NON-AQUEOUS
SOLVENT SYSTEMS

NON-AQUEOUS SOLVENT SYSTEMS

Edited by

T. C. WADDINGTON

School of Molecular Sciences,
University of Warwick,
Coventry, England

1965

ACADEMIC PRESS

London and New York

List of Contributors

H. Bloom, Chemistry Department, University of Tasmania, Hobart, Tasmania, Australia (p. 353)

R. S. Dasso, Chemistry Department, University of Illinois, Urbana, Illinois, U.S.A. (p. 211)

R. J. Gillespie, Department of Chemistry, McMaster University, Hamilton, Ontario, Canada (p. 117)

C. J. Hialada, Department of Chemistry and Inorganic Materials Research Division of the Lawrence Radiation Laboratory, University of California, Berkeley, California, U.S.A. (p. 1)

J. W. Hastie, Chemistry Department, University of Tasmania, Hobart, Tasmania, Australia (p. 353) ...

H. H. Hyman, Chemistry Division, Argonne National Laboratory, Argonne, Illinois, U.S.A. (p. 47)

W. L. Jolly, Department of Chemistry, and Inorganic Materials Research Division of the Lawrence Radiation Laboratory, University of California, Berkeley, California, U.S.A. (p. 1)

J. J. Katz, Chemistry Division, Argonne National Laboratory, Argonne, Illinois, U.S.A. (p. 47)

D. S. Tayer, Chemistry Department, The University, Glasgow, Scotland (p. 201)

M. E. Peach, Anorganisch-Chemisches Institut der Universität, Göttingen, West Germany (p. 85)

R. E. Powell, Chemistry Department, University of Illinois, Urbana, Illinois, U.S.A. (p. 211)

E. O. Robinson, Department of Chemistry, University of Toronto, Toronto, Ontario, Canada (p. 117)

A. G. Sharpe, University Chemical Laboratory, Cambridge, England (p. 253)

T. C. Waddington, School of Molecular Sciences, University, Uxbridge, Warwick, Coventry, England (pp. 85, 253)

Contents

Page

LIST OF CONTRIBUTORS.. v

PREFACE.. vii

CHAPTER 1

Liquid Ammonia

W. J. JOLLY AND C. J. HALLADA

I. Introduction.. 1

II. Physical Properties of Ammonia.. 2

  A. Vapour Pressure of Solid Ammonia................................ 2

  B. Vapour Pressure of Liquid Ammonia.............................. 3

  C. Heat of Fusion of Ammonia...................................... 3

  D. Heat of Vapourization of Ammonia at Boiling Point.............. 3

  E. Heat Capacity of Ammonia....................................... 3

  F. Thermodynamic Functions for Ammonia Gas at 25°C............... 4

  G. Density of Liquid Ammonia...................................... 4

  H. Viscosity of Liquid Ammonia.................................... 4

  I. Dielectric Constant of Liquid Ammonia.......................... 5

  J. Surface Tension of Liquid Ammonia.............................. 5

  K. Crystal Structure.. 5

  L. Electrical Conductivity of Liquid Ammonia...................... 5

  M. Refractive Index of Liquid Ammonia............................. 5

  N. Some Derived Constants... 5

III. Physical Properties of Liquid Ammonia Solutions..................... 6

  A. Non-electrolytes... 6

  B. Electrolytes... 6

  C. Metals... 10

IV. Reactions in Liquid Ammonia... 19

  A. Comparison of Ammonia with Other Solvents...................... 19

  B. Ionic Solvation... 26

  C. Acid–Base Reactions 28

  D. Reactions of Metal Solutions................................... 34

  References.. 41

CHAPTER 2

Liquid Hydrogen Fluoride

H. H. HYMAN AND J. J. KATZ

I. Introduction.. 47

  A. Equipment for Studying Liquid Hydrogen Fluoride................ 50

Page

II. Properties of Pure Liquid Hydrogen Fluoride................ 52
   A. Physical Properties.. 52
   B. Vibronic Absorption Spectra.......................... 55
   C. Structure of the Liquid................................ 57
   D. Acidity... 62
III. Solutes in Liquid Hydrogen Fluoride...................... 64
   A. Metal Fluorides... 65
   B. Non-metallic, Non-acidic, Ionizing Fluorides.............. 67
   C. Proton Acceptors.. 68
   D. Acid Solutes: Fluoride Ion Acceptors..................... 72
   E. Salts in the Hydrogen Fluoride System as Solutes.......... 74
   F. Solution in Hydrogen Fluoride without Ionization......... 75
IV. Solution in Anhydrous Hydrogen Fluoride of Compounds of
       Biological Importance............................... 76

CHAPTER 3

The Higher Hydrogen Halides as Ionizing Solvents

M. E. PEACH AND T. C. WADDINGTON

I. Introduction... 83
   A. Some Physical Properties of the Liquid Hydrogen Halides... 84
   B. Self-ionization 86
   C. Experimental Methods................................... 88
II. Solutions in the Hydrogen Halides........................ 97
   A. Acids and Bases.. 97
   B. Solvolysis Reactions................................... 111
   C. Redox Reactions.. 112

CHAPTER 4

Sulphuric Acid

R. J. GILLESPIE AND E. A. ROBINSON

I. Introduction... 117
   A. Bases.. 118
   B. Acids.. 121
   C. Non-electrolytes 122
   D. Sulphates and Hydrogen Sulphates....................... 122
II. The Physical Properties of Sulphuric Acid and Its Solutions, In-
       cluding Experimental Methods of Investigation........ 123
   A. Properties of Sulphuric Acid........................... 123
   B. Properties of Solutions................................ 131

Page

III. Inorganic Solutes.. 162
   A. The Solutes Water and Sulphur Trioxide 162
   B. Boron... 164
   C. Silicon... 167
   D. Tin and Lead... 170
   E. Nitrogen and Phosphorus................................ 172
   F. Arsenic, Antimony and Bismuth.......................... 174
   G. Vanadium, Chromium and Manganese 177
   H. Sulphur, Selenium and Tellurium........................ 179
   I. Halogens... 180
   J. Transition Metal Complexes............................. 184
   K. Chelation by the Sulphate Group........................ 186
IV. Organic Solutes... 187
   A. Simple Bases... 187
   B. Polybasic Compounds.................................... 188
   C. Amides and Ureas....................................... 190
   D. Esters... 192
   E. Carboxylic Anhydrides.................................. 193
   F. Ethers... 194
   G. Nitriles... 195
   H. Carboxylic Acids....................................... 196
   I. Carbonium Ions... 198
   J. Aromatic Sulphonation.................................. 204
   References.. 205

CHAPTER 5

Co-ordinating Solvents

R. S. Drago and K. F. Purcell

I. Introduction.. 211
II. Criteria for Establishing Co-ordination..................... 215
   A. Ultra-violet and Visible Spectroscopy................... 215
   B. Infra-red Spectroscopy................................. 216
   C. Nuclear Magnetic Resonance Spectroscopy................ 217
   D. Cryoscopy... 219
   E. Conductivity.. 219
III. Energetics of the Co-ordination Process.................... 220
   A. Statement of the Problem............................... 220
   B. Evaluation of the Energy Terms......................... 222
IV. Solute Behaviour in Selected Solvents...................... 226
   A. *NN*-Dimethylacetamide (DMA).......................... 228
   B. *N*-Methylacetamide (NMA)............................. 230
   C. Dimethyl Sulphoxide (DMSO)............................ 230

                                                                    Page
    D. Nitromethane and Nitrobenzene (NM, NB)................ 234
    E. Acetone (Ac) 237
    F. Methanol and Ethanol (MeOH, EtOH) 239
    G. Pyridine (Py).. 241
    H. Acetronitrile (Me CN)................................ 243
    I. Tetramethylene Sulphone.............................. 245
V. Some Generalizations (Sulpholane–$TMSO_2$).................... 247
   References... 249

CHAPTER 6

Liquid Sulphur Dioxide

T. C. WADDINGTON

   I. Introduction... 253
  II. Solubilities in Liquid Sulphur Dioxide...................... 254
 III. Solvate Formation with Sulphur Dioxide..................... 256
 IV. Electrical Conductivity and Ionization in Liquid Sulphur Di-
    oxide Solutions...................................... 260
  V. Electrochemical Studies in Solutions in Liquid Sulphur Dioxide 264
    A. Electrolysis....................................... 264
    B. Electrode Potentials............................... 264
 VI. Chemical Reactions in Liquid Sulphur Dioxide............... 266
    A. Solvolysis.. 266
    B. Metathetical Reactions............................. 267
    C. Amphoteric Reactions.............................. 268
    D. Oxidation–Reduction Reactions 271
    E. Complex Formation................................. 272
 VII. Isotopic Exchange Reactions in Liquid Sulphur Dioxide....... 273
VIII. Conclusion and Summary................................. 280
   References... 282

CHAPTER 7

The Halogens and Interhalogens as Solvents

A. G. SHARPE

   I. The Halogens... 286
    A. Chlorine.. 287
    B. Bromine... 287
    C. Iodine.. 288
  II. The Interhalogens.................................... 290
    A. Compounds of Formula AB........................... 290
    B. Compounds of Formula AB_3....................... 292

Page

C. Compounds of Formula AB_5............................ 295
D. Compounds of Formula AB_7............................ 297
References... 298

CHAPTER 8

Halides and Oxyhalides of Group V Elements as Solvents

D. S. PAYNE

I. Introduction.. 301
II. Experimental Methods..................................... 306
  A. Qualitative Solubility Considerations.................... 306
  B. The Examination of Solid Phases........................ 307
  C. The Products of Electron Transfer...................... 307
  D. Conductance Measurements............................. 307
  E. Transport Number Measurements....................... 308
  F. Potentiometric Measurements........................... 308
  G. Titrations Using Indicators.............................. 309
  H. Spectrometric Measurements........................... 309
  I. Viscosity Measurements................................. 310
  J. Thermodynamic Measurements.......................... 310
  K. Isotopic Exchange Reaction............................ 310
  L. Ebullioscopic and Cryoscopic Measurements.............. 310
III. Halides as Solvents....................................... 311
IV. Oxyhalides as Solvents.................................... 327
V. Phosphoryl Chloride...................................... 332
VI. Uses of Group V Halide and Oxyhalides as Solvents.......... 348
References.. 349

CHAPTER 9

Molten Salts as Solvents

H. BLOOM AND J. W. HASTIE

I. Summary.. 353
II. Introduction... 354
III. The Nature of Molten Salts................................ 354
  A. Type of Entities Present................................ 355
  B. Holes and Free Volume in Ionic Melts................... 356
  C. Distribution Functions................................. 357
  D. Nature of the Interionic Forces (Bonding) in Simple Melts.. 357
IV. Solutions of Salt and Water................................ 357
V. Solutions of Salt and Organic Compounds.................... 358
  A. Solutions in an Organic Solvent........................ 358

Page

B. Solutions of Organic Compounds in Molten Salts........... 360

VI. Solutions of Non-metallic Elements in Molten Salts........... 361

    A. Sulphur... 361

    B. Iodine.. 361

VII. Solutions of Gases in Molten Salts........................... 361

    A. Simple Solutions of Gas and Salt...................... 362

    B. Complex Solutions of Gases in Molten Salts............. 362

VIII. Solutions of Metals in Molten Salts......................... 364

    A. Introduction....................................... 364

    B. Solutions Without Significant Interaction................. 365

    C. Solutions With Strong Solute–Solvent Interaction (i.e. Non-metallic Solutions).................................. 369

    D. Solutions of Metals in Salts of Another Metal—Displacement Solubility.. 373

IX. Solutions of Salt in Molten Salt............................. 374

    A. Molten Salt Systems with Incomplete Miscibility........... 375

    B. Molten Salt Systems with Complete Miscibility............ 377

    C. The Structure of Molten Salt Solutions................... 377

    D. Solvation and Complex Ion Formation in Molten Salt Mixtures... 382

    E. Complex Ions and Reaction Kinetics..................... 382

X. Application of Molten Salts as Solvents....................... 383

    A. Reactions Involving Organic Substances or Volatile Inorganic Liquids in Molten Salt Solvents............... 383

    B. Other Reactions Involving Inorganic Substances in Molten Salt Solvents... 385

    C. Future Developments................................. 387

    References... 387

AUTHOR INDEX... 391

SUBJECT INDEX... 405

CHAPTER 1

Liquid Ammonia

WILLIAM L. JOLLY AND CALVIN J. HALLADA

Department of Chemistry, and Inorganic Materials Research Division of the Lawrence Radiation Laboratory, University of California, Berkeley, California, U.S.A.

I. Introduction	1
II. Physical Properties of Ammonia	2
A. Vapour Pressure of Solid Ammonia	2
B. Vapour Pressure of Liquid Ammonia	3
C. Heat of Fusion of Ammonia	3
D. Heat of Vapourization of Ammonia at Boiling Point	3
E. Heat Capacity of Ammonia	3
F. Thermodynamic Functions for Ammonia Gas at 25°C	4
G. Density of Liquid Ammonia	4
H. Viscosity of Liquid Ammonia	4
I. Dielectric Constant of Liquid Ammonia	5
J. Surface Tension of Liquid Ammonia	5
K. Crystal Structure	5
L. Electrical Conductivity of Liquid Ammonia	5
M. Refractive Index of Liquid Ammonia	5
N. Some Derived Constants	5
III. Physical Properties of Liquid Ammonia Solutions	6
A. Non-electrolytes	6
B. Electrolytes	6
C. Metals	10
IV. Reactions in Liquid Ammonia	19
A. Comparison of Ammonia with Other Solvents	19
B. Ionic Solvation	26
C. Acid–Base Reactions	28
D. Reactions of Metal Solutions	34
References	41

I. INTRODUCTION

The chemistry of liquid ammonia has been studied so extensively that it cannot be adequately discussed in less than a book. In writing this chapter, we have decided not to attempt to cover all aspects of the solvent, but rather to discuss those aspects which are susceptible to quantitative treatment. We have emphasized the application of thermodynamics and kinetics to liquid ammonia chemistry. It should be recognized that this type of treatment is possible only as a result of many physical-chemical studies carried out in recent years. We hope, however, that it will be apparent that much remains to be done in the systematization of liquid ammonia chemistry.

In other books and review articles, liquid ammonia has normally been discussed in rather qualitative terms. The principal device for systematizing the chemistry has usually been analogy with aqueous chemistry. Some important literature sources are listed below. These chapters and articles are recommended as sources of information on topics not covered, or only touched on, in this chapter:

General

Chapters 3–6 in "Non-Aqueous Solvents" by Audrieth and Kleinberg (1953).

Chapter 4 in "Systematic Inorganic Chemistry" by Yost and Russell (1944).

"The Nitrogen System of Compounds" by Franklin (1935).

Chapter 2 in "Chemistry in Non-Aqueous Solvents" by Sisler (1961).

Chapter 3 in "Die Chemie in Wasserähnlichen Lösungsmitteln" by Jander (1949).

Review article: "Inorganic Reactions in Liquid Ammonia" by Fowles and Nicholls (1962).

Specific

Ammonolysis: Fernelius and Bowman (1940).

Alkali amides: Bergstrom and Fernelius (1933, 1937); Levine and Fernelius (1954).

Metal–ammonia solutions: Kraus (1953); Jolly (1959); Symons (1959); Lepoutre and Sienko (1964).

Reactions of metal–ammonia solutions: Birch (1950); Watt (1950); Birch and Smith (1958).

Chemical thermodynamics: Jolly (1956).

II. Physical Properties of Ammonia

In this section, we tabulate the important physical properties of ammonia.

A. Vapour Pressure of Solid Ammonia (Armstrong, 1953)

(Based on $0°C = 273.16°K$)

$T(°K)$	$\theta(°C)$	$P(mm)$
175	−98·16	4·85
180	−93·16	8·78
185	−88·16	15·42
190	−83·16	26·27
195	−78·16	43·57
195·46	−77·70	45·58 (triple point)

$$\log_{10}P = 9.98379 - \frac{1627.22}{T}$$

B. VAPOUR PRESSURE OF LIQUID AMMONIA (Armstrong, 1953)

(Based on 0°C = 273·16°K)

T(°K)	θ(°C)	P(mm)
195·46	−77·70	45·58 (triple point)
200	−73·16	64·92
210	−63·16	133·21
220	−53·16	253·97
230	−43·16	454·28
239·78	−33·38	760 (boiling point)
240	−33·16	768·43
250	−23·16	1237·5
260	−13·16	1914·8
270	−3·16	2857·1
280	6·84	4130·0
290	16·84	5804·2
298·16	25·00	7520·5
300	26·84	7956·6
320	46·84	14,028
340	66·84	23,089
360	86·84	35,973
380	106·84	53,597
400	126·84	77,334
405·6	132·4	85,400 (critical point)

$$\log_{10}P = 9{\cdot}95028 - \frac{1473{\cdot}17}{T} - 0{\cdot}0038603T \text{ (for } T < 250°\text{K)}$$

C. HEAT OF FUSION OF AMMONIA (Overstreet and Giauque, 1937)

$$\Delta H = 1351{\cdot}6 \text{ cal mole}^{-1}.$$

D. HEAT OF VAPOURIZATION OF AMMONIA AT BOILING POINT (Overstreet and Giauque, 1937)

$$\Delta H = 5581 \text{ cal mole}^{-1}.$$

E. HEAT CAPACITY OF AMMONIA (Overstreet and Giauque, 1937)

(Based on 0°C = 273·10°K and a temperature scale appreciably different from the International Temperature Scale)

T(°K)	C_p	T(°K)	C_p	T(°K)	C_p
20	0·368	110	6·877	200	17·58 (liq.)
30	1·033	120	7·497	210	17·75
40	1·841	130	8·102	220	17·90

$T(^\circ\mathrm{K})$	C_p	$T(^\circ\mathrm{K})$	C_p	$T(^\circ\mathrm{K})$	C_p
50	2·663	140	8·699	230	18·03
60	3·474	150	9·272	240	18·12
70	4·232	160	9·846		
80	4·954	170	10·42		
90	5·612	180	11·03		
100	6·246	190	11·71 (sol.)		

F. THERMODYNAMIC FUNCTIONS FOR AMMONIA GAS AT 25°C (Rossini *et al.*, 1952)

ΔH_f°	−11·04 kcal mole^{-1}
ΔF_f°	−3·976 kcal mole^{-1}
S°	46·01 e.u.
C_p°	8·523 cal mole^{-1} deg^{-1}

G. DENSITY OF LIQUID AMMONIA (Cragoe and Harper, 1921)

$\theta(^\circ\mathrm{C})$	Density (g/ml)	$\theta(^\circ\mathrm{C})$	Density (g/ml)
−70	0·7253	−20	0·6650
−60	0·7138	−10	0·6520
−50	0·7020	0	0·6386
−40	0·6900	10	0·6247
−34	0·6826	20	0·6103
−33	0·6814	25	0·6028
−30	0·6776	30	0·5952

H. VISCOSITY OF LIQUID AMMONIA

$\theta(^\circ\mathrm{C})$	Viscosity (centipoises)	$\theta(^\circ\mathrm{C})$	Viscosity (centipoises)
−33·5	0·2543 [a]	15	0·1457, 0·1479 [c,d]
−26	0·230 [b]	20	0·1411 [d]
−10	0·183 [b]	25	0·1350, 0·1345 [c,d]
−4	0·170 [b]	30	0·138 [b]
5	0·1618 [c]	50	0·125 [b]
10	0·152 [b]		

[a] Elsey (1920)   [b] Pinevich (1948a,b)
[c] Plank and Hunt (1939)   [d] Shatenshtein *et al.* (1949a,b)

I. DIELECTRIC CONSTANT OF LIQUID AMMONIA (Grubb *et al.*, 1936)

$\theta(°C)$	Dielectric constant
-60 ± 10	26·7
-33	(23) interpolated
5	18·94
15	17·82
25	16·90
35	16·26

J. SURFACE TENSION OF LIQUID AMMONIA (Berthoud, 1918a,b; Stairs and Sienko, 1956)

$\theta(°C)$	$\gamma(\text{erg cm}^{-2})$
11·10	23·38
34·05	18·05
58·98	12·95

where $\theta = °C$, $\gamma = 23·41 - 0·3371\theta - 0·000943\theta^2 (-75° < \theta < -39°)$

K. CRYSTAL STRUCTURE (Vegard and Hillesund, 1942)

Cubic, 4 molecules per unit cell.
at $-185°$, $a_o = 5·2253$ kX
$= 5·2358$ Å.
Calculated density $= 0·7881$ g cm^{-3}.

L. ELECTRICAL CONDUCTIVITY OF LIQUID AMMONIA (Hnizda and Kraus, 1949)

$L_o \sim 1 \times 10^{-11}$ ohm^{-1} cm^{-1} (very pure NH$_3$).

M. REFRACTIVE INDEX OF LIQUID AMMONIA (Franklin, 1935)

$\eta = 1·325$ at $16°$ for $\lambda = 5899$ Å.

N. SOME DERIVED CONSTANTS

Freezing point constant, $K_f = \dfrac{RT_f^2}{1000 \, \Delta H_f} = 0·9567$.

Boiling point constant, $K_b = \dfrac{RT_b^2}{1000 \, \Delta H_v} = 0·3487$.

III. Physical Properties of Liquid Ammonia Solutions

A. NON-ELECTROLYTES

Liquid ammonia is an excellent solvent for many non-electrolytes that are relatively insoluble in water (see Section IVA, 1). Most research on these solutions has centred on practical problems such as the separation by extraction and crystallization of materials which are difficultly separable. We shall mention here only a few basic studies in the area of non-electrolytic solutions.

Phase studies have been performed on several hydrocarbon–liquid ammonia systems by Ishida (1957, 1958, 1959, 1960a,b) and Fenske *et al.* (1955). It was found that the experimental data for both the critical composition and the activity coefficients are best interpreted by the solubility parameter theory if it is assumed that ammonia is associated nearly to a dimer as a liquid.

Some data are available on the heats of solution for non-electrolytes in liquid ammonia. It has been observed by Schmidt *et al.* (1941) that the molar heats of solution of normal alcohols in liquid ammonia decrease from 1960 cal for methanol to -100 cal for normal butanol. Gunn and Green (1960) found that the molar heats of solution for water and methylamine are independent of concentration.

It is interesting that nitrogen (Wiebe and Tremearne, 1933), hydrogen (Ipat'ev and Teodorovich, 1932), helium and argon (Cseko and Cornides, 1960) all obey Henry's Law up to pressures of about 100 atm when dissolved in liquid ammonia. The temperature dependence of the solubility of the mixture $N_2 + 3H_2$ in liquid ammonia was studied by Lefrancois and Vaniscotte (1960). They observed that the solubility follows a third order function of the temperature (°C).

The spectra, from 2500 to 6000 Å, of solutions of several nitrophenols and nitronaphthols in liquid ammonia have been interpreted by Dykhno and Shatenshtein (1948, 1951). Comparison was made with the spectra of these same molecules in 0·005 M NaOH solutions in water. General similarities were found in the spectra of both solvent systems; however the peaks were shifted to higher wavelengths in liquid ammonia. These shifts were attributed to the formation of acid–base complexes.

B. ELECTROLYTES

Solutions of electrolytes in liquid ammonia have been subjected to extensive research. Nearly all the types of measurements which have been made with aqueous solutions of electrolytes have also been made with liquid ammonia solutions even though the handling of liquid ammonia is more difficult than that of water. It is not possible to present the results of all the work which has been carried out in determining the nature of electrolyte–liquid ammonia solutions. However, some of the more important data and conclusions will be covered.

1. Molar Volumes

The densities of the solutions of several alkali metal halides and ammonium halides have been measured at various temperatures and concentrations (Johnson and Martens, 1936; Kikuchi and Kudo, 1944, 1948). It was found (Johnson and Martens, 1936) that the densities vary linearly with the temperature and that the apparent molar volumes, V, are a linear function of $c^{\frac{1}{2}}$ (in moles/litre). This behaviour is entirely similar to that found in aqueous solutions.

In more recent work, Gunn and Green (1962a) have determined the apparent molar volumes of several electrolytes in liquid ammonia at 0°C. They find that plots of V against $c^{\frac{1}{2}}$ (in equivalents/litre) have almost the same shapes for several alkali metal halides, ammonium halides, and barium nitrate. Even at concentrations where considerable ion pairing would be expected, the ion additivity rule is obeyed. Using estimated association constants, Gunn and Green extrapolate their data to infinite dilution to obtain the volumes given in Table I. The table includes the volumes of the same salts in water at 25°C (Harned and Owen, 1958).

TABLE I

Some Molar Volumes at Infinite Dilution in Ammonia and Water

Salt	V^0 in NH_3 at 0°C (cm^3)	V^0 in H_2O at 25°C (cm^3)
NaCl	-38	16·4
NaI	-55	35·1
KI	-6	45·4

From the data it may be noted that

$$V^0_{NaI}(NH_3,\ 0°) - V^0_{NaCl}(NH_3,\ 0°) = 23\ cm^3$$
$$V^0_{NaI}(H_2O,\ 25°) - V^0_{NaCl}(H_2O,\ 25°) = 18·7\ cm^3$$

thus
$$V^0_{I^-}(NH_3) - V^0_{Cl^-}(NH_3) \approx V^0_{I^-}(H_2O) - V^0_{Cl^-}(H_2O)$$

and
$$V^0_{KI}(NH_3,\ 0°) - V^0_{NaI}(NH_3,\ 0°) = 9\ cm^3$$
$$V^0_{KI}(H_2O,\ 25°) - V^0_{NaI}(H_2O,\ 25°) = 10·3\ cm^3$$

thus
$$V^0_{K^+}(NH_3) - V^0_{Na^+}(NH_3) \approx V^0_{K^+}(H_2O) - V^0_{Na^+}(H_2O).$$

Since there is no "absolute" way of finding the V^0 for any single ion, the ionic V^0 values still remain unknown. Ionic volumes obtained by assuming that $V^0_{K^+} = V^0_{Cl^-}$ have been given elsewhere (Jolly, 1959); a more detailed calculation will be given here. Using an expression similar to Hepler's (1957), one calculates a $V^0_{Na^+}$ (in ammonia at 0°C) of $-41\cdot5$ cm^3. The expression of Couture and Laidler (1956) yields the value -34 cm^3. If we take the average of these two, we calculate

$$V^0_{Na^+} = -37 \text{ cm}^3$$
$$V^0_{K^+} = -28 \text{ cm}^3$$
$$V^0_{Cl^-} = -1 \text{ cm}^3$$
$$V^0_{I^-} = +22 \text{ cm}^3.$$

2. *Thermochemistry*

The heats of solution of several electrolytes in liquid ammonia have been measured at 25°C and -33°C by Gunn and Green (1960). Table II gives the heats of solution of several salts in ammonia at 25°C and -33°C and in water at 25°C. The heats of solution are all for a mole ratio of solvent to solute of 500. It will be noted that the heats of solution are more negative in ammonia than in water, and are likewise more negative at 25°C than at -33°C.

TABLE II

Some Heats of Solution in Water and Ammonia (ΔH^0 in kcal/mole)

	H$_2$O(25°C)[a]	NH$_3$(25°C)[b]	NH$_3$(-33°C)[b]
H$_2$O(liq.)	0	$-3\cdot32$	$-2\cdot81$
CH$_3$NH$_2$(liq.)	$-5\cdot0$	$+0\cdot50$	—
HgI$_2$	—	$(-20\cdot8)$	$(-20\cdot15)$
NaCl	$+1\cdot02$	$-6\cdot75$	$-1\cdot57$
KI	$+4\cdot95$	$-9\cdot44$	$-7\cdot89$
CsI	$+7\cdot9$	$-5\cdot27$	—
NH$_4$Cl	$+3\cdot71$	$-8\cdot23$	$-6\cdot95$
NH$_4$I	$+3\cdot3$	$-16\cdot10$	$-13\cdot37$
Ba(NO$_3$)$_2$	$+9\cdot96$	$-15\cdot31$	—

[a] Rossini *et al.* (1952)   [b] Gunn and Green (1960).

The slope obtained from a plot of the heat of solution versus $c^{\frac{1}{2}}$ for KI solutions of low concentrations is 27 kcal mole$^{-3/2}$ litre$^{1/2}$. This is almost twelve times the calculated Debye-Hückel slope and undoubtedly is the result of a high degree of ionic association in liquid ammonia. Therefore the thermal effects accompanying dilution are principally due to dissociation of the ion pairs and solvation of the resulting ions; that is, KI in liquid ammonia is analogous to most "strong" 2–2 salts in water.

3. *Electrochemistry*

(a) Conductance. The conductances of several salts and acids in liquid ammonia have been determined. Unfortunately, the agreement between equivalent conductances measured by different experimenters has seldom been as good as that found for aqueous solutions. Some of the better conductance data are presented in Table III. The data are not exactly self-consistent. Thus, using the data of Hnizda and Kraus (1949) at $-34°$,

$$\Lambda^0_{KBr} - \Lambda^0_{NaBr} = 32\cdot5 = \lambda^0_{K^+} - \lambda^0_{Na^+}$$

while from the data of Monoszon and Pleskov (1931) at $-33\cdot5°$,

$$\Lambda^0_{KNO_3} - \Lambda^0_{NaNO_3} = 39 = \lambda^0_{K^+} - \lambda^0_{Na^+}.$$

TABLE III

Conductances of Salt Solutions in Ammonia and Water

Electrolyte	$\theta(°C)$	Λ^0 in NH_3	$10^8 \, \mathring{a}$	$K_{assoc.}$	Λ^0 in H_2O at 25°
KCl [a]	−34	348·0	6·7	1060	149·9
KBr [a]	−34	346·98	7·8	453	151·9
KI [a]	−34	345·1	6·6	183	150·4
NaBr [b]	−34	314·3	5·9	263	128·3
LiNO$_3$ [b]	−33·5	299			110·1
LiNO$_3$ [b]	−40	290			110·1
NaNO$_3$ [b]	−33·5	315			121·6
NaNO$_3$ [b]	−40	300			121·6
KNO$_3$ [b]	−33·5	354			145·0
KNO$_3$ [b]	−40	338			145·0
RbNO$_3$ [b]	−40	344			149·2
CsNO$_3$ [b]	−40	345			148·7
KNH$_2$ [c]	−33	343		13,700	

[a] Data are those of Hnizda and Kraus (1949). These data were recently treated by Kay (1960), using the extended form of the Onsager-Fuoss conductance theory (Fuoss and Accascina, 1959).

[b] Monoszon and Pleskov (1931).

[c] Hawes (1933).

Monoszon and Pleskov have used the transference data of Franklin and Cady (1904) to assign λ_+^0 to the alkali metal ions and λ_-^0 to the nitrate ion, but due to the lack of agreement in the nitrate and halide data, there is no advantage gained by assigning λ_-^0 values to the halide ions.

It will be noted that the association constants of the potassium halides follow the order expected from the relative sizes of the halide ions. However, it is surprising that the values for the closest distance of approach, $\mathring{a}$, of the potassium and halide ions which best fit the extended Onsager-Fuoss conductance theory are larger than they are in either water or methanol (Kay, 1960). The $\mathring{a}$ values for aqueous solutions often agree closely with the sum of the ionic radii (Fuoss and Accascina, 1959). However, this is apparently not true for the alkali metal halides in liquid ammonia.

(*b*) Polarography. Polarographic studies using the dropping mercury electrode have contributed much to our understanding of the nature of solutions of electrolytes in liquid ammonia, in spite of the fact that the freezing point of mercury ($-38\cdot9°C$) is very close to the boiling point of liquid ammonia ($-33\cdot4°C$). Polarograms, can indicate whether the reduction occurs in one or more steps and thereby also indicate the nature of intermediate species that are involved.

Thus Laitinen and Shoemaker (1950a) showed that the oxidation product of the Hg pool anode during polarographic measurements in liquid ammonia is Hg^{2+}, and that the $Hg-Hg^{2+}$ electrode behaves reversibly in liquid ammonia.

Table IV presents the half-wave potentials for several reduction processes in liquid ammonia at $-36°$. The half-wave potentials given are versus a $Pb/0\cdot1N\,Pb(NO_3)_2$ electrode.

When the cation of the indifferent electrolyte is non-reducible, platinum and mercury electrodes act as electron electrodes in liquid ammonia. The standard potential of the electron electrode relative to the standard hydrogen electrode at $-36°C$ is $-1\cdot9\,V$.

Schaap *et al.* (1961) have used a high-pressure polarographic cell for measurements at room temperature.

C. METALS

In spite of the large amount of work done on metal–ammonia solutions since they were first studied by Weyl (1864), there is still some uncertainty concerning the nature of the solutions. All metal–ammonia solutions are metastable and decompose to give hydrogen and the metal amide. Since this reaction is catalysed by certain impurities, the need for extreme care and cleanliness when working with these solutions cannot be over emphasized.

TABLE IV

Polarographic Half-Wave Potentials in Ammonia at $-36°$

Species reduced	$E_{\frac{1}{2}}$ (V)	Reversibility
Li^+	-1.67	Rev.[a]
Na^+	-1.31	Rev.[a]
K^+	-1.24	Rev.[a]
Rb^+	-1.21	Rev.[a]
Cs^+	-1.15	Rev.[a]
Tl^+	$+0.15$	Rev.[b]
$Cu^{2+} \rightarrow Cu^+$	$+0.16$	Rev.[b]
$Cu^+ \rightarrow$ amalgam	-0.21	Irrev.[b]
NH_4^+	-1.37	Rev.[b]
$Pb^{2+} \rightarrow Pb$ amalgam	-0.01	Rev.[c]
$Cd^{2+} \rightarrow Cd$	-0.45	Rev.[c]
$Ni^{2+} \rightarrow Ni$	-0.79	Irrev.[c]
Zn^{2+}	-0.89	Irrev.[c]
$Ca^{2+} \rightarrow Ca$	-1.96	—[d]
$Sr^{2+} \rightarrow Sr$	-1.68	—[d]
$Ba^{2+} \rightarrow Ba$	-1.59	—[d]

[a] Laitinen and Nyman (1948a, 1948b). [c] McElroy and Laitinen (1953).
[b] Laitinen and Shoemaker (1950b). [d] Nyman (1949).

This could well be the source of much of the disagreement found in the results obtained by various workers in these systems. It is generally agreed, however, that when a metal is dissolved in liquid ammonia, it dissociates into a metal ion and electron(s), at least in very dilute solutions.

1. *Phase Diagrams*

The metals which dissolve in liquid ammonia are those with low ionization potentials and high solvation energies. Thus the alkali metals, the alkaline earth metals heavier than beryllium, and those rare earths which exhibit the $+2$ oxidation state are soluble.

The solubilities of the alkali metals are given in Table V. The alkaline earth metals, europium and ytterbium do not exist in equilibrium with their solutions. These metals form solid hexammoniates. The hexammoniate of calcium separates out at a concentration of 10 mole per cent calcium at $-64°C$ and 11 mole per cent calcium at $0°C$. The ratio of ammonia to hexammoniate is about 4 to 5, which is about the same as the ratio of ammonia to metal for the alkali metals.

A portion of the phase diagram for the sodium–ammonia system is shown in Fig. 1. The significant features of this diagram (which are general for metal-ammonia systems) are: (1) a steep solubility curve for the metal or its hexammoniate, (2) a low temperature eutectic point, and (3) a miscibility gap in the liquid region corresponding to the co-existence of two different metal solutions. In the region of the miscibility gap, the more concentrated

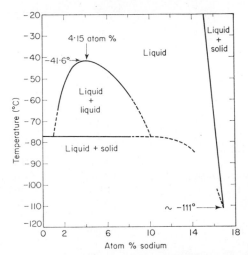

Fig. 1. Sodium–ammonia phase diagram (reproduced with permission from Jolly, 1959).

phase is bronze coloured and less dense than the blue phase, which is of considerably lower concentration at the lower temperatures. The alkali metals, except caesium, and the alkaline earth metals all show this behaviour. Sienko (1964) has reviewed the subject of metal–ammonia systems, and has proposed an electron model which predicts consolute concentrations of 3·9 atom per cent metal in ammonia, in remarkable agreement with observed values.

TABLE V

Solubilities of Metals in Liquid Ammonia

Metal	$\theta(^\circ C)$	Gram-atoms of metal per 1000 g NH_3	Moles NH_3 per gram-atom of metal
Lithium [a,b]	0	16·31	3·60
	−33·2	15·66	3·75
	−39·4	16·25	3·61
	−63·5	15·41	3·81
Sodium [c,d,e]	22	9·56	6·14
	0	10·00	5·87
	−30	10·63	5·52
	−33·8	10·72	5·48

Metal	$\theta(°C)$	Gram-atoms of metal per 1000 g NH_3	Moles NH_3 per gram-atom of metal
Sodium [c,d,e]	−33·5	10·93	5·37
	−50	10·89	5·39
	−70	11·29	5·20
	−105	11·79	4·98
Potassium [c,d,e,f]	0	12·4	4·68, 4·74
	−33·2	11·86	4·95
	−50	12·3	5·05, 4·79
	−100	12·2	4·82
	−33·5	12·05	4·87
Caesium [g]	−50	25·1	2·34

[a] Johnson and Piskur (1933).   [c] Johnson and Meyer (1932).   [e] Ruff and Geisel (1906).
[b] Kraus and Johnson (1925).   [d] Kraus and Lucasse (1921).   [f] Johnson and Meyer (1929).
[g] Hodgins (1949.)

There are other differences between the alkali metal– and alkaline earth metal–ammonia systems besides the difference in the solid species that exist in equilibrium with saturated solutions. Whereas the upper consolute temperature for the sodium–ammonia two-liquid equilibrium is − 41·6°, the upper consolute temperature for calcium–ammonia solutions is not yet reached at 50° (Jolly *et al.*, 1964). The concentration at which the second phase first begins to appear is much lower for calcium solutions than for sodium solutions (Hallada and Jolly, 1963). The eutectic temperatures are much lower for alkali metal–ammonia systems than for the alkaline earth metal–ammonia systems. The eutectic points of several systems are given in Table VI.

TABLE VI

Metal–Ammonia Eutectics (Birch and MacDonald, 1947, 1948)

Metal	$\theta(°C)$	Mole percentage metal
Li	−185	22
K	−157	15
Cs	−118	—
Ca	−87	12
Sr	−89	7
Ba	−89	7·7

2. *Molar Volumes*

When a metal is dissolved in liquid ammonia, there is a large net increase in volume. Table VII presents the densities of saturated solutions of lithium, sodium and potassium at several temperatures.

TABLE VII

Densities of Saturated Solutions of Alkali Metals in Ammonia

Lithium[a]		Sodium[b]		Potassium[b]	
$\theta(°C)$	Density	$\theta(°C)$	Density	$\theta(°C)$	Density
19	0·477	−31·6	0·576	−33·3	0·625
−80	0·495	−33·3	0·578	−39·0	0·627
		−40·7	0·581	−41·0	0·629
		−47·0	0·585	−46·4	0·636
		−51·0	0·587	−49·6	0·638

[a] Jaffe (1935).   [b] Johnson *et al.* (1950).

Gunn and Green (1962a) found that the apparent molar volumes at 0°C of alkali metals change only slightly over the concentration range 0·01–1·0 molar. They assign the following partial molar volumes at infinite dilution:

$$V^0_{Li} = 49 \text{ cm}^3$$
$$V^0_{Na} = 57 \text{ cm}^3$$
$$V^0_{K} = 65 \text{ cm}^3.$$

Using the values of the partial molar volumes at infinite dilution that were given earlier (Section IIIB,l) for KI and NaI, one obtains the molar volume of the solvated electron at infinite dilution:

$$V^0_K - V^0_{KI} = 65 - (-6) = 71 \text{ cm}^3 = V^0_{e^-} - V^0_{I^-}$$
$$V^0_{Na} - V^0_{NaI} = 57 - (-15) = 72 \text{ cm}^3 = V^0_{e^-} - V^0_{I^-}.$$

Since $$V^0_{I^-} = 22 \text{ cm}^3,$$
$$V^0_{e^-} = 94 \text{ cm}^3 \text{ mole}^{-1}.$$

This volume corresponds to a sphere of radius 3·34 Å. Other calculations have also led to values around 3 Å for the electron cavity radius (Jolly, 1959; Hutchison and O'Reilly, 1962a).

3. Thermochemistry

The alkali metals, except lithium, have very low heats of solution, but the metals that form solid ammoniates evolve large amounts of heat when they are dissolved in liquid ammonia. The heats of solution of several metals are given in Table VIII.

The heat of dilution of sodium is endothermic, and when NaI is present, the heat of dilution is greater (Gunn and Green, 1962b).

The heat of ammonation of the electron (that is, the heat of transfer from the gas phase to ammonia) is of considerable interest. Coulter (1953) calculated an ammonation heat of -11 kcal mole^{-1}. This seems to be too positive compared to the experimental photoelectric threshold energy, 33 kcal mole^{-1} (Hasing 1940); a value for the heat of ammonation of the electron of about -40 kcal mole^{-1} seems more reasonable (Jolly, 1959). Jortner (1959) theoretically calculated a heat solution of -39 kcal mole^{-1} for the electron in a cavity of radius 3·2–3·4 Å.

TABLE VIII

Heats of Solution of Metals in Ammonia at $-33°C$

Metal	Concentration (mole/litre)	ΔH^0 (kcal mole^{-1})
Li	0·067	-9·65 [a]
Na	0·4	$+1$·4 [b]
K	0·07	0·0 [b,c]
Rb	0·13	0·0 [c]
Cs	0·19	0·0 [c]
Ca	0·023	-19·7 [d]
Sr	—	-20·7 [e,f]
Ba	—	-19·0 [e,f]

[a] Coulter and Monchick (1951).　　[d] Wolsky et al. (1952).
[b] Kraus and Schmidt (1934).　　[e] Coulter (1953).
[c] Schmidt et al. (1938).　　[f] Wolsky (1952).

4. Electrical Conductance

The equivalent conductances of metal solutions in liquid ammonia are greater than those for any other type of electrolyte in any known solvent. The specific conductivities of concentrated solutions are of the same order of magnitude as the conductivities of metals, and the equivalent conductances of dilute solutions approach values near 1000, i.e. some five to ten times the values for salts in water (Kraus and Lucasse, 1921). The equivalent conductances of lithium, sodium and potassium are given in Fig. 2. It will be noticed that as the concentration increases from infinite dilution the equivalent conductance decreases to a minimum near 0·04 molar, and then increases very abruptly with increasing concentration.

Transference studies of sodium solutions have shown that the conductance of the electron, λ_-, has a minimum value at about 0·04 molar, whereas the conductance of the sodium ion, λ_+, decreases continuously as concentration

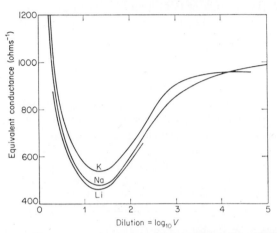

FIG. 2. Equivalent conductance of metal–ammonia solutions at −33·5°. V = litres of ammonia of density 0·674 in which one gram-atom of metal is dissolved (reproduced with permission from Jolly, 1959).

increases (Dye et al., 1960). The ratio T_-/T_+ varies from seven in dilute solutions to 280 at ∼ 0·9 molar (Kraus, 1914). These transference data show that the behaviour of the conductance curves is determined primarily by the mobility of the electron.

The temperature coefficient of specific conductivity for sodium,

$$\frac{\Delta K}{\Delta \theta} \cdot \frac{100}{K_{-33\cdot5°\mathrm{C}}},$$

is 1·9% per degree for dilute solutions, reaches a maximum of about 4% per degree at ∼ 1 molar, and falls almost to zero at higher concentrations (Kraus and Lucasse, 1922 and 1923). These data are not explicable by changes in viscosity, and must be due to quite different conduction mechanisms in the various concentration regions. A review of the many mechanisms that have been proposed for the low field conductance has been given elsewhere (Jolly, 1959).

In measurements of the Wien effect, fields of magnitude 15,000 V/cm gave a 4% increase in the conductivity of alkali metal solutions (Lepoutre and Patterson, 1955). Comparable increases in aqueous solutions of electrolytes require fields of magnitude 100,000 V/cm.

5. *Magnetic Properties*

The molar magnetic susceptibility of an alkali metal solution approaches that of a mole of free electron spins, $N\mu_0^2/kT$, at infinite dilution. As the concentration is increased, however, the molar susceptibility decreases rapidly (Freed and Sugarman, 1943). Comparison of static susceptibilities of sodium and potassium, and susceptibilities obtained from paramagnetic resonance measurements, has been interpreted to indicate that the radius of the cavity in which the electron resides is 3·0 Å (Hutchison and Pastor, 1953). This agrees well with the value calculated earlier from partial molar volumes. The paramagnetic resonance line width for potassium solutions is only about 0·03 gauss. The line width varies directly with viscosity (Levy, 1956) and has been interpreted as due to motionally narrowed hyperfine interactions between unpaired electrons and the protons bordering the electron cavity (Kaplan and Kittel, 1953).

The spin-spin relaxation times, T_1, and spin-lattice relaxation times, T_2, are about equal in dilute solutions, and again in concentrated solutions, of potassium; in the middle concentration range, T_1 is larger than T_2 (Hutchison and O'Reilly, 1961b). Within a limited concentration range, T_1 and T_2 are almost equal for solutions of lithium, sodium and calcium (Cutler and Powles, 1962). The equality of T_1 and T_2 is interpreted as meaning that the electron interaction is with the nitrogen nucleus of the ammonia, not with the protons. The relaxation times vary from 1 to 3 μsec depending on concentration and temperature (Pollak, 1961; Cutler and Powles, 1962).

It is now well known that the nuclear magnetic resonance absorption for a given species in metallic systems occurs at higher fields than normal (Knight, 1949). McConnell and Holm (1957) measured the Knight shifts of ^{14}N and ^{23}Na in sodium–ammonia solutions. They found that the average hyperfine contact density of ^{23}Na and an unpaired electron is 3×10^{-3} to 5×10^{-3} as large as the contact density in an isolated sodium atom when the NH_3/Na ratio of the solutions is 50 to 400. At NH_3/Na ratios less than 50, the contact density increases markedly. On the other hand, the average hyperfine contact density of ^{14}N and an unpaired electron is almost 0·1 that on a nitrogen atom at all solution concentrations. This supports the suggestion that the electron interaction is with the nitrogen nucleus (Pollak, 1961). The temperature dependence of the Knight shift for sodium solutions over a hundred-fold range of concentrations was measured by Acrivos and Pitzer (1962).

6. *Absorption Spectra*

The blue colour of dilute metal solutions is due to the short wavelength tail of a broad absorption band that peaks at approximately 15,000 Å. The spectra of the alkali metals, and at least calcium of the alkaline earth metals, are essentially the same (Gold and Jolly, 1962; Hallada and Jolly, 1963).

Furthermore, the alkali metals obey Beer's law at the lower wavelengths up to concentrations as high as 0·2 molar. At wavelengths beyond 20,000 Å, there may be a positive deviation from Beer's Law at the higher concentrations.

Up to concentrations at which phase separation occurs, calcium solutions also obey Beer's Law at all but the highest wavelengths. The molar extinction coefficients of the calcium solutions are very nearly twice the molar extinction coefficients of the alkali metal solutions at all wavelengths.

It has been reported that addition of NaI to sodium solutions produces a new band at 8000 Å (Clark *et al.*, 1959); however, this peak was not observed in independent experiments (Gold and Jolly, 1962). It is entirely possible that the 8000 Å peak is due to a short-lived species which disappears after a few minutes.

Reflection spectra on sodium solutions with NH_3/Na ratios of 5 to 168 were measured at 1–20 μ (Beckman and Pitzer, 1961). Dilute solutions show a strong peak near 1·5 μ. The concentrated solutions show high reflectivity over broad wavelength ranges.

7. *Models*

In the preceding paragraphs on the physical properties of metal–ammonia solutions, we have occasionally interpreted the data in terms of particular models. Now, in conclusion, it will be instructive to briefly review some of the microscopic models that have been proposed for metal–ammonia solutions, especially those for low and intermediate concentrations.

The early conductivity work of Kraus led him to the conclusion that, in very dilute solutions, metals dissociate to give ammoniated cations and electrons.

$$M = M^+ + e^-. \tag{1}$$

As the concentration is increased these species associate and the conductivity decreases. Eventually, incipient metallic behaviour occurs and the equivalent conductance increases rapidly.

When magnetic data became available it was obvious that the model Kraus proposed from conductivity data was not adequate, since it did not account for the pairing of electrons. The magnetic data were explained by Huster (1930), and Freed and Sugarman (1943) in terms of an equilibrium between the ionic species and diamagnetic metal atom dimers:

$$2M^+ + 2e^- = M_2. \tag{2}$$

Becker *et al.* (1956) showed that both the conductivity data and the susceptibility data can be approximately accounted for by considering both of the above equilibria. However, Arnold and Patterson (1964) have shown that the equilibrium constants for these reactions obtained from electrochemical data do not agree with those obtained from magnetic data. They resolve the discrepancy by postulating another diamagnetic species, M^-, and give the following equilibrium constants:

$$M = M^+ + e^- \qquad k = 9 \cdot 9 \times 10^{-3} \qquad (3)$$

$$M^- = M + e^- \qquad k = 9 \cdot 7 \times 10^{-4} \qquad (4)$$

$$M_2 = 2M \qquad k = 1 \cdot 9 \times 10^{-4}. \qquad (5)$$

Detailed models of the species involved in these equilibria have continually evolved.

All the data are fairly well explained by assuming that the electron-in-a-cavity retains its identity even when species such as M, M^- and M_2 are being formed. The M species may be described as an ion pair in which an ammoniated metal ion and an ammoniated electron are held together by coulombic forces with little distortion of the ammoniated electron, and the M^- and M_2 species may be pictured as quadrupolar ionic assemblies of either one or two ammoniated cations and two ammoniated electrons. The wave functions for the two electrons in the latter species overlap sufficiently so that the singlet state is lower in energy than the triplet by more than kT. The highly concentrated metal solutions are like molten metals in which the metal cations are ammoniated (Gold et al., 1962).

IV. REACTIONS IN LIQUID AMMONIA

A. COMPARISON OF AMMONIA WITH OTHER SOLVENTS

1. Solubilities

The most important function of a solvent is to dissolve other substances. Thus a knowledge of the kinds of substances which a solvent is capable of dissolving is of great importance. Hildebrand (1948) has discussed the properties of liquid ammonia which are significant in comparing solubilities in ammonia with solubilities in other solvents, and, in the following paragraphs, we shall cite solubility data to illustrate the effects of these properties.

The dielectric constant of ammonia (about 23 at the boiling point) is considerably lower than that of water (78·5), and yet significantly greater than that of acetic acid (6·4). As one might expect, the solubilities of ionic salts in ammonia lie, in general, between the values for the same salts in water and acetic acid. This generalization does not hold for salts whose anions are highly polarizable, because of London forces which are discussed in a later paragraph. Some typical solubilities for these three solvents are presented in Table IX. Salts with polynegative anions, such as sulphates, carbonates, and phosphates, are practically insoluble in liquid ammonia. In such salts, the solvation energy of the ions in ammonia is insufficient to compensate for the high lattice energy.

The abnormally high boiling point of ammonia is evidence of the tendency for ammonia to form hydrogen bonds. Substances which are capable of forming hydrogen bonds with ammonia have high solubilities in ammonia, just as they have in other hydrogen-bonding solvents such as water and hydrogen fluoride. Thus sugars, esters, amines, and phenols are very soluble in liquid ammonia.

TABLE IX

Solubilities of some Ionic Salts in Water, Ammonia, and Acetic Acid [a]
(g/100 g of solvent at 25°)

	Water	Ammonia	Acetic Acid
$LiNO_3$	52·2	243·7	10·3 (30°)
$NaNO_3$	91·8	97·6	0·17
KNO_3	37·8	10·4	0·18
NH_4OAc	148 (4°)	253·2	39·3
NaCl	37	3·02	0·073 (30°)

[a] Solubilities taken largely from Jander (1949) and Audrieth and Kleinberg (1953).

The basic character of ammonia is largely responsible for the high solubility of carboxylic acids, alcohols, and phenols in ammonia. In many cases, it may be difficult to distinguish the effects of ammonia's basicity from the effects of its tendency to hydrogen bond. A characteristic closely related to the basicity of ammonia is its tendency to co-ordinate to transition metal ions

TABLE X

Comparison of the Dispersion and Orientation Potentials for Water and Ammonia

	Dispersion potential	Orientation potential
H_2O	47	190
NH_3	93	84

such as Ni^{2+}, Cu^{2+}, Zn^{2+}, Ag^+, etc. Salts of such metal ions usually have high solubilities in ammonia. This co-ordinating characteristic of ammonia is clearly shown by the high solubilities of the silver halides in ammonia. At 25°, the solubilities (in g/100 g of ammonia) are 0·83, 5·92 and 206·8 for AgCl, AgBr, and AgI, respectively (Jander, 1949).

Molecules which do not react chemically with one another nevertheless are attracted by London, or Van der Waals, forces which arise from a coupling of the motion of the electrons in the separate atoms. The London interaction energy between two molecules may be approximated by the relation

$$E_{AB} = - \frac{3\alpha_A \alpha_B}{2R^6} \frac{I_A I_B}{I_A + I_B}$$

where α_A and α_B denote the polarizabilities of the molecules, R their distance apart, and I_A and I_B their ionization potentials. In the case of molecules which not only have high dipole moments, but also have enough electrons to be highly polarizable, the London forces may outweigh the dipole orientation effect. In Table X, the London and orientation potentials for water and ammonia are compared. It will be noted that the attractive potential for water depends mainly on its dipole moment, whereas that for ammonia depends almost equally on its dipole moment and its polarizability. Thus, although ammonia is generally a poorer solvent than water for ionic salts

TABLE XI

Solubility Parameters and Solubilities in Ammonia [a]

	$(\Delta E_v/V)^{\frac{1}{2}}$	Solubility in liquid NH_3
n-Hexane	7·3	5·1% at 20° [b] (compare with 0·014% at 15·5° for H_2O)
Carbon tetrachloride	8·6	soluble
Benzene	9·2	moderately soluble
Yellow phosphorus	13·1	soluble
Ammonia	13·1	
Water	23·8	infinitely miscible because of hydrogen-bonding, etc.
Mercury	30·7	practically insoluble

[a] Solubility parameters from Hildebrand and Scott (1962).   [b] Ishida (1958).

and highly polar molecules, it is a better solvent for non-polar molecules, particularly those with many electrons. The higher polarizability of the thiosulphate ion as compared with that of the sulphate ion is probably why sodium thiosulphate dissolves to the extent of 0·17 g/100 g of ammonia, whereas sodium sulphate has no detectable solubility in ammonia.

Similarly, the increase in anionic polarizability on going from chloride to iodide is probably the main cause of the increase in solubility on going from AgCl to AgI, for which the data are quoted above.

The "solubility parameter", or the square root of the energy of vapourization per cc, is a useful criterion of solubility. In the absence of strong dipole and acid–base effects, substances are most soluble in one another when their solubility parameters are of the same order of magnitude. The solubility parameters for several substances, and their solubilities in ammonia, are presented in Table XI.

2. Available Oxidation Potential Range*

If all reactions in liquid ammonia were thermodynamically controlled (as opposed to kinetically controlled), no oxidizing agent more powerful than nitrogen, and no reducing agent more powerful than hydrogen, would be capable of existence in liquid ammonia. The NH_3—N_2 and H_2—NH_3 couples, and their potentials in volts at 25°, in both acid and basic solutions are given below.

Acid Solutions $(1 \text{ M } NH_4^+)$:

$$\tfrac{1}{2}H_2 + NH_3 = NH_4^+ + e^- \qquad\qquad E^0 = 0 \qquad\qquad (6)$$

$$4NH_3 = \tfrac{1}{2}N_2 + 3NH_4^+ + 3e^- \qquad\qquad E^0 = -0.04. \qquad\quad (7)$$

Basic Solutions $(1 \text{ M } NH_2^-)$:

$$\tfrac{1}{2}H_2 + NH_2^- = NH_3 + e^- \qquad\qquad E^0 = 1.59 \qquad\qquad (8)$$

$$3NH_2^- = \tfrac{1}{2}N_2 + 2NH_3 + 3e^- \qquad\qquad E^0 = 1.55. \qquad\qquad (9)$$

Obviously with only a 0.04 V range available, hardly any species are thermodynamically stable in ammonia. Fortunately, however, both the hydrogen couple and the nitrogen couple usually exhibit "overvoltages" of about 1 V. So in acid solutions, the practical range of potentials for dissolved species is from 1.0 to −1.0 V. In basic solutions, where the hydrogen and nitrogen couples have potentials of about 1.6 V, the practical range extends from 2.6 to 0.6 V. Thus it is possible to work in liquid ammonia with species which are extremely strong reducing agents (such as the alkali metals) and with species which are extremely strong oxidizing agents (such as permanganates, ozonides, and superoxides).

In Fig. 3, the oxidation potentials for several couples are plotted against pH (pH = 0 corresponds to 1 M NH_4^+, and pH = 27 corresponds to 1 M NH_2^-). The dotted lines in Fig. 1 correspond to the approximate boundaries of the stability zones for redox couples. Thus we see that the ammoniacal electron is thermodynamically unstable with respect to hydrogen evolution at all pH values; however, in alkaline solutions and in the absence of catalysts, the

---

* A table of oxidation potentials in ammonia and a discussion of their application to liquid ammonia chemistry is given by Jolly (1956).

decomposition reaction is slow. In general, solid metals show negligible overvoltage effects in the reduction of ammonia. Thus, although the zinc couple falls within the dotted line boundaries, metallic zinc causes hydrogen

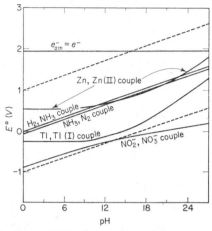

FIG. 3. Oxidation potentials in ammonia at 25° as a function of pH.

evolution both in acid solutions and in alkaline solutions (Bergstrom and Fernelius, 1933). The probable net reaction in alkaline solutions is

$$Zn + 2NH_2^- + 2NH_3 = Zn(NH_2)_4^{2-} + H_2. \tag{10}$$

Metallic thallium is, of course, inert toward ammonia at all pH values, and it happens that neither Tl^+ nor $Tl(NH_2)_2^-$ reacts with ammonia (Bergstrom and Fernelius, 1933). The nitrate ion is essentially inert toward ammonia in acid solutions, but in alkaline solutions nitrogen evolution slowly occurs (Bergstrom, 1940):

$$3K^+ + 3NH_2^- + 3NO_3^- = 3KOH + N_2 + 3NO_2^- + NH_3. \tag{11}$$

3. *Available Acid–Base Range*

The basicity of ammonia is about 10^{12} times greater than that of water, and the acidity of ammonia is about 10^{-25} times smaller than that of water. Consequently acids for which pK is less than ~ 12 in aqueous solutions are "strong" acids in liquid ammonia, and acids for which pK is greater than ~ 39 in aqueous solutions have practically no acidity in liquid ammonia. Acids of intermediate strength are weak acids in ammonia, and they may be differentiated according to their acid strengths. In Fig. 4, the pK ranges in which differentiation of acid strength is possible are indicated for the solvents acetic acid, water, ammonia, and benzene. On the same graph the aqueous pK values of several acids are indicated. It will be noted that, because of the smaller ionization constant of ammonia, a

wider range of acid strengths may be studied in ammonia than in the other
protonic solvents. In addition, because ammonia is more basic than either
acetic acid or water, the pK values of the acids which can be differentiated
are higher for ammonia than for acetic acid and water. Finally it may be

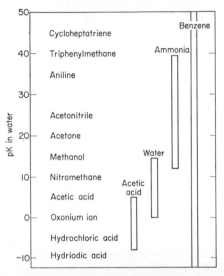

Fig. 4. Ranges of acidity differentiation for several solvents. Most of the pK values were
taken from Cram (1963). (The values for HCl and HI are taken from Pauling, 1960.)

noted that inasmuch as benzene is an aprotic solvent, it is possible in principle
to study any acid in benzene. In practice, however, difficulty is often encountered in dissolving ionic species in benzene.

Acids for which aqueous pK <12 react completely with ammonia to form
the corresponding ammonium salts. However, it must not be thought that
these acids (or ammonium salts) are strong in the sense that they are completely dissociated to independent ions in liquid ammonia. All salts, ammonium salts included, are weakly dissociated in ammonia. The "strength" of an
acid is best measured in terms of the equilibrium constant of the reaction

$$HX + NH_3 = (NH_4^+)(X^-). \tag{12}$$

However, rather than always indicate the formation of ion-pairs when these
are the principal species, it is customary to write the ions as independent
species, keeping in mind that considerable ionic aggregation takes place in
moderately concentrated solutions. Thus we write

$$HOAc + NH_3 = NH_4^+ + OAc^- \tag{13}$$

even though the ion-pair dissociation constant for ammonium acetate is
$7 \cdot 7 \times 10^{-5}$ (Gur'yanova and Pleskov, 1936).

Bases whose conjugate acids have aqueous pK values greater than $\sim$39 undergo essentially complete ammonolysis in liquid ammonia to form the amide ion. Two examples of such ammonolysis are given below.

$$KH + NH_3 = K^+ + NH_2^- + H_2 \tag{14}$$

$$Na_2O + NH_3 = NaNH_2 + NaOH. \tag{15}$$

The aqueous ionization constants of H_2 and OH^- have been estimated to be 10^{-38} and $<10^{-36}$, respectively (Latimer, 1952). Thus the criterion for basic ammonolysis is just barely satisfied in these cases.

Some oxidizing agents react with liquid ammonia to form nitrogen-containing products which can be looked upon either as oxidation-reduction products or as ammonolysis products. Consider, for example, the reactions of chlorine, bromine, and iodine:

$$X_2 + 2NH_3 = NH_4^+ + X^- + NH_2X. \tag{16}$$

(The halamine NH_2X reacts further at a lower rate to form species such as hydrazine and nitrogen.) The initial reaction can be looked upon as a self-oxidation-reduction of the halogen to the $+1$ and -2 oxidation states, but it is equally valid to consider the reaction as the ammonolytic cleavage of the X—X bond. Similarly, consider the following reaction (Franklin, 1934):

$$3K^+ + 3NH_2^- + NO_3^- = N_3^- + 3KOH + NH_3. \tag{17}$$

This reaction corresponds to the oxidation of amide to azide by nitrate, but it may be looked upon as the basic ammonolysis of the nitrate ion. (The $O{=}\overset{+}{N}\overset{\diagup O^-}{\diagdown O^-}$ ion is converted to the $\overset{-}{N}{=}\overset{+}{N}{=}\overset{-}{N}$ ion by replacing the $O{=}\overset{+}{N}$ bond by an $\overset{-}{N}{=}\overset{+}{N}$ bond and by replacing the $\overset{+}{N}\overset{\diagup O^-}{\diagdown O^-}$ bonds by an $\overset{+}{N}{=}\overset{-}{N}$ bond.)

4. *Ease of Handling*

The low boiling point of ammonia $(-33\cdot4°)$ is an obvious disadvantage when working with this solvent. However, in many types of work it is not necessary to use any refrigeration when handling liquid ammonia. Because of the high heat of vapourization, the liquid may be kept at its boiling point in open containers such as beakers, flasks etc., without too rapid boiling of the ammonia. The rate of evaporation of ammonia in dewar flasks (even when unsilvered for ease in observation) is practically negligible. The vapour pressure of the liquid at room temperature (8–10 atm) is low enough so that it may be handled in sealed glass ampoules without much danger of explosion. Techniques for handling liquid ammonia are discussed by Audrieth and Kleinberg (1953), Franklin (1935), Jolly (1960) and Sanderson (1948).

The viscosity of ammonia at its boiling point is only one-quarter that of water at room temperature. The low viscosity of ammonia is a definite advantage when filtering ammonia solutions and when carrying out heterogeneous reactions which require the diffusion of solutes through the liquid.

B. IONIC SOLVATION

1. *Thermodynamic Functions for Ammonation and Hydration Processes*

The free energies of formation of pairs of oppositely-charged ions are found to be of approximately the same magnitude in ammonia as they are in water, if one restricts the comparison to ions which do not form abnormally strong ammonia complexes (Jolly, 1953, 1956). The data for a few pairs of ions of this type are presented in Table XII. We shall claim as a reasonable

TABLE XII

Free Energies of Formation in Water and Ammonia

Ion pair	ΔF_f^0(kcal mole^{-1})(25°) in water	in ammonia
$Na^+ + F^-$	$-128 \cdot 7$	$-124 \cdot 4$
$Li^+ + I^-$	$-82 \cdot 6$	-83
$Rb^+ + NO_3^-$	$-93 \cdot 9$	$-90 \cdot 3$
$NH_4^+ + Br^-$	$-43 \cdot 6$	$-42 \cdot 6$
$Na^+ + ClO_3^-$	$-63 \cdot 2$	$-61 \cdot 3$

approximation for ions of the type given in Table XII, that the free energy of transfer of an individual ion from water to ammonia is zero. We shall therefore assume that the free energy of transfer of an ion which forms strong ammonia complexes can be equated to the sum of the free energies of transfer of that ion and an equivalent number of non-ammonia-complexing counter-ions. We shall call such ionic free energies of transfer "experimental" free energies of transfer. It is interesting to compare such "experimental" free energies of transfer with the free energies of the aqueous reactions of type

$$M(H_2O)_x^{Z+} + xHN_3 = M(NH_3)_x^{Z+} + xH_2O. \tag{18}$$

The free energy (in kcal mole^{-1}) of such a reaction, using the 1 M solution as the standard state for both water and ammonia, is given by the expression

$$\Delta F_K^\circ = -1 \cdot 36 \, (\log K + x \log 55) \tag{19}$$

where K is the usual equilibrium constant for aqueous solutions. In Table XIII, values for ΔF_K° may be compared with the corresponding "experimental" free energies of transfer, ΔF_t^0. It can be seen that the correspondence is very close. Hence we may estimate the standard free energy of formation of an ion in liquid ammonia from the relation:

$$\Delta F_f^0(NH_3) = \Delta F_f^0(H_2O) + 16Z - 1 \cdot 36 \, (\log K + x \log 55)$$

where $\Delta F_f^0(NH_3)$ and $\Delta F_f^0(H_2O)$ are the standard free energies of formation in ammonia and water, respectively, and Z is the charge (taking account

TABLE XIII

Calculated and "Experimental" Free Energies of Transfer from Water to Ammonia
(kcal mole^{-1} at 25°)

Ion	x	$-\Delta F_K^0$	$-\Delta F_t^0$
Hg^{2+}	4	36	40
Cu^{2+}	5	29	29
Zn^{2+}	4	22	22
Cu^+	2	20	20
H^+	1	15	16
Ag^+	2	14	17

of sign) of the ion. The term $16Z$ arises from the fact that $\Delta F_f^0 = 0$ for the hydrogen ion in both solvents, and $\Delta F_t^0 = -16$ kcal mole^{-1} for the hydrogen ion. Similar equations have been given for estimating ionic entropies and heats of formation in ammonia (Jolly, 1956).

2. Kinetics of Ammonia Exchange Reactions

The ammoniated hydrogen ion, or ammonium ion, is the simplest ion one can have in liquid ammonia. The rate at which protons move from ammonium ions to ammonia molecules (or the rate at which solvent ammonia molecules displace ammonia molecules from ammonium ions) is much too great to measure by classical chemical techniques (Nyman *et al.*, 1950). However Ogg (1954) has shown that it is possible to measure this rate by n.m.r. techniques. The proton magnetic resonance spectrum of pure liquid ammonia consists of three peaks, due to the spin-spin coupling of the protons with the ^{14}N nucleus. A trace of ammonium salt causes the signal to change to a single line. The change is attributed to the reaction

$$NH_3 + NH_4^+ \rightleftharpoons NH_4^+ + NH_3 , \qquad (19)$$

and from a rough estimate of the ammonium ion concentration required to cause collapse of the triplet, Ogg calculated a rate constant of about 5×10^8 litre mole^{-1} sec^{-1}. He estimated rate constants of the same order of magnitude for the reactions

$$NH_3 + NH_2^- \rightleftharpoons NH_2^- + NH_3 \tag{20}$$

and

$$NH_3 + H_2O \rightleftharpoons NH_4^+ + OH^-. \tag{21}$$

Wiesendanger *et al.* (1957) have shown, using ^{15}N, that the exchange of ammonia molecules between the solvent and the ions $Ag(NH_3)_2^+$, $Cu(NH_3)_4^{2+}$, and $Ni(NH_3)_6^{2+}$ is too fast to measure by classical methods, but they were able to show that the ions $Cr(NH_3)_6^{3+}$ and $Co(NH_3)_6^{3+}$ exchange their ammonia molecules relatively slowly with the solvent. In the case of $Cr(NH_3)_6^{3+}$, a bimolecular rate constant $1 \cdot 3 \times 10^{-6}$ litre mole^{-1} sec^{-1} was measured. Hunt *et al.* (1963) measured the rate of exchange of ^{14}N between $Ni(NH_3)_6^{2+}$ and the solvent ammonia molecules by n.m.r. line broadening measurements. Because the rate of the corresponding exchange reaction in water was found to be independent of the ammonia concentration and to be of practically the same magnitude as that for the exchange in anhydrous ammonia, they proposed that the reaction is unimolecular and reported the rate constant $k = 4 \cdot 7 \times 10^4$ sec^{-1} at 25°.

C. ACID–BASE REACTIONS

1. *The Nature of the Ammonium and Amide Ions*

The ammonium ion and amide ion are analogs of the oxonium ion and hydroxide ion, respectively. Thus the neutralization of a strong acid with a strong base in ammonia is represented by the equation

$$NH_4^+ + NH_2^- \rightarrow 2\,NH_3 \tag{22}$$

whereas the analogous reaction in water is usually written as

$$H^+ + OH^- \rightarrow H_2O. \tag{23}$$

The analogy breaks down, however, when one considers the mobilities of the ions. The aqueous oxonium ion and aqueous hydroxide ion have ionic

TABLE XIV

Ionic Conductances in Ammonia and Water

Ion	Equivalent ionic conductance (cm^2 ohm^{-1} eq.$^{-1}$)	
	Liquid NH_3, $-33 \cdot 5$°	Water,[c] 25°
Na^+	158 [a]	50·1
NH_4^+	142 [a]	73·4
H^+		349·8
NO_3^-	177 [a]	71·4
NH_2^-	166 [b]	
OH^-		198·0

[a] Laitinen and Shoemaker (1950).   [b] Hawes (1933).   [c] MacInnes (1939).

conductances which are several times as large as the conductances of ordinary $+1$ and -1 ions (see Table XIV). These abnormally high conductances are explained in terms of a mechanism, the essentials of which were first described by de Grotthuss (1806). Oxonium ion migration is accomplished when the proton of an oxonium ion moves the small distance necessary to partially break its bond to the oxygen atom and to form a bond to the oxygen atom of the adjacent hydrogen-bonded water molecule:

$$
\begin{array}{cccc}
\text{H} & \text{H} & \text{H} & \text{H} \\
| & | & | & | \\
\text{H—O—H} \cdots \text{O—H} \rightarrow \text{H—O} \cdots \text{H—O—H} \\
+ & & & +
\end{array}
$$

Hydroxide ion migration is quite similar:

$$
\begin{array}{cccc}
\text{H} & \text{H} \ \text{H} & \text{H} \\
| & | \ | & | \\
\text{O} \cdots \text{H—O} \rightarrow \text{O—H} \cdots \text{O} \\
- & & -
\end{array}
$$

Analogous processes do not contribute appreciably to the mobilities of the NH_4^+ and NH_2^- ions in ammonia because of the much weaker hydrogen bonds in this solvent. (The weaker a hydrogen bond, the higher the barrier between the two equilibrium positions for the proton.) It is clear from the data in Table XIV that the mobilities of the ammonium and amide ions in ammonia are similar to the mobilities of ordinary univalent ions in the same solvent. We have noted above that the rate constants for the reactions

$$NH_4^+ + NH_3 \rightarrow NH_3 + NH_4^+ \tag{24}$$
$$NH_2^- + NH_3 \rightarrow NH_3 + NH_2^- \tag{25}$$

are of the order of magnitude 5×10^8 litre mole^{-1} sec^{-1}. The rate constants for the corresponding aqueous reactions

$$H_3O^+ + H_2O \rightarrow H_2O + H_3O^+ \tag{26}$$
$$OH^- + H_2O \rightarrow H_2O + OH^- \tag{27}$$

are $1 \cdot 1 \times 10^{10}$ and 5×10^9 litre mole^{-1} sec^{-1}, respectively (Loewenstein and Szöke, 1962).

2. Determination of Ammonium Ion Concentration

Platinum black electrodes show very little hydrogen overvoltage in liquid ammonia and, when equilibrated with hydrogen, may be used as reversible hydrogen electrodes. Pleskov and Monoszon (1935) used the hydrogen electrode in ammonia at $-50°$ to determine the activity coefficients for NH_4NO_3 and NH_4Cl. By studying the cell

Pt, H_2 | $0 \cdot 1$ M NH_4NO_3 | saturated KNO_3 | $KNH_2(C)$ | Pt, H_2,

they determined the self-ionization constant for liquid ammonia:

$$2NH_3 = NH_4^+ + NH_2^- \qquad K = 1 \cdot 9 \times 10^{-33} \text{ at } -50°.$$

Using the heat of reaction, $\Delta H° = 26·1$ kcal/mole (Mulder and Schmidt, 1951), one calculates $K = 5·1 \times 10^{-27}$ at 25°. This is to be compared with the value $2·2 \times 10^{-28}$ calculated from the free energy of solution of sodium amide (Coulter *et al.*, 1959). For most purposes, the value $K = 10^{-27}$ is sufficiently accurate. If we set up a pH scale using the relation pH = $-\log [\text{NH}_4^+]$, we calculate that pure liquid ammonia has a pH of 13·5 at 25°.

Zintl and Neumayr (1930) were unsuccessful with the hydrogen electrode, but they did find the quinhydrone electrode to be reproducible. They obtained self-consistent results with the concentration cell

Pt | quinhydrone (C_1), NH$_4$Cl (c_1) | | quinhydrone (C_2), NH$_4$Cl (c_2) | Pt

at $-50°$.

Heyn and Bergin (1953) attempted the use of glass electrodes in liquid ammonia solutions. Their cells were of the type

Pb | 0·1 M_1Pb(NO$_3$)$_2$, NH$_4$NO$_3$ (C) | glass membrane |

0·1 M Pb(NO$_3$)$_2$, 0·1 M NH$_4$NO$_3$ | Pb.

Each of the several glasses tried failed to show glass-electrode response. It appears that the ammonium ions in liquid ammonia are not in equilibrium with ions on the surface of the glass electrode. Perhaps the ammonia dehydrates the glass to such an extent that protons are no longer mobile in the glass. It would be interesting to try a sheet of cation exchange resin in the ammonium form as a pH-sensitive membrane.

A number of acid–base indicators, including some that are used in aqueous solutions, have been studied in liquid ammonia (Shatenshtein, 1939, and Franklin and Kraus, 1900). Some of these are listed in Table XV with their

TABLE XV

Acid–Base Indicators in Liquid Ammonia

Indicator	Colour of solution in pure NH$_3$	Basic solution	Acidic solution
Phenolphthalein	pale red	deep red	colourless
Carmine	dirty red	blue	red
Saffranine	crimson	blue	crimson
m-Nitroaniline	yellow	green	yellow
p-Nitroaniline	yellow	orange	yellow
o-Nitroaniline	yellow	red	yellow

colours in acid and basic solutions. Cuthrell *et al.* (1963) have determined the ionization constants and dissociation constants for the weak acids *o*- and *p*-nitroacetanilide by a spectrophotometric method. These compounds are colourless in acidic solutions and yellow-brown in alkaline solutions. The ionization, to form an ion pair, may be represented by the general equation

$$HX + NH_3 = NH_4^+X^-; \qquad K_i = [NH_4^+X^-]/[HX]$$

and the dissociation by the equation

$$NH_4^+X^- = NH_4^+ + X^-; \qquad K_d = [NH_4^+][X^-]/[NH_4^+X^-].$$

The equilibrium constants, corrected to infinite dilution, are:

o-nitroacetanilide: $K_i = 2 \cdot 2 \times 10^{-2}$; $\qquad K_d = 2 \cdot 2 \times 10^{-4}$

p-nitroacetanilide: $K_i = 9 \cdot 3 \times 10^{-2}$; $\qquad K_d = 0 \cdot 89 \times 10^{-4}$.

In solutions of very high pH, the concentration of amide ion may be determined spectrophotometrically. The amide ion absorbs at 3410 Å (Ogg et al., 1933).

Watt et al. (1955) have potentiometrically titrated several acids in liquid ammonia with potassium amide. A "difference indicator" electrode system was used, in which one electrode is immersed in the solution being titrated, and the other is immersed in a solution having a composition the same as the initial composition of the titrated solution but separated from the bulk of the solution by a capillary tube (Zintl et al., 1931; Watt and Sowards, 1955). From the positions of the inflection points in the titration of mixtures of acids, the following order of acid strength was determined:

$$NH_4^+ > H_2NC(NH)NH_3^+ > H_2NC(S)NH_2 > H_2NC(O)NH_2 > H_2NC(NH)NH_2 >$$
$$H_2NC(S)NH^- > H_2NC(O)NH^- > H_2NC(NH)NH^- > NH_3.$$

Unfortunately this method is not suitable for the quantitative measurement of acid strength.

3. Base-Catalysed Exchange Reactions

Weak acids exchange their hydrogen for deuterium when they are dissolved in liquid ND_3. The exchange rate constants for several hydrocarbons

TABLE XVI

Comparison of Deuterium Exchange Rate Constants at 120° with Aqueous pK Values
(No Amide Catalyst Added)

Hydrocarbon	Rate constant [a] (sec^{-1})	Aqueous pK [b]
Indene	4×10^1	~ 21
Fluorene	2×10^{-2}	~ 31
Triphenylmethane	2×10^{-7}	~ 40
Diphenylmethane	7×10^{-9}	~ 42

[a] Shatenshtein (1962). [b] Cram (1963).

are given in Table XVI. It will be noted that the more acidic a hydrocarbon, the more rapidly it exchanges its hydrogen with ammonia. Probably these rate constants correspond to the rate constants for the ionization of the hydrocarbons.

Extremely weak acids such as benzene do not undergo exchange in deuteroammonia in the absence of a catalyst. However, in the presence of a strong base such as potassium amide, exchange takes place. The mechanism for exchange is probably of the following type:

$$RH + ND_2^- \rightarrow R^- + NHD_2 \tag{28}$$
$$R^- + ND_3 \rightarrow RD + ND_2^-. \tag{29}$$

Some experimental rate constants for benzene are presented in Table XVII. These constants are pseudo first-order rate constants, calculated assuming (for convenience) that the rate is independent of the potassium amide concentration. It can be seen that in dilute solution the rate is approximately proportional to the potassium amide concentration, and that at higher concentrations the apparent rate constant falls off. This fall in catalyst activity is probably attributable to the formation of ion pairs.

TABLE XVII

Deuterium Exchange Rate Constants for Benzene in Potassium Amide Solutions
(Shatenshtein, 1962)

(Constants, in sec^{-1}, calculated assuming rate = k[benzene].)

$\theta(°C)$	Molarity of potassium amide					
	0·010	0·014	0·021	0·059	0·19	0·43
−30				4×10^{-7}		
0	4×10^{-6}		$7·3 \times 10^{-6}$			$8·9 \times 10^{-5}$
25	$4·4 \times 10^{-5}$	$5·7 \times 10^{-5}$	$8·6 \times 10^{-5}$	$1·8 \times 10^{-4}$	$4·2 \times 10^{-4}$	
40	$1·6 \times 10^{-4}$	$3·1 \times 10^{-4}$				

It has been found that the rate of exchange of a deuterium atom in the *ortho* position of a substituted benzene is highly sensitive to the electronegativity of the substituent group. Thus the rate constant for fluorobenzene is more than 10^7 times greater than the rate constant for toluene. If we plot the logarithm of the relative exchange rate constants for substituted benzenes against the aqueous pK values for the corresponding substituted acetic acids, a straight line is obtained, as shown in Fig. 5. This is further evidence that the rate of exchange parallels the acidity of the hydrocarbon.

The exchange of hydrogen between organic compounds and ammonia can be used for the preparation of deuterated compounds. Some compounds which have been fully deuterated in this way are benzene, naphthalene,

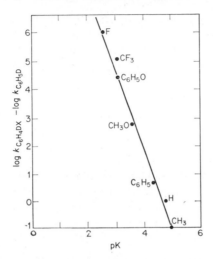

FIG. 5. Correlation between exchange rate constants for substituted benzenes and aqueous pK values for the corresponding substituted acetic acids.

phenanthrene, biphenyl, triphenylmethane, diphenylmethane, bibenzyl, and pyridine (Shatenshtein, 1962).

Wilmarth and Dayton (1953) observed that the conversion of *para*-hydrogen to *ortho*-hydrogen is catalysed by liquid ammonia solutions of potassium amide. The exchange of deuterium gas was found to proceed at approximately the same rate in these solutions, and the initial product was found to be HD. In each case, the rate was found to be proportional to the concentrations of amide ion and hydrogen (*para*-hydrogen or deuterium). They reported a rate constant at $-50°$ of 130 litre mole^{-1} sec^{-1}. The data are consistent with the following type of mechanism:

$$D_2 + NH_2^- \rightarrow D^- + NH_2D \tag{30}$$
$$D^- + NH_3 \rightarrow HD + NH_2^-. \tag{31}$$

A study of the deuterium exchange reaction over a wide concentration range at various temperatures indicated that the reaction is catalysed both by the free amide ion and by the undissociated potassium amide (Bar-Eli and Klein, 1962). The calculated rate constants at $-61°$ are $k_{NH_2^-} = 36$ litre mole^{-1} sec^{-1} and $k_{KNH_2} = 1.7$ litre mole^{-1} sec^{-1}. The activation energy for the amide ion reaction was found to be 7.5 kcal mole^{-1}. From the exchange rates for D_2, HD, and HT, and from the *para*-hydrogen conversion rate, the following isotope effects were calculated:

$$2k_{HD}/k_{D_2} = 1.28 \pm 0.03$$
$$k_{HD}/k_{HT} = 1.64 \pm 0.07$$
$$2k_{H_2}/k_{D_2} = 2.36 \pm 0.30.$$

The amide-catalysed exchange of hydrogen with ammonia is under serious consideration as the basis of a method for concentrating deuterium in ammonia (Haul *et al.*, 1961; Dirian and Grandcollot, 1961; Bourke and Lee, 1961a,b; Brown and Roberts, 1961; Rebora, 1962).

4. *Acid-Catalysed Reactions*

Many esters undergo ammonolysis when treated with liquid ammonia.

$$RCO_2R + NH_3 \rightarrow RCONH_2 + ROH. \tag{32}$$

Ammonium salts catalyse such ammonolyses, just as aqueous acids catalyse the corresponding hydrolyses. The order of catalytic activity for ammonium salts is, however, the reverse of the order of acid strengths based on conductance studies. For example, in the ammonolysis of ethyl benzoate, Fellinger and Audrieth (1938) found the catalytic effect to decrease in the following order: ammonium benzoate$>NH_4Cl>NH_4Br>NH_4ClO_4$. It was later observed that sodium salts are also capable of catalysing ester ammonolysis. Such electrolytes are not as effective as the ammonium salts, but it seems clear that all these catalysed ester ammonolyses are best looked upon as examples of electrolyte catalysis (Audrieth and Kleinberg, 1953).

The exchange of nitrogen between carboxylic acid amides and liquid ammonia has been studied by the use of ^{15}N-labelled ammonia (Heyns *et al.*, 1958). The exchange is catalysed by ammonium chloride, and the following mechanism has been proposed:

$$
\overset{\displaystyle +}{\underset{\displaystyle \downarrow}{\overset{\displaystyle OH_2}{\underset{\displaystyle \quad}{\quad}}}}
$$

$$RCONH_2 + {}^{15}NH_4^+ \rightleftharpoons R-\underset{\displaystyle \underset{\displaystyle NH_2}{|}}{\overset{\displaystyle \overset{\displaystyle +OH_2}{|}}{C}}-{}^{15}NH_2 \tag{33}$$

$$\downarrow$$

$$RCO^{15}NH_2 + NH_4^+$$

D. REACTIONS OF METAL SOLUTIONS

1. *Systematics*

An enormous number of synthetic reactions involving metal–ammonia solutions have been carried out. These reactions have been reviewed by Birch (1950), Birch and Smith (1958), Watt (1950 and 1957), and Fowles and Nicholls (1962). Practically nothing is known of the mechanisms of these reactions; nevertheless some systematization is possible by considering the products of the reactions. Most reactions involving metal–ammonia solutions may be considered as being initiated by one of the following three steps:

(1) simple electron addition without bond cleavage,

$$e_{am}^- + X \to X^- \tag{34}$$

(2) bond cleavage by the addition of one electron,

$$e_{am}^- + X\!-\!Y \to X\!\cdot + Y^- \tag{35}$$

or (3) bond cleavage by the addition of two electrons,

$$2e_{am}^- + X\!-\!Y \to X^- + Y^-. \tag{36}$$

Electron addition without bond cleavage. The reactions of the electron with molecular oxygen and the nitrite ion involve the formation of products which have reasonable kinetic stabilities in liquid ammonia:

$$e_{am}^- + O_2 \to O_2^- \tag{37}$$

$$e_{am}^- + NO_2^- \to NO_2^{2-}. \tag{38}$$

The rates of these reactions in liquid ammonia are unknown. Thus it is interesting that, even though the electron and the O_2^- and NO_2^{2-} ions are extremely short-lived species in water, the rates of these reactions in water have been measured (Czapski and Schwarz, 1962; Dorfman, 1963).

Some very interesting reductions of transition metal ions appear to involve the simple addition of one or more electrons:

$$e_{am}^- + MnO_4^- \to MnO_4^{2-} \tag{39}$$

$$2e_{am}^- + Ni(CN)_4^{2-} \to Ni(CN)_4^{4-} \tag{40}$$

$$2e_{am}^- + Pd(CN)_4^{2-} \to Pd(CN)_4^{4-} \tag{41}$$

$$2e^- + Pt(NH_3)_4^{2+} \to Pt(NH_3)_4 \tag{42}$$

$$2e^- + Pt(en)_2^{2+} \to Pt(en)_2. \tag{43}$$

Bond cleavage by the addition of one electron. The reactions of the electron with protonic acids fall in this category. The kinetics and mechanisms of the following three examples are discussed in the following sections.

$$e_{am}^- + NH_3 \to NH_2^- + \tfrac{1}{2}H_2 \tag{44}$$

$$e_{am}^- + NH_4^+ \to NH_3 + \tfrac{1}{2}H_2 \tag{45}$$

$$e_{am}^- + EtOH \to EtO^- + \tfrac{1}{2}H_2. \tag{46}$$

The reaction of the electron with organic sulphides may be interpreted in terms of the intermediate formation of R· radicals:

$$e_{am}^- + R_2S \to RS^- + \tfrac{1}{2}R_2. \tag{47}$$

The following reaction is an unusual case in which a stable radical is formed:

$$e_{am}^- + (C_2H_5)_3SnBr \to (C_2H_5)_3Sn\!\cdot + Br^-. \tag{48}$$

Bond cleavage by the addition of two electrons. When a bond is broken by the addition of two electrons, either two anions or a "di-anion" form:

$$2e_{am}^- + Ge_2H_6 \rightarrow 2GeH_3^- \tag{49}$$

$$2e_{am}^- + C_6H_5NHNH_2 \rightarrow C_6H_5NH^- + NH_2^- \tag{50}$$

$$2e_{am}^- + C_6H_5 - N{=}O \rightarrow C_6H_5 - N^- - O^-. \tag{51}$$

However, one of the anions usually undergoes ammonolysis, as in the following examples:

$$2e_{am}^- + N{\equiv}N^+ - O^- \rightarrow N{\equiv}N + O^{2-}$$

$$\downarrow NH_3$$

$$OH^- + NH_2^- \tag{52}$$

$$2e_{am}^- + N{\equiv}C - O^- \rightarrow N{\equiv}C^- + O^{2-}$$

$$\downarrow NH_3$$

$$OH^- + NH_2^- \tag{53}$$

$$2e_{am}^- + Br - C_2H_5 \rightarrow Br^- + C_2H_5^-$$

$$\downarrow NH_3$$

$$C_2H_6 + NH_2^- \tag{54}$$

$$2e_{am}^- + RCH{=}CH_2 \rightarrow RCH - CH_2^{2-}$$

$$\downarrow 2NH$$

$$RCH_2CH_3 + 2NH_2^-. \tag{55}$$

It has been observed that many reductions which take place in liquid ammonia solutions containing both an alkali metal and a protonic acid such as an alcohol or water do not occur at all in the absence of the protonic acid (Birch, 1950; Birch and Smith, 1958). Thus benzene does not appreciably react with sodium in ammonia. However, in the presence of alcohol, reduction to 1,4-dihydrobenzene takes place. Behaviour of this type is probably best explained in terms of the buffering action of the alcohol or other protonic acid. The reduction of a species X to H_2X may be considered to proceed by the following type of mechanism:

In most cases, the intermediate X^{2-} is thermodynamically very unstable; consequently practically no reaction proceeds via this intermediate. The ratio between the concentrations of HX and X^- depends on the pH of the solution. In the absence of any added protonic acid, the pH will soon reach quite high values as a consequence of the reaction proceeding to a slight extent; hence, unless HX is an exceedingly weak acid, the HX concentration will drop, and the reaction will essentially stop. In the presence of an added protonic acid, the solution will be buffered at a pH depending on the strength of the acid. If the added acid is sufficiently strong, the $[HX]/[X^-]$ ratio will be high, and the reduction will proceed steadily.

2. *The Reaction of Metals with Ammonia*

All metal-ammonia solutions are metastable. If they are allowed to stand for long periods, or if suitable catalysts are present, decomposition to hydrogen and the metal amide occurs:

$$M + xNH_3 \rightarrow \frac{x}{2}H_2 + M(NH_2)_x. \tag{56}$$

In dilute solutions of sodium or potassium (the amides of which are soluble), the net reaction is

$$e_{am}^- + NH_3 \rightarrow NH_2^- + \tfrac{1}{2}H_2. \tag{57}$$

If pure reagents and clean apparatus are used, and if the solutions are kept cold, decomposition may be held to 0·1% per day (Dewald and Lepoutre, 1954). Warshawsky (1963) has pointed out that an initial hydrogen evolution from metal–ammonia solutions in glassware is attributable to reaction of the metal with a strongly adsorbed layer of water on the glass surface. This water may be removed from a Pyrex surface by baking at 400° for 200 hours *in vacuo.*

The reaction of potassium with liquid ammonia at room temperature has been followed spectrophotometrically by Chou *et al.* (1963). These investigators found that the reaction was first order in metal for the first 75% of reaction and reported half-times of 9-13 hours for initial concentrations in the range 2×10^{-4}—$1\cdot 13 \times 10^{-3}$ M. Because the reaction was observed to take place at different rates in different reaction vessels, and because other investigators have observed entirely different rates, it is believed that the reaction is wall-catalysed. I. Warshawsky (unpublished results) has observed that the decomposition of dilute ($< 10^{-4}$ M) solutions of sodium in ammonia at $-78°$ in the presence of platinum foil is zero order in sodium. A rate constant of $1\cdot 5 \times 10^{-9}$ moles of H_2 cm^{-2} h^{-1} was reported. The first-order and zero-order behaviours observed in the above studies indicate that the rates are independent of the ammonium ion concentration and the amide ion concentration (in the concentration ranges under study).

A reaction of more fundamental interest than the surface-catalysed reactions described above is the homogeneous reaction of the electron with ammonia. It may be that this reaction is too slow to observe directly. If we assume that the rate of the homogeneous reaction is less than that of the presumably heterogeneous reaction observed by Chou *et al.*, we calculate, for the first-order rate constant, $k < 1\cdot5 \times 10^{-5}$ sec^{-1}. This may be compared with the rate constant $k < 4\cdot4 \times 10^{4}$ sec^{-1} for the relatively fast reaction of the aqueous electron with water (Dorfman and Taub, 1963):

$$e_{aq}^{-} + H_2O \rightarrow H + OH^{-}. \tag{58}$$

The large difference in the reactivity of the electron in water and ammonia is not unexpected. A higher activation energy for the liquid ammonia process,

$$e_{am}^{-} + NH_3 \rightarrow H + NH_2^{-} \tag{59}$$

than for the aqueous process is consistent with the estimated heats of reaction, $+33$ kcal mole^{-1} for the liquid ammonia process, and -10 kcal mole^{-1} for the aqueous process.

The mechanism of the homogeneous reaction is, of course, unknown. One can postulate that the atomic hydrogen formed in the initial step dimerizes,

$$2H \rightarrow H_2, \tag{60}$$

or that it reacts further with electrons to form the hydride ion,

$$H + e_{am}^{-} \rightarrow H^{-} \tag{61}$$

$$H^{-} + NH_3 \rightarrow H_2 + NH_2^{-}. \tag{62}$$

3. *The Reaction of Metals with the Ammonium Ion*

The ammonium ion reacts very rapidly with the electron in ammonia.

$$NH_4^{+} + e_{am}^{-} \rightarrow NH_3 + \tfrac{1}{2}H_2 \tag{63}$$

The half-time for the reaction of 10^{-4} M electrons with 10^{-4} M ammonium ions is less than 1 second. This observation places a lower limit of 10^{4} litre mole^{-1} sec^{-1} on the second-order rate constant. We believe that the rate constant for the $NH_4^{+} + e_{am}^{-}$ reaction cannot be greater than the rate constant of the exchange of protons between NH_4^{+} and NH_3, for which the value 5×10^{8} litre mole^{-1} sec^{-1} has been reported. Therefore we place the $(NH_4^{+} + e^{-})$ rate constant between the limits of 10^{4} and 5×10^{8} litre mole^{-1} sec^{-1}.

The rate constant for the corresponding reaction of the aqueous electron and the aqueous proton is $2\cdot3 \times 10^{10}$ litre mole^{-1} sec^{-1} (Dorfman and Taub, 1963):

$$e_{aq}^{-} + H_{aq}^{+} \rightarrow H. \tag{64}$$

There are at least two ways in which it should be possible to determine the rate of reaction of the electron with the ammonium ion in liquid ammonia. First, it should be possible to utilize the same techniques of pulse radiolysis (Dorfman, 1963) and photolysis (Swenson *et al.*, 1963) which have been used to study reactions of the aqueous electron. Second, it should be possible to study the decomposition of metals in solutions which are buffered at an ammonium ion concentration such that the reaction proceeds at a conveniently measurable rate. We have interpreted data on the reaction of sodium in ethanol–ethoxide solutions in this way in the following section.

4. The Reaction of Sodium with Ethanol

Kelly *et al.* (1962) followed the reaction of sodium with ethanol in liquid ammonia at $-33.4°$ by measuring the evolved hydrogen as a function of time

$$e_{am}^- + \text{EtOH} \rightarrow \text{EtO}^- + \tfrac{1}{2}\text{H}_2. \tag{65}$$

They obtained data over a remarkably wide time interval. The data for a run in which the sodium was in excess are presented in Table XVIII in the form of the fraction of the alcohol reacted as a function of time. The investigators noted that, during the first 25% of reaction, the reaction was first-order in alcohol and essentially zero-order in sodium. During the second 25% of reaction, the reaction did not appear to be of definite kinetic order, but for the last half of the reaction, the reaction was first-order in both alcohol and sodium, or second-order overall. We believe that the data are most easily explained in terms of the following mechanism:

$$\text{EtOH} + \text{NH}_3 \overset{k_1}{\underset{k_2}{\rightleftharpoons}} \text{NH}_4^+ + \text{EtO}^- \tag{66}$$

$$\text{NH}_4^+ + e_{am}^- \overset{k_3}{\rightarrow} \text{NH}_3 + \tfrac{1}{2}\text{H}_2. \tag{67}$$

If we assume a low, steady-state concentration for the ammonium ion, we calculate the rate law:

$$-\frac{d[\text{EtOH}]}{dt} = \frac{k_1[\text{EtOH}][e_{am}^-]}{(k_2/k_3)[\text{EtO}^-] + [e_{am}^-]}.$$

Qualitatively the data fit this rate law. At the beginning of the reaction, when the EtO^- concentration is very low, the rate law reduces to

$$-\frac{d[\text{EtOH}]}{dt} = k_1[\text{EtOH}].$$

Under these conditions, the rate-determining step is the ionization of the ethanol. During the last stages of the reaction, when $(k_2/k_3)[\text{EtO}^-] \gg [e_{am}^-]$, the rate law reduces to

$$-\frac{d[\text{EtOH}]}{dt} = \frac{k_1[\text{EtOH}][e_{am}^-]}{(k_2/k_3)[\text{EtO}^-]}.$$

Under these conditions, the rate-determining step is the reaction of the ammonium ion with the electron. The accuracy with which the data may be quantitatively represented by the complete rate law can be seen from the "Powell plot" in Fig. 6 (Frost and Pearson, 1961). Here we have plotted the fraction of reaction, f, against the logarithm of time, t. The circles correspond to the experimental points, and the solid curve has been calculated from the complete rate law, using the constants $k_1 = 0 \cdot 0303$ sec^{-1} and $k_2/k_3 = 460$. The discrepancy between the experimental points and the calculated

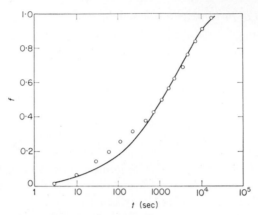

Fig. 6. Plot of fraction reaction *vs* logarithm, of time for sodium–ethanol reaction (Kelly *et al.*, 1962).

curve in the region $f = 0 \cdot 10$ to $f = 0 \cdot 40$ is not understood. It does not appear that the discrepancy may be accounted for by ion-pairing, by assuming an initial reaction of the sodium with the ammonia, or by a rate-law term first order in ethanol and first order in sodium.

TABLE XVIII

The Reaction of Sodium with Ethanol (from data of Kelly *et al.*, 1962)

Initial sodium: 0·96 M
Initial ethanol: 0·34 M

t (sec)	f (fraction reaction)	t (sec)	f (fraction reaction)
~3	0·012	1200	0·495
10	0·065	1680	0·565
30	0·141	2400	0·620
60	0·198	3600	0·687
120	0·254	4800	0·760
240	0·315	7200	0·840
480	0·377	10,800	0·910
720	0·425	18,000	0·975
		28,800	1·000

The pK_a of ethanol in water is ~ 17 (Cram, 1963). If we use the rule that pK values in ammonia are 12 units lower than those in water, and estimate an ion-pair dissociation constant of 10^{-4} for NH_4OEt in ammonia, we may calculate an overall ionization and dissociation constant for ethanol (k_1/k_2) in ammonia of 10^{-9}. From our values for k_1 and k_2/k_3 we may then calculate the rate constant for the reaction of the electron with the ammonium ion, $k_3 \sim 10^5$ litre mole^{-1} sec^{-1}. It will be noted that this value lies within the limits which was imposed above.

5. Comparison with Other Metal Solutions

Solutions of alkali metals in aliphatic amines are extensively used by organic chemists as reducing agents (Birch, 1950; Birch and Smith, 1958). The advantages of amines over ammonia include higher boiling points, higher solubilities for organic compounds, and stronger reducing power in their metal solutions. The metal–amine solutions, however, are much more unstable with respect to decomposition to amide and hydrogen.

Down et al. (1959) found that potassium and NaK dissolve slightly (or the order of 10^{-4} M) in certain ethers to give unstable blue solutions. The ethers which show the highest solubilities are the "glyme" solvents (dimethyl ethers of ethylene glycols), 1-methoxymethyltetrahydrofuran, and the cyclic tetramer of propylene oxide. The solubility of potassium in such ethers accounts for the successful use of these solvents in various reactions of potassium, such as the reactions with transition metal carbonyls to form potassium "carbonylates".

$$2K + Mn_2(CO)_{10} \rightarrow 2Mn(CO)_5^- + 2K^+. \tag{68}$$

Aromatic hydrocarbons such as naphthalene react with potassium and sodium in glyme ethers to form green solutions of electron addition compounds (Scott et al., 1936):

$$K + C_{10}H_8 \rightarrow K^+ + C_{10}H_8^-. \tag{69}$$

These relatively stable solutions are very useful as strong reducing agents in circumstances in which it is necessary to avoid solvolysis by protonic solvents. Thus Chatt and Watson (1962) have prepared zero-oxidation-state transition-metal complexes of the type $M[(CH_3)_2PCH_2CH_2P(CH_3)_2]_3$ by the reduction of higher-valent complexes with sodium naphthalenide in tetrahydrofuran.

This work was supported in part by the United States Atomic Energy Commission.

References

Acrivos, J. V. and Pitzer, K. S. (1962) J. Phys Chem. **66**, 1693.
Armstrong, G. T. (1953) U.S. National Bureau of Standards Report 2626, "A Critical Review of theLiterature Relating to the Vapor Pressure of Ammonia and Trideutero-ammonia", Washington, D.C.

Arnold, E. and Patterson, A., Jr. (1964) Chapter in "Solutions Metal-Ammoniac", (Lepoutre, G. and Sienko, M. J., eds.). W. A. Benjamin, New York.
Audrieth, L. F. and Kleinberg, J. (1953) "Non-Aqueous Solvents". Wiley, New York.
Bar-Eli, K. and Klein, F. S. (1962) *J. chem. Soc.* 1378.
Becker, E., Lindquist, R. H. and Alder, B. J. (1956) *J. chem. Phys.* **25**, 971
Beckman, T. A. and Pitzer, K. S. (1961) *J. phys. Chem.* **65**, 1527.
Bergstrom, F. W. (1940) *J. Amer. chem. Soc.* **62**, 2381.
Bergstrom, F. W. and Fernelius, W. C. (1933) *Chem. Rev.* **12**, 43.
Bergstrom, F. W. and Fernelius, W. C. (1937) *Chem. Rev.* **20**, 413.
Berthoud, A. (1918a) *Helv. chim. acta* **1**, 84.
Berthoud, A. (1918b) *Chem. Abstr.* **12**, 1849.
Birch, A. J. and MacDonald, D. K. C. (1947) *Nature, Lond.* **159**, 811.
Birch, A. J. and MacDonald, D. K. C. (1948) *Trans. Faraday Soc.* **44**, 735.
Birch, A. J. (1950) *Quart. Rev.* **4**, 69.
Birch, A. J. and Smith, H. (1958) *Quart. Rev.* **12**, 17.
Bourke, P. J. and Lee, J. C. (1961a) *Trans. Inst. chem. Engrs. (Lond.)* **39**, 280.
Bourke, P. J. and Lee, J. C. (1961b) *Chem. Abstr.* **55**, 26615i.
Brown, J. and Roberts, N. W. (1951) Brit. Pat. 867, 848.
Brown, J. and Roberts, N. W. (1962) *Chem. Abstr.* **56**, Pl 48c.
Chatt, J. and Watson, H. R. (1962) *J. chem. Soc.* 2545.
Chou, D. Y. P., Pribble, M. J., Jackman, D. C. and Keenan, C. W. (1963) *J. Amer. chem. Soc.* **85**, 3530.
Clark, H. O., Horsfield, A. and Symons, M. C. R. (1959) *J. chem. Soc.* 2478.
Coulter, L. V. and Monchick, L. (1951) *J. Amer. chem. Soc.* **73**, 5867.
Coulter, L. V. (1953) *J. phys. Chem.* **57**, 553.
Coulter, L. V., Sinclair, J. R., Cole, A. G. and Roper, G. C. (1959) *J. Amer. chem. Soc.* **81**, 2986.
Couture, A. M. and Laidler, K. J. (1956) *Canad. J. Chem.* **34**, 1209.
Cragoe, C. and Harper, D. (1921) *Bur. Stds. Sc. Pp.* **420**, 313.
Cram, D. J. (1963) *Chem. Engng News* **93**, 92.
Cseko, G. and Cornides, I. (1960) *J. inorg. nucl. Chem.* **14**, 139.
Cuthrell, R. E., Fohn, E. C. and Lagowski, J. J. (1963) Paper 30 presented before the Division of Inorganic Chemistry, American Chemical Society Meeting, New York, pp. 13N–14N.
Cutler, D., and Powles, J. G. (1962) *Proc. Phys. Soc. (Lond.)* **80**, 130.
Czapski, G. and Schwarz, H. A. (1962) *J. phys. Chem.* **66**, 471.
De Grotthuss, C. J. T. (1806) *Annls Chim.* **58**, 54.
Dewald, J. F. and Lepoutre, G. (1954) *J. Amer. chem. Soc.* **76**, 3369.
Dirian, G. and Grandcollot, P. (1961a) *Comm. energie at. (France)*, *Rappt.* No. 1981.
Dirian, G. and Grandcallot, P. (1961b) *Chem. Abstr.* **55**, 26623d.
Dorfman, L. M. (1963) *Science* **141**, 493.
Dorfman, L. M. and Taub, I. A. (1963) *J. Amer. chem Soc.* **85**, 2370.
Down, J. L., Lewis, J., Moore, B. and Wilkinson, G. (1959) *J. chem. Soc.* 3767.
Dye, J. L., Sankuer, R. F. and Smith, G. E. (1960) *J. Amer. chem. Soc.* **82**, 4797.
Dykhno, N. and Shatenshtein, A. (1948) *J. phys. chem. (U.S.S.R.)* **22**, 461.
Dykhno, N. and Shatenshtein, A. (1951) *Zh. fiz. khim.* **25**, 670.
Elsey, H. M. (1920) *J. Amer. chem. Soc.* **42**, 2454.
Fellinger, L. L. and Audrieth, L. F. (1938) *J. Amer. chem. Soc.* **60**, 579.
Fenske, M. R., McCormick, R. H., Lawroski, H. and Geier, R. G. (1955) *A. I. Ch. E. Journal* **1**, 335.

Fenske, M. R., McCormick, R. H., Lawroski, H. and Geier, R. G. (1956) *Chem. Abstr.* **50**, 2154b.

Fernelius, W. C. and Bowman, G. B. (1940) *Chem. Rev.* **26**, 3.

Fowles, G. W. A. and Nicholls, D. (1962) *Quart. Rev.* **16**, 19.

Franklin, E. C. (1934) *J. Amer. chem. Soc.* **56**, 568.

Franklin, E. C. (1935) "The Nitrogen System of Compounds". Reinhold Publishing Corp., New York.

Franklin, E. C. and Kraus, C. A. (1900) *Amer. chem. J.* **23**, 227.

Franklin, E. C. and Cady, H. P. (1904) *J. Amer. chem. Soc.* **26**, 499.

Freed, S. and Sugarman, N. (1943) *J. chem. Phys.* **11**, 354.

Frost, A. A. and Pearson, R. G. (1961) "Kinetics and Mechanism", 2nd edition. Wiley, New York.

Fuoss, R. M. and Accascina, F. (1959) "Electrolytic Conductance". Interscience, New York.

Gold, M. and Jolly, W. L. (1962) *Inorg. Chem.* **1**, 818.

Gold, M., Jolly, W. L. and Pitzer, K. S. (1962) *J. Amer. chem. Soc.* **84**, 2264.

Grubb, H. M., Chittum, J. F. and Hunt, H. (1963) *J. Amer. chem. Soc.* **58**, 776.

Gunn, S. R. and Green, L. R. (1960) *J. phys. Chem.* **64**, 1066.

Gunn, S. R. and Green, L. R. (1962a) *J. chem. Phys.* **36**, 363.

Gunn, S. R. and Green, L. R. (1962b) *J. chem. Phys.* **36**, 368.

Gur'yanova, E. N. and Pleskov, V. A. (1936) *J. phys. Chem.* (*U.S.S.R.*) **8**, 345.

Hallada, C. J. and Jolly, W. L. (1963) *Inorg. Chem.* **2**, 1076.

Harned, H. S. and Owen, B. B. (1958) "The Physical Chemistry of Electrolytic Solutions", 3rd edition. Reinhold Publishing Corp., New York.

Hasing, J. (1940) *Annln Phys.* **37**, 509.

Haul, R., Ihle, H., Schierholz, H. and Blennemann, D. (1961) *Chemie-Ingr.-Tech.* **33**, 713.

Hawes, W. W. (1933) *J. Amer. chem. Soc.* **55**, 4422.

Hepler, L. G. (1957) *J. phys. Chem.* **61**, 1426.

Heyn, A. H. A. and Bergin, M. J. (1953) *J. Amer. chem. Soc.* **75**, 5120.

Heyns, K., Brockmann, R. and Roggenbuck, A. (1958) *Liebigs Ann.* **614**, 97.

Hildebrand, J. H. (1948) *J. chem. Educ.* **25**, 74.

Hildebrand, J. H. and Scott, R. L. (1962) "Regular Solutions". Prentice-Hall, Englewood Cliffs, N.J.

Hnizda, V. F. and Kraus, C. A. (1949) *J. Amer. chem. Soc.* **71**, 1565.

Hodgins, J. W. (1949) *Canad. J. Res.* **27**, 861.

Hunt, J. P., Dodgen, H. W. and Klanberg, F. (1963) *Inorg. Chem.* **2**, 478.

Huster, E. (1938) *Annln Phys.* **33**, 477.

Hutchison, C. A., Jr. and O'Reilly, D. E. (1961a) *J. chem. Phys.* **34**, 163.

Hutchison, C. A., Jr. and O'Reilly, D. E. (1961b) *J. chem. Phys.* **34**, 1279.

Hutchison, C. A., Jr. and Pastor, R. C. (1953) *J. chem. Phys.* **21**, 1959.

Ipat'ev, V. V. and Teodorovich, V. P. (1932) *J. gen. Chem., Moscow* **2**, 305.

Ishida, K. (1957) *Kogyo Kagaku Zasshi* **60**, 864.

Ishida, K. (1958) *Bull. chem. Soc. Japan* **31**, 143.

Ishida, K. (1959) *Chem. Abstr.* **53**, 980lh.

Ishida, K. (1960a) *Bull. chem. Soc. Japan* **33**, 693.

Ishida, K. (1960b) *Chem. Abstr.* **54**, 23687f.

Jaffe, H. (1935) *Z. Phys.* **93**, 741.

Jander, G. (1949) "Die Chemie in Wasserähnlichen Lösungsmitteln", Springer-Verlag, Berlin.

Johnson, W. C. and Martens, R. I. (1936) *J. Amer. chem. Soc.* **58**, 15.

Johnson, W. C. and Meyer, A. W. (1929) *J. phys. Chem.* **33**, 1922.

Johnson, W. C. and Meyer, A. W. (1932) *J. Amer. chem. Soc.* **54**, 3621.

Johnson, W. C., Meyer, A. W. and Martens, R. D. (1950) *J. Amer. chem. Soc.* **72**, 1842.

Johnson, W. C. and Piskur, M. M. (1933) *J. phys. Chem.* **37**, 93.

Jolly, W. L. (1953) *J. phys. Chem.* **58**, 250.

Jolly, W. L. (1956) *J. chem. Educ.* **33**, 512.

Jolly, W. L. (1959) *Prog. inorg. Chem.* **1**, 235.

Jolly, W. L. (1960) "Synthetic Inorganic Chemistry". Prentice-Hall, Englewood Cliffs, N.J.

Jolly, W. L., Hallada, C. J. and Gold, M. (1964) Chapter in "Solutions Metal-Ammoniac" (edited by Lepoutre, G. and Sienko, M. J.), W. A. Benjamin, New York.

Jortner, J. (1959) *J. chem. Phys.* **30**, 839.

Kaplan, J. and Kittel, C. (1953) *J. chem. Phys.* **21**, 1429.

Kay, R. L. (1960) *J. Amer. chem. Soc.* **82**, 2099.

Kelly, E. J., Secor, H. Y., Keenan, C. W. and Eastham, J. F. (1962) *J. Amer. chem. Soc.* **84**, 3611.

Kikuchi, S. and Kudo, S. (1944) *J. Soc. chem. Ind. Japan* **47**, 302.

Kikuchi, S. and Kudo, S. (1948) *Chem. Abstr.* **42**, 6208i.

Knight, W. D. (1949) *Phys. Rev.* **76**, 1259.

Kraus, C. A. (1914) *J. Amer. Chem. Soc.* **36**, 864.

Kraus, C. A. and Johnson, W. C. (1925) *J. Amer. chem. Soc.* **47**, 725.

Kraus, C. A. and Lucasse, W. W. (1921) *J. Amer. chem. Soc.* **43**, 2529.

Kraus, C. A. and Lucasse, W. W. (1922) *J. Amer. chem. Soc.* **44**, 1941.

Kraus, C. A. and Lucasse, W. W. (1923) *J. Amer. chem. Soc.* **45**, 2551.

Kraus, C. A. and Schmidt, F. C. (1934) *J. Amer. chem. Soc.* **56**, 2297.

Kraus, C. A. (1953) *J. chem. Educ.* **30**, 83.

Laitinen, H. A. and Nyman, C. J. (1948a) *J. Amer. chem. Soc.* **70**, 2241.

Laitinen, H. A. and Nyman, C. J. (1948b) *J. Amer. chem. Soc.* **70**, 3002.

Laitinen, H. A. and Shoemaker, C. E. (1950a) *J. Amer. chem. Soc.* **72**, 663.

Laitinen, H. A. and Shoemaker, C. E. (1950b) *J. Amer. chem. Soc.* **72**, 4975.

Latimer, W. M. (1952). "Oxidation Potentials", 2nd edition, pp. 34–36. Prentice-Hall, Englewood Cliffs, N.J.

Lefrancois, B. and Vaniscotte, C. (1960) *Chal. et Industr.* **41**, 183.

Lepoutre, G. and Patterson, A., Jr. (1955) *C.R. Acad. Sci., Paris* **240**, 1644.

Lepoutre, G. and Sienko, M. J., Editors (1964) "Solutions Metal-Ammoniac". W. A. Benjamin, New York.

Levine, R. and Fernelius, W. C. (1954) *Chem. Rev.* **54**, 449.

Levy, R. A. (1956) *Phys. Rev.* **102**, 31.

Loewenstein, A. and Szöke, A. (1962) *J. Amer. chem. Soc.* **84**, 1151.

MacInnes, D. A. (1939) "The Principles of Electrochemistry". Reinhold Publishing Corp., New York.

McConnell, H. M. and Holm, C. H. (1957) *J. chem. Phys.* **26**, 1517.

McElroy, A. D. and Laitinen, H. A. (1953) *J. phys. Chem.* **57**, 564.

Monoszon, A. M. and Pleskov, V. A. (1931) *Z. phys. Chem.*, Abt. A. **156**, 176.

Mulder, H. D. and Schmidt, F. C. (1951) *J. Amer. chem. Soc.* **73**, 5575.

Nyman, C. J. (1949) *J. Amer. chem. Soc.* **71**, 3914.

Nyman, C. J., Si Chang Fung and Dodger, H. W. (1950) *J. Amer. chem. Soc.* **72**, 1033.

Ogg, R. A., Jr. (1954) *Disc. Faraday Soc.* No. 17, 215.

Ogg, R. A., Jr., Leighton, P. A. and Bergstrom, F. W. (1933) *J. Amer. chem. Soc.* **55**, 1754.

Overstreet, R. and Giauque, W. F. (1937) *J. Amer. chem. Soc.* **59**, 254.

Pauling, L. (1960) "The Nature of the Chemical Bond", 3rd edition, p. 621. Cornell University Press, Ithaca, N.Y.

Pinevich, G. (1948a) *Kholod. Tekh.* **20**, No. 3, 30.

Pinevich, G. (1948b) *Chem. Abstr.* **43**, 8813e.

Plank, C. J. and Hunt, H. (1939) *J. Amer. chem. Soc.* **61**, 3590.

Pleskov, V. A. and Monoszon, A. M. (1935a) *Acta Phys.-chim. URSS* **1**, 713.

Pleskov, V. A. and Monoszon, A. M. (1935b) *Acta Phys-chim. URSS* **2**, 615.

Pollak, V. L. (1961) *J. chem. Phys.* **34**, 864.

Rebora, P. L. (1962a) *Energia nucl.* **9**, 338.

Rebora, P. L. (1962b) *Chem. Abstr.* **57**, 16078a.

Rossini, F. D., Wagman, D. D., Evans, W. H., Levine, S. and Jaffe, I. (1952). National Bureau of Standards Circular 500, "Selected Values of Chemical Thermodynamic Properties". Washington, D.C.

Ruff, O. and Geisel, E. (1906) *Ber. dtsch. chem. Ges.* **39**, 828.

Sanderson, R. T. (1948) "Vacuum Manipulation of Volatile Compounds". Wiley, New York.

Schaap, W. B., Conley, R. F. and Schmidt, F. C. (1961) *Analyt. chem.* **33**, 498.

Schmidt, F. C., Sottysiak, J., Tajkowski, E. and Denison, W. A. (1941) *J. Amer. chem. Soc.* **63**, 2669.

Schmidt, F. C., Studer, F. J. and Sottysiak, J. (1938) *J. Amer. chem. Soc.* **60**, 2780.

Scott, N. D. Walker, J. F. and Hansley, V. L. (1936) *J. Amer. chem. Soc.* **58**, 2442.

Shatenshtein, A. I. (1939) *Acta Phys.-chem. URSS* **10**, 121.

Shatenshtein, A. I. (1962) "Isotopic Exchange and the Replacement of Hydrogen in Organic Compounds". Consultants Bureau, New York.

Shatenshtein, A. I., Izrailevich, E. A. and Ladyshnikova, N. I. (1949a) *Zh. fiz. khim.* **23**, 497.

Shatenshtein, A. I., Izrailevich, E. A. and Ladyshnikova, N. I. (1949b) *Chem. Abstr.* **43**, 6024c.

Sisler, H. H. (1961) "Chemistry in Non-Aqueous Solvents". Reinhold Publishing Corp., New York.

Stairs, R. A. and Sienko, M. J. (1956) *J. Amer. chem. Soc.* **78**, 920.

Swenson, G. W., Zwicker, E. F. and Grossweiner, L. I. (1963) *Science* **141**, 1042.

Symons, M. C. R. (1959) *Quart. Rev.* **13**, 99.

Vegard, L. and Hillesund, S. (1942) Avhandl. Norske Videnskaps-Akad. Oslo I. Mat.-Naturv. Klasse, No. 8; Wyckoff, R. W. G. (1948, 1951) "Crystal Structures", Vol. I. Interscience, New York.

Warshawsky, I. (1963) *J. inorg. nucl. Chem.* **25**, 601.

Watt, G. W. (1950) *Chem. Rev.* **46**, 289, 317.

Watt, G. W. (1957) *J. chem. Educ.* **34**, 533.

Watt, G. W. and Sowards, D. M. (1955) *J. electrochem. Soc.* **102**, 46.

Watt, G. W., Sowards, D. M. and McBride, W. R. (1955) *J. Amer. chem. Soc.* **77**, 5835.

Weyl, W. (1864) *Annln Phys.* **121**, 601.

Wiebe, R. and Tremearne, T. H. (1933) *J. Amer. chem. Soc.* **55**, 975.

Wiesendanger, H. U. D., Jones, W. H., and Garnet, C. S. (1937) *J. chem. Phys.* **27**, 668.

Wilmarth, W. K. and Dayton, J. C. (1953) *J. Amer. chem. Soc.* **75**, 4553.

Wolsky, S. P. (1952) Thesis, Boston University, Boston, Massachusetts.

Wolsky, S. P., Zdanuk, E. J. and Coulter, L. V. (1952) *J. Amer. chem. Soc.* **74**, 6196.

Yost, D. M. and Russell, H., Jr. (1944). "Systematic Inorganic Chemistry". Prentice-Hall, Englewood Cliffs, N.J.

Zintl, E., Goubeau, J. and Dullenkopf, W. (1931) *Z. phys. Chem.* **A154**, 1.

Zintl, E. and Neumayr, S. (1930) *Ber. dtsch. chem. Ges.* **63**B, 237.

CHAPTER 2

Liquid Hydrogen Fluoride

H. H. HYMAN AND J. J. KATZ

Chemistry Division, Argonne National Laboratory, Argonne, Illinois, U.S.A.

I. Introduction.. 47
    A. Equipment for Studying Liquid Hydrogen Fluoride..................... 50
II. Properties of Pure Liquid Hydrogen Fluoride............................. 52
    A. Physical Properties... 52
    B. Vibronic Absorption Spectra..................................... 55
    C. Structure of the Liquid... 57
    D. Acidity... 62
III. Solutes in Liquid Hydrogen Fluoride.................................... 64
    A. Metal Fluorides.. 65
    B. Non-metallic, Non-acidic, Ionizing Fluorides........................ 67
    C. Proton Acceptors.. 68
    D. Acid Solutes: Fluoride Ion Acceptors............................. 72
    E. Salts in the Hydrogen Fluoride System as Solutes..................... 74
    F. Solution in Hydrogen Fluoride without Ionization..................... 75
IV. Solution in Anhydrous Hydrogen Fluoride of Compounds of Biological Importance 76

I. INTRODUCTION

Hydrogen fluoride is an interesting and important member of the class of non-aqueous ionizing solvents. It is a simple binary compound, and the anion and cation species formed by self-ionization are the smallest and most mobile ionic species found in any solution. Investigations of this powerful solvent have been severely handicapped in the past by the reactivity of glass and quartz with hydrogen fluoride. Ordinary laboratory equipment thus cannot be used, and this circumstance, together with the extraordinarily unpleasant physiological properties of the compound, prevented until very recently any systematic investigation of the solvent behaviour of hydrogen fluoride.

The advent of nuclear energy has changed all this. The urgent necessity for the manipulation of uranium hexafluoride for the separation of the uranium isotopes generated a keen interest in hydrogen fluoride and in fluorine chemistry generally, and resulted ultimately in a wide variety of laboratory tools that make the study of hydrogen fluoride a practical undertaking. It is not surprising, therefore, that many recent developments have occcurred in laboratories supported by Atomic Energy authorities. Particularly noteworthy is the development of fluorine-containing plastics that are completely inert to hydrogen fluoride. Polytetrafluoroethylene and polychlorotrifluoroethylene are available on a large scale as sheets, rods, or tubes, are easily worked, and, in the case of polychlorotrifluoroethylene, are

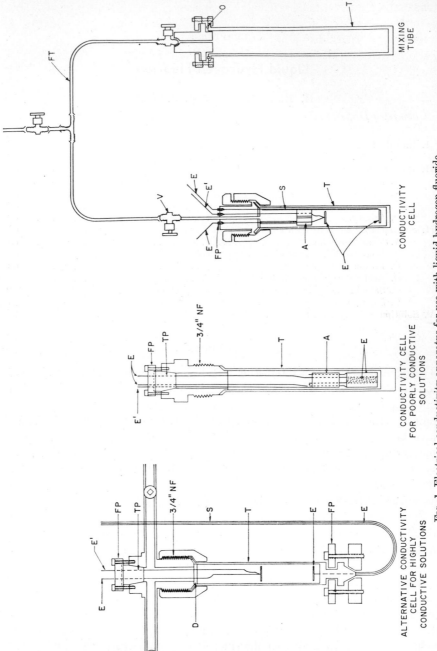

Fig. 1. Electrical conductivity apparatus for use with liquid hydrogen fluoride.

transparent. Apparatus fabricated from these resistant plastics have indeed revolutionized research with hydrogen fluoride, and have converted hydrogen fluoride to a tractable and useful substance.

Hydrogen fluoride is of interest from many points of view. It is important in the preparation of elemental fluorine, in the synthesis of inorganic and

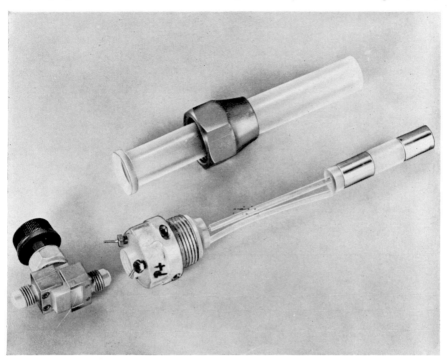

FIG. 2. A cell for electrical conductivity measurements in liquid hydrogen fluoride. For this cell the geometry of the electrodes is fixed, and results are reproducible, though the design is somewhat different from that found in ordinary conductivity cells.

FIG. 1. (*Facing page.*)

A	An aligning block, polytetrafluoroethylene.
D	A polychlorotrifluoroethylene porous disc.
E	Electrodes and leads of platinum.
E′	Platinum–rhodium alloy lead used to make thermocouple.
FP	A forcing plate used to squeeze a wedge-shaped polytetrafluoroethylene seal around the fine lead.
FT	Flexible polychlorotrifluoroethylene tubing.
O	An o-ring type flanged seal. Major parts are polychlorotrifluoroethylene, o-rings are polytetrafluoroethylene. Metal bolts and flanges are used.
NF	A nickel or nickel alloy flare fitting. (A threader hollow ring of any metal with a polychlorotrifluoroethylene centre may be substituted.)
S	A sheath of polychlorotrifluoroethylene tubing.
T	The polychlorotrifluoroethylene tube may be injection molded, machined, or fabricated from extruded tubing.
TP	A polytetrafluoroethylene plug forced around the electrical leads.
V	Valves (a variety of plastic and metal valves have been used).

organic fluorine compounds, and as a solvent. Emphasis here will be focused
on its solvent properties. Extensive reviews on other important aspects of
hydrogen fluoride are given by Simons (1950, 1964) and Mellor (1956).

A. EQUIPMENT FOR STUDYING LIQUID HYDROGEN FLUORIDE

Modern techniques make it possible to carry out on hydrogen fluoride
solutions all the physical chemical observations that can be made on aqueous
solutions. Such measurements include, by way of example, electrical conductivity; vapour pressure; absorption spectrophotometry in the ultra-violet,
visible, and infra-red; Raman spectroscopy; proton magnetic resonance;
polarimetry; and refractometry.

Fig. 3. A 1 mm cell for spectrophotometry with liquid hydrogen fluoride solutions.

Electrical conductivity measurements can be conveniently made in all
polychlorotrifluoroethylene (Kel-F) systems (Quarterman et al., 1957, 1961).
Hydrogen fluoride can be prepared in very pure form by distillation in all
polychlorotrifluoroethylene apparatus (Runner et al., 1956). Hydrogen
fluoride prepared in this way has the lowest electrical conductivity of any
hydrogen fluoride routinely prepared and is eminently suitable as a solvent
for electrical conductivity measurements (Figs. 1 and 2).

Absorption spectrophotometry in the visible and ultra-violet has become a simple process by the use of absorption cells fitted with synthetic sapphire (Al_2O_3) windows that are highly transparent and completely resistant to hydrogen fluoride (Fig. 3). In the infra-red region silver chloride windows are quite resistant to almost all hydrogen fluoride solutions, and measurements can be made in this region with little difficulty. Alternative windows may often be substituted in a single cell (Fig. 4) (Quarterman *et al.*, 1957). Raman spectra can be observed with sapphire tubes, but many recent investigations have depended on polychlorotrifluoroethylene tubing. Such tubing, in smaller sizes, has also been successfully used for nuclear magnetic resonance studies.

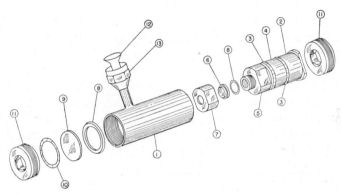

FIG. 4. A variable light path cell for spectrophotometry with liquid hydrogen fluoride solutions. 1. Body. 2. Polychlorotrifluoroethylene barrel. 3. Polytetrafluoroethylene o-rings for sliding seal. 4. Kel-F spacer. 5. Kel-F adjustment nut for sliding seal. 6. Inner window sapphire or silver chloride. 7. Kel-F end piece for inner assembly. 8. Teflon gasket. 9. Outer window sapphire or silver chloride. 10. Teflon o-ring. 11. Brass plug. 12. Flared lip. 13. Brass flare nut.

The availability of extruded polychlorotrifluoroethylene tubing and solid forms suitable for machining has greatly facilitated the construction of vacuum lines for the preparation and manipulation of hydrogen fluoride solutions. Valves, tees, elbows, unions, and similar fittings can be easily fabricated from this transparent thermoplastic. Threads may be machined directly in the plastic, but metal threads are generally more satisfactory, and a variety of fittings have been fabricated employing plastic to plastic seals between threaded or flanged metal connections, as in the connections shown in Figs. 1 and 2. Split rings of threaded metal are assembled around flanged plastic tubes. This type of connection or closure has been found to be widely applicable (cf. Katz and Hyman, 1953; Adams and Katz, 1956, 1957; Hyman *et al.*, 1957, 1961).

Polytetrafluoroethylene (Teflon) is softer than Kel-F, opaque, and not readily fusible. However, it is also completely resistant to hydrogen fluoride solutions, and so finds considerable use. It can be employed at much higher temperature than can the chlorine-containing plastic. Ordinarily, however, hydrogen fluoride is used at near ambient temperatures, and under such conditions lower-melting plastics are more readily fabricated and equally satisfactory in use. Other fluorine-containing elastomers (e.g. Viton A) are also useful for hydrogen fluoride resistant equipment. The moral of this very brief description is that practical means exist for fabricating practically any kind of apparatus for experimenting with hydrogen fluoride. The problems encountered in the past have for the most part been solved, and the experimental problems associated with hydrogen fluoride are now less severe than for many substances commonly encountered in the laboratory.

II. Properties of Pure Liquid Hydrogen Fluoride

A. PHYSICAL PROPERTIES

Table I describes the melting and boiling points, density, refractive index, viscosity, surface tension, dielectric constant, and electrical conductivity of hydrogen fluoride. Some of these data have not been checked recently and may have been determined on impure material. Small amounts of water or other impurities can seriously affect many of the values quoted.

However, the data given in Table I provide an entirely adequate basis for qualitative conclusions about the solvent properties of liquid hydrogen fluoride.

These physical properties indicate at once that it is an unusual solvent. The high boiling point, long liquid range, and high dielectric constant suggest that, like water, hydrogen fluoride is an associated liquid, that hydrogen bonding and proton transfer reaction will be important in hydrogen fluoride solution, and that ionization will frequently accompany solution.

The relatively low surface tension and viscosity of liquid hydrogen fluoride are very different from those of water and rule out the presence of three-dimensional networks such as those found in water or sulphuric acid. The structure of liquid hydrogen fluoride will thus be markedly different from these other high dielectric solvents. The molecular processes taking place in pure liquid hydrogen fluoride are important and will be discussed in detail below.

The heat of formation of hydrogen fluoride has recently been reinvestigated. Feder *et al.* (1963) combine results based on precision fluorine bomb calorimetry, e.g. for the heat of formation of SiF_4, with data on the heat of hydrolysis, e.g. $SiF_4 + 2H_2O \rightarrow SiO_2 + 4HF$. The results suggest a value of $-64 \cdot 9$ kcal mole^{-1} for the heat of formation of gaseous monomeric hydrogen fluoride at 25°C.

The vapour pressure p of liquid hydrogen fluoride was measured by Jarry and Davis (1953). Their data is represented by either of two equations:*

$$\log p(\text{torr}) = 8 \cdot 38036 - 1952 \cdot 55/(335 \cdot 52 + t) \tag{1}$$

$$\log p(\text{torr}) = -1 \cdot 91173 - 918 \cdot 24/T + 3 \cdot 21542 \log T. \tag{2}$$

Table II gives the vapour pressure at selected temperatures as calculated from each of these equations. Jarry and Davis arrive at a boiling point,

* t refers to °C, T to °K.

19·51°C, which is close to that found by many other workers, but the heat of vapourization determined from their vapour pressure curve, 1·608 kcal mole^{-1} at this boiling point, does not agree with the value found by earlier workers

TABLE I

Some Properties of Liquid Hydrogen Fluoride

Property	Value*
Melting point	$-89·37°C^a$
Boiling point	$19·51°C^b$
Density (g/ml)	$1·0020-(2·2625\times10^{-3}t)$
	$+(3·125\times10^{-6}t^2)^c$
	1·1231 at $-50°C^c$
	1·0606 at $-25°C^c$
	1·002 at $0°C^c$
	0·9546 at $25°C^d$
	0·908 at $50°C^e$
	0·796 at $100°C^e$
	0·646 at $150°C^e$
Critical density	0·29 ($\pm0·03$) at $188°C^e$
Refractive index	
$n^{25°C}$	$1·15436+0·001025/\gamma(A)^f$
$n_D^{25°C}$	$1·1574^f$
$\Delta n_D/\Delta t$	$-0·0004^f$
Viscosity	
(at $-50°C$)	0·570 centipoise
	0·507 centistoke^g
(at $-25°C$)	0·350 centipoise
	(= 0·330 centistoke)^g
(at $0°C$)	0·256 centipoise
	(= 0·256 centistoke)^g
Surface tension	$40·7\ (1-T/503·2)^{1·78c}$
(dynes/cm)	17·7 at $-81·8°C^c$
	12·0 at $-23·2°C^c$
	10·1 at $0°C^c$
	8·62 at $18·2°C^c$
Dielectric constant	175 at $-73°C^h$
	134 at $-42°C^h$
	111 at $-27°C^h$
	84 at $0°C^h$
Electrical conductivity	$1·4\times10^{-5}$ at $-15°C^i$
(ohm^{-1} cm^{-1})	$\sim\times10^{-6}$ at $0°C^k$

[a] Hu et al., 1953.
[b] Jarry and Davis, 1953.
[c] Simons and Bouknight, 1932.
[d] Hyman et al., 1963.
[e] Franck and Spalthoff, 1957.
[f] Perkins, 1965.
[g] Simons and Dresdner, 1944.
[h] Fredenhagen and Dahmlos, 1929.
[i] Fredenhagen and Cadenbach, 1929.
[k] Runner et al., 1956.

* In equations, t is used for °C, T for °K.

(cf. Mellor, 1956) or by Hu *et al.* (1953). The thermochemical data determined by this latter group are summarized in Table III. The discrepancy between the two values for the heat of vapourization has not been satisfactorily resolved.

TABLE II

Vapour Pressure of Liquid Hydrogen Fluoride

Temperature °C	Vapour pressure (torr)	
	Equation 1[a]	Equation 2[b]
−80	5·55	4·84
−50	34·82	33·52
−25	123·7	122·5
0	363·8	363·8
10	536·2	536·7
20	773·2	774·1
25	921·4	922·5
50	2069·0	2069·0
100	7891·0	7894·0
150		23,460[b]
188[c]		48,690[b]

[a] According to Jarry and Davis, 1953 (see text).
[b] Franck and Spalthoff, 1957.
[c] Critical temperature (188 ± 3°C), and pressure (48,700 ± 2500 torr).

TABLE III

Fusion and Vapourization of Hydrogen Fluoride[a]

Melting point	189·79 ± 0·02°K
Heat of Fusion	46·93 ± 0·04 cal/g at the melt-ing point
	= 0·939 kcal mole^{-1} [b]
Entropy of fusion	4·942 e.u.
Boiling point	292·61 ± 0·1°K at 741·4 mm
Heat of vapourization	89·45 ± 0·20 cal/g at the above boiling point
	= 1·789 kcal mole^{-1} [b]
Entropy of vapourization	= 6·117 e.u.
Molar entropy of gaseous hydrogen fluoride at 741 mm and 292·61°K	= 23·9 e.u.
Molar entropy of monomeric gaseous hydrogen fluoride (spectroscopic)	41·5 e.u. at 298·16°K

[a] According to Hu *et al.*, 1953. See text.
[b] The formula molecular weight is taken as 20·006 g/mole.

B. VIBRONIC ABSORPTION SPECTRA

The absorption spectrum of hydrogen fluoride has been employed to investigate the molecular properties of four different states of aggregation, gaseous monomer and polymer, liquid, and solid.

To observe the vibration and rotation spectrum of gaseous monomeric hydrogen fluoride, measurement must be carried out at low pressure and moderately elevated temperature to assure complete disaggregation.

Calcium fluoride, silver chloride, and polyethylene are suitably inert window materials. The fundamental HF stretching vibration is found in the 3μ region, the rotation bands in the far infra-red. Highly precise observations are available (Kuipers *et al.*, 1956; Kuipers, 1958; Rothschild, 1964) on the gas and need not concern us directly in our discussion of liquid hydrogen fluoride. Some of the pertinent data on the monomeric gas are summarized in Table IV.

TABLE IV

Some Spectroscopic Data for Monomeric HF Gas

Constant[a]	Value (cm^{-1})
ν_0 $(0\leftarrow1)$	3961·64
$(0\leftarrow2)$	7751·24
$(0\leftarrow3)$	11372·7
$(0\leftarrow4)$	14831·6
B_0	20·56
D_0	0·00211
ω_e	4137·25
$x_e\omega_e$	88·73
$y_e\omega_e$	0·533
B_e	20·95
D_e	0·00213
α_e	0·789
γ_e	0·0087

[a] Standard spectroscopic notation, cf. e.g. Herzberg, 1950.

At lower temperatures and higher pressures hydrogen fluoride associates into polymers. This association is discussed in detail in a later section. The infra-red absorption spectrum has been invaluable in ascertaining the nature of the polymer species in the gas (Smith, 1958).

The nature of the absorption bands in the 3μ region is the most significant in the study of gas polymers, since these absorptions arise from the hydrogen stretching fundamentals in the HF polymers.

Liquid hydrogen fluoride likewise has a number of infra-red absorption bands, and Figs. 5 and 6 summarize the situation in two regions of the spectrum. These absorption bands appear to be primarily due to h.f. vibrations in polymer molecules (Maybury *et al.*, 1955; Hyman *et al.*, 1957).

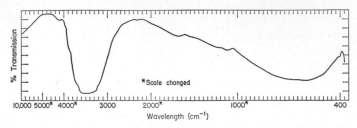

FIG. 5. Infra-red spectrum of liquid hydrogen fluoride (according to Maybury *et al.*, 1955) (cell thickness, 6μ).

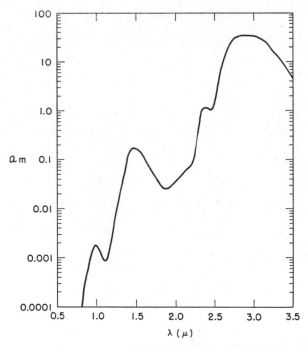

FIG. 6. Near infra-red spectrum of liquid hydrogen fluoride (Hyman *et al.*, 1957).

For infra-red studies with liquid hydrogen fluoride, silver chloride appears to be the most suitable window material. Since, as is also the case with liquid water, hydrogen fluoride absorbs intensely in the infra-red, very short light paths are needed. A typical infra-red cell with a very short and variable light path is shown in Fig. 7. The intense and broad absorption band in the

3μ region exhibited by liquid hydrogen fluoride reduces the utility of infra-red analysis for the study of dilute solutions, but infra-red studies have been applied effectively to more concentrated solutions (Adams and Katz, 1957).

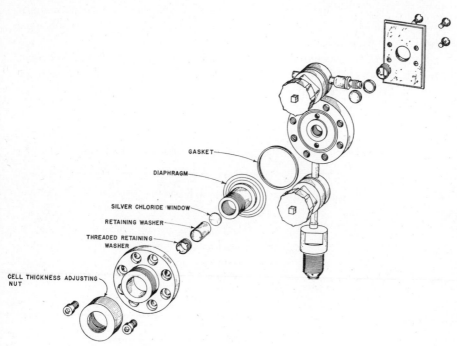

GASKET

DIAPHRAGM

SILVER CHLORIDE WINDOW

RETAINING WASHER

THREADED RETAINING WASHER

CELL THICKNESS ADJUSTING NUT

FIG. 7. A cell for infra-red absorption spectrophotometry with liquid hydrogen fluoride solutions. The flexible diaphragm permits variation in light path.

Finally, the infra-red absorption spectrum of solid hydrogen fluoride has been studied (Table V). The interpretation involves some speculation as to the structure of the solid and thus is briefly discussed in connection with association.

C. STRUCTURE OF THE LIQUID

It is obvious from its physical properties that liquid hydrogen fluoride has a complex structure. At least two types of molecular interaction appear to play an important role in liquid hydrogen fluoride. These are self-ionization and intermolecular association.

1. *Self-ionization*

As in most protonic ionizing solvents, the ionic species formed by self-ionization are probably part of a hydrogen-bonded network; individual molecules cannot readily be distinguished. A naked, unsolvated proton is clearly unrealistic, and the formal self-ionization equation in its simplest form must approximate:

$$2HF \rightleftharpoons H_2F^+ + F^-. \tag{3}$$

It is highly likely that the proton is in fact attached not to monomeric hydrogen fluoride but to hydrogen fluoride polymers. The fluoride ion must also be heavily solvated.

The extent to which self-ionization takes place in pure liquid hydrogen fluoride is not yet completely established. The most useful criterion for determining the extent of self-ionization is the electrical conductivity, but

TABLE V

Absorption Bands in the Spectra of Pure HF and DF Crystals

DF^a (cm^{-1})	HF (cm^{-1})	
	a	b
	3581 w	3590 w
2527	3414 s	3420 s
	3270 w	3270 w
2284	3060 s	3060 s
855	1200	1204
715	971	(955–1010)
570	790	
405	555	547
	515	
	370	366

[a] Sastri and Hornig, 1963.
[b] Giguère and Zengin, 1958.

the true minimum value for this parameter is still uncertain. The impurity contributing most to enhanced conductivity is water, which must be rigorously removed in order to assess the extent of self-ionization of pure hydrogen fluoride. Commercial hydrogen fluoride drawn directly from cylinders shows high electrical conductivity. To purify hydrogen fluoride, not only must adventitious water itself be rigorously excluded, but virtually all other metal oxides as well. Hydrogen fluoride reacts with oxides to yield water, and even the usual protective oxide film on nickel metal equipment reacts in this way. Fredenhagen and Cadenbach (1929) were able to prepare very dry hydrogen fluoride with a conductivity of $1\cdot4\times10^{-5}$ ohm^{-1} cm^{-1} at 0°C in platinum equipment. Such a conductivity is now known to correspond to a water content of less than 0·0002% H_2O. More recently, hydrogen fluoride with a conductivity as low as 10^{-6} ohm^{-1} cm^{-1} has been obtained by distillation in a polychlorotrifluoroethylene fractionating column (Runner et al., 1956), but only a few measurements have been made on hydrogen fluoride of this purity.

If the equivalent conductivity of the ionic species present in pure HF at 0°C is assumed to have a value of 700, a specific conductivity of 10^{-6} ohm^{-1} cm^{-1} corresponds to an H^+ or F^- concentration of $1\cdot4\times10^{-6}$ mole/litre, or an equilibrium constant for self-ionization K_{HF} of 2×10^{-12}. The true equilibrium constant for self-ionization will probably be lower, and may even approach that of water itself in the rigorous absence of all impurities.

Both the proton and the fluoride ion show high equivalent conductances in liquid hydrogen fluoride. The high equivalent conductance is undoubtedly due to a chain conductivity mechanism, quite comparable to that observed in water or anhydrous sulphuric acid. Chain conductivity for the fluoride ion and especially for the proton was only established many years after such a mechanism was first suspected to play a role in conductivity. The low viscosity of hydrogen fluoride reduces differences between chain conductivity and ordinary ionic mobility. Experimental difficulties have also been encountered in obtaining solutions free enough from basic impurities to measure accurately the conductivity of low concentrations of strong acids. It has now become clear, however, that a chain conductivity mechanism is operative in the migration of ions in hydrogen fluoride (Kilpatrick and Lewis, 1956; Hyman et al., 1963).

2. Polymerization

The association or polymerization of hydrogen fluoride has been studied most directly in the gas phase. The average molecular weight as a function of temperature and pressure is now reasonably well known (Table VI). The data indicate that HF in the gas phase is extensively associated. Indeed, gaseous hydrogen fluoride is probably the most imperfect gas known.

The infra-red absorption studies of Smith (1958) have helped resolve the debate as to the nature of the high molecular weight species present in the gas. Smith's observations confirm the early suggestion of Simons and Hildebrand (1924) that at elevated pressures aggregates of the type $(HF)_6$ are the predominant form. Dielectric polarization measurements strongly support the ring hypothesis for the structure of the hexamer. At lower pressures the tetramer, dimer, and monomer become increasingly important species. Smith notes, however, that the cyclic hexamer is present in higher concentration than the tetramer even at rather low pressures where both become minor constituents, and rejects the existence of linear zig-zag chains of $(HF)_n$

units (where n is statistically distributed around a mean value which grows with increasing pressure) (cf. Fig. 8) (Briegleb, 1953; Strohmeier, 1953). Franck and Meyer (1959) accept the ring form as dominant, but give equilibrium constants allowing for both chain and ring polymers.

X-Ray diffraction of solid hydrogen fluoride shows the solid to possess a linear zig-zag arrangement (Atoji and Lipscomb, 1954) (Fig. 8). The infrared absorption spectrum of solid hydrogen fluoride is consistent with linear

TABLE VI

Association Factor for Gaseous Hydrogen Fluoride

Temperature 0°C	Pressure (torr)	Z (molecules HF/polymer)
0·0	363·8	4·717[a]
	244·5	3·118[b]
	200·2	2·597[b]
19·5	760·0	3·76[a]
25·0	921·4	3·553[a]
26·0	488·5	1·708[b]
	401·0	1·422[b]
	342·5	1·279[b]
38·0	639·0	1·354[b]
	501·0	1·184[b]
	407·0	1·118[b]
50·0	2069·0	3·015[a]
100·0	7891·0	2·453[a]
160·0	26,500·0	1·70[a]
200·0	37,600·0	1·32[c]
	58,800·0	2·05[c]
300·0	57,500·0	1·09[c]
	173,000·0	1·43[c]

[a] Jarry and Davis, 1953.
[b] Long et al., 1943.
[c] Franck and Spalthoff, 1957; Spalthoff and Franck, 1957.

zig-zag chains (Sastri and Hornig, 1963). The extra absorption peaks attributed to lattice combinations in HF (and not found in DF) suggest unusually strong interactions between the chains in solid hydrogen fluoride. The differences in molecular configuration between solid and gaseous HF have not been adequately explained.

There is no direct evidence of the extent of association or the configuration of the polymeric molecules that exist in the liquid state. The heat of vapourization of the liquid is low for a highly associated liquid. Since the heat of dissociation of the polymer is substantial, it can tentatively be concluded that not much change occurs in the average number of polymer units in the transition from liquid to gas. From vapour density measurements of saturated vapour in equilibrium with the liquid, it appears that the average number of hydrogen fluoride units in gas aggregates is about 3·5, and this probably is close to the average size of the molecular aggregates in the liquid.

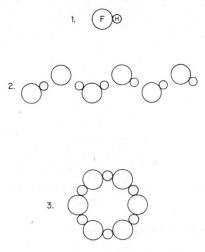

FIG. 8. Some possible structural arrangements in hydrogen fluoride.

The nature and extent of molecular association in liquid hydrogen fluoride are greatly influenced by the presence of ionizing impurities. For example, the density, acidity, and proton nuclear magnetic resonance behaviour of liquid hydrogen fluoride vary as a function of added water in a way that can best be explained by assuming drastic changes in the size and arrangement of $(HF)_n$ polymers. Thus, the density of aqueous hydrogen fluoride solutions shows a maximum value (1·25 g/ml at 0°C) at about 75% HF. This is a remarkable increase of 25% over the density of either pure component. As water is added to liquid hydrogen fluoride, the concentration of hydrogen fluoride molecules per litre actually increases and attains a maximum value at about 88% hydrogen fluoride. In this connection the density of the solid (1·653 g/ml at −93·8°C (Le Boucher *et al.*, 1932)) is noteworthy. The change in volume on melting is exceptionally large.

The variation in density can be explained in terms of a transition from a high concentration of the ring polymer in pure liquid HF to linear chains in the solid, or in the liquid phase under conditions of substantial ionization (Fig. 9). The electrical conductivity approaches the very high value of 1 ohm⁻¹ cm⁻¹ in these maximum density HF–H₂O solutions, and more than 2% of the fluorine atoms present are calculated to exist as fluoride ions. The displacement of ring-chain equilibria can also be used to interpret the behaviour of other proton acceptors in liquid hydrogen fluoride solutions.

D. ACIDITY

Liquid anhydrous HF has long been recognized to be a very acidic substance. Many organic compounds with a variety of functional groups dissolve readily in liquid HF. Such solutions usually exhibit substantial ionic conductivity even though ordinary ionic dissociation is highly improbable. The

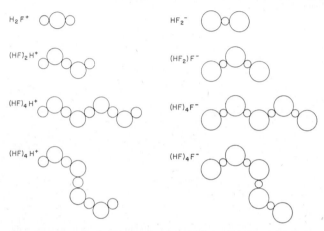

FIG. 9. Hypothetical arrangement of H^+ and F^- in liquid HF.

available data are best interpreted in terms of substantial proton transfer from the solvent to the solute in question (Simons, 1950):

$$R + HF \rightleftharpoons RH^+ + F^-. \tag{4}$$

In dilute aqueous solution, however, HF is a rather weak acid. The weak acid character of dilute aqueous hydrofluoric acid is at first sight surprising, and must be accounted for by any explanation that pretends to interpret acid–base interactions between molecules. Pauling (1956) suggests that the solvation stabilizing the ions increases in the sequence $I^- < Br^- < Cl^- < F^-$ as a linear function of the electronegativity of the halogen. The stability of the hydrogen halide molecule, in aqueous solution as in the gas phase, however, follows a quadratic function of the electronegativity difference between the halogen and hydrogen. Therefore, it is not surprising that the order of acid strength of the hydrogen halides in water is $HI > HBr > HCl > HF$. Indeed the differences in acid ionization constants are roughly in agreement with simple calculations based on the electronegativity differences tabulated by Pauling. He further points out that it is similarly true that water is a much weaker acid than the other hydrides of the sixth group elements, hydrogen sulphide, selenide, and telluride. The difference in acid strength between H_2O and H_2Te is very comparable to that between HF and HI. These relationships may be accepted without much argument, but it is nevertheless surprising that the equilibrium

$$H_2O + HF \rightleftharpoons H_3O^+ + F^- \qquad (5)$$

proceeds in dilute aqueous solution only to the extent indicated by an ionization constant

$$K = \frac{[H_3O^+][F^-]}{[HF]} \qquad (6)$$

of about $3-7 \times 10^{-4*}$ (Roth, 1959). The surprise is occasioned by the observation that proton transfer by anhydrous HF to an indicator is no less than 10^{17} times as great as it is in pure H_2O.

We have noted that no significant concentration of HF molecules exists as such in liquid hydrogen fluoride, and the same is true of individual H_2O molecules in liquid H_2O. Proton transfer from the aggregated molecules making up the HF matrix to an isolated H_2O molecule is very different from proton transfer from an isolated HF molecule to the group of molecules associated in the H_2O matrix. In the former case the fluoride ion remaining after proton transfer is part of a relatively stable zig-zag hydrogen fluoride chain (Fig. 9). In the latter case the fluoride ion is solvated only by water molecules. Therefore, the ease with which the HF unit loses a proton increases steadily as the concentration of hydrogen fluoride in the system is increased. The attempt to describe this in terms of a single addition of F^- to HF to yield an HF_2^- ion is a crude approximation, and we should not be surprised at the failure to find a satisfactory equilibrium constant.

While a number of acidity scales have been advanced, the H_0 function first proposed by Hammett (1935, 1940) (Hammett and Deyrup, 1932) appears to be the most useful for strong proton acids. H_0 is defined as

$$H_0 = pK_{In} - \frac{\log C_{InH^+}}{\log C_{In}}.$$

To measure H_0 a series of neutral indicators is employed. The indicators are selected to be of decreasing basicity, and to have uncharged and protonated species of markedly different absorption spectra

$$In + HA \rightarrow InH^+ + A^-.$$

---

* Unfortunately, there is no agreement on an accurate value for this constant. The ionization has usually been treated as a two-step process:

$$H_2O + HF \rightleftharpoons H_3O^+ + F^- \quad K_1 = \frac{(H_3O^+)(F^-)}{HF}$$

$$HF + F^- \rightleftharpoons HF_2^- \quad K_2 = \frac{(HF_2^-)}{(HF)(F^-)}.$$

Literature values of K_1 range from $2 \cdot 4 - 7 \cdot 2 \times 10^{-4}$ and K_2 from $5 - 25$ (Mellor, 1956), but the experimental data usually show K's that are far from constant.

The method has been reviewed by Paul and Long (1957) and indicator constants (K_{In}) are given there for a number of useful reagents. The H_0 values for some hydrogen fluoride solutions are given in Table VII.

TABLE VII

Acidity Constant (H_0) for Liquid Hydrogen Fluoride

H_0	Impurity concentration (moles/litre)	Electrical conductivity (ohm^{-1} cm^{-1} at 0°C)
$-10\cdot98$ ⎫	$< 10^{-4}$	3×10^{-5}
$-10\cdot65$ ⎬ [a]		5×10^{-5}
$-9\cdot72$ ⎭	$\sim 2\cdot5 \times 10^{-4}$	10^{-4}
$-10\cdot2$ ⎫	$< 10^{-3}$	
$-9\cdot6$ ⎪ [b]	$0\cdot1$	
$-8\cdot86$ ⎬	$1\cdot0$ (H_2O)	
$-8\cdot4$ ⎭	$1\cdot0$ (NaF)	

[a] Hyman et al., 1963.   [b] Hyman et al., 1957.

The H_0 value for anhydrous sulphuric acid is -11, about the same value found for hydrogen fluoride. Since the H_0 scale is related to pH and is intended to represent a continuous set of acidity values on a logarithmic scale, these H_0 values show hydrogen fluoride and sulphuric acid to be exceptionally strong acids.

The acid strength of anhydrous hydrogen fluoride, as well as dilute solutions, must be influenced by ring-chain equilibrium. It has been suggested (Hyman et al., 1963) that the fluoride ion and solvated proton are stabilized by chain structures, and that the neutral HF molecule is stabilized by ring structures. The detailed shape of the acid strength versus impurity content curve is affected by this transformation. A much more detailed analysis of the structure of liquid hydrogen fluoride than is yet available will be necessary for the validity of this hypothesis to be established.

III. Solutes in Liquid Hydrogen Fluoride

As technical difficulties are overcome, hydrogen fluoride becomes an increasingly interesting solvent, and more of its potentialities are being realized. A vast array of solutes dissolve freely in liquid hydrogen fluoride. As previously described, hydrogen fluoride is a low molecular weight solvent of high volatility, an ionizing solvent of exceptionally high dielectric constant, and a very strong acid. Hydrogen fluoride has essentially neither oxidizing nor reducing powers. While it can be reduced with evolution of hydrogen by most of the reagents that reduce water, it cannot be oxidized to elemental fluorine by any chemical oxidant. It thus becomes of interest in the study of extremely powerful oxidizing agents in solution.

Solutes in liquid hydrogen fluoride may be classified in a number of ways. The binary fluorides have been studied most extensively as solutes and may well be considered as a separate class. As the most electronegative element, fluorine forms binary fluorides with every element except helium, neon, and argon. Fluorides can be further classified with respect to the ionic species they yield in hydrogen fluoride solution. The metal fluorides, where the metal oxidation number is four or less, behave as simple bases to yield a metal-containing cation and the fluoride ion:

$$HF + MF_x \rightleftharpoons MF_{x-1} + HF_2^-. \tag{9}$$

Non-metal fluorides are usually volatile and often are liquids. When they dissolve in hydrogen fluoride, they may remain unionized, or they may react with hydrogen fluoride with the gain or loss of a fluoride ion:

$$HF + MF_x \rightleftharpoons MF_{x-1}^+ + HF_2^- \tag{10}$$

$$HF + MF_x \rightleftharpoons H_2F^+ + MF_{x+1}^-. \tag{11}$$

Which reaction occurs and its extent depends on a number of factors, but the geometry of the original fluoride and the product ions plays an important and often a dominant role.

Fluorides that increase the concentration of the HF_2^- ion are bases in the hydrogen fluoride system, although the solutions may be very acidic indeed by the usual standards. Solutes that increase the concentration of H_2F^+ ion are classified as acids.

A. METAL FLUORIDES

The simplest solutes in hydrogen fluoride are the metal fluorides. On dissolution, metal fluorides yield a new cation (e.g. Na^+), while the concentration of fluoride anion is increased. The simple alkali metal fluorides thus are bases in liquid hydrogen fluoride and correspond to metal hydroxides in the water system. The solubilities of some metallic fluorides, derived mainly from the work of Jache and Cady (1952), are summarized in Table VIII. The alkali metal fluorides are highly soluble, as are the alkaline earths. Silver(I) fluoride is likewise very soluble, and mercury(I) fluoride is appreciably so. Silver and mercury sulphates are soluble in sulphuric acid, while the oxides are very insoluble in water. In this respect the water system may be distinguished from the strong acid systems.

Many sparingly soluble fluorides are more soluble in the presence of a variety of complexing agents such as acetic acid, citric acid, methyl cyanide, 7,10-phenanthroline, 8-hydroxyquinoline, dithizone and carbon monoxide (Clifford and Sargent, 1957).

Ionization of dilute solutions of the alkali metal fluorides in liquid hydrogen fluoride is essentially complete. The electrical conductivity of sodium and potassium fluoride dissolved in hydrogen fluoride is shown in Fig. 10 (Simons,

TABLE VIII

Solubility of Metal Fluorides in Hydrogen Fluoride

Fluoride	Solubility in HF (g/100 g)	Temperature °C
LiF	10·3	12
NaF	30·1	11
KF	36·5	8
RbF	110·0	20
CsF	199·0	10
NH_4F	32·6	17
AgF	83·2	19
Hg_2F_2	0·87	12
TlF	580·0	12
CuF_2	0·010	12
AgF_2	0·048	12
CaF_2	0·817	12
SrF_2	14·83	12
BaF_2	5·60	12
BeF_2	0·015	11
MgF_2	0·025	12
ZnF_2	0·024	14
CdF_2	0·201	14
HgF_2	0·54	12
PbF_2	2·62	12
FeF_2	0·006	12
CrF_2	0·036	14
NiF_2	0·037	12
AlF_3	<0·002	11
CeF_3	0·043	12
TlF_3	0·081	12
SbF_3	0·536	12
BiF_3	0·010	12
MnF_3	0·164	12
FeF_3	0·008	12
CoF_3	0·257	12
ZrF_4	0·009	12
CeF_4	0·10	12
ThF_4	<0·006	18
NbF_5	6·8	25
TaF_5	15·2	25
SbF_5	∞	25

1950; Kilpatrick and Lewis, 1956). The data are far from precise by the standard of aqueous conductivity measurements, but the equivalent conductivities of these solutes at 0°C seem to be about 400. Transference measurements (Kilpatrick and Lewis, 1956) suggest that approximately 70% of the current is carried by the fluoride ion. Taking into account the low viscosity of liquid hydrogen fluoride, this transference number, while less than that found for KOH in water, has been explained in terms of a chain mechanism for fluoride ion conduction.

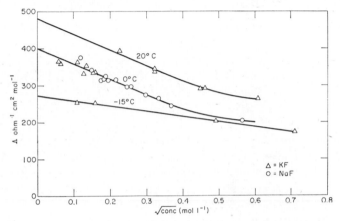

FIG. 10. Electrical conductivity of sodium and potassium fluoride solutions in anhydrous hydrogen fluoride.

As noted above, it seems likely that the fluoride ion is substantially solvated in liquid hydrogen fluoride, at least to the extent of forming HF_2^-, and finite concentrations of the higher species $H_2F_3^-$ and even $H_4F_5^-$ probably exist as well. The infra-red absorption spectra of hydrogen fluoride solutions is best interpreted in terms of the formation of a hydrogen bonded solvate of the fluoride ion (Adams and Katz, 1957). It is of course well-known that many metal fluorides have been isolated from hydrogen fluoride as salts of the HF_2^- anion.

B. NON-METALLIC, NON-ACIDIC, IONIZING FLUORIDES

The halogen fluorides constitute the most interesting members of this category. Chlorine trifluoride and bromine trifluoride are completely miscible with hydrogen fluoride and are appreciably ionized (Rogers et al., 1956a,b, 1957):

$$ClF_3 + HF \rightleftharpoons ClF_2^+ + HF_2^- \tag{12}$$

$$BrF_3 + HF \rightleftharpoons BrF_2^+ + HF_2^-. \tag{13}$$

Although the halogen fluorides are bases in the hydrogen fluoride system, hydrogen fluoride is itself an acid in the halogen fluoride system.

Halogen fluoride–hydrogen fluoride solutions may be neutralized from either direction in the appropriate solvent system. Neutralization can be followed by conductivity measurements, and the salt formed can be isolated by evaporation of excess solvent.

$$(BrF_2^+ + HF_2^-) + (H_2F^+ + SbF_6^-)^* \rightarrow BrF_2SbF_6 + HF \uparrow \qquad (14)$$
$$* \text{ (Acidic hydrogen fluoride solution)}$$

$$(BrF_2^+ + HF_2^-) + (K^+ + BrF_4^-)^* \rightarrow KHF_2 + BrF_3 \uparrow \qquad (15)$$
$$* \text{ (Basic bromine trifluoride solution)}$$

While much of the chemical behaviour of the halogen fluoride–hydrogen fluoride solutions can be explained in terms of the ionic species present, ionization need not take place to any great extent.

For most systems the maximum ionization observed is less than one per cent of complete ionization.

C. PROTON ACCEPTORS

The simple fluorides are the least interesting bases, in the sense that they present few anomalies. In liquid hydrogen fluoride, perhaps to an even greater extent than in anhydrous sulphuric acid, there are many materials, both organic and inorganic, that accept a proton from hydrogen fluoride and exist in solution as an ionized fluoride. Water is an obvious and interesting example. In anhydrous hydrogen fluoride, water behaves primarily as $H_3O^+HF_2^-$, a conclusion based on the sharp rise in conductivity as water is added:

$$H_2O + 2HF \rightarrow H_3O^+ + HF_2^-. \qquad (16)$$

If the electrical conductivity data of Fredenhagen is accepted at face value, water does not increase the conductivity of hydrogen fluoride as much as an equal concentration of sodium or potassium fluoride, or as much as a proton acceptor such as methyl alcohol or acetic acid. The best explanation for this observation is probably the incorporation of H_2O molecules into hydrogen-bonded polymers which carry a single proton $(H_2O)_n \cdot H_3O^+$, or $(H_2O)_n \cdot (HF)_n H_3O^+$:

$$nH_2O + 2HF \rightarrow (H_2O)_n H^+ + HF_2^- \qquad (17)$$
$$ROH + 2HF \rightarrow (ROH)H^+ + HF_2^-. \qquad (18)$$

Therefore, in terms of base strength,

$$1 \text{ mol ROH} \cong n \text{ mols } H_2O. \qquad (19)$$

A large number of organic compounds are bases in hydrogen fluoride. Most substances containing oxygen, nitrogen, or sulphur atoms that are not co-ordinatively saturated offer a lone electron pair capable of binding protons. A very large number of organic compounds fall into this category (Simons,

1950; Mellor, 1956). Alcohols, acids, aldehydes, ketones, ethers and amines are illustrative of classes of compounds that dissolve in hydrogen fluoride with extensive ionization. Saturated hydrocarbons are relatively insoluble.

Many soluble organic compounds seem to act as simple proton acceptors and may be recovered unchanged on removal of the hydrogen fluoride. Others, however, do undergo change as a result of solution in hydrogen fluoride. Butadiene and other unsaturated compounds polymerize and undergo rearrangement. Highly coloured solutions are frequently formed. Only on a few occasions has the behaviour of even a moderately complicated solute been studied in detail. The addition of a proton has usually, and justifiably, been assumed as the initial step.

A number of aromatic hydrocarbons are soluble in liquid hydrogen fluoride. The behaviour of the aromatic nucleus as a proton acceptor group is of some interest and has led to a number of studies in this solvent. For example, the question of the relative base strength of the methyl benzenes in solution in hydrogen fluoride has been explained using electrical conductivity measurements (Kilpatrick and Luborsky, 1953), thermochemical methods (Mackor *et al.*, 1958), and nuclear magnetic resonance measurements (MacLean and Mackor, 1962).

Some simple rules governing proton transfer in hydrogen fluoride are illustrated in Figs. 11 and 12. Acetic acid and trifluoroacetic acid, and ethanol and trifluoroethanol are each miscible with anhydrous hydrogen fluoride without any chemical reaction. Acetic acid ionizes essentially completely in dilute solution in anhydrous hydrogen fluoride to form the protonated acetic acid cation:

$$CH_3COOH + 2HF \rightleftharpoons CH_3CO_2H_2^+ + HF_2^-. \tag{20}$$

Trifluoroacetic acid is of course a much stronger acid than acetic acid, and it accordingly functions as a weaker base. It is no surprise, therefore, that trifluoroacetic acid has a much lower electrical conductivity in hydrogen fluoride solution than does acetic acid itself. It must be emphasized, however, that the lower extent of ionization results from the decrease in basicity occasioned by the substitution of fluorine for hydrogen in the methyl group of the acid. The acid strength of the molecule is thus not the determining factor. Ethanol is, as expected, essentially completely ionized in hydrogen fluoride solution, but trifluoroethanol solutions are like those of trifluoroacetic acid, and are only weakly ionized. This circumstance must be due to the decreased basicity of CF_3CH_2OH, for trifluoroethanol hardly qualifies as a strong acid.

Finally, attention is directed to the effect of dielectric constant on electrical conductivity of hydrogen fluoride solutions (Fig. 13). Nitrobenzene, a weak base with a high dielectric constant, and diethyl ether, a strong base with a low dielectric constant, are both miscible in all proportions with anhydrous

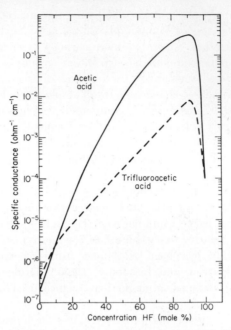

Fɪɢ. 11. Electrical conductivity of acetic and trifluoroacetic acids in liquid hydrogen fluoride.

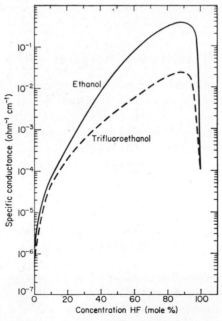

Fɪɢ. 12. Electrical conductivity of ethanol and trifluoroethanol in liquid hydrogen fluoride.

hydrogen fluoride. Concentrated solutions of diethyl ether exhibit essentially no electrical conductivity, although diethyl ether is observed to be completely ionized in dilute solution in hydrogen fluoride. Nitrobenzene on the other hand shows appreciable conductivity in moderately concentrated solution, but even in very dilute solution is only slightly ionized. In any acid–base system, proton transfer depends on the relative strength of the two proton acceptors, but ionization and extensive electric conductivity are found only in solvents of high dielectric constant.

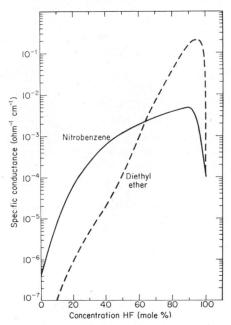

FIG. 13. Electrical conductivity of nitrobenzene and diethyl ether in liquid hydrogen fluoride.

The behaviour of nitrobenzene in hydrogen fluoride is easy to correlate with its behaviour in fuming sulphuric acid. Nitrobenzene functions as an acid-base indicator in both acids. It must be emphasized that solubility in strong acids such as hydrogen fluoride and sulphuric acid, while often associated with proton transfer and ionization, may take place even when the solute is a weak base, and no proton transfer actually occurs. Solubility under such circumstances has also been described as a weak acid-base interaction while not involving atom transfer or the formation of bonds which can be identified by absorption spectra or other simple observations (Hammett, 1940; Kilpatrick and Hyman, 1958).

Terms such as dipole–dipole interaction, acid–base interaction, and proton transfer are used to describe solvent–solute interactions, often without great precision, but usually with an adequate picture of the process taking place.

Infra-red absorption spectrophotometry has been applied to a number of hydrogen fluoride solutions studied over a range of concentrations (Adams and Katz, 1957). The solutes include most of those mentioned above, diethyl ether, ethanol, trifluoroethanol, nitrobenzene and others. Both the dipole alignment and the ionization processes affect the HF vibrations and the range of concentration in which each process dominated was noted in this study.

D. ACID SOLUTES: FLUORIDE ION ACCEPTORS

The extreme acidity of liquid hydrogen fluoride is the basis for both technological and scientific interest in the solvent. By the criterion of the Hammett acidity function, H_0, anhydrous hydrogen fluoride is an extremely strong acid with an H_0 value close to -11. This value is close to that of anhydrous sulphuric acid, and hydrogen fluoride is thus a member of the small class of super-acids. Some ambiguity exists in the exact value because the indicator must affect the concentration of anions and cations present, but H_0 values near -12 have been observed for hydrogen fluoride solutions which clearly contain an excess of acidic species (Hyman et al., 1963).

Because of the high acidity, only a limited number of solutes will act as acids in hydrogen fluoride. Only a few solutes increase the concentration of protonated solvent molecules. Perchloric and fluorosulphonic acids appear to be sufficiently strong and stable enough acids to fall into this category. The most important and interesting group of acids in liquid hydrogen fluoride solutions, however, are the fluoride ion acceptors. The majority of these compounds are Group V fluorides, of which antimony pentafluoride is the most frequently cited example. In hydrogen fluoride the net result of the addition of a fluoride ion acceptor is precisely the same as the addition of a proton donor, namely an increase in the concentration of solvated protons:

$$SbF_5 + 2HF \rightarrow H_2F^+ + SbF_6^-. \tag{21}$$

That antimony pentafluoride and arsenic pentafluoride can act as fluoride ion acceptors has been established in a number of ways (Clifford et al., 1957; Hyman et al., 1961, 1963). The electrical conductivity of HF–SbF$_5$ solutions is very high. When a base such as water is added to this system, the conductivity decreases, and the antimony pentafluoride can be titrated in this way. With further addition of water, the conductivity then increases (Hyman et al., 1963) (Fig. 14). The Raman spectrum of arsenic pentafluoride and antimony pentafluoride solutions in hydrogen fluoride provide most convincing evidence for the abilities of these solutions to act as acids in this solvent system. In dilute solution, the strong Raman line associated with the octahedral AsF_6^- ion or SbF_6^- ion is easily observed at the predicted frequency. Arsenic pentafluoride forms slightly less conductive solutions than SbF_5 and therefore is a weaker acid than is antimony pentafluoride. Niobium and tantalum pentafluorides have only limited solubility in anhydrous hydrogen fluoride. The solubility of NbF_5 and TaF_5 is sufficient, nevertheless, to show that these substances act as acids, although they are somewhat weaker acids than the more soluble arsenic and antimony compounds. Boron trifluoride appears to be the only fluoride ion acceptor other than the Group V fluorides that has definitely been shown to have acid properties in hydrogen fluoride. The low solubility of BF_3 (and low electrical conductivity of $HF-BF_3$ solutions) suggests that this solute is a rather weak acid (Kilpatrick and Luborsky, 1954). Group IV fluorides, i.e. titanium tetrafluoride and silicon

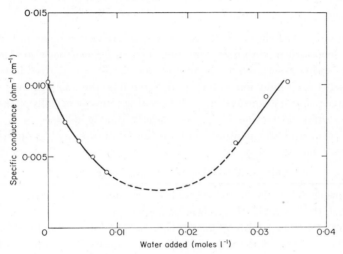

FIG. 14. Conductometric titration of antimony pentafluoride by water in liquid fluoride (SbF_5 0·02 M).

tetrafluoride, are essentially insoluble in anhydrous hydrogen fluoride, and have not been shown to increase the hydrogen ion concentration of the pure solvent. However, in multi-phase systems, titanium tetrafluoride appears to increase the solubility of some hydrocarbons and to function as a catalyst in hydrocarbon re-arrangement (McCauley et al., 1956; McCauley and Lien, 1951, 1957). This behaviour is very much like that of TaF_5 and MoF_5 in similar systems and is interpreted to involve acidic behaviour by TiF_4 and TaF_5. The solubility and acidity of sparingly soluble weak acid fluorides is significantly increased by the presence of a proton acceptor:

$$R + TaF_5 + HF \rightarrow RH^+ + TaF_6^- \tag{22}$$

$$R + 2TiF_4 + HF \rightarrow RH^+ + Ti_2F_9^-. \tag{23}$$

The fluorides may easily be ranked in terms of acid–base properties. The acid strength of fluorides increases regularly from the basic alkali metal fluorides to the pentafluorides, which are the most acidic.

In general, this order corresponds to the acid–base properties of the oxides in water:

strong bases: $$NaF + HF \rightarrow Na^+ + HF_2^- \tag{24}$$

$$Na_2O + H_2O \rightarrow 2Na^+ + 2OH^- \tag{25}$$

weak acids: $$AlF_3 + HF + NaF \rightarrow Na^+ + AlF_4^- + HF* \tag{26}$$

$$Al_2O_3 + 3H_2O + 2NaOH \rightarrow 2Na^+ + 2Al(OH)_4^-* \tag{27}$$

strong acids: $$SbF_5 + 2HF \rightarrow H_2F^+ + SbF_6^- \tag{28}$$

$$SO_3 + 3H_2O \rightarrow 2H_2O^+ + SO_4^{2-} \tag{29}$$

$$Cl_2O_7 + 3H_2O \rightarrow 2H_2O^+ + 2ClO_4^-. \tag{30}$$

Differences in the behaviour of oxides and fluorides are presumably due to specific geometrical stabilizing factors. The difference between the single electron charge associated with fluoride ion transfer and the electron pair associated with oxide ion transfer also renders the analogy less precise. In the hydrogen fluoride system octahedral symmetry stabilizes the monovalent hexafluoride anion MF_6^-. No strictly analogous species is possible with oxygen, and the pentoxide of antimony shows acid properties only with strong bases:

$$Sb_2O_5 + 2NaOH + 5H_2O \rightarrow Na^+ + 2Sb(OH)_6^-*. \tag{31}$$

On the other hand, the hydrogen acids of tetrahedral monovalent tetroxide anions, i.e. (ClO_4^-) of the Group VII elements are very strong acids in water. Acids derived from Group VI atoms (i.e. H_2SO_4) follow closely. Of the oxygen acids, only perchloric acid appears to be sufficiently acidic for the perchlorate anion to be stable as such in liquid hydrogen fluoride. The mixed fluorine-oxygen acid fluoro-sulphonic acid also appears to be in this category.

The solubility and ionization behaviour of hydrogen chloride or bromide in liquid hydrogen fluoride have not been adequately investigated. Fredenhagen (Fredenhagen and Cadenbach, 1930) originally suggested that the concentration of chloride or bromide in hydrogen fluoride solution is vanishingly small. However, it is possible to precipitate insoluble silver chloride from hydrogen fluoride solution, particularly at low temperatures near the melting point of hydrogen fluoride. This suggests a much higher solubility for the remaining halogen acids in hydrogen fluoride than has previously been suspected (Fredenhagen, 1939).

E. SALTS IN THE HYDROGEN FLUORIDE SYSTEM AS SOLUTES

So many solutes are protonated in liquid hydrogen fluoride that the number of true salts is limited. Solvolysis in hydrogen fluoride is the rule for many compounds which are salts in water. For example, potassium nitrate

---

* The anions containing aluminium or antimony which are actually present are more complicated, and their composition varies with concentration.

in anhydrous hydrogen fluoride is converted to KF, $H_3O^+F^-$, and $NO_2^+F^-$ (Del Greco and Gryder, 1961):

$$KNO_3 + 6HF \rightleftharpoons K^+ + NO_2^+ + H_3O^+ + 3HF_2^-. \tag{32}$$

Potassium perchlorate, on the other hand, does seem to be a true salt:

$$KClO_4 + HF \rightleftharpoons K^+ + ClO_4^- + HF. \tag{33}$$

Alkali metal sulphates are usually converted to fluorosulphonates, which then act as normal salts. Other oxygenated anions also usually yield the H_3O^+ cation and an oxide or oxyfluoride. The resulting oxygen compound may then react further to yield the free element. For example, chlorates appear to form chlorine dioxide, whereas bromates give free bromine.

The alkali metal salts of boron trifluoride and the Group V non-metal fluorides are typical salts in liquid hydrogen fluoride. A number of these have been identified by Clifford and Morris (1957). $AgPF_6$, $NaPF_6$, and $Ba(PF_6)_2$ are described as soluble in liquid hydrogen fluoride. $NaAsF_6$ and $NaSbF_6$ are sparingly soluble, $AgBF_4$ is rather insoluble (Clifford and Kongpricha, 1957), and KBF_4 is appreciably soluble.

Evaporation of hydrogen fluoride solutions of BaF_2 or NaF and weak volatile acids as TeF_6 or GeF_4 form solids to which the formulas $Ba(TeF_7)_2$ or $NaGeF_5$ have been assigned. No compelling evidence for the existence of ions such as TeF_7^- in hydrogen fluoride has been adduced. The identity of only a limited number of anions in liquid hydrogen fluoride has been established, and little is known of their behaviour or about the properties of the salts they may form.

F. SOLUTION IN HYDROGEN FLUORIDE WITHOUT IONIZATION

Solution in liquid hydrogen fluoride is not necessarily accompanied by ionic processes, even though proton transfer does occur in a very large number of instances. Weak bases, as noted above, dissolve in anhydrous hydrogen fluoride with only a slight increase in the electrical conductivity. Many such weak bases are organic compounds whose base strength has been lowered by substituents such as nitro or trifluoromethyl groups. In view of the high dielectric constant of hydrogen fluoride, hydrogen bonding usually leads to proton transfer and extensive ionization in dilute solution. Where no such process occurs, it may be inferred that the tendency toward hydrogen bond formation is very weak. Acid–base interactions and hydrogen bond formation play such important roles in understanding solution behaviour in acidic solvents like hydrogen fluoride that we are not quite sure how to treat solutions of weak bases that are miscible in all proportions with liquid hydrogen fluoride. However poorly understood, these solutes may in practice be useful diluents for hydrogen fluoride. Trifluoroacetic acid and liquid sulphur dioxide are miscible with anhydrous hydrogen fluoride in all proportions, do not seem to significantly reduce the acidity of the hydrogen fluoride, and are in fact useful diluents.

In addition, there are a substantial number of inert and rather insoluble compounds. Sparingly soluble and non-ionizing solutes include many simple inorganic molecules including binary fluorides.

The influence of geometrical stabilization in acidic solutes has been discussed. Most pentafluorides have acidic properties because formation of the octahedrally symmetrical hexafluoride anions is favoured. Stable hexafluorides can then be expected to dissolve in liquid hydrogen fluoride without fluoride ion transfer. To the extent that this has been investigated, this appears to be the situation. The uranium hexafluoride–hydrogen fluoride system shows a liquid miscibility gap, the solubility of solid uranium hexafluoride in hydrogen fluoride is rather slight, and there is no evidence for either ionization or compound formation (Rutledge et al., 1953). Investigation by nuclear magnetic resonance methods of a number of hexafluorides containing hydrogen fluoride confirm the absence of interaction (Muetterties and Phillips, 1959). No systematic studies of dilute solutions in hydrogen fluoride appear to have been carried out as yet.

The clear exception is xenon hexafluoride. The high solubility, rapid fluorine exchange, and extensive ionization found for this compound in hydrogen fluoride (Hyman and Quarterman, 1963; Hindman and Svirmickas, 1963) are in agreement with other observations that suggest a symmetry lower than octahedral for xenon hexafluoride (Gillespie, 1963; Smith, 1963).

While the octahedrally symmetrical compounds offer the best examples of non-interaction in solution in liquid hydrogen fluoride, other structures may also be important. Tetrahedral SiF_4 and CF_4 (Muetterties and Phillips, 1959) and the square planar XeF_4 (Hindman and Svirmickas, 1963; Brown et al., 1963) are examples.

IV. Solution in Anhydrous Hydrogen Fluoride of Compounds of Biological Importance

It might seem at first sight that a substance with as ferocious a reputation as anhydrous hydrogen fluoride would have little utility as a solvent for complex and labile organic compounds. Nevertheless, carbohydrates and proteins dissolve readily in anhydrous hydrogen fluoride, frequently with only minor chemical consequences. Despite the fact that anhydrous hydrogen fluoride is certainly one of the most hygroscopic substances known, complex organic compounds potentially capable of eliminating the elements of water often dissolve without dehydration. It is important that dissolution be carried out in such a way that the heat of solution, which is generally high, is dissipated without a concomitant rise in the temperature of the solution. If solutions are prepared at low temperatures, in vessels of good thermal conductivity, and with care taken to maintain a liquid phase at all times, then clear solutions of carbohydrates and proteins can be achieved without difficulty.

Fredenhagen and Cadenbach (1933) appear to have been the first to observe that cellulose is freely soluble in liquid hydrogen fluoride. Cellulose forms conducting solutions in hydrogen fluoride, and the material recovered from such solutions, designated by Fredenhagen as a glucosan, yields glucose on mild hydrolysis. This procedure was in fact suggested as a method for the saccharification of cellulose. Little has appeared in the literature subsequent to this early work that sheds light on the fate of carbohydrates in liquid hydrogen fluoride. Pedersen (1962, 1963) (Pedersen and Fletcher, 1960) has very recently examined the behaviour of a variety of sugar esters with hydrogen fluoride. Prolonged treatment of penta-O-acetyl-β-D-glucopyrannose with anhydrous hydrogen fluoride leads to the formation of derivatives of mannose and altrose; partial hydrolysis and isomerization result. It does not appear that any particular precautions were taken to render or maintain the solutions water-free. Even so, chemical attack on the sugar esters was slow. It would be interesting to study these solutes with strict exclusion of water.

Anhydrous hydrogen fluoride is a powerful solvent for proteins. Not only are the water-soluble proteins freely soluble in hydrogen fluoride, but many fibrous proteins normally insoluble in water, silk fibroin for instance, are also very soluble. Proteins found to dissolve freely are: ribonuclease, insulin, trypsin, serum albumin, serum globulin, edestin, haemoglobin and collagen. Although chemical reactions may ensue, these are not necessarily incompatible with retention of biological activity. Insulin can be recovered from hydrogen fluoride solution with essentially full retention of biological activity (Katz, 1954). The enzymes ribonuclease and lysozyme may be dissolved and re-covered from hydrogen fluoride or HF–SO$_2$ mixtures in a form indistinguishable in enzymatic properties from the original, provided the temperature is kept low and the time of exposure is short (Koch *et al.*, 1958). At higher temperatures, inactivation occurs, but it appears that inactivation results from the splitting of a small number of peptide bonds, without causing a decrease in molecular weight but leading to an increase in hydrodynamic volume. Model experiments on compounds containing disulphide linkages strongly indicate that disulphide bonds in proteins are stable in hydrogen fluoride solution.

Anhydrous hydrogen fluoride swells collagen and disorients it, but probably does not break peptide bonds. Low molecular weight gelatins sometimes observed on recovery from hydrogen fluoride probably arise by hydrolysis with adventitious water (Veis and Katz, 1956). To further indicate the ability of hydrogen fluoride to function as a protein solvent, attention is directed to the polymerization of N-carboxy anhydrides in hydrogen fluoride to form poly-α-amino acids (Kopple and Katz, 1956). Polypeptides with chain lengths of 30 are readily obtained. An unexpected side-reaction, the elimination of carbon monoxide from the N-carboxy anhydride, probably accounts for the relatively short chain length (Kopple et al., 1962).

Some possible chemical consequences for proteins dissolved in hydrogen fluoride have been the subject for recent investigations by Hess and co-workers (Lenard et al., 1964; Shin et al., 1962; Sakakibara et al., 1962). These workers have shown that serine- and threonine-containing peptides undergo an N to O acyl shift in hydrogen fluoride. It has been known for a long time that under the influence of strong acids, such as concentrated sulphuric acid, that a reversible, pH-dependent rearrangement occurs at peptide links involving amino acids containing an aliphatic hydroxy group in the side chain. Migration occurs, and the peptide bond is converted to an ester group, with the peptide nitrogen now appearing as a free amino group. An hydroxy-oxazolidine is considered to be the intermediate in the N to O acyl migration:

$$
\underset{\substack{\text{O} \quad \text{HO—CH}_2 \quad \text{O} \\ \parallel \qquad | \qquad \parallel}}{\text{R—C—NH—CH—C—NHR}'}
\underset{\text{OH}^-}{\overset{\text{H}^+}{\rightleftharpoons}}
\quad\quad
\underset{\text{OH}^-}{\overset{\text{H}^+}{\rightleftharpoons}}
$$

$$
\underset{\substack{\text{NH}_3^+\text{—CH—C—NHR}'}}{\overset{\substack{\text{O} \\ \parallel \\ \text{R—C—O—CH}_2 \quad \text{O}}}{}}
\qquad\qquad (34)
$$

Since the ester group formed in the acyl migration is very sensitive to hydrolysis, this furnishes the basis of a useful method for the chemical cleavage of peptide chains at peptide linkages adjacent to seryl or threonyl amino acid residues. Specific cleavage also appears to occur at C—methionyl peptide bonds. This work constitutes the most detailed analysis of the chemical consequences on proteins resulting from dissolution in hydrogen fluoride. The reactions that do occur are highly specific and may have value in protein structure determinations. Singer (1962) has recently reviewed the effects of non-aqueous solvents generally on protein conformation, and has directed particular attention to the effects of strong protonic solvents.

The observation that the iron-containing proteins cytochrome c and haemoglobin are soluble in liquid hydrogen fluoride to form solutions that have absorption spectra very similar to those in water has prompted examination of other metal co-ordination compounds in hydrogen fluoride. The ability of metal complex compounds to persist in hydrogen fluoride seems to be general, for metal phthalocyanines, cobalt(III) amines, and many other co-ordination compounds dissolve without destruction of the complex. Particularly interesting solutes are the biologically important metal co-ordination compounds chlorophyll and vitamin B_{12}. Chlorophyll yields solutions in hydrogen fluoride with absorption spectra characteristic of the more usual solvents. Vitamin B_{12} forms a deep olive-green solution in hydrogen fluoride as contrasted to its normal deep-red. This cobalt(III) co-ordination compound survives dissolution in hydrogen fluoride despite its very complicated structure and numerous functional groups. Vitamin B_{12} can be readily regenerated from the recovered solute and possesses full B_{12} activity.

REFERENCES

Adams, R. M. and Katz, J. J. (1956) *J. opt. Soc. Amer.* **46**, 895.
Adams, R. M. and Katz, J. J. (1957) *J. mol. Spectroscopy* **1**, 306.
Atoji, M. and Lipscomb, W. N. (1954) *Acta crystallogr.* **7**, 173.
Briegleb, G. and Strohmeier, W. (1953) *Z. Electrochem.* **57**, 668.
Brown, T. H., Whipple, E. B. and Verdier, P. H. (1963) "Noble Gas Compounds" (H. H. Hyman, ed.), pp. 263–9. University of Chicago Press, Chicago.
Clifford, A. F. and Kongpricha, S. (1957) *J. inorg. nucl. Chem.* **5**, 76.
Clifford, A. F. and Morris, A. G. (1957) *J. inorg. nucl. Chem.* **5**, 71.
Clifford, A. F. and Sargent, J. (1957) *J. Amer. chem. Soc.* **79**, 4041.
Clifford, A. F., Beachell, H. C. and Jack, W. M. (1957) *J. inorg. nucl. Chem.* **5**, 57.
Del Greco, F. P. and Gryder, J. W. (1961) *J. phys. Chem.* **65**, 922.
Feder, H. M., Hubbard, W. N., Wise, S. S. and Margrave, J. L. (1963) *J. phys. Chem.* **67**, 1148.
Franck, E. U. and Meyer, F. (1959) *Z. Elektrochem.* **63**, 571.
Franck, E. U. and Spalthoff, W. (1957) *Z. Elektrochem.* **61**, 348.
Fredenhagen, H. (1939) *Z. anorg. Chem.* **242**, 23.
Fredenhagen, K. and Cadenbach, G. (1929) *Z. anorg. Chem.* **178**, 289.
Fredenhagen, K. and Cadenbach, G. (1930) *Z. phys. Chem.* **146A**, 245.
Fredenhagen, K. and Cadenbach, G. (1933) *Angew. Chem.* **46**, 113.
Fredenhagen, K. and Dahmlos, J. (1929) *Z. anorg. Chem.* **178**, 272.
Giguère, P. A. and Zengin, N. (1958) *Canad. J. Chem.* **36**, 1013.
Gillespie, R. J. (1963) "Noble Gas Compounds" (H. H. Hyman, ed.), pp. 333–9. University of Chicago Press, Chicago.
Hammett, L. P. (1935) *Chem. Rev.* **16**, 67.
Hammett, L. P. (1940) "Physical Organic Chemistry". McGraw-Hill Book Co., New York.
Hammett, L. P. and Deyrup, A. J. (1932) *J. Amer. Chem. Soc.* **54**, 2721.
Herzberg, G. (1950) "Molecular Spectra and Molecular Structure. I. Spectra of Diatomic Molecules," 2nd edition. D. van Nostrand Co., Inc., New York.
Hindman, J. C. and Svirmickas, A. (1963) *In* "Noble Gas Compounds" (H. H. Hyman, ed.), pp. 251–62. University of Chicago Press, Chicago.
Hu, J.-H., White, D. and Johnston, H. L. (1953) *J. Amer. chem. Soc.* **75**, 1232.
Hyman, H. H. and Quarterman, L. A. (1963) "Noble Gas Compounds" (H. H. Hyman, ed.), p. 275. University of Chicago Press, Chicago.
Hyman, H. H., Kilpatrick, M. and Katz, J. J. (1957) *J. Amer. chem. Soc.* **79**, 3668.
Hyman, H. H., Lane, T. I. and O'Donnell, T. A. (1963) 145th Meeting A. C. S. Abstracts, p. 63T.
Hyman, H. H., Quarterman, L. A., Kilpatrick, M. and Katz, J. J. (1961) *J. phys. Chem.* **65**, 123.
Jache, A. W. and Cady, G. H. (1952) *J. phys. Chem.* **56**, 1106.
Jarry, R. L. and Davis, W. J. (1953) *J. phys. Chem.* **57**, 600.

Katz, J. J. (1954) *Archs Biochem. Biophys.* **51**, 293.

Katz, J. J. and Hyman, H. H. (1953) *Rev. sci. Instrum.* **24**, 1066.

Kilpatrick, M. and Hyman, H. H. (1958) *J. Amer. chem. Soc.* **80**, 77.

Kilpatrick, M. and Lewis, J. I. (1956) *J. Amer. chem. Soc.* **78**, 5186.

Kilpatrick, M. and Luborsky, F. (1953) *J. Amer. chem. Soc.* **75**, 577.

Kilpatrick, M. and Luborsky, F. (1954) *J. Amer. chem. Soc.* **76**, 5863.

Koch, A. L., Lamont, W. A. and Katz, J. J. (1956) *Archs Biochem. Biophys.* **63**, 106.

Kopple, K. D. and Katz, J. J. (1956) *J. Amer. chem. Soc.* **78**, 6199.

Kopple, K. D., Quarterman, L. A. and Katz, J. J. (1962) *J. org. Chem.* **27**, 1062.

Kuipers, G. A. (1958) *J. mol. Spectroscopy* **2**, 75.

Kuipers, G. A., Smith, D. F. and Neilson, A. H. (1956) *J. chem. Phys.* **25**, 275.

Le Boucher, L., Fischer, W. and Biltz, W. (1932) *Z. anorg. Chem.* **206**, 61.

Lenard, J. I., Schally, A. V. and Hess, G. P. (1964) *Biochem. Biophys. Research Commun.* **14**, 498.

Long, R. W., Hildebrand, J. H. and Morell, W. E. (1943) *J. Amer. chem. Soc.* **65**, 182.

McCaulay, D. A. and Lien, A. P. (1951) *J. Amer. chem. Soc.* **75**, 2013.

McCaulay, D. A. and Lien, A. P. (1957) *J. Amer. chem. Soc.* **79**, 2495.

McCaulay, D. A., Higley, W. S. and Lien, A. P. (1956) *J. Amer. chem. Soc.* **78**, 3009.

Mackor, E. L., Hofstra, A. and Van de Waals, J. H. (1958) *Trans. Faraday Soc.* **54**, 186.

MacLean, C. and Mackor, E. L. (1961) *J. chem. Phys.* **34**, 2207.

MacLean, C. and Mackor, E. L. (1962) *Discuss. Faraday Soc.*, No. 34, 165.

Maybury, R. H., Gordon, S. and Katz, J. J. (1955) *J. Chem. Phys.* **23**, 1277.

Mellor's Comprehensive Treatise on Inorganic and Theoretical Chemistry. (1956) Supplement A, Part I. Longmans, Green and Co., London. Chapter I. Fluorine Section 3, 72–84. The preparation of hydrofluoric acid. Section 4, 85–146. The physical and chemical properties and uses of hydrogen fluoride and its aqueous solutions.

Muetterties, E. L. and Phillips, W. D. (1959) *J. Amer. chem. Soc.* **81**, 1084.

Paul, M. A. and Long, F. A. (1957) *Chem. Rev.* **57**, 1.

Pauling, L. (1956) *J. chem. Educ.* **33**, No. 1, 16–17.

Perkins, A. (1965) *J. phys. Chem.* (in the press).

Pedersen, C. (1962) *Acta chem. Scand.* **16**, 1831.

Pedersen, C. (1963) *Acta chem. Scand.* **17**, 673.

Pedersen, C. and Fletcher, H. G., Jr. (1960) *J. Amer. chem. Soc.* **82**, 941.

Quarterman, L. A., Hyman, H. H. and Katz, J. J. (1957) *J. phys. Chem.* **61**, 912.

Quaterman, L. A., Hyman, H. H. and Katz, J. J. (1961) *J. phys. Chem.* **65**, 90.

Rogers, M. T., Speirs, J. L. and Panish, M. B. (1956a) *J. Amer. chem. Soc.* **78**, 3288.

Rogers, M. T., Speirs, J. L. and Panish, M. B. (1956b) *J. phys. Chem.* **61**, 366.

Rogers, M. T., Speirs, J. L., Panish, M. B. and Thompson, H. B. (1956) *J. Amer. chem. Soc.* **78**, 936.

Roth, W. A. (1939) *Annls Chim. Phys.* **542**, 35.

Rothschild, W. G. (1964) *J. opt. Soc. Amer.* **54**, 20.

Runner, M. E., Balog, G. and Kilpatrick, M. (1956) *J. Amer. chem. Soc.*, 5183.

Rutledge, G. P., Jarry, R. L. and Davis, W., Jr. (1953) *J. phys. Chem.* **57**, 541.

Sakakibara, S., Shin, K. H. and Hess, G. P. (1962) *J. Amer. chem. Soc.* **84**, 4921.

Sastri, M. L. N. and Hornig, D. F. (1963) *J. chem. Phys.* **39**, 3497.

Shin, K. H., Sakakibara, S., Schneider, W. and Hess, G. P. (1962) *Biochem. Biophys. Res. Commun.* **8**, 288.

Simons, J. H. (1950) "Fluorine Chemistry" Vol. I, p. 225. Academic Press, New York.

Simons, J. H. (1964) "Fluorine Chemistry" Vol. V, p. 2–15, Academic Press, New York.

Simons, J. H. and Bouknight, J. W. (1932) *J. Amer. chem. Soc.* **54**, 129.

Simons, J. H. and Dresdner, R. D. (1944) *J. Amer. chem. Soc.* **66**, 1070.

Simons, J. H. and Hildebrand, J. H. (1924) *J. Amer. chem. Soc.* **46**, 2183.

Singer, S. J. (1962) *Adv. Protein Chem.* **17**, 1.

Smith, D. F. (1958) *J. chem. Phys.* **28**, 1040.

Smith, D. F. (1963) "Noble Gas Compounds" (H. H. Hyman, ed.), pp. 295–303. University of Chicago Press, Chicago.

Spalthoff, W. and Franck, E. U. (1957) *Z. Elektrochem.* **61**, 993.

Strohmeier, W. and Briegleb, G. (1953) *Z. Electrochem.* **57**, 662.

Veis, A. and Katz, J. J. (1956) *Biochim. biophys. Acta* **22**, 96.

CHAPTER 3

The Higher Hydrogen Halides as Ionizing Solvents

M. E. PEACH AND T. C. WADDINGTON

Anorganisch-Chemisches Institut der Universität, Göttingen, West Germany
School of Molecular Sciences, University of Warwick, Coventry, England

I. Introduction... 83
    A. Some Physical Properties of the Liquid Hydrogen Halides............... 84
    B. Self-ionization... 86
    C. Experimental Methods... 88
II. Solutions in the Hydrogen Halides..................................... 97
    A. Acids and Bases.. 97
    B. Solvolysis Reactions.. 111
    C. Redox Reactions... 112

I. INTRODUCTION

The higher hydrogen halides (HCl, HBr, HI) have interest as ionizing solvents both in their own right and also because of the comparison that can be made between their properties and those of liquid hydrogen fluoride, to which they are so similar and at the same time so different. Most of the work discussed in this paper will refer to liquid hydrogen chloride. It is interesting to note how much more important, in the past, the temperature factor has been than the extreme reactivity of hydrogen fluoride. Fremy was using platinum apparatus in his preparation of anhydrous hydrogen fluoride in 1856, whereas the work of Archibald, McIntosh and Steele at the beginning of this century was seriously handicapped by lack of high vacuum apparatus and a limited supply of solid carbon dioxide for producing low temperatures.

The first experiments using liquid hydrogen chloride as a solvent were performed about a century ago by Gore (1865). The experiments were rather hazardous, as he worked in an enclosed system, making hydrogen chloride from sulphuric acid and sal ammoniac. Only qualitative visual observations were made, but these did not augur well for the future: of the 66 compounds studied only 10 dissolved, and he concluded that "Liquid hydrogen chloride has but a feeble solvent power for solid bodies in general".

In spite of Gore's conclusions, the study of hydrogen chloride, bromide, and iodide as non-aqueous solvents was resumed for about a decade just after the turn of the century at McGill University, Canada. The vast majority of these results is collected together and discussed in a lengthy paper, published in English and German, divided into four sections, each of which is complete in itself, describing work impeccably performed under difficult experimental conditions (Steele, McIntosh and Archibald, 1905, 1906).

The first section describes the measurement of physical and thermodynamic constants of the hydrogen halides. The variation of vapour pressure and density were studied as a function of the temperature; the surface energy (by Ramsay and Shield's method) and viscosity (by rate of capillary flow) were also measured. The accuracy of this work can be judged from the fact that the latent heat of vapourization of liquid hydrogen chloride was calculated, from the vapour pressure curve, to be 3·54 kcal mole^{-1} the currently accepted value is 3·86 kcal mole^{-1} (Mellor). The main inaccuracy must have been the measurement of small volumes of the liquid hydrogen halides in graduated tubes. The second section describes solubility, conductivity and ebullioscopic measurements. The results obtained from the variation of conductivity with dilution and the ebullioscopic measurements were rather strange and very difficult to interpret. It is hoped to be able to present an explanation later in this review, based on the assumption that triple ions are formed in all but the most dilute solutions. The third section describes work that was very difficult experimentally, the measurement of transport numbers in liquid hydrogen bromide, and no attempt has yet been made to extend these observations. The validity of Faraday's Laws for these solutions was confirmed and the actual transport numbers were determined by Hittorf's method. In the last section there is a detailed discussion of the results, but little relationship was found between dissolving power, dielectric constant, conductivity and deviations in molecular weight determinations.

Direct study of some reactions in liquid hydrogen chloride was then resumed in the late 1950's in Cambridge (Waddington and Klanberg, 1960a) although a good deal of work bearing on the solvent properties, such as the study of phase diagrams, had been studied in the interim. Some further studies have also been made recently of the solvent properties of liquid hydrogen bromide and iodide by Waddington and White (1960a,b, 1963) and Klanberg and Kohlschutter (1961).

A. SOME PHYSICAL PROPERTIES OF THE LIQUID HYDROGEN HALIDES

Some of the physical properties of the liquid hydrogen halides and water, for comparative purposes, are listed in Table I.

From the table it can be seen that there are some quite marked similarities between water and hydrogen fluoride on the one hand, and the other hydrogen halides on the other hand, and some great differences between these two groups. Hydrogen chloride, bromide and iodide have a relatively narrow liquid range, thus increasing some of the experimental difficulties, and low dielectric constants. The consequences of these low dielectric constants can be seen experimentally when it is found that only salts with low lattice energies, such as the tetra-alkylammonium halides, are soluble, whereas "ordinary simple salts", such as ammonium chloride, with a high lattice energy, are insoluble. Another consequence of this low dielectric constant is the complex variation of the equivalent conductivity with concentration, discussed later in Section IC,2.

The Trouton's constants are high for water and hydrogen fluoride, indicating that some association, due to hydrogen bonding, must be occurring. In the other hydrogen halides, hydrogen bonding, although it can occur, is very much weaker than in hydrogen fluoride: this is reflected in the normal Trouton's constants, which indicate little association in the liquid.

TABLE I

Some Physical Constants of the Hydrogen Halides and Water

	H_2O	HF	HCl	HBr	HI
Mol. wt.	18·0	20·0	36·5	80·9	127·9
M.p. (°C)	0	−83·0	−114·6	−88·5	−50·9
B.p. (°C)	100	19·5	−84·1	−67·0	−35·0
Liquid range (°C)	100	102·5	30·5	21·5	15·9
Density of liquid	1·00	1·20	1·187	2·603	2·85
(g/ml near m.p.)	(0°)	(−80°)	(−114°)	(−84°)	(−47°)
Latent heats:					
Fusion	1440[a]	1094	476	600	686
Vapourization	9720[a]	7230[a]	3860	4210	4724
(cal/mol)					
Trouton's constant	26·0	24·7	20·4	20·4	19·8
Dielectric constant	84·2	175	9·28	7·0[a]	3·39[a]
of liquid	(0°)	(−73°)	(−95°)	(−85°)	(−50°)
Viscosity	1·00	0·24	0·51[f]	0·83[f]	1·35[f]
(centipoises)	(22°)	(0°)	(−95°)	(−67°)	(−35·4°)
Specific conductivity	0·05[b]	0·1[d]	0·0035[g]	0·0014[h]	0·00085[i]
(μ mho cm^{-1})	(18°)	(−80°)	(−85°)	(−84°)	(−45°)
H.Hal stretching Frequency	3568*[c]	3961[e]	2886[e]	2558[e]	2230[e]
(gas, cm^{-1})					

* Value for the OH radical.

[a] "Handbook of Chemistry and Physics" Chemical Rubber Publishing Co.
[b] Glasstone: "Textbook of Physical Chemistry."
[c] Herzberg: "Infra-red and Raman Spectra of Polyatomic Molecules."
[d] Runner et al. (1956).
[e] Grange et al. (1960).
[f] Steele et al. (1905).
[g] Glockler and Peck (1936).
[h] Waddington and White (1963).
[i] Smyth and Hitchcock (1933).

All other values are quoted from Mellor's "Comprehensive Inorganic Chemistry".

4

B. SELF-IONIZATION

The self-conductances of the liquid hydrogen halides, except the fluoride, are somewhat less than that of water, but to account for these conductivities some form of self-ionization must be postulated. It is known that water ionizes into a proton and a hydroxide ion,

$$H_2O \rightleftharpoons H^+ + OH^- \tag{1}$$

and that this equation is more usually written with the proton solvated, as the hydroxonium ion, although further solvation of both ions must occur,

$$2H_2O \rightleftharpoons H_3O^+ + OH^-. \tag{2}$$

Similarly the hydrogen halides, HHal, can ionize,

$$HHal \rightleftharpoons H^+ + Hal^- \tag{3}$$

but in these systems solvation of both proton and the halide ion is known to occur :

$$3HHal \rightleftharpoons H_2Hal^+ + HHal_2^-. \tag{4}$$

The only well authenticated example of an H_2Hal^+ ion in solution is the hydrofluoronium ion, H_2F^+, which has been detected, together with the SbF_6^- ion, in the hydrogen fluoride—antimony pentafluoride system by conductivity measurements, Raman spectra and infra-red spectra (Hyman et al., 1961). The H_2Cl^+ ion may exist in the compounds $HCl . HClO_4$, which is explosive, $HCl . H_2SO_4$, which it was not possible to isolate as a solid (Hantzsch, 1930) and in $HCl . HBr$ (Klemenc and Kohl, 1927). This last compound has been claimed to have a structure $H_2Cl^+Br^-$ and not $H_2Br^+Cl^-$ by a dubious argument equating the H_2Cl^+ ion with the K^+ ion and the H_2Br^+ ion with the Rb^+ ion, as the nuclear charge and number of electrons are the same in both instances, and comparing the lattice energies of potassium bromide and rubidium chloride (del Fresno, 1928). There is, as yet, no evidence for the H_2Br^+ and H_2I^+ ions in solution, or in solids.

The existence of the hydrogen difluoride ion, HF_2^-, has long been known, and that of the hydrogen dichloride ion, HCl_2^-, is now well established. It was first postulated as an intermediate in some organic reactions in nitrobenzene (Herbrandson et al., 1954), and was then prepared as tetramethylammonium hydrogen dichloride (Waddington, 1958a, b) and as some carbonium ion dichlorides (Sharp, 1958). Recently this ion has been encountered in several compounds. The reported preparation of caesium hydrogen dichloride by West (1957), has later proved to be false ; the compound was in fact $CsCl . \frac{3}{4}HCl . \frac{3}{4}H_2O$ (Vallée and McDaniel, 1963; Maki and West, 1963) with a structure $4Cs^+Cl^- . 3H_3O^+Cl^-$. Caesium hydrogen dichloride has been prepared from hydrogen chloride and caesium chloride at $-78°$, and has a high dissociation pressure (c. 4·4 atm, at room temperature)

(Valleé and McDaniel, 1962). The infra-red spectra of some of these compounds have been examined and frequencies assigned to the hydrogen dichloride ion (Waddington, 1958b; Sharp, 1958). The infra-red data is consistent with that of a linear ion $(Cl-H-Cl)^-$; the symmetric position of the proton has been confirmed by entropy measurements (Chang and Westrum, 1962). The heat of formation of the HF_2^- ion in the gas phase has been calculated to be 58—5 kcal mole^{-1} (Waddington, 1958a). The heats of formation for the HX_2^- ion with large cations are reported to approach limiting values of $+14 \cdot 2$ kcal mole^{-1} for HCL_2^-, $+12 \cdot 8$ kcal mole^{-1} for HBr_2^-, and $+12 \cdot 4$ kcal mole^{-1} for the HI_2^- ion (Valleé and McDaniel, 1963). The hydrogen dichloride and dibromide ions have been found as their tropenium

TABLE II

The Infra-red Vibration Frequencies of the Hydrogen Dihalide Ions

Anion	ν_3 cm^{-1} (Assymetric stretch)	ν_2 cm^{-1} (Bending)	Salt
HF_2^-	1450	1223	KHF_2
HCl_2^-	1565	1180	Me_4NHCl_2[a]
	1565	1160	Me_4NHCl_2[b]
	1540	1150	$n-Bu_4NHCl_2$[b]
	1625	1150	$Si(acac)_3HCl_2$[b]
HBr_2^-	1670	1170	Et_4NHBr_2[b]
	1690	1170	$n-Bu_4NHBr_2$[b]
HI_2^-	1650	1165	$n-Bu_4NHI_2$[b]
$HBrCl^-$	1650	1100	$n-Bu_4NHBrCl$[c]
$HClI^-$	2000	990	$n-Bu_4NHClI$[c]

[a] Waddington (1958a, b).   [b] Valleé and McDaniel (1963).
[c] Salthouse and Waddington (1965).

salts, $C_7H_7^+HX_2^-$, which were prepared from the reaction of a solution of tropenyl methyl ether with a saturated ethereal solution of the hydrogen halide (Harmon and Davis, 1962). The hydrogen dibromide ion has also been prepared as the tetra-n-butylammonium and tetraphenylarsonium salts (Waddington and White, 1960a) and the hydrogen di-iodide ion as the tetra-n-butylammonium salt. Salts of mixed dihalide ions such as $HClBr^-$ and $HClI^-$, have also recently been prepared (Salthouse and Waddington, 1965).

A summary of the infra-red data on these ions is given in Table II.

If the self-ionization of the hydrogen halides can be represented by equation (4), two definitions of acids and bases are applicable, based upon a difference of emphasis, rather than of principle. This arises from the fact that either halide ion- or proton-transfer can be regarded as the primary step in the equilibrium. Acids can be defined as proton donors or halide ion acceptors, and bases as proton acceptors or halide ion donors: the halide ions in this concept must always be solvated as the hydrogen dihalide ions, similarly the protons are solvated as hydrohalonium ions H_2Hal^+. Thus hydrogen chloride shows some of the characteristics of a chloridotropic solvent such as arsenic trichloride (Gutmann, 1956), and some of an acidic solvent, such as sulphuric acid (Gillespie and Leisten, 1954; Gillespie and Robinson, 1959 and Chapter 4 of this book).

C. EXPERIMENTAL METHODS

1. *Preparation of the Pure Solvents, and Handling Techniques*

The main method used in the study of these solvents has been conductimetric measurements. Spectroscopic techniques have not been extensively used. The most sensitive test of the purity of the hydrogen halides is the specific conductivity of the liquid, although a rough guide can be obtained from vapour pressure measurements. The conductivity is very sensitive to traces of impurity, such as water, and very high purity solvent can only be obtained by repeated distillations. As the hydrogen halides, except the fluoride, are gases at room temperature, they must be handled in an enclosed vacuum system. The temperatures at which the solvents are usually studied are $-111.6°$ (melting carbon disulphide) and $-95.0°$ (melting toluene) for hydrogen chloride, $-83.6°$ (melting ethyl acetate) for hydrogen bromide, and $-45.2°$ (melting chlorobenzene) for hydrogen iodide.

2. *Conductimetric Measurements*

The conductivity of solutions in liquid hydrogen chloride and bromide, was studied by Steele *et al.* (1905, 1906) but not used as a means for following titrations of the acid–base type. This latter type of titration has been used extensively in recent work on these solvents. The conductivities of the pure solvents are shown in Table I, while a selection of conductivities of solutes in the various solvents are shown in Table III.

From this table it is seen that the conductivities of the solvobases are very much greater than those of the solvoacids. This is due to the highly acidic nature of these solvents, making it very difficult to find acids that are stronger than the solvents themselves. It is also seen that the conductivities in liquid hydrogen chloride are higher than in the bromide or iodide. The mechanism of the conduction is not known, but it can be postulated that it occurs by chloride ion transfer, in basic liquid hydrogen chloride solutions, viz:

$$Cl\!-\!\!-\!H\!-\!\!-\!Cl^- \ .. \ H\!-\!\!-\!Cl$$
$$\downarrow$$
$$Cl\!-\!\!-\!H \ ... \ Cl\!-\!\!-\!H\!-\!\!-\!Cl^-$$

If this represents a true picture of the mode of conduction the molar conductances of all univalent bases should be approximately the same at infinite dilution: unfortunately it is not yet possible to measure these conductances with any degree of accuracy (Peach and Waddington, 1963a). Transport

TABLE III

Conductances of Some Solutions

Solvent	Solute	Concentration (mole/litre)	Specific conductivity (μ mho cm^{-1})	Molar conductances (cm^2 ohm^{-1} mole^{-1})	solution
HCl	PCl$_5$	0·36	9350	25·9	Basic[a]
HCl	Me$_4$NCl	0·32	6790	21·5	Basic[a]
HCl	BCl$_3$	0·32	0·13	4.0×10^{-4}	Acidic[a]
HCl	BF$_3$	1·43	0·09	0.6×10^{-4}	Acidic[a]
HCl	POF$_3$	0·25	3·6	1.5×10^{-2}	Basic[b]
HBr	Me$_4$NBr	0·023	9·8	0·432	Basic[c]
HBr	SnBr$_4$	0·064	0·024	3.8×10^{-4}	Acidic[c]
HI	Ph$_3$MeNI	0·10	243	2·55	Basic[d]
HI	Pyridine	0·38	125	0·32	Basic[d]

[a] Waddington and Klanberg (1960a).   [c] Waddington and White (1960a).
[b] Peach and Waddington (1962b).   [d] Klanberg and Kohlschütter (1961).

TABLE IV

Cation Transport Numbers in Liquid Hydrogen Bromide[a]

Substance	Concentration (mole/litre)	Mean value of t_+
Ether, (C$_2$H$_5$)$_2$O	1·0	0·82
Triethylamine, Et$_3$N	0·5	0·18
Triethylamine, Et$_3$N	0·62–0·75	0·22
Triethylamine, Et$_3$N	1·04	0·35
Acetone, Me$_2$CO	1·0	0·38
Acetone, Me$_2$CO	1·82	0·95
Methyl hexyl ketone	0·9	0·39
Methyl hexyl ketone	1·8	0·77

[a] Steele et al. (1905, 1906).

numbers have not yet been measured in liquid hydrogen chloride, but they have been measured for some hydrogen bromide solutions (Steele *et al.*, 1905, 1906). The results are summarized in Table IV. It will be seen from the table that the cation transport number is always increased by increase of concentration. This change probably indicates an increase in the complexity of the cation as the solution becomes stronger.

The hydrogen halides, except the fluoride, have low dielectric constants. Fuoss and Kraus studied the variation of conductivity with concentration in solvents of low dielectric constant (Krauss and Fuoss, 1933; Fuoss and Krauss, 1933). They found that plots of $\log\varLambda$ against $\log c$ ($\varLambda$ = equivalent

TABLE V

Values of c_m, $\varLambda_m$ and $\varLambda_\infty$ in Hydrogen Chloride Solution[a]

Variable	Plot	Kraus and Fuoss[b, c]	Me$_2$S	Me$_3$N	Me$_3$NHBCl$_4$	MeCOCl
c_m	$\begin{cases}\varLambda-c^{\frac{1}{2}} \\ \varLambda c^{\frac{1}{2}}-c \\ \log\varLambda-\log c\end{cases}$	$\epsilon = 9\cdot0$ $0\cdot025$	$0\cdot0196$ $0\cdot0197$ $0\cdot020$	$0\cdot0064$ $0\cdot0069$ $0\cdot0072$	$0\cdot01538$ $0\cdot0133$ $0\cdot01514$	$0\cdot0625$ $0\cdot114$ $0\cdot0603$
$\varLambda_m$	$\begin{cases}-c^{\frac{1}{2}} \\ \log\varLambda-\log c\end{cases}$	$5\cdot6$	$0\cdot85$ $0\cdot76$	$0\cdot85$ $0\cdot87$	$0\cdot79$ $0\cdot80$	$0\cdot00485$ $0\cdot00516$
$\varLambda_\infty$	$\varLambda-c^{\frac{1}{2}}$	40	$3\cdot65$	$1\cdot90$	$2\cdot50$	$0\cdot0151$

[a] Peach and Waddington (1963a).   [b] Kraus and Fuoss (1933
[c] Fuoss and Kraus (1933).

conductance, c = concentration) showed a minimum and that this minimum moved to higher concentrations as the dielectric constant increased; with aqueous solutions this minimum was at concentrations too high to be observed. The variation of the conductances of hydrogen chloride, hydrogen bromide and hydrogen iodide solutions was studied by Steele *et al.* (1905, 1906), Peach and Waddington (1963a), and by Waddington and White (1963). In all these cases it was found that in plots of $\varLambda$ and $\sqrt{c}$ the value of $\varLambda$ tended to come to a minimum at low values of $\sqrt{c}$. The position of this minimum concentration, c_m, has been found for hydrogen chloride solutions of the bases dimethylsulphide and trimethylamine, the salt, trimethylammonium tetrachloroborate, and the weak electrolyte, (see Fig. 1) acetyl chloride; the values are shown in Table V (Peach and Waddington, 1963a). Extrapolation of these curves to infinite dilution is very difficult.

This variation of conductance with concentration in hydrogen chloride solutions is very much the same as that observed by Fuoss and Kraus with a

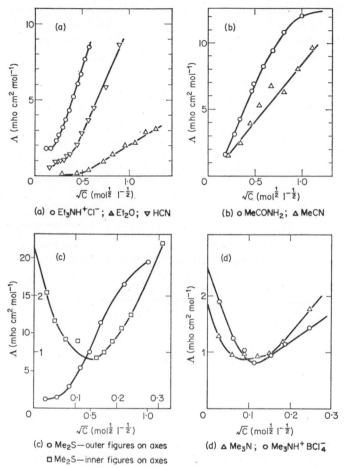

(a) o $Et_3NH^+Cl^-$; $\triangle Et_2O$; $\triangledown HCN$

(b) o $MeCONH_2$; $\triangle MeCN$

(c) o Me_2S—outer figures on axes
□ Me_2S—inner figures on axes

(d) $\triangle Me_3N$; o $Me_3NH^+ BCl_4^-$

Fig. 1. The results of conductivity dilution experiments in liquid hydrogen chloride.

solvent of about the same dielectric constant. To account for these results it is assumed that two modes of ionization for an ion pair, A^+B^-, are possible:

$$A^+B^- \overset{K_5}{\rightleftharpoons} A^+ + B^- \tag{5}$$

$$A^+B^- + A^+ \overset{K_6}{\rightleftharpoons} A_2B^+ \tag{6}$$

$$A^+B^- + B^- \overset{K_7}{\rightleftharpoons} AB_2^-. \tag{7}$$

Ionization of type (5) occurs in very dilute solutions, and of types (6) and (7) in more concentrated ones. Calculations from this basic operation, involving some drastic assumptions, show that the ionization of strong electrolytes in hydrogen chloride solutions can be represented by equations (5), (6), and (7) (Peach and Waddington, 1963a): similar reasoning must also apply to hydrogen bromide and iodide solutions. It is also possible to calculate the dissociation constants K_5, K_6 and K_7 (see Table V). The variation of the conductance of weak electrolytes with concentration is more complicated, and cannot easily be explained.

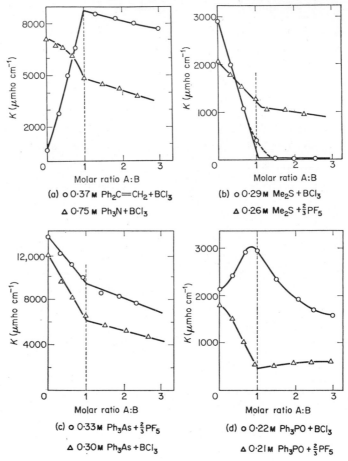

(a) o 0·37 M $Ph_2C\!\!=\!\!CH_2 + BCl_3$
　　△ 0·75 M $Ph_3N + BCl_3$

(b) o 0·29 M $Me_2S + BCl_3$
　　△ 0·26 M $Me_2S + \frac{2}{3}PF_5$

(c) o 0·33 M $Ph_3As + \frac{2}{3}PF_5$
　　△ 0·30 M $Ph_3As + BCl_3$

(d) o 0·22 M $Ph_3PO + BCl_3$
　　△ 0·21 M $Ph_3PO + \frac{2}{3}PF_5$

Fig. 2. Some conductimetric titrations in liquid hydrogen chloride.

For simplicity the ionization of all salts, when discussed further in the text, will be assumed to be of type (5), although ionization of types (6) and (7) must occur.

Reactions involving changes in the ionic species present in the solution can be followed conductimetrically, for example the acid–base reaction (Waddington and Klanberg, 1960a):

$$Me_4N^+HCl_2^- + BCl_3 \rightarrow Me_4N^+BCl_4^- + HCl \qquad (8)$$

or an oxidation reaction where ions are formed (Salthouse and Waddington, 1965)

$$PCl_3 + Cl_2 + HCl \rightarrow PCl_4^+ \, HCl_2^-. \qquad (9)$$

Several plots of conductimetric titrations are shown in Fig. 2 of bases against the solvoacids boron trichloride or phosphorus pentafluoride.

Phosphorus pentafluoride acts as a source of fluorophosphoric acid, HPF_6, one molecule of which is formed from one and a half molecules of phosphorus pentafluoride. Boron trichloride can react with bases to form either tetrachloroborates or a boron trichloride adduct; obviously it can only form tetrachloroborates with bases that readily lose a chloride ion, e.g. tetramethylammonium chloride. Phosphorus pentafluoride can only form hexafluorophosphates. There are four main types of conductimetric titrations. They are:

(1) salt formation, e.g. $Ph_3N + BCl_3$, $Me_2S + PF_5$, $Ph_3PO + PF_5$;

(2) adduct formation, e.g. $Me_2S + BCl_3$;

(3) ionization, e.g. $Ph_2C{=}CH_2 + BCl_3$;

(4) a mixture of two, or three, of the above, e.g. $Ph_3PO + BCl_3$.

TABLE VI

Conductances at Equivalence Points

Base	Acid	Λ_B	Λ_E	Λ_B/Λ_E	Product in solution
Ph_3N	BCl_3	12·6	7·8	1·62	Salt[a]
Ph_3As	BCl_3	39·5	20·4	1·94	Salt[a]
Ph_3As	PF_5	40·3	27·8	1·45	Salt[b]
Me_2S	BCl_3	10·05	0·033	304·6	Adduct[a]
Me_2S	PF_5	7·8	4·1	1·90	Salt[b]
$Ph_2C{=}CH_2$	BCl_3	1·77	23·8	0·074	Salt[c]
$PhC{\equiv}CH$	BCl_3	0·72	0·68	1·06	Salt[c]
Me_2O	BCl_3	0·43	0·012	25·8	Adduct[a]
$PhCN$	BCl_3	1·43	0·0052	27·5	Adduct[c]
Ph_2SO	BCl_3	6·65	1·60	4·15	Salt[d]

Λ_B = Conductance of free base (cm² ohm⁻¹ mole⁻¹).
Λ_E = Conductance at equivalence point (cm² ohm⁻¹ mole⁻¹).

[a] Peach and Waddington (1961).   [c] Peach and Waddington (1962a).
[b] Peach and Waddington (1963b).   [d] Peach and Waddington (1962b).

The shape of these curves is characteristic of the reactions occurring. In salt and adduct formation, the conductance per mole of base steadily decreases up to the equivalence point as the acid is added; it reaches a very low value when an adduct is formed in solution, but remains higher if a salt is formed. This is well illustrated by the figures show in Table VI for the conductances at the beginning and equivalence point in various titrations.

When the molar conductance at the equivalence point is low, below $c.\ 0.1\ cm^2\ ohm^{-1}\ mole^{-1}$, it can be assumed that an adduct has been formed in solution, assuming, of course, that no precipitation has occurred during the titration. Using this technique it is possible to detect the formation of salts in solution, which are unstable at room temperature. For example boron trichloride undoubtedly reacts with triphenylarsine to form the salt $Ph_3AsH^+BCl_4^-$, but it was only possible to isolate the adduct, $Ph_3As\ .\ BCl_3$ at room temperature. It is noteworthy that the conductimetric curve is usually smooth in the equivalence point region when an adduct has been formed, but there is a sharp break associated with salt formation.

When ionization occurs during a titration the conductance increases as the acid is added, presumably due to the salt being more stable than the free base (see Fig. 2(a)). Sometimes it is impossible to assign a curve to one of the above categories, e.g. triphenylphosphine oxide and boron trichloride (see Fig. (2d)): the reaction is probably a mixture of at least two types, ionization and salt formation.

3. Spectroscopic

The spectra of solutions in hydrogen halides have been very little studied. One of the difficulties is the low temperatures involved, unless the experiments are performed at fairly high pressures. It has been possible to study some n.m.r. spectra of solutions in hydrogen chloride at room temperature, using tubes under pressure. Such spectra have confirmed the presence of $(C_6H_5)_2C\ .\ CH_3^+$ and $(C_6H_5)C(CH_3)^{2+}$ ions in solutions of unsymmetrical diphenyl ethylene and phenyl acetylene in liquid hydrogen chloride.

No experimental measurements have been made on solutions in the hydrogen halides, either at room temperature, or low temperature, of the Raman, infra-red, and ultra-violet spectra. In certain cases, such as the ultra-violet spectra of the aromatic olefins, this would provide valuable further evidence for the proposed mode of ionization (Peach and Waddington, 1962a).

$$Ph_2C{=}CH_2 + 2HCl \rightarrow Ph_2MeC^+ + HCl_2^-. \tag{10}$$

Spectroscopic measurements have been extensively used for solutions in hydrogen fluoride, where measurements can be made at about room temperature: the presence of the ions H_2F^+ and SbF_6^- has been detected in solutions of antimony pentafluoride in hydrogen fluoride by Raman and infra-red spectra, as well as by conductivity measurements (Hyman et al., 1961).

Raman spectroscopy has been used in the study of some hydrogen chloride addition compounds. The spectra of the compounds $CH_3\ .\ CO\ .\ NH_2\ .\ HCl$ and $(CH_3\ .\ CO\ .\ NH_2)_2HCl$, show that the hydrochloride is probably

$CH_3 . CO . NH_3^+ Cl^-$; the spectra of the hemihydrochloride was difficult to interpret (Kahovec and Knollmüller, 1941). The spectra of the compounds of dimethyl ether and hydrogen chloride, $Me_2O . HCl$, $Me_2O . 3HCl$, and $Me_2O . 4HCl$, reveal that the latter two compounds are ionic, whereas the monohydrochloride has a hydrogen-bonded structure. However the compounds $Me_2O . DCl$ and $Me_2O . HBr$ do have an ionic structure, the ether oxygen being protonated (Vidale and Taylor, 1956).

4. Phase Diagrams

Study of phase diagrams in which one of the hydrogen halides is one component, will not reveal very much about the nature of the solutions, but it does give indications of some of the compounds that can be formed in them. Study of the phase diagram of water and hydrogen chloride showed that three compounds are formed $HCl . 3H_2O$, m.p. $-24 \cdot 4°$; $HCl . 2H_2O$, m.p. $-17 \cdot 7°$; and $HCl . H_2O$, m.p. $-15 \cdot 4°$ (Rupert, 1909). The last compound would be formed when some water is present in the liquid hydrogen chloride, but it is insoluble (Waddington and Klanberg, 1960a): the crystal structure of $H_2O . HCl$ shows that it is $H_3O^+Cl^-$, with every hydrogen atom joined by hydrogen bonds to the nearest chloride atom ion (Yoon and Carpenter, 1959).

The phase diagrams of solvoacids and solvobases can yield valuable information about the nature of the solvated protons and halide ions. The system, boron trichloride and hydrogen chloride does not show any compound formation (Graff, 1933): it can therefore be concluded that boron trichloride must be very weak solvoacid in hydrogen chloride. Although the phase diagram of the hydrogen chloride—chlorine system shows that the compounds formed are $2HCl . Cl_2$, m.p. $-121°$ and $HCl . Cl_2$, m.p. $-115°$ (Wheat and Browne, 1940), there is no evidence that chlorine solutions in hydrogen chloride are acidic (M. E. Peach and T. C. Waddington, unpublished results), although they can act as oxidizing agents (J. A. Salthouse and T. C. Waddington, unpublished results).

The diagrams of several compounds that are solvobases with hydrogen chloride or bromide have been studied. Some of the first observations were made by Maas and McIntosh (1913), although workers in Archibald's school had previously been able to isolate some hydrogen halide adducts with oxygen containing compounds. In the phase diagram of ethyl ether and hydrogen chloride the compounds detected were $Et_2O . HCl$, m.p. $-92°$; $Et_2O . 2HCl$, m.p. $-88°$; $Et_2O . 5HCl$, m.p. $-89°$ (Maas and McIntosh, 1913): from these results it seems reasonable to suppose that the ether is protonated, Et_2OH^+, and the chloride ion solvated $Cl(HCl)_x$ where $x = 0, 1$, or 4.

More recently, phase diagrams of hydrogen chloride with π-orbital donor molecules have been studied. It was found that some aliphatic olefins and acetylenes formed very low melting point compounds of compositions 1 : 1, 2 : 1 and 4 : 1 (HCl: hydrocarbon): similar results showing 1 : 1 and 2 : 1 (HCL : hydrocarbon) adducts were obtained with aromatic hydrocarbons (Cook et al., 1956). The nitriles have also been studied as n-bond systems (Murray and Schneider, 1955): in the case of acetonitrile and hydrogen chloride the compounds detected were $CH_3CN . HCL$, m.p. $-63.2°$; $2CH_3CN . 3HCl$, m.p. $-88°$; $CH_3CN . 5HCl$, m.p. $-123.6°$; and $CH_3CH . 7HCl$, m.p. $-125.0°$. These can again be interpreted as $CH_3CNH^+Cl(HCl)_x^-$. Infra-red study of a compound of composition, $CH_3CN . 2HCl$ shows that it is ionic, $CH_3C{=}NH^+HCl_2^-$ (Janz and Danyluk, 1959). Although complete phase diagrams have not been studied the compounds n-$Bu_4NCl(HCl)_2$, n-Bu_4NBr $(HCl)_2$ and n-$Bu_4NI(HCl)_2$ have recently been isolated at low temperature (Salthouse and Waddington, 1965).

5. Cryoscopic and Ebullioscopic Measurements

Cryoscopic (Beckmann and Waentig, 1910) and ebullioscopic (Steele et al., 1905, 1906) measurements have been made on some solutions in hydrogen chloride, bromide and iodide. Experiments of this type are likely to lead to results which would be extremely difficult to interpret, due to the complex mode of ionization. This was in fact observed: Beckmann and Waentig (1910) concluded that some form of association was occurring in solution. Further interpretation of these results would be extremely difficult, but it ought to be possible to correlate them with the variation of conductivity with dilution for a particular solute.

6. Preparative Methods

Because of their low boiling points and consequent easy removal, the liquid hydrogen halides as solvents are good media for certain preparations. By using the hydrogen halide and the corresponding boron trihalide it is easy to prepare tetrahaloborates (Waddington and Klanberg, 1959, 1960; Waddington and White, 1960a,b): particularly easy are the tetra-chloroborates where the excess of solvent and boron trichloride can be removed by low temperature distillation at c. $-80°$. Hexachlorodiborates can be prepared from diboron tetrachloride in the same way (Holliday et al., 1961). This method must be limited to reactions between two compounds, the excess of one of which can be removed either with the solvent, or by pumping on the compound under a high vacuum. If both of the reactants are involatile, care must be exercised in interpreting the results, as the product may be an equimolecular mixture of the reactants. Most of the compounds prepared in the liquid hydrogen halides have been isolated at the end of conductimetric titrations, where, although the amount recovered may only be of the order of a millimole there is sufficient for analysis and character-ization. By using a somewhat different reaction cell it is possible to study the products of a reaction by the increase in weight observed. Solvolysis reactions where one product is volatile can be studied similarly. However, if one of the products is insoluble and the other is soluble, the solute can be recovered by decantation in an inverted Y-shaped cell and evaporation of the solvent (Peach and Waddington, 1961). Solvolytic reactions are not very valuable preparative methods, as the chloro-, bromo-, and iodo-compounds which are formed can often be obtained more easily by other methods. A good method has been developed for the preparation of small quantities of high purity nitryl chloride by the solvolysis of dinitrogen pentoxide with liquid hydrogen chloride.

II. Solutions in the Hydrogen Halides

The experiments of Gore (1856) showed that a large variety of metals, non-metals and simple inorganic substances were insoluble in liquid hydrogen chloride. However he must have observed some solvolytic reactions, as he reported that materials such as cadmium sulphide turned white and the solid recovered contained no sulphide. The solubilities of a further large selection of inorganic materials were reported by Steele et al. (1905, 1906) who found that ionic halides, such as the alkali metal halides, were insoluble in hydrogen chloride. They did find that covalent chlorides, such as stannic chloride and phosphorus oxychloride were soluble. When the low dielectric constants and highly acidic nature of the solvents are borne in mind, later workers have been more successful in finding suitable solutes for hydrogen chloride, bromide, and iodide solutions.

A. ACIDS AND BASES

The hydrogen halides are highly acidic solvents, whose acidity increases in the order

$$HF < HCl < HBr < HI.$$

Consequently it is often very difficult to find any reasonably strong solvo-acids, particularly in hydrogen chloride, bromide and iodide which are appreciably more acidic solvents than hydrogen fluoride. Conversely there are very many solvo-bases, some of which act as very strong electrolytes.

1. Bases

It is possible for basic solutions to be formed by two distinct types of solute.

(a) Salts which ionize readily to give a free halide ion, solvated in the solution: the best examples of this type of compound are the tetra-alkylammonium halides, R_4NHal.

(b) Compounds containing atoms with a lone pair of electrons, or a π-bond system, which can easily be protonated, e.g. triphenylamine in liquid hydrogen chloride (Peach and Waddington, 1961).

A selection of conductances of basic solutions in hydrogen chloride are shown in Tables II and VII.

(a) *Salt type*. Bases of type (a) which can be found are rather few: if the compound exists as an ionic species in the solid state at room temperature, it must have a large cation, and consequent low lattice energy, as the solvent's dielectric constants are low. Generally salts of the Group V elements, $R_3^1MR^+Hal^-$, will act as solvo-bases (Waddington and Klanberg, 1960a;

TABLE VII

Conductances of Some Bases in Hydrogen Chloride at $-95°$ [a]

Solute	Concentration (mole/litre)	Specific conductivity (μ mho cm^{-1})	Molar conductance (cm^2 ohm^{-1} mole^{-1})
Ph_3Cl	0·25	10640	42·9
Ph_3SiCl	Saturated	1·53	—
Ph_3As	0·20	7700	39·3
AsH_3	Saturated	26·3	—
H_2S	Saturated	2·8	—
Me_2O	0·26	114·4	0·43
Me_2S	0·35	3950	11·3
$Ph_2C=CH_2$	0·37	650	1·77
MeCN	0·42	1220	2·94
Me_2CO	0·41	4300	10·4
MeCOCl	0·30	2·9	0·0097
Ph_2SO	Saturated	1500	—
$COCl_2$	0·39	0·27	0·0007

[a] Peach and Waddington (1961, 1962a,b).

Waddington and White, 1960a, 1963; Klanberg and Kohlschütter, 1961), but when R = H these salts can be formed *in situ* and are classified as bases of type (b). Bases are also formed when phosphorus pentachloride and bromide are dissolved in the corresponding solvent (Waddington and Klanberg, 1960a; Waddington and White, 1960a, 1963).

$$PCl_5(s) + 2HCl = PCl_4^+ + HCl_2^-. \qquad (11)$$

Such solutions provide a ready source of $PHal_4^+$ ions, and further salts can be prepared after reaction with a solvo-acid. Although phosphorus penta-chloride exists in the solid state as $PCl_4^+ PCl_6^-$, it has not been possible to detect the PCl_6^- ion in liquid hydrogen chloride (Waddington and Klanberg, 1960a), indeed there is surprisingly little evidence for the existence of the PCl_6^-

ion in any other salts containing "ordinary cations", although hexachloro-phosphates of the cations $EtCCl_2 \cdot PCl_3^+$ (Kirsanov and Fedorova, 1960) and $(Cl_3P=N-(PCl_2N)_x-PCl_3)^+$ (Fluck, 1962) have been reported.

Carbon–halogen compounds, in which the carbon–halogen bond is easily broken with the formation of a stable carbonium ion, can act as solvo-bases. The triphenylmethyl carbonium ion, Ph_3C^+, can be readily formed from triphenylmethyl chloride in hydrogen chloride (Peach and Waddington, 1961), and is also probably formed from the chloride in hydrogen iodide (Klanberg and Kohlschütter, 1961). Detection of this ion in solution is easy as it is highly coloured; the colour must be caused by the presence of the triphenylmethyl carbonium ion, and not the hydrogen dichloride, as most other basic solutions are colourless. Attempts to prepare the ions Ph_3M^+ (M = Si, Ge, Sn, Pb) by dissolving the chlorides Ph_3MCl in hydrogen chloride failed (Peach and Waddington, 1961): with the tin and lead compounds partial replacement of the phenyl group by halogen was observed.

(b) *Protonation of Groups IV, V and VI elements.* Bases of type (b), involving protonation, have been studied with derivatives of Group IV, V and VI elements, various olefins, acetylenes, nitriles, azo compounds, and compounds containing doubly-bonded oxygen. Study of protonation reactions is easier in liquid hydrogen chloride than sulphuric acid, where similar reactions have been observed, as the undesirable side effects of sulphonation are avoided (Gillespie and Leisten, 1954). Triphenyl- and trimethylamine are both strong bases in liquid hydrogen chloride (Peach and Waddington, 1961, 1962a). A freshly purchased sample of triphenylamine gave a pale brown solution, but when the sample had been kept for six months and then vacuum sublimed the solution was blue: this colour change was not a function of the concentration, and might well have been due to the formation of the ion Ph_3N^+, as some ions of this type are reported as being blue (Peach and Waddington, 1961). It is possible to protonate the nitrogen in hydrazo-benzene in hydrogen chloride, but rearrangement occurs to give benzidine (Peach and Waddington, 1961). Pyridine acts as an excellent base in all three solvents (Waddington and Klanberg, 1960a; Waddington and White, 1960a,b) and it is easy to prepare pyridinium tetrahalogenborates.

The phosphorus atom in phosphine and triphenylphosphine is also easily protonated in hydrogen chloride, bromide, and iodide (Peach and Waddington, 1961; Klanberg and Kohlschütter, 1961). If phosphine is used as a solvo-base in hydrogen chloride or bromide the phosphonium ion is formed and in this way phosphonium tetrachloroborate, chlorotrifluoroborate, and tetrabromoborate have been prepared (Waddington and Klanberg, 1960a; Waddington and White, 1960b). However, if diphosphine is employed, it is not possible to detect any diphosphonium ions as decomposition occurs (Peach and Waddington, 1961). Triphenylarsine can be readily protonated in hydrogen chloride, forming a strong base. It is not possible to isolate this protonated form at room temperature as a tetrachloroborate, after reaction with boron trichloride, since hydrogen chloride is lost and an adduct formed.

$$Ph_3As + 2HCl \rightarrow Ph_3AsH^+ HCl_2^- \qquad (12)$$

$$Ph_3AsH^+ + BCl_3 + HCl_2^- \rightarrow Ph_3AsH^+ BCl_4^- + HCl \qquad (13)$$

$$\downarrow$$

$$Ph_3As \cdot BCl_3$$

Attempts to use arsine to prepare arsonium salts were unsuccessful, as arsine reacts with the solvent. Triphenylstibine or triphenylbismuthane do not form stable protonated species in liquid hydrogen chloride; they react with the solvent and become partially chlorinated (Peach and Waddington, 1961).

The basic properties of various derivatives of oxygen and sulphur, ROR′ and RSR′, have been examined in liquid hydrogen chloride (Peach and Waddington, 1961). Early workers had shown that it is possible to detect protonated alcohols and ethers, derivatives of hydrogen chloride, bromide, or iodide (Maas and McIntosh, 1913; McIntosh, 1908) and that some alcohols and ethers form highly conducting solutions (Walker et al., 1904). Water and hydrogen sulphide are both insoluble in liquid hydrogen chloride (Waddington and Klanberg, 1960a; Peach and Waddington, 1961), but when one or both of the hydrogen atoms is replaced by a methyl or phenyl group, basic solutions are formed. Dimethyl sulphide is the strongest base, as is shown by its conductivity (see Tables VII and IX).

Conductimetric titrations of these bases against boron trichloride in hydrogen chloride do not reveal much useful information, except in the cases of dimethyl ether and sulphide where an adduct is formed in solution (see Fig. 2(b)). It is not possible to isolate any protonated oxygen or sulphur compounds from these solutions after reaction with boron trichloride. Adducts are formed and decomposition of these adducts produces oxygen and sulphur substituted boron chlorides (Peach and Waddington, 1961). An unstable protonated derivative of dimethyl sulphide could be isolated after its reaction in liquid hydrogen chloride with phosphorus pentafluoride (Peach and Waddington, 1963b).

(c) *Protonation of π-bond systems.* Aromatic olefins, such as 1,1-diphenylethylene can easily be protonated, with the formation of a carbonium ion:

$$Ph_2C{=}CH_2 + H^+ \rightarrow Ph_2CMe^+. \qquad (14)$$

Reactions such as this have been observed in sulphuric acid and hydrogen chloride (Gold and Tye, 1952; Peach and Waddington, 1962a). The conductimetric titration of 1,1-diphenylethylene against boron trichloride in liquid hydrogen chloride shows the interesting phenomena of ionization occurring as the acid is added (see Fig. 3): a sharp end-point was found at a mole ratio of $1 : 1 :: BCl_3 : Ph_2C{=}C\,H$. In similar experiments using styrene and α-methylstyrene there is some evidence for the formation of carbonium ions in solution; this is based mainly on the colour of the solutions, as conductimetric titrations were inconclusive. This must reflect the stability of the carbonium ions which would have been formed:

$$Me_3C^+, \; PhMeHC^+, \; PhMe_2C^+ \ll Ph_2MeC^+ < Ph_3C^+.$$

A doubly charged carbonium ion $(C_6Me_5)ClC^{2+}$ has been detected in a solution of pentamethyltrichloromethylbenzene in sulphuric acid (Hart and Fish, 1958). Conductimetric study of the reaction of phenylacetylene with boron trichloride in hydrogen chloride indicated that the doubly charged carbonium ion $PhMeC^{2+}$ was formed (Peach and Waddington, 1962a), an end-point being found at a mole ratio of $2:1$ ($BCl_3 : PhC{\equiv}CH$) (see Fig. 3)

$$PhC{\equiv}CH + 4HCl \rightarrow PhMeC^{2+} + 2HCl_2^- \qquad (15)$$

$$PhMeC^{2+} + 2HCl_2^- + 2BCl_3 \rightarrow PhMeC^{2+} + 2BCl_4^- + 2HCl. \qquad (16)$$

Diphenyl acetylene formed a much less basic solution and there was little evidence for the formation of the ion $PhC . CH_2Ph^{2+}$. The nitriles contain

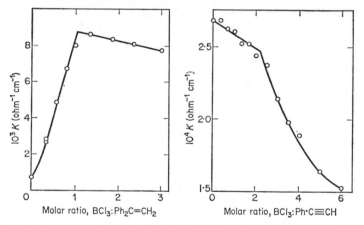

Fig. 3. Conductimetric titrations of $Ph_2C{=}CH_2$ and $PhC{\equiv}CH$ with BCl_3 in liquid hydrogen chloride. (Reproduced by permission from the *Journal of the Chemical Society*.)

a triple bond which it is easy to protonate, and with hydrogen chloride, bromide, and iodide, it has been possible to prepare the compounds $MeCN . 2HHal$. The infra-red spectra of these compounds indicate two distinct types of structure $MeC{\equiv}NH^+HCl_2^-$ and $MeBrC{=}NH_2^+ Br^-$ (Janz and Danyluk, 1959). Both aceto- and benzonitriles have been found to be reasonably strong bases in liquid hydrogen chloride (Peach and Waddington, 1962a). In the reaction of all these basic solutions with boron trichloride it was not possible to isolate a tetrachloroborate, and hence examine further the structure of the cation. In the case of the nitriles an adduct was isolated, but with the ethylenes and acetylenes decomposition to tarry products occurred. It is impossible to say whether the acetonitrile adduct formed in solution, or as the product was warmed to room temperature, because precipitation occurred during the titration. After reaction of acetonitrile with phosphorus pentafluoride it was not possible to isolate a stable salt or adduct (Peach and Waddington, 1963b).

Azo compounds also contain a π-bond system, which it ought to be possible to protonate. Azobenzene and m-azotoluene both formed saturated basic solutions in liquid hydrogen chloride, from both of these solutions stable tetrachloroborates were isolated after reaction with boron trichloride (Peach and Waddington, 1962a). The position of the proton cannot be located from the infra-red spectra: other evidence, such as pKa measurements (Yeh and Jaffée, 1959) and the ultra-violet spectra of protonated azo compounds (Gerson and Heilbronner, 1962) suggests that the proton is located on the bond. Azoxybenzene and nitrobenzene are also reasonably strong bases in liquid hydrogen chloride. A boron trichloride adduct can be isolated from the reaction of an azoxybenzene solution and boron trichloride: the structure of this adduct is uncertain, as is the position of the original proton attachment. Nitrosobenzene in hydrogen chloride reacted with boron trichloride to form a compound which exploded just below room temperature, although a hydrochloride, of unknown structure, could be isolated from solution (Peach and Waddington, 1962a).

(d) *Protonation of doubly-bonded oxygen.* Carbonyl, nitro, phosphoryl, sulphonyl and sulphuryl groups all have at least one oxygen atom bonded to the central atom. The bonding is often considered to be polar, particularly in the carbonyl group,

$$\overset{\backslash}{\underset{/}{C}} = O \leftrightarrow \overset{\backslash}{\underset{/}{C^+}} - O^- \tag{17}$$

and easy protonation of the oxygen atom would be expected. A fairly large variety of organic compounds containing these groups has been studied in liquid hydrogen chloride, the conductivities of which are shown in Table VIII.

Examination of this table reveals that most of the carbonyl compounds are strong bases, the exceptions being the aldehydes. In the case of the amides and esters, protonation may not have occurred at the carbonyl oxygen; acetamide hydrochloride is known to contain protonated nitrogen, $MeCONH_3^+Cl^-$ (Smyth and Hitchcock, 1933). The reactions of most of these carbonyl compounds with boron trichloride are complex, for instance with benzaldehyde the adduct $3PhCHO \cdot 2BCl_3$ is formed, which pyrolyses to benzylidene dichloride (Fraser *et al.*, 1957). Compounds containing carbonyl groups always give, with boron trichloride in liquid hydrogen chloride, adducts and not tetrachloroborates (Peach and Waddington, 1962a). Trimethylamine oxide hydrochloride, $Me_3NOH^+Cl^-$ and triphenylphosphine oxide both act as strong solvo-bases. From the triphenylphosphine oxide solution a hydrochloride was isolated and, after reaction with phosphorus pentafluoride, a hexafluorophosphate, but with boron trichloride a mixture of the tetrachloroborate and adduct was formed. The protonated form of trimethylamine oxide was not retained on reaction with boron trichloride but

TABLE VIII

Conductances of Some Doubly-Bonded Oxygen Compounds in Liquid Hydrogen Chloride[a]

Compound	Concentration (mole/litre)	Specific conductivity (μmho cm^{-1})	Molar conductance (cm^2 ohm^{-1} mole^{-1})
MeCHO	Saturated	1·60	—
PhCHO	Saturated	1·81	—
Me$_2$CO	0·41	4300	10·4
Ph$_2$CO	0·25	1810	7·15
MeCONH$_2$	Saturated	1640	—
PhCONH$_2$	0·23	800	3·48
PhCO$_2$Et	0·33	3200	9·74
MeNO$_2$	Saturated	1·3	—
PhNO$_2$	0·31	490	0·16
Me$_2$SO	Saturated	1200	—
Ph$_2$SO	Saturated	1500	—
Me$_2$SO$_2$	0·23	47	0·20
Ph$_2$SO$_2$	0·21	110	0·51
Ph$_3$PO	0·22	2200	9·61

[a] Peach and Waddington (1962a,b).

an adduct was formed. Similar types of reaction were found with liquid hydrogen chloride solutions of dimethyl- and diphenylsulphoxide; the solution was fairly basic but after reaction with boron trichloride the adduct was recovered, although with phosphorus pentafluoride, dimethylsulphoxidium hexafluorophosphate was formed (Peach and Waddington, 1962b, 1963b).

The basic properties of the nitro compounds and sulphones were considerably less than that of the same type of compound containing only one doubly-bonded oxygen atom. This is probably due to resonance forms effectively reducing the charge on the oxygen atoms, as compared with that in a compound containing only one doubly-bonded oxygen, e.g. trimethylamine oxide and nitromethane

$$\underset{Me}{\overset{Me}{\diagdown}}N\rightarrow O \leftrightarrow \underset{Me}{\overset{Me}{\diagdown}}\overset{+}{N}-O^- \quad cf. \quad Me-\overset{\diagup O}{N}\underset{\diagdown O}{} \leftrightarrow Me-\overset{+}{N}\underset{\diagdown O}{\diagup O^-} \leftrightarrow Me-\overset{+}{N}\underset{\diagdown O^-}{\diagup\!\!\!/ O} \quad (18)$$

The basic properties of compounds such as benzoyl chloride in liquid hydrogen chloride can be due either to protonation of the carbonyl oxygen or loss of a chloride ion,

$$PhCOCl + 2HCl \rightleftharpoons PhCClOH^+ + HCl_2^- \qquad (19)$$

$$PhCOCl + HCl \rightleftharpoons PhCO^+ + HCl_2^-. \qquad (20)$$

The available evidence suggests that the compound ionizes as in equation (19): if ionization as in equation (20) occurs, solvolysis of benzoic acid would be expected, which is not observed (Reach and Waddington, 1962a).

$$PhCO_2H + 3HCl = PhCO^+HCl_2^- + H_3O^+Cl^-. \qquad (21)$$

Further evidence supporting this mechanism is found in the reactions of diphenylphosphoryl chloride, Ph_2POCl, in hydrogen chloride. If this compound ionizes by loss of a chloride ion, as equation (20), then the compound formed after reaction with boron trichloride ought to have the structure $Ph_2PO^+BCl_4^-$. All the available evidence suggests that this compound is in fact $Ph_2PClO–BCl_3$ (Peach and Waddington, 1962c), and that the tetrachloroborate is initially formed in the hydrogen chloride solution and then loses hydrogen chloride on removal of the solvent:

$$Ph_2PClOH^+HCl_2^- + BCl_3 \rightarrow Ph_2PClOH^+BCl_4^- + HCl$$
$$\downarrow \qquad\qquad\qquad (22)$$
$$Ph_2PClO–BCl_3 + HCl$$

Attempts to try and prepare the ion PCl_3OH^+ from the interaction of strong aquo-acids and phosphorus oxychloride in hydrogen chloride also failed (Peach and Waddington, 1962b). Most of the chloro compounds examined in liquid hydrogen chloride were weak bases, except diphenylphosphoryl chloride, and in most cases reaction with boron trichloride yielded an adduct, often unstable, or nothing (Peach and Waddington, 1962b). Some of the reactions of nitrosyl chloride observed in liquid hydrogen chloride (Waddington and Klanberg, 1960b) can be accounted for if no ionization of the solute is encountered.

When the molar conductances of solutions of the compounds in HCl described in this section and section (b) are examined, an interesting correlation is seen to exist between the conductance of the base and the negative inductive effect of the ligands attached to the atom which is protonated, as is seen in the Tables IX and X.

If the basicity, as measured by the molar conductance at comparable dilution, is controlled by the negative charge on the oxygen, or sulphur, then a direct relationship with the negative inductive effect as measured by the ionization in water of the corresponding substituted acetic acid is to be expected; this is observed. There are some exceptions as the figures in Tables IX and X show. Anomalies are ethyl benzoate, where protonation of

TABLE IX

K Classical for Substituted Acetic Acids, XCH_2CO_2H[a]

X	Me	H	Ph	OMe	I	Br	Cl	F
10^5K	1·34	2·1	5·6	33·5	75	138	155	217

[a] Peach and Waddington (1962b).

TABLE X

Variation of Molar Conductances with Ligands for Hydrogen Chloride Solutions[a]

	XYO				XYS		
	Molar conductance ($cm^2\ ohm^{-1}\ mole^{-1}$)				Molar conductance ($cm^2\ ohm^{-1}\ mole^{-1}$)		
X	Y			X	Y		
	Me	H	Ph		Me	Ph	
Me	0·43	0·13	0·021	Me	11·8	—	
H	0·13	—	0·019	H	0·054	0·030	
Ph	0·021	0·019	0·0017	Ph	—	0·15	

	X_2SO_2		X_3PO		PhCOX	
X	Molar conductance ($cm^2\ ohm^{-1}\ mole^{-1}$)	X	Molar conductance ($cm^2\ ohm^{-1}\ mole^{-1}$)	X	Molar conductance ($cm^2\ ohm^{-1}\ mole^{-1}$)	
Me	0·20	Ph	9·61	Ph	7·15	
Ph	0·51	Cl	0·20	Cl	0·046	
Cl	—	F	0·015	OEt	0·74	

[a] Peach and Waddington (1962b).

the ethoxide oxygen can also occur, diphenyl sulphide, the sulphones and diphenylphosphoryl chloride; in all the latter cases protonation of the aromatic nucleus can also occur. Protonation of an aromatic nucleus causes highly coloured compounds to be formed: coloured liquid hydrogen chloride solutions were formed by anisole (pale pink) and diphenyl sulphide (purple) (Peach and Waddington, 1961), and by triphenylphosphine oxide (pale yellow) and diphenylphosphoryl chloride (yellow) (Peach and Waddington,

TABLE XI

Acid Conductances

Solvent	Solute	Concentration (mole/litre)	Specific conductivity (μmho cm^{-1})	Molar conductance (cm^2 ohm^{-1} mole^{-1})
HCl	MeSO$_3$H	Saturated	9·0	—[a]
HCl	CF$_3$SO$_3$H	Saturated	2·0	—[a]
HCl	ClSO$_3$H	0·38	2·7	$7·0 \times 10^{-3}$ [b]
HCl	SiF$_4$	0·13	0·98	$7·7 \times 10^{-3}$ [c]
HCl	PF$_5$	0·25	1·9	$7·5 \times 10^{-3}$ [c]
HCl	SO$_2$	Saturated	0·15	—[a]
HCl	P$_4$O$_{10}$	Saturated	0·82	—[a]
HCl	BCl$_3$	0·32	0·13	$4·0 \times 10^{-4}$ [b]
HCl	BF$_3$	1·43	0·09	$0·6 \times 10^{-4}$ [b]
HBr	Al$_2$Br$_6$	Saturated	0·073	—[d]
HBr	SnBr$_4$	0·064	0·024	$3·8 \times 10^{-4}$ [d]

[a] Peach and Waddington (1962b).   [c] Peach and Waddington (1963b).
[b] Waddington and Klanberg (1960a).   [d] Waddington and White (1960a).

1962b). In the series of phosphoryl compounds, X$_3$PO, it is seen that the molar conductance of phosphoryl chloride lies between that of triphenylphosphine oxide and phosphoryl fluoride, thus giving further support to the view that its mode of ionization probably involves protonation and not loss of a chloride ion.

2. Acids

There are two distinct possible types of acid in the hydrogen halide solvents, as is expected from the two different, but complementary, definitions of acids. They can either be halide ion acceptors, such as the boron halides, or proton donors, such as the strong aquo-acids. A selection of conductances is shown in Tables III and XI.

(a) *Group III Halide Ion Acceptors.* Boron compounds are well known acceptors and the trihalides function as solvo-acids in the corresponding hydrogen halide:

$$BHal_3 + 2HHal \rightleftharpoons H_2Hal^+ + BHal_4^-. \tag{23}$$

The extent of the ionization is small: the phase diagram of hydrogen chloride and boron trichloride shows that there is no compound formation (Graff, 1933). It is however very easy to prepare tetrahalogenoborates from a base and boron trihalide in the corresponding solvent (Waddington and Klanberg, 1959, 1960a; Waddington and White, 1960a,b). When boron trichloride is used as a solvo-acid in hydrogen chloride, some difficulty may be experienced because of adduct formation when the base is formed by protonation, e.g. with dimethylsulphoxide (Peach and Waddington, 1962b).

$$Me_2SOH^+HCl_2^- + BCl_3 \rightarrow Me_2SOH^+BCl_4^- + HCl \qquad (24)$$
$$\downarrow$$
$$Me_2SOBCl_3$$

However in many titrations sharp end-points are found (see Fig. 4). If diboron tetrachloride is employed as a solvo-acid in hydrogen chloride, salts of hexachlorodiboric acid, $H_2B_2Cl_6$ are formed (Holliday $et\ al.$, 1961)

$$2Me_4N^+HCl_2^- + B_2Cl_4 \rightarrow (Me_4N^+)_2B_2Cl_6^{2-} + 2HCl. \qquad (25)$$

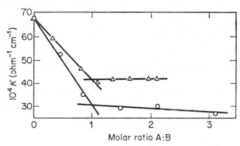

FIG. 4. Conductimetric titrations of boron halides against tetramethyl ammonium chloride in liquid hydrogen chloride; Δ, Me$_4$NCl + BCl$_3$; O, Me$_4$NCl + BF$_3$. (Reproduced by permission from the $Journal\ of\ the\ Chemical\ Society$.)

Sharp end-points at 2 : 1 (Base: B_2Cl_4) are found. The acceptor properties of other boron compounds for chloride ions in liquid hydrogen chloride appear to be somewhat limited. When boron trifluoride is used as a solvo-acid in hydrogen chloride, salts of trifluorochloroboric acid, HBF_3Cl, can be isolated and several have been characterized (Waddington and Klanberg, 1959, 1960a): this is the only known method of making these salts. Conductimetric titrations with boron trifluoride show sharp 1 : 1 end-points (see Fig. 4). However diborane, triethylboron, triphenylboron, and dimethylboron chloride do not function as solvo-acids in hydrogen chloride, but there is some evidence that methylboron dichloride acts as a very weak solvo-acid (M. E. Peach and T. C. Waddington, unpublished results). In liquid hydrogen bromide, compounds of the type BR_3Br^- were not prepared: boron trifluoride showed no acidic properties and boron trichloride was completely solvolysed to the tribromide (Waddington and White, 1960a, 1963). However boron tribromide

functions as a solvo-acid and in titrations with bromide ion donors, sharp
1 : 1 end points are found (see Fig. 5).

   (b) *Group IV Halide Ion Acceptors.* Germanium tetrachloride showed no
acidic properties in hydrogen chloride (see Fig. 6) (Waddington and Klanberg, 1959). Stannic halides are acidic in hydrogen chloride and bromide

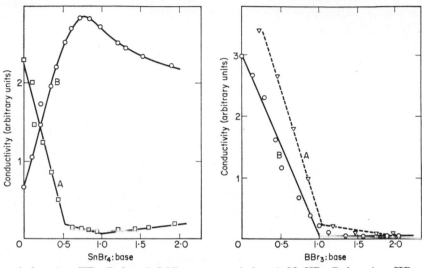

A, base is pyHBr; B, base is POBr₃   A, base is Me₄NBr; B, base is pyHBr

Fig. 5. Conductimetric titrations in liquid hydrogen bromide. (Reproduced by permission
from the *Journal of the Chemical Society.*)

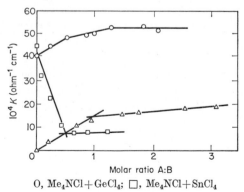

O, Me₄NCl+GeCl₄; □, Me₄NCl+SnCl₄

Fig. 6. Conductimetric titrations of Group IV chlorides against tetramethylammonium
chloride. (Reproduced by permission from the *Journal of the Chemical Society.*)

(Waddington and Klanberg, 1960a; Waddington and White, 1960a, 1963) and it
was possible to detect and isolate salts of hexachloro- and hexabromostanic
acid in titrations (see Figs. 5 and 6). Attempts have been made to prepare
the ions $SiF_4Cl_2^{2-}$ and $GeF_4Cl_2^{2-}$ by using the respective fluorides as acids in

hydrogen chloride. Silicon tetrafluoride exhibited no tendency to accept a chloride ion: germanium tetrafluoride appeared to be acidic, but it was not possible to isolate a definite product, as solvolysis took place (Peach and Waddington, 1963b).

(c) *Group V Halide Ion Acceptors*. Phosphorus trichloride is neutral in liquid hydrogen chloride (Waddington and Klanberg, 1960a): the acidic properties of the other Group V tervalent chlorides have not been studied. Phosphorus trifluoride showed no acidic properties and was not solvolysed in hydrogen chloride, but, in contrast, arsenic trifluoride was totally solvolysed, so its acidic properties could not be studied (Peach and Waddington, 1963b).

Phosphorus pentachloride and pentabromide both act as solvo-bases in the respective hydrogen halides, and there is no evidence for the formation of the $PHal_6^-$ ion in solution (Waddington and Klanberg, 1960a; Waddington and White, 1960a, 1963). Antimony pentachloride is a very powerful electron acceptor, and as such, ought to be able to form the $SbCl_6^-$ ion with bases in hydrogen chloride: no such reactions have been reported. The properties of the Group V pentafluorides in hydrogen chloride have been more thoroughly studied. Phosphorus pentafluoride reacts with strong bases to form hexa-fluorophosphates: the stoichiometry of this reaction is shown in the equation

$$2Me_4NCl + 3PF_5 \rightarrow 2Me_4NPF_6 + PF_3Cl_2. \tag{26}$$

Conductimetric titration curves showed a break when the molar ratio of base : PF_5 was 2 : 3 (see Fig. 2): unfortunately in these experiments it was not possible to isolate any of the covalent form of phosphorus dichloro-trifluoride (m.p. $-125°$, b.p. $7·1°$), as this constituted only c. $0·5\%$ of the solvent removed at low temperature. When phosphorus pentachloride was used as a base in liquid hydrogen chloride, both the ionic and covalent forms of phosphorus dichlorotrifluoride were formed:

$$2PCl_5 + 3PF_5 \rightarrow PCl_4^+PF_6^- + PF_3Cl_2. \tag{27}$$

There was no indication that there is any interconversion of these two forms of phosphorus dichlorotrifluoride. Phosphorus pentafluoride has been em-ployed as a solvoacid in reactions with bases that form boron trichloride adducts in solution, e.g. dimethyl sulphoxide; in all cases a hexafluoro-phosphate was formed in the solution, but sometimes this decomposed on warming to room temperature. Phosphorus pentafluoride is, then, the strongest acid yet found in liquid hydrogen chloride that will not form adducts with protonated bases (Peach and Waddington, 1963b).

Arsenic pentafluoride was solvolysed to tetrachloroarsonium hexa-fluoroarsenate in liquid hydrogen chloride:

$$2AsF_5 + 4HCl \rightarrow AsCl_4AsF_6 + 4HF. \tag{28}$$

Similarly solvolysis, or partial solvolysis, was observed with antimony pentafluoride, but a definite product could not be isolated (Peach and Waddington, 1963b): from the reaction of nitrosyl chloride and antimony pentafluoride in liquid hydrogen chloride it had been possible to isolate nitrosyl chloropentafluorantimonate, but the role of the solvent in these reactions is not understood (Waddington and Klanberg, 1960b).

The mechanism for the superficially similar reactions of phosphorus pentafluoride and arsenic pentafluoride in liquid hydrogen chloride are not known. The difference between them is that the phosphorus pentafluoride disproportionation will only occur in the presence of strong bases, and no free hydrogen fluoride is produced.

$$2MCl + 3PF_5 \rightarrow 2MPF_6 + PF_3Cl_2. \tag{29}$$

Neither reaction proceeds through the formation of a stable MF_5Cl^- ion, although this may be an intermediate, as in the scheme:

$$PF_5 + HCl_2^- \rightarrow PF_5Cl^- + HCl \tag{30}$$

$$PF_5Cl^- + PF_5 \rightarrow PF_6^- + PF_4Cl \tag{31}$$

$$PF_4Cl + HCl_2^- \rightarrow PF_4Cl_2^- + HCl \tag{32}$$

$$PF_4Cl_2^- + PF_5 \rightarrow PF_6^- + PF_3Cl_2. \tag{33}$$

A similar scheme involving free fluoride ions, which would react immediately with the solvent to form hydrofluoric acid, will explain the reaction of arsenic pentafluoride:

$$AsF_5 + HCl_2^- \rightarrow AsF_5Cl^- + HCl \tag{34}$$

$$AsF_5Cl^- + 2HCl \rightarrow AsF_4Cl + HF + HCl_2^- \tag{35}$$

$$AsF_4Cl + HCl_2^- \rightarrow AsF_4Cl_2^- + HCl \tag{36}$$

$$AsF_4Cl_2^- + 2HCl \rightarrow AsF_3Cl_2 + HF + HCl_2^-. \tag{37}$$

$$2AsF_3Cl_2 \rightarrow AsCl_4^+ AsF_6^-.$$

The compounds PF_4Cl, AsF_4Cl, AsF_3Cl_2 are unknown, but PF_3Cl_2, $PCl_4^+PF_6^-$ and $AsCl_4^+AsF_6^-$ are relatively stable (Holmes 1963; Holmes and Gallagher, 1963). It is interesting to note in this context that although the compound $SbCl_4^+SbF_6^-$ is known (Holmes, 1963) there is no indication of this being formed in the hydrogen chloride solution (Peach and Waddington, 1963b).

(d) *Group VII Halide Ion Acceptors.* The oxidation reactions of these compounds will be dealt with in a later section, but here we are concerned with their reactions as Lewis acids in the liquid hydrogen halides. Neither chlorine in liquid hydrogen chloride nor bromine in liquid hydrogen bromide function as halide ion acceptors. Iodine is fairly insoluble in hydrogen chloride and again does not function as an acceptor; there is no evidence for the formation of ions such as I_2Cl^- or I_3^-. However both bromine and iodine monochloride are acceptors in hydrogen chloride and in conductimetric titrations against tetra-alkylammonium chlorides in the solvents end-points were obtained at mole ratios of $1:1$ and the compounds R_4NBr_2Cl and R_4NICl_2 were isolated (J. A. Salthouse and T. C. Waddington, unpublished results).

(e) *Strong aquo-acids and anhydrides.* No strong oxy-acids appear to be sufficiently powerful to act as titratable solvo-acids in the hydrogen halides. Tri-
fluoromethane, methane and chlorosulphuric acids, showed no acidic properties
in liquid hydrogen chloride (Waddington and Klanberg, 1960a; Peach and
Waddington, 1962b). It was possible to isolate some new chlorosulphonates
from the solutions, but reaction may well have occurred after removal of
the solvent. Other oxy-acids studied in liquid hydrogen chloride were nitric
and phosphoric, which may have been weakly basic; here again no reaction
was observed (Peach and Waddington, 1962b).

Hydrogen bromide and hydrogen iodide are both very strong acids in
aqueous solutions and their properties were investigated in liquid hydrogen
chloride. In titrations against tetramethylammonium chloride in the solvent
neither gave an end-point thought there was a steady drop in conductivity
during their addition (Salthouse and Waddington, unpublished results). On
removal of the solvent tetramethylammonium bromide and iodide were left,
respectively. When a larger cation, such as tetra-n-butylammonium, was used
the mixed hydrogen dihalides, tetra-n-butylammonium hydrogen bromide
chloride, $(n-Bu)_4NHBrCl$, and tetra-n-butylammonium hydrogen chloride
iodide, $(n-Bu)_4NHClI$, were recovered (Salthouse and Waddington, 1965)
(see Section IB and Table II). It thus appears that both hydrogen bromide
and iodide can function as acids in liquid hydrogen chloride and that
the reactions

$$HCl_2^- + HBr \rightarrow HClBr^- + HCl \qquad (38)$$

$$HCl_2^- + HI \rightarrow HClI^- + HCl \qquad (39)$$

do occur. Like some acids in water they are so weak that the end-points of
titrations with them cannot be determined conductimetrically.

Various oxyacidan hydrides, such as sulphur dioxide, might also function
as acid anhydrides in the hydrogen halides, but the acid anhydrides dinitrogen tetroxide, phosphorus pentoxide and sulphur dioxide all showed no
acidic tendencies in liquid hydrogen chloride (Peach and Waddington, 1962b).

B. SOLVOLYSIS REACTIONS

A solvolysis reaction can be said to occur when a ligand is replaced by
a halogen atom, viz.:

$$MX + HHal \rightarrow MHal + HX. \qquad (40)$$

This type of reaction has been observed in solutions in hydrogen chloride
when X is phenyl, hydroxyl, or fluorine. The only hydroxyl compound
found to be solvolysed was triphenylcarbinol (Peach and Waddington, 1961):

$$Ph_3COH + 3HCl \rightarrow Ph_3C^+HCl_2^- + H_3O^+Cl^-. \qquad (41)$$

The driving force in such a reaction may be the insolubility of the hydroxonium chloride, or the extreme stability of the triphenylmethyl carbonium ion,

or more probably, a combination of both. It was not possible to solvolyse either benzoic acid or ethyl benzoate in hydrogen chloride solution (Peach and Waddington, 1962a): this was somewhat surprising as the latter compound is readily solvolysed in sulphuric acid solution (Gillespie and Leisten, 1954).

Triphenylstannyl chloride was found to be quantitatively solvolysed in solution in hydrogen chloride to diphenyldichlorostannane and benzene (Peach and Waddington, 1961):

$$Ph_3SnCl + HCl \rightarrow Ph_2SnCl_2 + PhH. \qquad (42)$$

The mechanism for this reaction is obscure. A similar type of solvolysis was also observed in solutions of the higher triphenyl metal chlorides, Ph_3MCl, of Group IV and the higher triphenyl derivatives, Ph_3M, of the Group V elements in hydrogen chloride (Peach and Waddington, 1961).

The most commonly observed solvolysis reactions are the replacement of a lighter halogen atom by a heavier. Strong fluorinating agents, such as antimony trifluoride, react in solution in hydrogen chloride to form the chloride and hydrogen fluoride (Peach and Waddington, 1963b):

$$SbF_3 + 3HCl \rightarrow SbCl_3 + 3HF. \qquad (43)$$

Boron trifluoride is not solvolysed in hydrogen chloride or bromide (Waddington and Klanberg, 1960a; Waddington and White, 1960a, 1963), but boron trichloride reacts in hydrogen bromide to form the tribromide (Waddington and White, 1960 a, 1963) and both the trichloride and the tribromide are solvolysed in hydrogen iodide to the tri-iodide (Klanberg and Kohlschütter, 1961):

$$BCl_3 + 3HI \rightarrow BI_3 + 3HCl. \qquad (44)$$

This difference presumably reflects the great stability of the B—F bond. Similar types of solvolysis have been observed with triphenylmethyl chloride and germanium tetrachloride in hydrogen iodide solution; in both cases the iodide was formed (Klanberg and Kohlschütter, 1961).

C. REDOX REACTIONS

The basic oxidation and reduction reactions in the hydrogen halide solvent systems can be represented by:

$$Hal^- \rightleftharpoons \tfrac{1}{2}Hal_2 + \epsilon, \quad E_{ox} \qquad (45)$$

$$\tfrac{1}{2}H_2 \rightleftharpoons H^+ + \epsilon, \quad E_{red} \qquad (46)$$

where E represents the standard oxidation potential. If as in water, $E_{red} > E_{ox}$, materials with $E < E_{red}$ will reduce the solvent and with $E > E_{ox}$ will oxidize the solvent. The strongest thermodynamically stable oxidizing agent in liquid hydrogen chloride must be chlorine, which shows no acidic properties.

Chlorine, bromine and iodine monochloride are all readily soluble in the solvent and it proved possible to study the oxidation reactions of these species conductimetrically. Iodine is relatively insoluble in liquid hydrogen chloride and in solutions of halides in the solvent. In all the reactions so far studied it does not appear to act as an oxidizing agent. The reactions of these oxidizing agents with simple halide ions are instructive. Chlorine oxidizes the iodide ion in two stages, to ICl_2^- and then to ICl_4^-, and both stages can be detected conductimetrically (see Fig. 7). Bromide ion is oxidized by chlorine to $BrCl_2^-$, and the end-point can again be detected conductimetrically (see Fig. 7). Bromine oxidizes the iodide ion to IBr_2^- and in a conductimetric titration a 1 : 1 end-point is found for the bromine and iodide ion (J. A. Salthouse and T. C. Waddington, unpublished results).

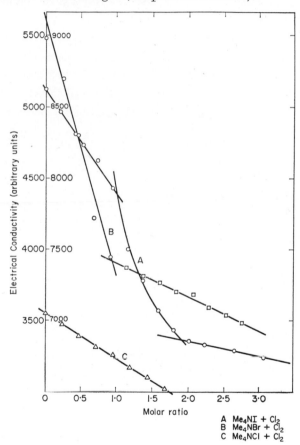

A $Me_4NI + Cl_2$
B $Me_4NBr + Cl_2$
C $Me_4NCl + Cl_2$

FIG. 7. The titrations of chlorine against tetra-alkylammonium halides in liquid hydrogen chloride. (Reproduced by permission from the *Journal of the Chemical Society*.)

The reactions of iodine monochloride are a little more complicated. In titrations of iodine monochloride against iodide ion, two end-points are found at 1 : 1 and 2 : 1 [ICl : I⁻]. Iodine is first liberated:

$$I^- + ICl + HCl \rightarrow I_2 \downarrow + HCl_2^- \tag{47}$$

and the ICl_2^- ion is then formed:

$$ICl + HCl_2^- \rightarrow HCl + ICl_2^-. \tag{48}$$

The second stage is not an oxidation reaction but the reaction of a Lewis acid in the solvent.

These reactions of halide ions with oxidizing agents in the solvent enable more complicated oxidation reactions in the solvent, such as the oxidation of phosphorus trichloride, to be interpreted. Phosphorus trichloride, itself a very poor conductor in liquid hydrogen chloride, is oxidized by chlorine to the pentachloride, a good conductor, and the reaction can be followed conductimetrically, a 1 : 1 end-point being found:

$$PCl_3 + Cl_2 + HCl \rightarrow PCl_4^+ + HCl_2^-. \tag{49}$$

Oxidation of phosphorus trichloride by bromine leads to the production of the ion PCl_3Br^+:

$$PCl_3 + Br_2 + HCl \rightarrow PCl_3Br^+ + HClBr^-. \tag{50}$$

On removal of the solvent the ion decomposes, but if boron trichloride is added the salt $PCl_3Br^+BCl_4^-$ can be isolated (J. A. Salthouse and T. C. Waddington, unpublished results).

REFERENCES

Beckmann, E. and Waentig, P. (1910) *Z. anorg. Chem.* **67**, 17.
Chang, S. and Westrum, E. F., Jr. (1962) *J. chem. Phys.* **36**, 2571.
Cook, D., Lupien, Y. and Schneider, W. G. (1956) *Canad. J. Chem.* **34**, 957, 964.
Del Fresno, C. (1928) *Z. anorg. Chem.* **170**, 222.
Fluck, E. (1962) *Z. anorg. Chem.* **315**, 191.
Fuoss, R. M. and Krauss, C. A. (1933) *J. Amer. chem. Soc.* **55**, 2387.
Fraser, M. J., Gerrard, W. and Lappert, M. F. (1957) *J. chem. Soc.* 639.
Gerson, F. and Heilbronner, E. (1962) *Helv. chim. acta* **45**, 51.
Gillespie, R. J. and Leisten, J. A. (1954) *Quart. Rev.* **8**, 40.
Gillespie, R. J. and Robinson, E. A. (1959) *Adv. inorg. Chem. Radiochem.* **1**, 385.
Glasstone, S. (1960) "Textbook of Physical Chemistry", pp. 637, 647, 891, 2nd edition, Macmillan, London.
Glockler, G. and Peck, R. E. (1936) *J. chem. Phys.* **4**, 658.
Gold, V. and Tye, F. L. (1952) *J. chem. Soc.* 2172.
Gore, G. (1865) *Phil. Mag.* (4) **29**, 541.
Graff, W. (1933) *C.R. Acad. Sci., Paris*, **197**, 754.
Grange, P., Lascombe, J. and Josien, M. L. (1960) *Spectrochim. Acta*, **16**, 981.
Gutmann, V. (1956) *Quart. Rev.* **10**, 451.
"Handbook of Chemistry and Physics", (1957–8) 39th edition, Chemical Rubber Publishing Co.
Hantzsch, A. (1930) *Ber. dtsch. chem. Ges.* **63**B, 1789.
Harmon, K. M. and Davis, S. (1962) *J. Amer. chem. Soc.* **84**, 4359.
Hart, H. and Fish, R. W. (1958) *J. Amer. chem. Soc.* **80**, 5894.
Herbrandson, H. F., Dickerson, R. T. and Weinstein, J. (1954) *J. Amer. chem. Soc.* **76**, 4046.
Herzberg, G. (1945) "Infrared and Raman Spectra of Polyatomic Molecules", p. 280. Van Nostrand, New York.

Holliday, A. K., Peach, M. E. and Waddington, T. C. (1961) *Proc. chem. Soc., Lond.* 220.

Holmes, R. R. (1963) *J. chem. Educ.* **40**, 125.

Holmes, R. R. and Gallagher, W. P. (1963) *Inorg. Chem.* **2**, 433.

Hyman, H. H., Quarterman, L. A., Kilpatrick, M. and Katz, J. J. (1961) *J. phys. Chem.* **65**, 123.

Janz, G. J. and Danyluk, S. S. (1959) *J. Amer. chem. Soc.* **81**, 3846, 3850, 3854.

Kahovec, L. and Knollmüller, K. (1941) *Z. phys. Chem.* B**51**, 49.

Kirsanov, O. V. and Fedorova, G. K. (1960) *Dopov. Akad. Nauk ukr. R.S.R.* 1960, 1086 (*Chem. Abstr.* (1962) **56**, 15142).

Klanberg, F. and Kohlschütter, H. W. (1961) *Z. Naturf.* **16**b, 69.

Klemenc, A. and Kohl, O. (1927) *Z. anorg. Chem.* **168**, 163.

Krauss, C. A. and Fuoss, R. M. (1933) *J. Amer. chem. Soc.* **55**, 21.

Maas, O. and McIntosh, D. (1913). *J. Amer. chem. Soc.* **35**, 535.

McIntosh, D. (1908) *J. Amer. chem. Soc.* **30**, 1097.

Maki, A. G. and West, R. (1963) *Inorg. Chem.* **2**, 657.

Mellor, J. W. (1961). "Comprehensive Treatise on Inorganic and Theoretical Chemistry", p. 415, Supplement 2, Part I. Longmans, London.

Murray, F. E. and Schneider, W. G. (1955) *Canad. J. chem.* **33**, 797.

Peach, M. E. and Waddington, T. C. (1961) *J. chem. Soc.* 1238.

Peach, M. E. and Waddington, T. C. (1962a) *J. chem. Soc.* 600.

Peach, M. E. and Waddington, T. C. (1962b) *J. chem. Soc.* 2680.

Peach, M. E. and Waddington, T. C. (1962c) *J. chem. Soc.* 3450.

Peach, M. E. and Waddington, T. C. (1963a) *J. chem. Soc.* 69.

Peach, M. E. and Waddington, T. C. (1963b) *J. chem. Soc.* 799.

Runner, M. E., Balog, G. and Kilpatrick, M. (1956) *J. Amer. chem. Soc.* **78**, 5183.

Rupert, E. F. (1909) *J. chem. Soc.* **31**, 851.

Salthouse, J. A. and Waddington, T. C. (1965) *J. chem. Soc.* (in the press).

Sharp, D. W. A. (1958) *J. chem. Soc.* 2558.

Sharp, D. W. A. (1960) *Adv. Fluorine Chem.* **1**, 105.

Smyth, C. P. and Hitchcock, C. S. (1933) *J. Amer. chem. Soc.* **55**, 1830.

Steele, B. D., McIntosh, D. and Archibald, E. H. (1905) *Phil. Trans.* **205**, 99.

Steele, B. D., McIntosh, D. and Archibald, E. H. (1906) *Z. phys. Chem.* **55**, 129.

Valleé, R. E. and McDaniel, D. H. (1962) *J. Amer. chem. Soc.* **84**, 3412.

Valleé, R. E. and McDaniel, D. H. (1963) *Inorg. Chem.* **2**, 997.

Vidale, G. L. and Taylor, R. C. (1956) *J. Amer. chem. Soc.* **78**, 294.

Waddington, T. C. (1958a) *Trans Faraday Soc.* **54**, 25.

Waddington, T. C. (1958b) *J. chem. Soc.* 1708.

Waddington, T. C. and Klanberg, F. (1959) *Naturwissenshaften*, **46**, 578.

Waddington, T. C. and Klanberg, F. (1960a) *J. chem. Soc.* 2329, 2332.

Waddington, T. C. and Klanberg, F. (1960b) *Z. anorg. Chem.* **304**, 185.

Waddington, T. C. and White, J. A. (1960a) *Proc. chem. Soc., Lond.* 85.

Waddington, T. C. and White, J. A. (1960b) *Proc. chem. Soc., Lond.* 315.

Waddington, T. C. and White, J. A. (1963) *J. chem. Soc.* 2701.

Walker, J. W., McIntosh, D. and Archibald, E. (1904) *J. chem. Soc.* **85**, 1098 (1904).

West, R. (1957) *J. Amer. chem. Soc.* **79**, 4568.

Wheat, J. A. and Browne, A. W. (1940) *J. Amer. chem. Soc.* **62**, 1577.

Yeh, S.-J. and Jaffée, H. H. (1959) *J. Amer. chem. Soc.*, **81**, 3279.

Yoon, Y. K. and Carpenter, G. B. (1959) *Acta crystallogr.* **12**, 17.

CHAPTER 4

Sulphuric Acid

R. J. GILLESPIE AND E. A. ROBINSON

Department of Chemistry, McMaster University, Hamilton, Ontario, Canada
Department of Chemistry, University of Toronto, Toronto, Ontario, Canada

I. Introduction... 117
    A. Bases... 118
    B. Acids... 121
    C. Non-Electrolytes 122
    D. Sulphates and Hydrogen Sulphates.................................... 122
II. The Physical Properties of Sulphuric Acid and Its Solutions, Including Experimental Methods of Investigation... 123
    A. Properties of Sulphuric Acid... 123
    B. Properties of Solutions.. 131
III. Inorganic Solutes... 162
    A. The Solutes Water and Sulphur Trioxide.............................. 162
    B. Boron.. 164
    C. Silicon.. 167
    D. Tin and Lead.. 170
    E. Nitrogen and Phosphorus... 172
    F. Arsenic, Antimony and Bismuth....................................... 174
    G. Vanadium, Chromium and Manganese................................... 177
    H. Sulphur, Selenium and Tellurium..................................... 179
    I. Halogens... 180
    J. Transition Metal Complexes.. 184
    K. Chelation by the Sulphate Group..................................... 186
IV. Organic Solutes... 187
    A. Simple Bases.. 187
    B. Polybasic Compounds... 188
    C. Amides and Ureas.. 190
    D. Esters.. 192
    E. Carboxylic Anhydrides... 193
    F. Ethers.. 194
    G. Nitriles.. 195
    H. Carboxylic Acids.. 196
    I. Carbonium Ions.. 198
    J. Aromatic Sulphonation... 204
References 205

I. INTRODUCTION

Sulphuric acid is a good solvent for compounds that ionize as electrolytes, as might be expected from its high dielectric constant, the polarity of its molecules, and their ability to form strong hydrogen bonds. Electrolytes may be classified in the usual way according to the solvo-system definition of acids and bases. Acids give the sulphuric acidium, $H_3SO_4^+$, ion

$$HA + H_2SO_4 = H_3SO_4^+ + A^-; \tag{1}$$

5

and bases give the hydrogen sulphate, HSO_4^-, ion

$$B + H_2SO_4 = BH^+ + HSO_4^-. \tag{2}$$

Because of the high acidity of sulphuric acid, bases are the largest class of electrolytes. Sulphuric acid has a levelling effect on the strengths of bases in the same way that water has a levelling effect on the strengths of acids. Acids of the sulphuric acid system are rarer but several examples are known. Many of the electrolytes of the sulphuric acid solvent system are unfamiliar as they are not known in aqueous solution; many compounds that do not have basic properties in water, including many that behave as acids in aqueous solution, are readily protonated in sulphuric acid, while many electrolytes that are encountered in water are not stable in sulphuric acid.

Sulphuric acid has proved a particularly valuable solvent in the study of the protonation of very weak bases such as ketones and nitro-compounds and in the preparation of stable solutions of reactive ions such as carbonium ions, NO_2^+ and I_3^+ that are unstable in more basic solvents such as water. Sulphuric acid resembles water as a solvent in many ways despite its greater acidity and a comparison of such properties as the conductivities, viscosities, densities and activities of electrolyte solutions in sulphuric acid with those of aqueous electrolyte solutions is proving valuable in aiding our understanding of electrolyte solutions in general.

There have been several previous reviews of the properties of sulphuric acid as a solvent (Gillespie and Leisten, 1954; Gillespie, 1959; Gillespie and Robinson, 1959). The purpose of this chapter is to provide a general introduction to the sulphuric acid solvent system and to cover in some detail recent work on the behaviour of solutes in this solvent.

A. BASES

1. *Metal Hydrogen Sulphates*

The alkali and some other metal hydrogen sulphates behave as fully ionized binary electrolytes. They are thus strong bases, analogous to hydroxides in water, e.g.

$$KHSO_4 = K^+ + HSO_4^- \tag{3a}$$
$$KOH = K^+ + OH^-. \tag{3b}$$

The corresponding normal sulphates are converted into the hydrogen sulphates and, formally, they are analogous to metal oxides in water,

$$K_2SO_4 + H_2SO_4 = 2K^+ + 2HSO_4^- \tag{4a}$$
$$K_2O + H_2O = 2K^+ + 2OH^-. \tag{4b}$$

Salts of other familiar inorganic acids are either insoluble, for example, AgCl, $CuBr_2$, $AlCl_3$, and $AlPO_4$, or undergo complete solvolysis as is illustrated in the following examples:

$$NH_4ClO_4 + H_2SO_4 = NH_4^+ + HSO_4^- + HClO_4 \qquad (5)$$
$$Na_3PO_4 + 3H_2SO_4 = 3Na^+ + 3HSO_4^- + H_3PO_4 \qquad (6)$$
$$KNO_3 + H_2SO_4 = K^+ + HSO_4^- + HNO_3. \qquad (7)$$

All such soluble salts thus give rise to strongly basic solutions. Solvolysis occurs because of the relatively high concentration of $H_3SO_4^+$ ions present in sulphuric acid as a result of its self-dissociation, and because the acids from which these salts are derived are either exceedingly weak or do not behave as acids at all in sulphuric acid. Thus perchloric acid is an exceedingly weak acid and both phosphoric acid and nitric acid react further as bases.

2. *Other Simple Bases*

A very large number of other substances behave as bases, forming their conjugate acids by the addition of a proton. Thus very many organic compounds, with the exception of aliphatic hydrocarbons, some aromatic hydrocarbons, and their halogen derivatives, are soluble in sulphuric acid. This can be attributed to their possessing atoms such as O, N, or P with lone pairs of electrons which can accept a proton from sulphuric acid.

Examples include ketones

$$R_2CO + H_2SO_4 = R_2COH^+ + HSO_4^- \qquad (8)$$

carboxylic acids

$$RCO_2H + H_2SO_4 = RCO_2H_2^+ + HSO_4^- \qquad (9)$$

esters

$$RCO_2R' + H_2SO_4 = RCO_2R'H^+ + HSO_4^- \qquad (10)$$

amines

$$RNH_2 + H_2SO_4 = RNH_3^+ + HSO_4^- \qquad (11)$$

amides

$$RCONH_2 + H_2SO_4 = R\overset{+}{C}(OH)NH_2 + HSO_4^- \qquad (12)$$

and phosphines

$$R_3P + H_2SO_4 = R_3PH^+ + HSO_4^-. \qquad (13)$$

Even triphenylamine and triphenylphosphine, which are normally regarded as exceedingly weak bases behave as strong bases in sulphuric acid. Some substances, such as nitro-compounds, dialkyl sulphones and nitriles, with only very weakly basic properties are incompletely protonated in sulphuric acid.

Molecules containing more than one basic group often form multi-charged cations. For example *o*-phenylenediamine is diprotonated, some amino acids are protonated on both the NH_2 and CO_2H groups, and hexamethylenetetramine accepts protons on all four nitrogen atoms.

Solutions of a very large number of organic compounds are quite stable at room temperature and the organic compound may be recovered unchanged by pouring the solution onto ice. Protonation often serves to deactivate the compound and thus prevent further reaction, such as aromatic sulphonation, which might otherwise occur.

Water and phosphoric acid provide examples of inorganic substances which behave as strong bases:

$$H_2O + H_2SO_4 \rightarrow H_3O^+ + HSO_4^- \tag{14}$$

$$H_3PO_4 + H_2SO_4 \rightarrow H_4PO_4^+ + HSO_4^-, \tag{15}$$

while selenium dioxide is a weak base:

$$SeO_2 + H_2SO_4 \rightleftharpoons HSeO_2^+ + HSO_4^-. \tag{16}$$

3. Complex Bases

A large number of oxy and hydroxy compounds behave as bases because they are dehydrated by the solvent. The simplest examples of this type of behaviour are given by a number of substances of the general formula XOH which are converted to the hydrogen sulphate XSO_4H:

$$XOH + 2H_2SO_4 = XSO_4H + H_3O^+ + HSO_4^-. \tag{17}$$

Ethyl alcohol is a base of this type, being converted into ethyl hydrogen sulphate

$$C_2H_5OH + 2H_2SO_4 = C_2H_5SO_4H + H_3O^+ + HSO_4^-. \tag{18}$$

Similarly iodic acid is converted to iodyl hydrogen sulphate

$$HIO_3 + H_2SO_4 = IO_2HSO_4 + H_3O^+ + HSO_4^-. \tag{19}$$

In addition the hydrogen sulphate itself sometimes acts as a base either by forming its conjugate acid

$$XSO_4H + H_2SO_4 = XSO_4H_2^+ + HSO_4^- \tag{20}$$

or by ionizing to X^+ and HSO_4^-.

Nitric acid, triphenyl carbinol, and mesitoic acid all provide examples of a hydrogen sulphate XSO_4H which is fully ionized to X^+ and HSO_4^- so that the overall ionizations of these compounds are:

$$HNO_3 + 2H_2SO_4 = NO_2^+ + H_3O^+ + 2HSO_4^- \tag{21}$$

$$Ph_3C.OH + 2H_2SO_4 = Ph_3C^+ + H_3O^+ + 2HSO_4^- \tag{22}$$

$$Me_3C_6H_2CO_2H + 2H_2SO_4 = Me_3C_6H_2CO^+ + H_3O^+ + 2HSO_4^-. \tag{23}$$

It has been shown recently that some interesting ions containing two carbonium ion centres can be obtained in sulphuric acid, e.g.

$$(C_6H_5)_2C\text{—}\langle\text{—}\rangle\text{—}C\text{-}(C_6H_5)_2 + 4H_2SO_4 = (C_6H_5)_2\overset{+}{C}\text{—}\langle\text{—}\rangle\text{—}\overset{+}{C}(C_6H_5)_2$$
$$\underset{OH}{|} \qquad\qquad \underset{OH}{|} \qquad\qquad\qquad\qquad + 2H_3O^+ + 4HSO_4^-. \tag{24}$$

Many of these cations are very strongly electrophilic and can only exist in very weakly basic solutions such as sulphuric acid, or in a suitable non-protonic solvent. Their formation in sulphuric acid is due not only to its high acidity but also to the very low activity of water in dilute solution in sulphuric acid. This low water activity is a consequence of its extensive conversion to H_3O^+. One advantage of sulphuric acid for the formation of such ions is that it is a good solvent for electrolytes whereas non-protonic solvents are often poor solvents for electrolytes. Thus relatively concentrated solutions of these reactive ions may be obtained in sulphuric acid.

Even some anhydrides react to give a hydrogen sulphate with the elimination of water

$$X_2O + 3H_2SO_4 = 2XSO_4H + H_3O^+ + HSO_4^-. \tag{25}$$

Hexamethyldisiloxane and arsenic (III) oxide behave in this way

$$[(CH_3)_3Si]_2O + 3H_2SO_4 = 2(CH_3)_3Si.SO_4H + H_3O^+ + HSO_4^- \tag{26}$$

$$As_2O_3 + 3H_2SO_4 = 2AsO.SO_4H + H_3O^+ + HSO_4^-. \tag{27}$$

Trimethylsilicon hydrogen sulphate is a non-electrolyte but $AsO.SO_4H$ is partially ionized. Dinitrogen pentoxide forms the fully ionized nitronium hydrogen sulphate:

$$N_2O_5 + 3H_2SO_4 = 2NO_2^+ + H_3O^+ + 3HSO_4^-. \tag{28}$$

B. ACIDS

The majority of substances that behave as acids in aqueous solution do not exhibit acidic properties in sulphuric acid but behave as bases of various types, as is shown by the following examples:

$$CH_3CO_2H + H_2SO_4 = CH_3CO_2H_2^+ + HSO_4^- \tag{29}$$

$$H_3PO_4 + H_2SO_4 = H_4PO_4^+ + HSO_4^- \tag{30}$$

$$HNO_3 + 2H_2SO_4 = NO_2^+ + H_3O^+ + 2HSO_4^- \tag{31}$$

$$H_3BO_3 + 6H_2SO_4 = B(HSO_4)_4^- + 3H_3O^+ + 2HSO_4^- \tag{32}$$

$$H_2SO_3 + H_2SO_4 = SO_2 + H_3O^+ + HSO_4^- \tag{33}$$

$$HF + 2H_2SO_4 = HSO_3F + H_3O^+ + HSO_4^-. \tag{34}$$

Even perchloric acid, which is often regarded as the strongest known mineral acid, is only very slightly ionized in sulphuric acid, and metal perchlorates undergo complete solvolysis

$$MClO_4 + H_2SO_4 = M^+ + HClO_4 + HSO_4^-. \tag{35}$$

The first acids of the sulphuric acid system to be recognized were disulphuric acid, $H_2S_2O_7$, and the higher polysulphuric acids, $H_2S_3O_{10}$ etc., which are present in oleums. These acids are weak acids of the sulphuric acid system. Another very weak acid is fluorosulphuric acid, HSO_3F.

Evidence has been obtained for the existence of a strong acid of the sulphuric acid solvent system, namely, the complex acid tetra(hydrogen sulphato)boric acid, $HB(HSO_4)_4$. Solutions of this acid can be obtained by dissolving boric acid in oleum

$$H_3BO_3 + 3H_2S_2O_7 = H_3SO_4^+ + B(HSO_4)_4^- + H_2SO_4. \qquad (36)$$

Solutions of some other complex sulphato acids such as hexa(hydrogen sulphato)stannic acid, $H_2Sn(HSO_4)_6$, and hexa(hydrogen sulphato)plumbic acid, $H_2Pb(HSO_4)_6$, have also been obtained.

C. NON-ELECTROLYTES

Rather few compounds that are soluble in sulphuric acid behave as non-electrolytes because the hydrogen-bonding interactions between the sulphuric acid molecules are sufficiently strong that unless a solute is strongly solvated, either because it is ionic, or because it can strongly hydrogen-bond with sulphuric acid, it is unlikely to be able to sufficiently disrupt the structure of the solvent to enable it to dissolve. Yet if a molecule is sufficiently basic to form strong hydrogen bonds with sulphuric acid it is likely that some proton transfer along the hydrogen bonds will occur, resulting in at least a small degree of ionization. Thus in order to behave as a non-electrolyte a solute must be sufficiently basic to form strong hydrogen bonds with the solvent but not basic enough to protonate. The only non-electrolytes that are known at present are alkyl sulphonyl fluorides and sulphonyl chlorides, sulphuryl chloride, picric acid, a few other polynitro-aromatic compounds and probably diphenyl sulphone and most of the sulphonic acids. Trichloroacetic acid and chlorosulphuric acid may also be non-electrolytes although the evidence is not conclusive (Gillespie et al., 1950; Brayford and Wyatt, 1955; Gillespie et al., 1956; Gillespie and Solomons, 1957; Hall and Robinson, 1964).

D. SULPHATES AND HYDROGEN SULPHATES

Because only a few anions are known that do not undergo extensive, if not complete, solvolysis in sulphuric acid, investigations have been mainly confined to the behaviour of sulphates and hydrogen sulphates, which are the analogues of the oxides and hydroxides in water. It should not be concluded, however, that the chemistry of solutions in sulphuric acid is therefore without any great interest, because many varieties of cations are known, a number of which cannot exist in aqueous solutions. When an oxide or hydroxide is dissolved in sulphuric acid there is a tendency for it to be converted to a sulphate or hydrogen sulphate with the elimination of water, although the extent to which this occurs varies widely from one element to another. Thus, for example, the oxides and hydroxides of the more electropositive metals are completely converted to the corresponding hydrogen sulphates, while phosphoric acid is merely protonated and undergoes no conversion to a sulphate derivative. In general a wide variety of compounds intermediate between the oxides and hydroxides of the aqueous system and the sulphates and hydrogen sulphates of the sulphuric acid system may be formed.

II. The Physical Properties of Sulphuric Acid and Its Solutions Including Experimental Methods of Investigation

A. PROPERTIES OF SULPHURIC ACID

1. *Structure*

The high viscosity, boiling point and surface tension (Table I), of sulphuric acid indicate that it is a highly associated liquid, doubtless because of strong hydrogen bonding between the molecules. It has been shown that the solid has a layer-type structure (Pascard, 1955) in which each sulphuric acid molecule is hydrogen bonded to four others. Unfortunately no great precision is claimed for the interatomic distances given in this X-ray determination. The structure of the liquid is likely to resemble that of the solid, just as the structure of liquid water is related to that of ice.

TABLE I

Some Physical Constants of Sulphuric Acid

H_2SO_4		
Freezing-point	10·371°	
Boiling-point	290–317°	
Viscosity (centipoise)	24·54	25°
Density (d_4^{25})	1·8269	25°
Dielectric constant	100	25°
Specific conductivity (ohm^{-1} cm^{-1})	$1·0439 \times 10^{-2}$	25°
Heat capacity (cal deg^{-1} g^{-1})	0·3373	25°
Heat of fusion (cal mole^{-1})	2560	10·37°
D_2SO_4		
Freezing-point	14·35°	
Viscosity (centipoise)	24·88	25°
Density (d_4^{25})	1·8573	25°
Specific conductivity (ohm^{-1} cm^{-1})	$0·2568 \times 10^{-2}$	25°

Extensive studies have been made of the vibrational spectrum of sulphuric acid, (Section IIA, 6). Symmetric and asymmetric stretching frequencies due to the SO_2 group and the $S(OH)_2$ group are readily identified and approximate stretching force constants derived from these frequencies (SO_2, $k = 10·3 \times 10^5$ dynes cm^{-1}; $S(OH)_2$, $k = 5·9 \times 10^5$ dynes cm^{-1}), indicate an S—O bond order of about 1·8 and an S—OH bond order near to 1·3 (Gillespie and Robinson, 1963b). The best single representation of the molecular structure is I in which the $d_{x^2-y^2}$ and d_{z^2} orbitals on sulphur are used in double bonds with oxygen.

$$
\begin{array}{ccc}
\text{HO} & & \text{O} \\
& \diagdown \; \diagup & \\
& \text{S} & \\
& \diagup \; \diagdown & \\
\text{HO} & & \text{O} \\
& \text{I} &
\end{array}
$$

2. Self-dissociation

The properties of 100% sulphuric acid are affected to an important extent by its rather extensive self-dissociation, and in order to understand the behaviour of solutes dissolved in sulphuric acid it is necessary to know the nature and extent of the self-dissociation processes.

Despite its high acidity, sulphuric acid is also appreciably basic, and belongs to the general group of solvents, like water, liquid ammonia, and liquid hydrogen fluoride, which are *amphoteric* or *amphiprotic*. This shows itself in the appreciable autoprotolysis of these solvents

$$2HA = H_2A^+ + A^- \tag{37}$$

in which one molecule behaves as an acid and the other as a base. The extent of autoprotolysis is determined by the acid and base strengths of the solvent and for sulphuric acid it is larger than for most protonic solvents (Table II).

TABLE II

Autoprotolysis Constants at 25°

Solvent	$-\text{Log } K_{\text{ap}}$	Solvent	$-\text{Log } K_{\text{ap}}$
NH_3	29·8	HF	9·7
C_2H_5OH	18·9	HCO_2H	6·2
D_2O	14·8	D_2SO_4	4·3
H_2O	14·0	H_2SO_4	3·6
CH_3CO_2H	12·6	H_3PO_4	~ 2
H_2O_2	12		

In addition to autoprotolysis

$$2H_2SO_4 = H_3SO_4^+ + HSO_4^- \tag{38}$$

sulphuric acid is also self-dissociated in other ways which are a consequence of a primary dissociation into water and sulphur trioxide.

$$H_2SO_4 = H_2O + SO_3. \tag{39}$$

Since water is extensively ionized according to the equation

$$H_2O + H_2SO_4 = H_3O^+ + HSO_4^- \tag{40}$$

and SO_3 forms disulphuric acid

$$SO_3 + H_2SO_4 = H_2S_2O_7 \qquad (41)$$

which is partially ionized as an acid,

$$H_2S_2O_7 + H_2SO_4 = H_3SO_4^+ + HS_2O_7^- \qquad (42)$$

and since the ions $H_3SO_4^+$ and HSO_4^- are in equilibrium as a result of the autoprotolysis reaction it follows that the ions H_3O^+ and $HS_2O_7^-$ must also be in equilibrium

$$2H_2SO_4 = H_3O^+ + HS_2O_7^-. \qquad (43)$$

This has been called the *ionic self-dehydration* reaction, with an equilibrium constant K_{id}. It has been found convenient to choose equations (38), (40), (42) and (43) to describe the complete self-dissociation of sulphuric acid. Values of the corresponding dissociation constants, K_{ap}, K_{H_2O}, $K_{H_2S_2O_7}$, and K_{id} for these reactions at 10°, 25° and 40° are given in Table III.

TABLE III

Equilibrium Constants for the Self-Dissociation Reactions of Sulphuric Acid

	10°	25°	40°
$K_{ap} = [H_3SO_4^+][HSO_4^-]$	1.7×10^{-4}	2.7×10^{-4}	4.0×10^{-4}
$K_{id} = [H_3O^+][HS_2O_7^-]$	3.5×10^{-5}	5.1×10^{-5}	8.1×10^{-4}
$K_{H_2S_2O_7} = [H_3SO_4^+][HSO_7^-]/[H_2S_2O_7]$	1.4×10^{-2}	1.4×10^{-2}	1.4×10^{-2}
$K_{H_2O} = [H_3O^+][HSO_4^-]/[H_2O]$	1	1	1

The values at 10° were obtained from a detailed study of the freezing points of solutions of metal hydrogen sulphates, water and disulphuric acid, each of which represses the self-dissociation of sulphuric acid in a different way (Bass *et al.*, 1960). Values of K_{ap} and K_{id} at 25° and 40° were obtained from the values at 10° and the heats of autoprotolysis and ionic self-dehydration, which have been measured by Wyatt and his co-workers; $\Delta H_{ap} = 5.0$ kcal mole^{-1}, $\Delta H_{id} = 6.0$ kcal mole^{-1} (Kirkbride and Wyatt, 1957; Dacre and Wyatt, 1961; Gillespie and Robinson, 1963).

Table IV gives values for the self-dissociation equilibrium constants of dideuterosulphuric acid, D_2SO_4. These have been obtained in a similar way to those for H_2SO_4 but are rather less precise. It may be noted that the auto-deuterolysis constant of D_2SO_4 is smaller than the autoprotolysis constant of H_2SO_4. The frequencies of the stretching vibrations of the SO_2 group of D_2SO_4 are slightly lower than those of the SO_2 frequencies of H_2SO_4, implying that D_2SO_4 is a slightly stronger base than H_2SO_4 (Gillespie and Robinson, 1962a;

TABLE IV

Equilibrium Constants for the Self-Dissociation Reactions of Dideuterosulphuric Acid

	14°	25°	40°
$K_{ap} = [D_3SO_4^+][DSO_4^-]$	$2 \cdot 9 \times 10^{-5}$	$4 \cdot 6 \times 10^{-5}$	$5 \cdot 2 \times 10^{-5}$
$K_{1d} = [D_3O^+][DS_2O_7^-]$	$5 \cdot 0 \times 10^{-5}$	$5 \cdot 5 \times 10^{-5}$	$6 \cdot 0 \times 10^{-5}$
$K_{D_2S_2O_7} = [D_3SO_4^+][DS_2O_7^-]/[D_2S_2O_7]$	$2 \cdot 8 \times 10^{-3}$	$2 \cdot 8 \times 10^{-3}$	$2 \cdot 8 \times 10^{-3}$
$K_{D_2O} = [D_3O^+][DSO_4^-]/[D_2O]$	$0 \cdot 2$	$0 \cdot 2$	$0 \cdot 2$

Gillespie and Robinson, 1963b). It would appear therefore that D_2SO_4 must be a weaker acid than H_2SO_4. It is interesting to note that the acid $D_2S_2O_7$ appears to be a weaker acid in D_2SO_4 than is the acid $H_2S_2O_7$ in H_2SO_4 (Gillespie *et al.*, 1956).

TABLE V

Molal Concentrations of the Self-Dissociation Species

H_2SO_4		D_2SO_4	
HSO_4^-	0·0150	DSO_4^-	0·0112
$H_3SO_4^+$	0·0113	$D_3SO_4^+$	0·0041
H_3O^+	0·0080	D_3O^+	0·0112
$HS_2O_7^-$	0·0044	$DS_2O_7^-$	0·0049
$H_2S_2O_7$	0·0036	$D_2S_2O_7$	0·0071
H_2O	0·0001	D_2O	0·0006
Total	0·0424	Total	0·0391

Table V gives the molal concentrations of each of the products of self-dissociation of H_2SO_4 and D_2SO_4 at the freezing points of the respective acids.

3. *Freezing Point*

At atmospheric pressure 100% sulphuric acid has a freezing point of 10·371° (Kunzler and Giauque, 1952c; Bass and Gillespie, 1960). The 100% acid is conveniently prepared by adding dilute oleum to slightly aqueous sulphuric acid until the maximum freezing point of 10·371° is reached. The freezing point of the hypothetical completely undissociated acid can be computed from the concentration of self-dissociation species and the cryo-scopic constant to be 10·625° (Bass *et al.*, 1960). The freezing point curve of the H_2O–SO_3 system in the vicinity of the composition H_2SO_4 is shown in Fig. 1 together with the curve calculated on the basis of the equilibrium

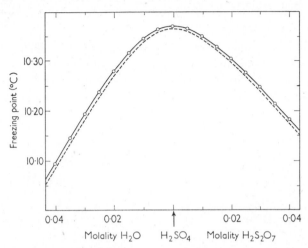

FIG. 1. Freezing points of the H_2O–SO_3 system in the region of the composition H_2SO_4. —O—O—, experimental curve; – – – –, calculated curve.

constants given in Table III. The small difference between the experimental and calculated curves may be attributed to the non-ideality of the solutions. The freezing point of D_2SO_4 is 14·34° (Flowers *et al.*, 1956b).

4. *Density*

Values of the densities of H_2SO_4 and D_2SO_4 at 25° are given in Table I. The temperature variation of the densities may be represented by the equations

$$H_2SO_4 : d_4^t = 1\cdot8516 - 1\cdot000 \times 10^{-3}t \tag{44}$$

$$D_2SO_4 : d_4^t = 1\cdot8816 - 0\cdot980 \times 10^{-3}t. \tag{45}$$

The molar volumes are 53·69 for H_2SO_4 and 53·89 for D_2SO_4 at 25°. It has been suggested that this rather large increase in molar volume on deuterium substitution might be due to the intermolecular deuterium bond being longer than the hydrogen bond (Greenwood and Thompson, 1959).

5. *Viscosity*

Values of the viscosity of H_2SO_4 and D_2SO_4 at 25° are given in Table I. The temperature dependence can be represented by the following equation (Greenwood and Thompson, 1959)

$$\eta = \eta_0 \exp (C_\eta/RT). \tag{46}$$

The energy of activation E_η is given by $E_\eta = 2C_\eta/T$ and decreases from 6·78 kcal mole^{-1} at 10° to 5·76 kcal mole^{-1} at 60° for H_2SO_4 and from 6·99 kcal mole^{-1} at 10° to 5·62 kcal mole^{-1} at 60° for D_2SO_4. This decrease in the activation energy is probably due to a progressive breaking of hydrogen bonds with increasing temperature.

6. *Dielectric Constant*

The dielectric constant of sulphuric acid has proved difficult to measure, mainly because of its high electrical conductivity. In 1953, Brand *et al.* using wave guide techniques made measurements in the frequency range 100–3000 Mc/s. They found that dielectric dispersion occurs at these fre-

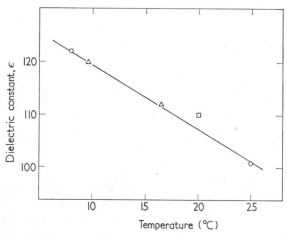

Fig. 2. The dielectric constant of sulphuric acid. □, Brand *et al.* (1953); ○, Gillespie and Cole (1956); △, Gillespie and White (1958).

quencies and they obtained the static dielectric constant by extrapolation. Two attempts have been made to obtain the static dielectric constant directly. Gillespie and Cole (1956) used a conventional bridge method for determining the capacity of a condenser containing sulphuric acid. The separation of the electrodes of the condenser could be varied and the large polarization capacity of the electrodes resulting from the high conductivity was thereby eliminated. An attempt has also been made (Gillespie and White, 1958) to use the force method first suggested by Furth in which the torque exerted by an electric field on a platinum ellipsoid suspended in the liquid is measured, although the high conductivity of the liquid caused considerable experimental difficulties. The values obtained are summarized in Fig. 2. They indicate a roughly linear dependence of the dielectric constant on the temperature in this range. Values of 120 at 10° and 100 at 25° are obtained by interpolation.

7. *Electrical Conductivity*

The relatively high concentration of ions in the pure liquid is responsible for the rather high conductivity of 100% sulphuric acid. The specific conductivities of both H_2SO_4 and D_2SO_4 at various temperatures are given in Table VI (Kunzler and Giauque, 1952a; Flowers *et al.*, 1956b; Gillespie *et al.*,

TABLE VI

Specific Conductivities of Sulphuric Acid and Dideuterosulphuric Acid at the 100% Composition and at the Composition of Minimum Conductance

Temperature	κ $(10^{-2} \text{ ohm}^{-1} \text{ cm}^{-1})$	κ $(10^{-2} \text{ ohm}^{-1} \text{ cm}^{-1})$	Composition at minimum conductance
	H_2SO_4	"Minimum"	(moles H_2O kg$_{\text{solution}}^{-1}$)
9·66°	0·570	0·5685	0·0023
25·00°	1·0439	1·0432	0·0019
40·00°	1·711	1·710	0·0015
	D_2SO_4	"Minimum"	(moles $D_2S_2O_7$ kg$_{\text{solution}}^{-1}$)
10·00°	0·133	—	—
25·00°	0·2568	0·2540	0·0045
40·00°	0·446	—	—

1956). Minima in the conductivities of the H_2O–SO_3 and D_2O–SO_3 systems occur almost, but not exactly, at the compositions H_2SO_4 and D_2SO_4. For the former the minimum occurs slightly on the aqueous side of the composition H_2SO_4, in the range 10–40°, and shifts towards the composition H_2SO_4 as the temperature increases. At 25° a minimum occurs slightly on the oleum side of the composition D_2SO_4. The position of the minimum depends on the concentrations and the mobilities of all the ions present, and it has been used in conjunction with other data to obtain important information concerning the values of these quantities. 100% Sulphuric acid can be conveniently prepared by first adjusting the composition to the minimum conductivity and then adding dilute oleum until the conductivity corresponding to 100% acid is obtained. The activation energy for the specific conductivity of sulphuric acid is very similar to that for the viscosity, but as Greenwood and Thompson (1959) pointed out this is almost certainly coincidental and has no implication for the mechanism of conduction in sulphuric acid. The conductivity of crystalline sulphuric acid is at least two powers of ten less than that of the liquid (Greenwood and Thompson, 1959).

8. *Heat Capacity and Heat of Fusion*

The specific heat of sulphuric acid is 0.3373 cal deg^{-1} g^{-1} (Kirkbride and Wyatt, 1957). The specific heat of the H_2O–SO_3 system has a small but sharp maximum at the composition H_2SO_4. This is due to the fact that a small part of the heat capacity of absolute sulphuric acid arises from the temperature coefficient of the heat of self-dissociation (Kunzler and Giauque, 1952b). The heat of fusion is 2560 cal mole^{-1} (Kunzler and Giauque, 1952c).

TABLE VII

Assignment of the Fundamental Vibrational Frequencies of H_2SO_4 and D_2SO_4 (frequencies in cm^{-1})

| | H_2SO_4 | | | | D_2SO_4 | | | | Approximate description |
| | liquid | | | Crystal | liquid | | | Crystal | |
	(a)	(b)	(c)	(d)	(a)	(b)	(c)	(d)	
$\nu_2(a_1)$	1195	1170	1140	1170	1170	—	—	1190	SO_2 sym. stretch.
$\nu_4(a_1)$	910	907	905	907	907	—	—	910	$S[OH(D)]_2$ sym. stretch.
$\nu_5(a_1)$	563	549	741	548	522	—	—	550–566	SO_2 bend.
$\nu_6(a_1)$	392	332	381	386	356	—	—	363	$S[OH(D)]_2$ bend.
$\nu_8(a_2)$	392	—	417	—	356	—	—	—	Torsion.
$\nu_{11}(b_1)$	973	967	1370	967	980	—	—	980	$S[OH(D)]_2$ asym. stretch.
$\nu_{12}(b_1)$	563	420	1190	623	560	—	—	628	SO_2 rock.
$\nu_{13}(b_2)$	1368	1365	965	1365	1340	—	—	1350	SO_2 asym. stretch.
$\nu_{15}(b_2)$	422	372	564	412	395	—	—	371	$S[OH(D)]_2$ rock.
$\nu_1(a_1)$	2450	2450	2430	2450	—	1860	1820	1860	O—H(D) sym. stretch.
$\nu_3(a_1)$	1137	1170	1170–1240	1170	—	—	—	—	O—H(D) bend.
$\nu_7(a_2)$	—	740	420	—	—	—	305	518	O—H(D) sym. wag.
$\nu_9(b_1)$	2970	2970	3000	2970	—	2280	2230	2280	O—H(D) asym. stretch.
$\nu_1(b_1)$	—	1240	1800	1240	—	—	—	930	O—H(D) bend.
$\nu_{14}(b_2)$	—	675	675	650	—	—	475	478	O—H(D) asym. wag.

(a) Gillespie and Robinson (1962a).
(b) Giguere and Savoie (1960).
(c) Walrafen and Dodd (1961).
(d) Giguere and Savoie (1963).

9. Infra-red and Raman Spectra

The infra-red and Raman spectra of sulphuric acid, and D_2SO_4, have been investigated by several groups of workers. Much of the earlier work has been discussed by Gillespie and Robinson (1962a) by Giguere and Savoie (1960), and by Walrafen and Dodd (1961). Most of the measurements have been on the liquids but recently Giguere and Savoie (1963) have obtained the infra-red spectra of solid H_2SO_4 and D_2SO_4. They also attempted to measure the infra-red spectra in the gas phase but these measurements were apparently unsuccessful since the spectra obtained were identical with those obtained for the liquids. The generally agreed assignments of the frequencies of the fundamental vibrations of H_2SO_4 and D_2SO_4 are given in Table VII. Giguere and Savoie (1960) and Walrafen and Dodd (1961) have calculated thermodynamic data from the vibrational frequencies.

10. Sulphuric Acid as a Primary Analytical Standard

Kunzler (1953) has proposed the use of 100% sulphuric acid as a primary analytical standard. He concluded that it is much easier, and less time consuming to prepare a precisely accurate sulphuric acid standard than other common standards. He showed that:

(i) by following the change in the freezing point it is possible to adjust the composition to within 0·001% of 100% H_2SO_4;

(ii) constant boiling point sulphuric acid can be prepared with an accuracy of at least 0·01% and the effect of pressure on the composition of the constant boiling mixture is much smaller than it is for constant boiling hydrochloric acid;

(iii) minimum conducting sulphuric acid can be prepared with a composition is within 0·002% of 99·996% H_2SO_4;

(iv) the "water titration" or "fair and foggy" method developed by Brand (1946) in which water or aqueous sulphuric acid is added to oleum until the fuming ceases can be used to prepare acid that has a composition within 0·02% of 100%;

(v) that sulphuric acid solutions can be analysed to within 0·05% by Somiya's (1927) thermometric titration which utilizes the enormous difference between the partial molar heat content of water in oleum and in concentrated aqueous acid.

B. PROPERTIES OF SOLUTIONS

1. Cryoscopic Properties

(a) *Freezing Point Depressions*. Sulphuric acid has a relatively large molal freezing point depression or cryoscopic constant, k, of 6·12 g mole^{-1} kg (Wyatt, 1953; Gillespie, 1956). It has been shown that the contribution of the heat of self-dissociation to the cryoscopic constant is negligible (Gillespie, 1956), so that $k = 6·12$ for the hypothetical undissociated acid as well as for 100% H_2SO_4. The high value for the cryoscopic constant and the convenient freezing point of $10\cdot371°$ make sulphuric acid an ideal solvent for cryoscopy provided that adequate precautions are taken to prevent absorption of water from the atmosphere, and due allowance is made for the solvent self-dissociation. Usually the Beckmann method is used and then the techniques involved are straightforward. Suitable apparatus has been described by several workers (Hammett and Deyrup, 1933; Newman *et al.*, 1949; Gillespie *et al.*, 1950).

Cryoscopic measurements may be used to obtain the value of ν, the number of moles of particles (molecules or ions), produced in solution by one mole of solute and hence to obtain information concerning the modes of ionization of solutes.

In general we have

$$\theta(1+0\cdot002\theta) = k\phi\Sigma m_i \tag{47}$$

where θ is the freezing point depression measured from the freezing-point of hypothetical undissociated sulphuric acid ($10\cdot625°$), k is the cryoscopic constant, Σm_i is the total concentration of all solute species (including the self-dissociation ions and molecules), and ϕ is the molal osmotic coefficient (Bass *et al.*, 1960). In general ϕ is not known and it is necessary to set it equal to unity. Then if m_d is the total concentration of solvent self-dissociation species, if m is the stoichiometric molality of the added solute and if each mole of solute reacts with, and therefore uses up, s moles of solvent, i.e.

$$A + sH_2SO_4 = P + Q + R \tag{48}$$

we have

$$\theta(1-0\cdot002\theta) = k\frac{\nu m}{1-0\cdot098\ ms} + m_d \tag{49}$$

and therefore

$$\nu = \frac{\theta(1+0\cdot002\theta - 0\cdot098\ ms)}{6\cdot12\ m} - \frac{m_d}{m}. \tag{50}$$

The total concentration of self-dissociation species m_d can be calculated for any concentration of added electrolyte using the equilibrium constants K_{ap}, K_{id}, $K_{H_2S_2O_7}$, and K_{H_2O} (Table III), and equations representing the composition and electrical neutrality of the solutions. Values of m_d have been tabulated (Bass *et al.*, 1960) for solutions of a strong base B, a strong acid HA, water, disulphuric acid, and the complex base XOH ionizing according to

$$XOH + 2H_2SO_4 = X^+ + H_3O^+ + HSO_4^-. \tag{51}$$

Similar calculations can be made for more complex electrolytes but it has been shown that for an electrolyte E ionizing according to the general equation

$$E = aH_3O^+ + bX^+ + (a+b)HSO_4^- + cY \tag{52}$$

the concentration of self-dissociation species for a given stoichiometric concentration of added base may be calculated with sufficient accuracy by assuming that the autoprotolysis is independent of the other self-dissociation equilibria and that the concentration of autoprotolysis ions, m_α, is determined only by the concentration of HSO_4^-, while the concentration of ions and molecules resulting from the other self-dissociation processes, m_β, is determined only by the concentration of $H_3O.HSO_4$ (Bass *et al.*, 1960). Values for m_α can then be obtained from the tabulated values for a strong base, and for m_β from the tabulated values for water. These values are given in Table VIII. We then have $m_d = m_\alpha + m_\beta$.

TABLE VIII

Values of m_α and m_β

m^s_{HSO}	m_α	$m^s_{H_3O^+}$	m_β
0·00	0·0263	0·00	0·0160
0·01	0·0191	0·01	0·0081
0·02	0·0142	0·02	0·0041
0·03	0·0110	0·03	0·0030
0·04	0·0088	0·04	0·0020
0·06	0·0063	0·06	0·0014
0·08	0·0045	0·08	0·0009
0·10	0·0036	0·10	0·0009
0·12	0·0028	0·12	0·0006
0·14	0·0023	0·14	0·0006
0·16	0·0017	0·16	0·0004
0·18	0·0012	0·18	0·0004
0·20	0·0010	0·20	0·0003
0·24	0·0003	0·24	0·0002
0·28	0·0001	0·28	0·0000

Considerable controversy arose between early workers because of their lack of understanding of the self-dissociation equilibria of sulphuric acid. The importance of the solvent self-dissociation was first clearly appreciated by Hammett and Deyrup (1933) who established the rather general practice of using as solvent sulphuric acid containing sufficient water to lower the freezing point to about 9·8–10° in order to largely repress the solvent self-dissociation. Then $\Delta\theta$, the freezing point depression measured from the freezing point of the slightly aqueous solvent is given approximately by

$$\Delta\theta = vkm. \tag{53}$$

Small additions of other bases, e.g. $KHSO_4$ may also be used to depress the freezing point of the initial acid. The symbol i, the van't Hoff i-factor, is used by many workers for the approximate value of ν that is given by this equation.

This procedure is not completely satisfactory as the self-dissociation is by no means completely repressed, and some allowance for this should be made, and the presence of a third electrolyte, e.g. $H_3O.HSO_4$ or $KHSO_4$ has been shown to cause complications (Brayford and Wyatt, 1955; Gillespie and Robinson, 1957a). Another type of difficulty arises in the case of solutes that are capable of dehydrating sulphuric acid, e.g. carboxylic acid anhydrides. In slightly aqueous acid, acetic anhydride gives a freezing point depression corresponding to $\nu = 2$ and it might therefore be erroneously concluded that it is simply protonated, i.e.

$$(CH_3CO)_2O + H_2SO_4 = (CH_3CO)_2OH^+ + HSO_4^-. \tag{54}$$

However, in 100% H_2SO_4 the freezing point depression corresponds to $\nu = 4$. This result and the fact that conductivity measurements indicate the formation of one hydrogen sulphate ion show that acetic anhydride is capable of dehydrating sulphuric acid to give the carboxylic acidium ion according to the equation

$$(RCO)_2O + 3H_2SO_4 = 2RCO_2H_2^+ + HSO_4^- + HS_2O_7^-. \tag{55}$$

Leisten (1961, 1964a) has however pointed out how advantage may be taken of differences in the cryoscopic behaviour of a solute in sulphuric acid solvents containing small amounts of water or other electrolytes to obtain more detailed information concerning the ionization of the solute than is provided by measurements in any one of these solvents alone. He has proposed the use of the following cryoscopic mixtures

(i) sulphuric acid containing water, i.e. H_3O^+, HSO_4^-;
(ii) sulphuric acid containing $H_2S_2O_7$, $HS_2O_7^-$;
(iii) sulphuric acid containing $HS_2O_7^-$, HSO_4^-;
(iv) sulphuric acid containing $H_3SO_4^+$, H_3O^+;
(v) sulphuric acid containing $H_3SO_4^+$, $H_2S_2O_7$.

In general the reaction of any solute may be represented by the equation

$$S + nH_2SO_4 \rightarrow aS_1 + bHSO_4^- + cH_3SO_4^+ + dH_2O + eH_2S_2O_7. \tag{56}$$

The resultant increase or decrease in the total number of moles of particles in solution as a consequence of adding one mole of H_2O, $H_2S_2O_7$, HSO_4^- or $H_3SO_4^+$ is given in Table IX. A given solute will have a different cryoscopic behaviour in at least three of the cryoscopic mixtures and since either b or c and either d or e must be zero the determination of the cryoscopic behaviour of the solute in three appropriate solvents (cryoscopic mixtures) will enable a and either b or c and either d or e to be determined. Almost always this allows the mode of ionization of the solute to be unambiguously determined.

(b) *Osmotic Coefficients.* Treffers and Hammett (1937) first suggested that interionic forces are very small in sulphuric acid because solutions of electro-

TABLE IX

Number of Moles of Particles Resulting from Various Solutes in Some Cryoscopic Solvent Mixtures

Solute	(i)	(ii)	(iii)	(iv)	(v)
H_2O	2	-1	0	0	-1
HSO_4^-	1	0	1	-1	-1
$H_2S_2O_7$	-2	1	0	0	1
$H_3SO_4^+$	-1	0	-1	1	1

lytes appear to behave ideally. Gillespie *et al.* (1950) suggested that this might be due to a very high dielectric constant, and they showed that the apparent deviations from ideality that did occur could plausibly be attributed

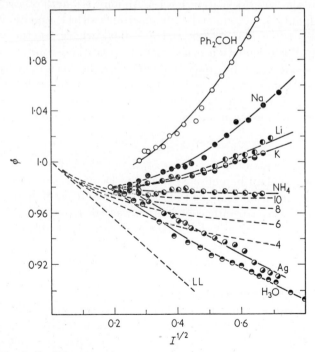

FIG. 3. Osmotic Coefficients. – – – –, calculated curves $(1+\phi^{el})$, with the values of $\mathring{a}$ indicated. LL = Debye-Hückel limiting law.

to ionic solvation. They attempted to make some allowance for this by a somewhat arbitrary assignment of solvation numbers. However, measurements of the dielectric constant of sulphuric acid (Section IIA, 6), showed that although it is high it is not so high that interionic forces may be completely ignored. Therefore in order to see if the effects of interionic forces could be detected, and to generally investigate deviations from ideal behaviour, some careful measurements of the freezing points of solutions of some completely ionized metal hydrogen sulphates were made by Bass and Gillespie (1960), using the method of equilibrium cryoscopy in which they determined the composition of the equilibrium solution by means of very accurate conductivity measurements. Molal osmotic coefficients ϕ were calculated from the results by means of equation (47). Figure 3 shows the osmotic coefficients plotted against the square root of the ionic strength of the solutions, $I^{\frac{1}{2}}$. The interpretation of these curves is not quite straightforward as they do not refer to solutions of single electrolytes but to mixtures of an electrolyte with the molecules and ions remaining from the solvent self-dissociation. The concentrations of the self-dissociation ions are negligibly small at the higher concentrations of electrolyte but become of increasing importance at lower concentrations until at infinite dilution the solution contains only the self-dissociation species. An ionic strength of less than that of 100% sulphuric acid cannot be obtained and all the osmotic coefficient curves terminate at $I^{\frac{1}{2}} = 0.0189$ and $\phi = 0.98$, which are the values for 100% H_2SO_4. For simplicity it is necessary to treat these solutions as if they contained a single electrolyte only, and agreement between the experimental and theoretical curves cannot be expected to be very good at low electrolyte concentrations. The variation of the osmotic coefficient with concentration may be accounted for by means of an equation of the form

$$\phi = 1 + \phi^{\text{el}} + b\Sigma m_i \qquad (57)$$

where ϕ^{el} is the contribution of electrostatic interionic forces to the osmotic coefficient, which may be obtained from the Debye-Huckel theory, b is an arbitrary parameter, and Σm_i is the total concentration of ionic species in the solution. The electrostatic contribution was calculated using a dielectric constant of 120 and various values of the parameter $\mathring{a}$, the distance of closest approach of cation and anion. The values of $\mathring{a}$ and b that give the best fit to the observed osmotic coefficient curve for each electrolyte are given in Table X.

Except for $H_3O.HSO_4$ and $AgHSO_4$ the values of $\mathring{a}$ are all of the order of 10Å which is considerably larger than the values generally obtained for electrolytes in water. Such a value, however, is not unreasonable if it is assumed, following Wicke and Eigen (1953), that for non-associated electrolytes there is always at least one solvent molecule between oppositely charged ions when they collide. Values of approximately 10Å may indeed be calculated on this basis from crystal radii and estimated values of the radii of a sulphuric acid molecule and a hydrogen sulphate ion (Bass et al., 1960).

The calculated osmotic coefficient curve for $\mathring{a} = 10$ and $b = 0$ is given in Fig. 3. For the concentrations that are accessible in sulphuric acid solutions the electrostatic contribution to the osmotic coefficient, although not negli-

TABLE X

$\mathring{a}$ and b Parameters and Solvation Numbers Calculated from Cryoscopic Measurements

| Cation | $\mathring{a}$ | b | Solvation Numbers | | |
			(a)	(b)	(c)
Ba^{2+}	10	0·32	11·5	6·5	3·0
Na^+	10	0·14	3·8	3·0	2·0
Li^+	10	0·08	2·6	2·3	3·4
K^+	10	0·07	2·4	2·1	0·6
NH_4^+	0	0·015	1·2	1·2	0·2
Ag^+	2	0	—	—	—
H_3O^+	2	0	—	—	4·0
$Ag^+(K_b = 1)$	10	0·07	2·4	2·1	—
$H_3O^+(K_b = 1)$	10	0·06	2·1	1·8	4·0
Me_2COH^+	—	0·025	1·5	1·0	—
$MePhCOH^+$	—	0·14	3·8	1·4	—
Ph_2COH^+	—	0·31	7·2	1·3	—
$(p\text{-}MeC_6H_4)_2COH^+$	—	0·34	7·8	1·1	—
$(p\text{-}ClC_6H_4)_2COH^+$	—	0·15	4·0	0·5	—
$PhNH_3^+$	—	0·025	1·5	0·8	—
$Ph_2NH_2^+$	—	0·14	3·8	0·6	—
Ph_3NH^+	—	0·31	7·2	0·6	—

(a) Calculated from equation (58).
(b) Calculated from equation (59).
(c) Aqueous solutions (Gluekauf, 1955).

gible, is almost constant and therefore differences between different electrolytes result almost entirely from differences in their interaction with the solvent. This is a consequence of the rather high dielectric constant and of the relatively large sizes of the sulphuric acid molecule and of the hydrogen sulphate ion.

The interpretation of the low osmotic coefficients of solutions of $AgHSO_4$ and $H_3O.HSO_4$ is not quite certain. It is possible that $AgHSO_4$ and $H_3O.HSO_4$

are incompletely dissociated in dilute solution in sulphuric acid. In the former case there could be some covalent contribution to the bonding between the silver and the hydrogen sulphate and in the latter there could be strong hydrogen bonding between an H_3O^+ and an HSO_4^- ion, as appears to be indicated by detailed investigation of the vibrational spectra of solutions of water in sulphuric acid (E. A. Robinson, unpublished results). In fact if a dissociation constant of the order of unity is assumed for both of these electrolytes then their osmotic coefficient curves are found to closely resemble those of the other electrolytes studied (Fig. 3).

(c) *Ion Solvation*. Robinson and Stokes (1948) have given a quantitative treatment of the activity coefficients of aqueous electrolyte solutions which allows for ionic solvation and assumes that the solvated ions and solvent molecules form an ideal solution (i.e. obey Raoult's Law). By applying their theory to sulphuric acid solutions Bass et al. (1960) showed that the parameter b is related to the solvation number s of an electrolyte by the expression

$$b = (2s - \nu)/40 \cdot 8. \tag{58}$$

Values of s calculated from this equation are given in Table X.

Gluekauf (1955) has pointed out that this treatment ignores the entropy of mixing of the solvent molecules and the solvated ions, which may have very different sizes. He showed how this additional effect could be taken into account, and he obtained solvation numbers for aqueous electrolytes which were often smaller, and in general varied with ion size in a more reasonable manner than the values obtained by Robinson and Stokes. Following Gluekauf's treatment it may be shown that the parameter b for sulphuric acid solutions is given by the expression

$$b = \frac{(r+s)^2}{40 \cdot 8} - \frac{r\nu}{20 \cdot 4} \tag{59}$$

where r is the ratio of the apparent molar volume of the unsolvated electrolyte to the molar volume of solvent. The values of the solvation numbers given by this equation are also given in Table X.

Since all the solutes studied have the hydrogen sulphate ion as a common anion the solvation numbers reflect the relative solvation numbers of the cations, and if, in view of the large size of the hydrogen sulphate ion, it is assumed that it is not solvated, then these values may be regarded as the solvation numbers of the cations.

Equation (59) gives a smaller and more reasonable solvation number for the highly solvated, and therefore large, barium ion, and also for the large organic cations than does equation (58). On the whole the solvation numbers obtained by the Gluekauf treatment are of reasonable magnitude for primary solvation numbers and show roughly the expected variation with ion size. Lithium appears to be anomalous in that its solvation number is less than that of sodium. This has been attributed to the fact that the co-ordination number of lithium ion for sulphuric acid molecules is only three while that of sodium is four (Gillespie and Oubridge, 1956; Bass *et al.*, 1960). Solvation numbers in sulphuric acid appear to be rather larger than in aqueous solution (Table X) and this is consistent with the probable greater polarity of the sulphuric acid molecule as compared with the water molecule.

(d) *Non-electrolytes.* As 2,4,6-trinitrotoluene was found to give a freezing point depression in slightly aqueous sulphuric acid somewhat greater than that expected for a non-electrolyte it was originally concluded that it was a weak base (Gillespie, 1950b). However, Brand *et al.* (1952) could find no spectrophotometric evidence for the ionization of this compound. Brayford and Wyatt (1955) have subsequently shown that picric acid, trinitrobenzene and trinitrotoluene all give greater than expected freezing point depressions for a non-electrolyte in sulphuric acid containing a little water but in sulphuric acid containing a small amount of $KHSO_4$ or $H_2S_2O_7$ the observed depressions are somewhat smaller than expected for a non-electrolyte. These authors suggest that these solutes are in fact non-electrolytes and that water "salts-out" the non-electrolyte whereas $KHSO_4$ and $H_2S_2O_7$ "salt-in" the non-electrolyte. This would have the consequence that the solubility of the non-electrolyte would be increased in the presence of $KHSO_4$ or $H_2S_2O_7$ but decreased in the presence of water. This conclusion has been verified experimentally (Kirkbride and Wyatt, 1958) although the increase in solubility produced by $KHSO_4$ is very small.

The unionized portion of weak bases similarly give an anomalously high freezing point depression in slightly aqueous solution. Thus the basicity of nitrobenzene obtained from cryoscopic measurements in slightly aqueous acid (Gillespie, 1950b) was higher than that obtained by conductimetric measurements (Gillespie and Solomons, 1957) but if 100% acid is used for the cryoscopic measurements good agreement is obtained with the conductimetric data (Gillespie and Robinson, 1957a).

2. *Densities and Apparent Molar Volumes*

The densities of solutions of a large number of solutes have been measured at 25° (Flowers *et al.*, 1960a; Gillespie and Wasif, 1953b). Solutions of $NaHSO_4$ and $KHSO_4$ have also been studied at 10° and 40°. Some additional information on ion-solvent interactions in sulphuric acid can be obtained from the apparent molar volumes of electrolytes, ϕ_v, which may be calculated from the densities of their solutions. If it is assumed that the molar volume of the hydrogen sulphate ion is 54 cm³ (equal to that of sulphuric acid), this value may be subtracted from the apparent molar volume of a fully ionized hydrogen sulphate to give the apparent molar volume of the cation, ϕ_v^+. If this value is then compared with the volume of the cation calculated from its crystallographic radius, V^+, the difference, δV, indicates the contraction produced in the solvent by the cation. It is reasonable to assume that this contraction is proportional to the extent of ion–solvent interaction or solvation. Then taking the solvation number for a given ion, e.g. Na^+, from cryoscopic measurements, solvation numbers, s, for the other cations can be obtained by simple proportion. The solvation numbers obtained in this way agree surprisingly well with those obtained from cryoscopy; they are presumably therefore also a measure of primary solvation.

The apparent molar volumes of the cations may be compared with their partial molar volumes in aqueous solution (Couture and Laidler, 1956) which are also given in Table XI. The close similarity in the values for univalent ions in the two solvents is remarkable.

TABLE XI

Apparent Molar Volumes and Solvation Numbers of Cations in Solutions of Their Hydrogen Sulphates

Cation	ϕ_v (cm³ mole⁻¹)	ϕ_v^+ (cm³ mole⁻¹)	$\overline{V}_{H_2O}^+$ (cm³ mole⁻¹)	r (Å)	V^+ (cm³ mole⁻¹)	δV (cm³ mole⁻¹)	s	s_{cyros}
Li	47	−7	−7·0	0·78	1·2	−8	2	2·3
Na	46	−8	−7·5	0·98	2·4	−10	3	3·0
K	53	−1	1·7	1·33	5·9	−7	2	2·1
Rb	59	+5	7·7	1·49	8·3	−3	1	—
Cs	68	+14	15·1	1·65	11·3	+3	0	—
Ag	53	−1	−7·0	1·13	3·6	−5	1·5	2·1
Tl	62	8	7·7	1·49	8·3	0	0	—
NH₄	59	5	—	1·48	8·2	−3	1	1·2
H₃O	61	7	12·0	1·48	8·2	−1	0·3	1·8
Ca	84	−24	−29·7	1·06	3·0	−27	8	—
Sr	87	−21	−30·2	1·27	5·8	−27	8	—
Ba	96	−12	−24·3	1·43	7·4	−19	5	6·5

Couture and Laidler (1956) showed that the partial molar volumes of ions in aqueous solution are proportional to the charge, z, and the cube of the ionic radius, r^3. Their results fit the relationship

$$\overline{V}^+ = 14 + 5 \cdot 6 r^3 - 26z. \tag{60}$$

A similar relationship, namely,

$$\phi_v^+ = 6 + 5 \cdot 6 r^3 - 18z \tag{61}$$

appears to hold for the apparent molar volumes of cations in sulphuric acid. The physical significance of these empirical relationships is not clear.

3. Viscosities

Viscosities of some electrolyte solutions in sulphuric acid are shown in

Fig. 4. Although sulphuric acid itself has a very high viscosity some electrolytes further increase the viscosity and, in fact, have a considerably greater

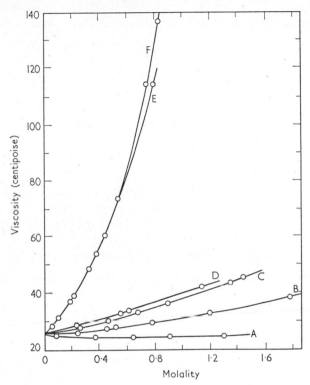

FIG. 4. Viscosities of some electrolyte solutions at 25°C: A, NH_4HSO_4; B, $KHSO_4$; C, $NaHSO_4$; D, $LiHSO_4$; E, $Ba(HSO_4)_2$; F, $Sr(HSO_4)_2$.

effect than do electrolytes in water. This again points to considerable ion–solvent interactions. The relative viscosities of electrolyte solutions may be described by an equation of the form (Jones and Dole, 1929)

$$\eta_r = \frac{\eta}{\eta_0} = 1 + Ac^{\frac{1}{2}} + Bc + Cc^2; \qquad (62)$$

the term $Ac^{\frac{1}{2}}$ is almost negligible in sulphuric acid and the viscosities are a very nearly linear function of the molar concentration up to approximately 0·4 molar in the case of uni-univalent electrolytes and 0·2 molar in the case of uni-divalent electrolytes. Values of the parameter B are given in Table XII.

If it is assumed that the hydrogen sulphate ion has a negligible effect on the viscosity these values can be attributed to the cations. It is generally believed (Gurney, 1953) that viscosity B-values are a measure of ion-solvent interaction and the values given in Table XII are certainly in the order that would be expected on this basis. It is interesting that the ammonium ion causes a small lowering of the viscosity of sulphuric acid in the same way that it causes a small lowering of the viscosity of water (Gurney, 1953). The hydronium ion decreases the viscosity of sulphuric acid quite appreciably while it has the opposite effect on the viscosity of water. This decrease in the viscosity

TABLE XII

Viscosity B-Values

	H_2SO_4	H_2O
H_3O^+	$-0\cdot4$	$+0\cdot07$
NH_4^+	$-0\cdot1$	$-0\cdot01$
K^+	$+0\cdot2$	$-0\cdot007$
Na^+	$+0\cdot8$	$+0\cdot09$
Li^+	$+1\cdot0$	$+0\cdot15$
Ba^{++}	$+4\cdot4$	$+0\cdot22$

due to the H_3O^+ ion could be regarded as evidence that the hydronium ion is a "structure-breaking" ion in sulphuric acid. It is apparently not strongly solvated as it is in water.

4. Electrical Conductivities

(a) *Proton-transfer Conduction by $H_3SO_4^+$ and HSO_4^-*. Some measurements of the specific conductivities of solutions in sulphuric acid were made by early workers (Oddo and Scandola, 1908; Hantzsch, 1907; Bergius, 1910; Kendall *et al.*, 1921), but there were considerable differences between their results and between the conclusions drawn from them, partly because of lack of understanding of the solvent self-dissociation and the contribution that it makes to the conductivities of solutions. It is only relatively recently that a detailed and precise study of the conductivities of electrolyte solutions in sulphuric acid has been made. The specific conductivities of the alkali metal hydrogen sulphates and some other electrolytes are summarized in Table XIII (Bass *et al.*, 1960). At low concentrations all these hydrogen sulphates have very similar specific conductivities which suggests that in these solutions the HSO_4^- carries most of the current. This was confirmed by the measurement of the transport numbers of metal cations in solutions of their hydrogen sulphates in sulphuric acid (Gillespie and Wasif, 1953a). The results of these measurements are summarized in Table XIV; they show that in a solution of a metal hydrogen sulphate only a few percent of the current is carried by the cation. That the $H_3SO_4^+$ ion has an abnormally high mobility is confirmed by the results of conductimetric acid–base titrations in sulphuric acid

TABLE XIII

Specific Conductivities of Some Electrolytes at 25°C

c(moles litre^{-1})	0·01	0·02	0·04	0·06	0·10	0·20	0·30	0·40	0·50	0·60	0·70	0·80
LiHSO$_4$	1·050	1·068	1·145	1·252	1·520	2·23	2·86	3·39	3·85	4·23	4·56	4·84
NaHSO$_4$	1·051	1·068	1·147	1·258	1·536	2·26	2·92	3·49	3·99	4·77	4·79	5·12
KHSO$_4$	1·052	1·073	1·156	1·274	1·558	2·33	3·04	3·68	4·23	4·72	5·16	5·56
RbHSO$_4$	1·052	1·08	1·17	1·29	1·61	2·40	3·14	3·77	4·40	4·84	5·37	—
CsHSO$_4$	1·052	1·08	1·17	1·29	1·61	2·41	3·15	3·79	4·47	5·00	5·51	—
AgHSO$_4$	1·053	1·075	1·16	1·26	1·58	2·29	3·00	3·62	4·15	4·62	5·07	5·48
TlHSO$_4$	1·053	1·08	1·17	1·29	1·61	2·45	3·19	3·87	4·48	5·01	5·52	—
NH$_4$HSO$_4$	1·053	1·075	1·161	1·278	1·590	2·38	3·11	3·79	4·39	4·94	5·44	—
H$_3$O.HSO$_4$	1·046	1·061	1·130	1·249	1·530	2·284	2·994	3·60	4·15	4·63	5·07	5·44
H$_2$S$_2$O$_7$	1·054	1·068	1·114	1·169	1·281	1·553	1·788	1·991	2·17	2·33	2·47	—
HB(HSO$_4$)$_4$	1·051	1·073	1·163	1·29	1·61	2·39	3·12	3·60	3·99	4·23	4·32	—
[(CH$_3$)$_2$COH]HSO$_4$	1·052	1·073	1·153	1·270	1·56	2·35	3·11	3·80	4·46	5·01	—	—
(CH$_3$.COH.C$_6$H$_5$)HSO$_4$	1·052	1·073	1·153	1·270	1·56	2·35	3·11	3·75	4·32	4·79	—	—
[(C$_6$H$_5$)$_2$COH]HSO$_4$	1·052	1·073	1·153	1·270	1·56	2·34	3·01	3·58	4·04	4·42	4·72	—
[(p-CH$_3$.C$_6$H$_4$)$_2$COH]HSO$_4$	1·052	1·073	1·153	1·270	1·55	2·29	2·47	3·48	3·88	4·23	4·45	—
[(p-Cl.C$_6$H$_4$)$_2$COH]HSO$_4$	1·052	1·073	1·153	1·270	1·56	2·30	2·48	3·49	3·88	—	—	—

(Flowers *et al.*, 1960b; Hall and Robinson, 1964); addition of $KHSO_4$ to a solution of an acid, e.g. $HB(HSO_4)_4$ causes a marked decrease in the conductivity as the highly mobile $H_3SO_4^+$ ion is replaced by the relatively poorly conducting K^+ ion.

TABLE XIV

Apparent Transport Numbers of Some Ions in Sulphuric Acid (25°C)

Ion	m_{MHSO_4}	t_+	Ion	$m_{M(HSO_4)_2}$	t_+
Ag^+	0·2490	0·026	Ba^{2+}	0·17	0·009
	0·31	0·022		0·23	0·010
K^+	0·62	0·030		0·31	0·008
	1·23	0·025		0·80	0·004
Na^+	0·79	0·021	Sr^{2+}	0·21	0·007
Li^+	0·56	0·013		0·82	0·003

Ionic mobilities generally have rather small values in sulphuric acid because of its high viscosity. The $H_3SO_4^+$ and HSO_4^- ions, however, have mobilities that are greater than any other ions in sulphuric acid and most ions in water;

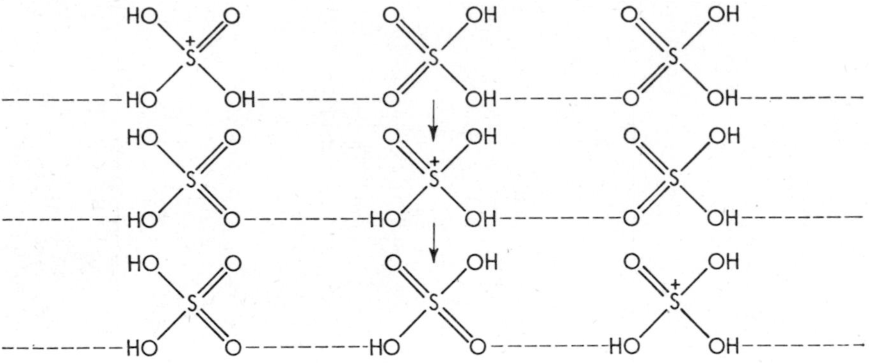

FIG. 5. Proton transfer conduction of the $H_3SO_4^+$ ion in sulphuric acid.

they are of the same order of magnitude as the abnormally conducting H_3O^+ and OH^- ions in water. The mobilities of the $H_3SO_4^+$ and HSO_4^- ions are unaffected by the high viscosity of the solvent because they conduct by a proton-transfer mechanism quite analogous to that which is generally accepted to account for the abnormally high mobilities of the H_3O^+ and OH^- ions in water. The mechanism is illustrated very diagrammatically for $H_3SO_4^+$ ions in Fig. 5. Successive transfers of protons along hydrogen bonds result in an effective movement of $H_3SO_4^+$ ions through the solution without the need for actual movement of individual ions. The details of this mechanism, and in particular the nature of the rate-determining step, are still under discussion (Greenwood and Thompson, 1959; Flowers *et al.*, 1960c). In general there must be a certain amount of molecular movement or re-orientation in order that suitable hydrogen-bonds may be formed to allow proton transfer to take place in the required direction. Thus hydrogen-bond

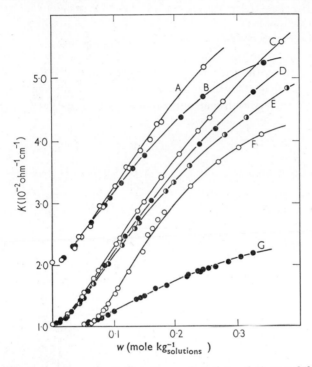

FIG. 6. Specific conductivities of some electrolyte solutions at 25°.

A, Acetone
B, Di-*p*-tolyl ketone ⎬displaced vertically by 1·0 (10^{-2} ohm^{-1} cm^{-1}) unit.
C, $CsHSO_4$.
D, $KHSO_4$.
E, $NaHSO_4$.
F, $HB(HSO_4)_4$ ⎬displaced horizontally by 0·05 w unit.
G, $H_2S_2O_7$

formation rather than proton transfer could be the rate-determining stage of the process.

(b) *Effect of Ion-solvent Interaction on the Mobility of HSO_4^-.* Although all simple bases have very similar conductivities at low concentrations differences become increasingly apparent at higher concentrations. The specific conductivities of some univalent metal hydrogen sulphates are shown in Fig. 6. All the curves are of the same general shape, commencing convex to the concentration axis as a result of repression of the self-dissociation of the solvent and then becoming concave to the concentration axis at relatively high concentrations. This shows that the mobility of the hydrogen sulphate ion apparently decreases with increasing concentration. Moreover it decreases to different extents in different metal hydrogen sulphate solutions. These differences between the conductivities of different electrolytes are much too great to be attributed to the very small differences in the mobilities of the cations and it was therefore concluded that the cations can have specific effects on the mobility of the hydrogen sulphate ion (Gillespie and Wasif, 1953c; Flowers *et al.*, 1960c).

After making allowance for the small contribution of the metal ions to the conductivity, values for the equivalent conductance or mobility of the hydrogen sulphate ion (λ_-) may be calculated from the specific conductivities of solutions of metal hydrogen sulphates and the values are given in Table XV.

TABLE XV

Values for the Mobility of the HSO_4^- Ion (λ_-) in Solutions of Hydrogen Sulphates

| | λ_- | | | | | |
| | Cation | | | | | |
m	Li^+	Na^+	K^+	Rb^+	Cs^+	NH_4^+
0·000	151·2	151·2	151·2	151·2	151·6	151·2
0·010	148·5	149·0	149·0	—	—	149·0
0·020	143·0	143·6	144·0	—	—	144·8
0·040	129·9	130·2	131·7	135·5	135·5	132·8
0·060	118·3	119·4	121·5	125·3	125·5	122·3
0·120	98·5	99·8	102·7	106·9	109·2	104·6
0·180	86·2	87·7	91·4	96·1	98·9	93·7
0·240	76·7	79·3	83·2	89·0	91·5	86·1

The order of decreasing conductance at any concentration is exactly the order that would be expected for increasing solvation of the cation (i.e. it is the order of decreasing ionic radius). It seems reasonable to suppose therefore that solvent molecules that are involved in solvating the cation cannot take part in the proton-transfer conduction process with the same ease as the "free" solvent molecules. Thus the mobility of the hydrogen sulphate ion decreases with increasing concentration of alkali metal hydrogen sulphate because of interaction of the cations with the solvent, and the magnitude of the decrease is related to the extent of this ion–solvent interaction. The lithium ion appears to have a greater interaction with the solvent than the sodium ion although cryoscopic measurements give a smaller solvation number for Li^+ than Na^+. This suggests that the ion–solvent interaction measured by conductivity measurements is not confined to the first solvation layer but is a more general interaction involving a number of layers of solvent around the ion, i.e. secondary solvation, whereas cryoscopic measurements give information on primary solvation. It may be noted that the conductivities of solutions of $H_3O.HSO_4$ and $Ag.HSO_4$ are normal and show no sign of the incomplete dissociation indicated by cryscopic measurements. There is at present no really satisfactory explanation for this. It is possible that water is fully ionized as $H_3O^+.HSO_4^-$ but that the ion-pairs are incompletely dissociated. Any incomplete dissociation would not affect the conductance of the solution if the life-time of the ion-pair were shorter than the average time between successive proton transfers.

(c) *Contribution of Asymmetric Autoprotolyses to the Conductance.* Wyatt (1961) has pointed out that the equivalent conductance of the hydrogen sulphate ion shows an unexpectedly large dependence on concentration, particularly for concentrations up to about 0·1 molal, since the equivalent conductance of HCl in water varies by only about 2% in the same concentration range. He therefore made the important suggestion that there may be a contribution to the conductance from asymmetric dissociation of the solvent in the applied field. He suggests that there is a slight bias towards the movement of protons from neutral molecules to their neutral neighbours (i.e. towards dissociation) in the direction of the field and that this contributes to the conductance. If a is the distance to which the autoprotolysis ions have to approach by a diffusion controlled process before neutralization can occur within a hydrogen-bonded complex, then in the self-dissociation or autoprotolysis it is the process of separating the charges by the distance a during the production of the autoprotolysis ions that gives the special contribution to the conductance. Wyatt derived the following expression for the contribution of asymmetric autoprotolysis to the conductance for a solvent HA

$$k_D = 3{\cdot}733 \times 10^{-11} k_R [H_2A^+][A^-] \left(\frac{\phi a^2}{T}\right) \tag{63}$$

where k_R is the rate of recombination of the autoprotolysis ions, and ϕ is the effective internal field for an external applied field of 1 V cm^{-1}. It is seen that the magnitude of the effect depends on the autoprotolysis constant, which is relatively large for sulphuric acid, and although the internal field, ϕ, and k_R are not known with certainty Wyatt showed that asymmetric solvent dissociation might reasonably contribute as much as 30% of the conductance of the 100% acid. Because of the much smaller autoprotolysis constant of water asymmetric solvent dissociation could only contribute negligibly to its conductance. If κ' is the specific conductivity of a solution of a metal hydrogen sulphate from which the small contribution of ions other than $H_3SO_4^+$ and HSO_4^- has been subtracted then

$$10^3 \kappa' = \rho \lambda_- (\mu m_+ + m_-) + 10^3 \kappa_D \tag{64}$$

where m_+ and m_- are the molalities of $H_3SO_4^+$ and HSO_4^- respectively, λ_- is the mobility of HSO_4^-, μ is the ratio of the mobilities of the $H_3SO_4^+$ and HSO_4^- ions, ρ the density of the solution, and κ_D the contribution due to asymmetric autoprotolysis. If λ_- and μ are constant then a plot of $10^3 \kappa'$ against $\mu m_+ + m_-$ should be a straight line with an intercept equal to κ_D.

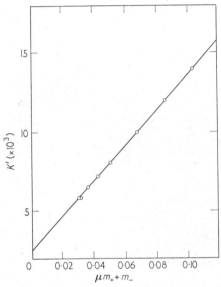

FIG. 7. Plot of $10^3 \kappa'$ (KHSO$_4$) against $\mu m_+ + m_-$ for the determination of the contribution of asymmetric dissociation to the conductivity of sulphuric acid.

From the position of the minimum conductivity in the H_2O–SO_3 system in the vicinity of 100% H_2SO_4 it can be deduced that $\mu = 1.5$ (Gillespie and Robinson, 1964). Using this value and values of m_+ and m_- calculated from the solvent self-dissociation constants plots of $10^3 \kappa$ against $\mu m_+ + m_-$ for various metal hydrogen sulphates were found to be straight lines with intercepts that gave $\kappa_D = 0.38 \times 10^{-2}$ and slopes that gave $\lambda_- = 166$ at 25° (Fig. 7). Thus the asymmetric dissociation does in fact contribute about 36% of the observed conductivity of the acid at 25° and λ_- remains satisfactorily constant at least up to 0.1 m.

(d) *Determination of γ.* That the mobilities of the $H_3SO_4^+$ and HSO_4^- ions are very much higher than those of other ions has the useful practical consequence that the conductivities of solutions of acids and bases in sulphuric acid are determined almost entirely by the concentrations of $H_3SO_4^+$ and/or HSO_4^- respectively. Consequently, γ, the number of moles of hydrogen sulphate ions, or the number of moles of sulphuric acidium ions, produced by one mole of an electrolyte can be obtained from the conductivities of solutions of any acid or base. It might be expected that at a given electrolyte

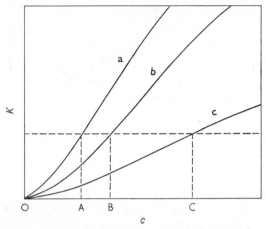

FIG. 8. Determination of γ from conductivity measurements. (a) Strong electrolyte, $\gamma > 1$; (b) standard strong electrolyte $\gamma = 1$ (e.g. $KHSO_4$); (c) weak electrolyte $\gamma < 1$.

concentration, the conductivity of a dihydrogen sulphate would be approximately twice that of a monohydrogen sulphate, but at low concentrations this is not the case because of the different extent to which the two

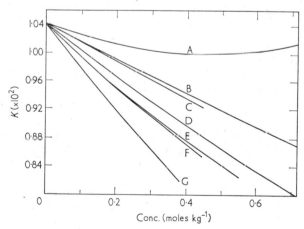

FIG. 9. Specific conductivities of solutions of non-electrolytes in H_2SO_4 at 25°: A, $MeSO_2F$; B, $MeSO_2Cl$; C, SO_2Cl_2; D, $EtSO_2Cl$; E, Ph_2SO_2; F, o-dinitrobenzene; G, 1 : 3 : 5 trinitrobenzene.

electrolytes repress the solvent autoprotolysis. However by comparing the concentration of a standard monohydrogen sulphate such as $KHSO_4$ needed to produce a given conductivity with the concentration of any other

6

electrolyte giving the *same* conductivity, the value of γ for the electrolyte may be obtained directly since the extent of repression of the autoprotolysis is the same for the two solutions that are compared. Figure 8 illustrates the application of this method for both a strong and a weak electrolyte. For the strong electrolyte $\gamma = OB/OA$ and for the weak electrolyte $\gamma = OB/OC$.

Recently Liler (1962) has attempted to allow for the effect on the conductivity of the unionized portion of a weak electrolyte since in general non-electrolytes reduce the conductivity of sulphuric acid. It is difficult to know how such a correction should be best made, however Liler was successful in obtaining values for the basic ionization constants of nitrocompounds which are in rather better agreement with those obtained from cryoscopy than were the earlier results of Gillespie and Solomons (1957).

(e) *Non-Electrolytes.* The conductivities of solutions of non-electrolytes are lower than that of the solvent itself (Fig. 9). This may be attributed to a decrease in the mobilities of the $H_3SO_4^+$ and HSO_4^- ions caused by the non-electrolyte and/or to a reduction in the concentrations of the autoprotolysis ions. A decrease in the mobilities of the characteristic solvent ions could be attributed to strong hydrogen bonding interactions between solute and solvent molecules which would hinder the orientation of the latter and hence decrease their effectiveness in the proton-transfer conduction process. A decrease in the concentrations of the autoprotolysis ions would result from a reduction in the concentration of "free" sulphuric acid as a consequence of solvent molecules removed into the solvation shell of solute molecules. For solutions of aromatic polynitro compounds it has been assumed that the decrease in conductivity is entirely due to the reduction in the concentration of the autoprotolysis ions and solvation numbers were thereby obtained. It was found, to a good approximation, that each nitro group is apparently solvated with one sulphuric acid molecule (Gillespie and Solomons, 1957). Recent measurements by Liler (1962) on the conductivities of $KHSO_4$ in H_2SO_4–SO_2Cl_2 mixtures have shown that sulphuryl chloride has a considerably greater effect on the conductivity of 100% H_2SO_4 than it does on solutions of $KHSO_4$ in H_2SO_4. It must be concluded therefore that the non-electrolyte sulphuryl chloride affects the concentrations of the autoprotolysis ions considerably more than it affects their mobilities, thus providing some support for the assumption used in interpreting the results for polynitro compounds. However this very simple approach does not appear to be entirely substantiated by recent measurements of the conductivities of solutions of some alkyl sulphonyl chlorides and fluorides. The conductivities of solutions of some sulphonyl compounds in sulphuric acid are given in Fig. 9. Despite the fact that $MeSO_2F$ is an intrinsically weaker base than $MeSO_2Cl$ (Hall and Robinson, 1964) it decreases the conductivity of sulphuric acid less than any other sulphonyl halide, at low concentrations, while at relatively high concentrations it actually increases the conductivity, which eventually rises

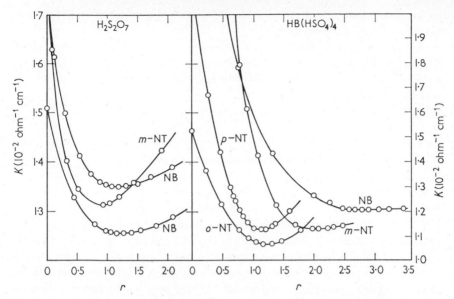

FIG. 10. Conductimetric titrations of weak bases with the acids $H_2S_2O_7$ and $HB(HSO_4)_4$. NB, nitrobenzene; o–NT, o-nitrotoluene; m–NT, m-nitrotoluene; p–NT, p-nitrotoluene.

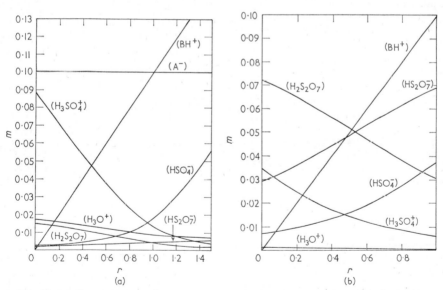

FIG. 11. (a) Concentrations of species in a strong acid–strong base reaction at 25° ($m^i_{HA} = 0.1$). (b) Concentrations of species in a disulphuric acid–strong base reaction at 25° ($m^i_{H_2S_2O_7} = 0.1$).

to a value greater than that for the solvent. These observations have not been satisfactorily explained.

(f) *Conductimetric Acid–Base Titrations:* (i) *Simple Bases.* Acid–base neutralization reactions can be carried out in sulphuric acid as in any other amphoteric solvent. The neutralization reaction is simply the reverse of the solvent autoprotolysis, i.e.

$$H_3SO_4^+ + HSO_4^- = 2H_2SO_4. \tag{65}$$

Since the ions $H_3SO_4^+$ and HSO_4^- have very much higher mobilities than any other ions neutralization reactions are conveniently followed by measuring the electrical conductivity of a solution. This decreases as base is added to acid and the highly conducting $H_3SO_4^+$ ion is removed by neutralization with HSO_4^-, passes through a minimum and then increases again as excess HSO_4^- ion is added to the solution (Fig. 10). The position of minimum conductivity depends on the dissociation constants of the acid and base, K_a and K_b, respectively, and if one dissociation constant is known it is possible to calculate the other from the experimentally determined position of minimum conductivity. A general treatment of the variation of the electrical conductivity during an acid–base reaction is possible and several special bases have been discussed (Flowers *et al.*, 1963). This treatment did not take into account asymmetric autoprotolysis of the solvent but this would affect only the magnitude and not the position of the conductivity minimum in an acid–base titration. The position of minimum conductivity may be described in terms of the ratio, $r = n_b/n_a^i$, of the number of moles of added base, n_b, to the initial number of moles of acid, n_a^i. Figure 11 shows how the concentrations of all the species in reactions of the strong acid HA and the acid $H_2S_2O_7$, respectively, with a strong base B vary with r for an initial concentration of acid m_{HA}^i or $m_{H_2S_2O_7}^i = 0.1$ molal. For a base–HA reaction:

$$r_{\min} = \left(\frac{1+0.018}{K_b}\right)\left[\left(\frac{1+0.013}{K_a}\right)^{-1} + \frac{0.0007}{m_a^i}\right]. \tag{66}$$

For a base–$H_2S_2O_7$ reaction:

$$r_{\min} = 0.56\left(1 + \frac{0.018}{K_b}\right). \tag{67}$$

Values of $r_{\min}$ for various values of K_a and K_b are given in Table XVI.

(ii) *Complex Bases.* For a simple base such as $KHSO_4$ added to an initially 0.1 M solution of $H_2S_2O_7$ the conductivity minimum occurs at $r = 0.56$, but in the case of a complex base, e.g. $Ph_3C.OH$ added to an initially 0.1 M solution of $H_2S_2O_7$ the minimum would be expected to occur at $r = 0.56/1+0.56) = 0.36$, since each molecule of $Ph_3C.OH$ ionizes to give a water molecule which reacts with a molecule of $H_2S_2O_7$ in addition to giving a triphenyl carbonium ion.

Nitric acid and mesitoic acid would be expected to behave similarly. In the case of N_2O_5 each molecule ionizes to give two nitronium ions as well as a molecule of water. In this case the conductivity minimum would be predicted at $r = \dfrac{0 \cdot 28}{1 + 0 \cdot 28} = 0 \cdot 22$.

TABLE XVI

Calculated Conductivity Minima for Acid–base Titrations

	Strong Acid ($K_a = \infty$)				
K_b	∞	$1 \cdot 0$	10^{-1}	10^{-2}	10^{-3}
r_{min}	$1 \cdot 01$	$1 \cdot 02$	$1 \cdot 19$	$2 \cdot 82$	$19 \cdot 1$
	Strong Base ($K_b = \infty$)				
K_a	∞	$1 \cdot 0$	10^{-1}	10^{-2}	10^{-3}
r_{min}	$1 \cdot 01$	$0 \cdot 98$	$0 \cdot 89$	$0 \cdot 44$	$0 \cdot 08$
	Disulphuric Acid				
K_b	∞	$1 \cdot 0$	10^{-1}	10^{-2}	10^{-3}
r_{min}	$0 \cdot 56$	$0 \cdot 57$	$0 \cdot 66$	$1 \cdot 58$	$11 \cdot 3$
	Water				
K_a	∞	$1 \cdot 0$	$0 \cdot 3$	10^{-1}	10^{-2}
r_{min}	$1 \cdot 00$	$1 \cdot 00$	$1 \cdot 00$	$0 \cdot 93$	$0 \cdot 42$

For the compound trichloromethylmesitylene which ionizes in sulphuric acid to give a carbonium ion and chlorosulphuric acid (R. J. Gillespie and E. A. Robinson, unpublished results) according to the equation

$$(CH_3)_3C_6H_2CCl_3 + 3H_2SO_4 = (CH_3)_3C_6H_2CCl_2^+ + HClSO_3 + H_3O^+ + 2HSO_4^-$$
$$(68)$$

titration in dilute oleum has been shown to give a conductivity minimum $r = 0 \cdot 37$. In this case disulphuric acid is used up both in neutralizing the base $(CH_3)_3C_6H_2CCl_2^+ . HSO_4^-$ and in the formation of $HClSO_3$, according to the equation

$$(CH_3)_3C_6H_2CCl_3 + 2H_2S_2O_7 = (CH_3)_3C_6H_2CCl_2^+ + HS_2O_7^- + HClSO_3 + H_2SO_4.$$
$$(69)$$

Thus for an initially $0 \cdot 1$ M solution of $H_2S_2O_7$ the conductivity minimum would be predicted at

$$r = \frac{0 \cdot 56}{1 + 0 \cdot 56} = 0 \cdot 36,$$

which is close to the observed value of $0 \cdot 37$. Mesitoyl chloride behaves similarly. Thus conductimetric acid–base titrations of $H_2S_2O_7$ with a complex electrolyte provide information that supplements the results of cryoscopic and conductimetric measurements.

5. *Thermal Properties*

Kirkbride and Wyatt (1957) have measured the partial molar heat contents of potassium, ammonium, and barium hydrogen sulphates, acetic acid and water at 25°. Their results for water are in good agreement with the earlier and less detailed results of Kunzler and Giauque (1952a) and have also been confirmed by new measurements carried out very recently by Mountford and Wyatt (1964). The partial molar heat contents were found to depend markedly on the concentration because of the repression of the solvent self-dissociation at low concentrations. They also found that, on the addition of water to a solution containing a metal sulphate, the partial molar heat content of the water still varied markedly with concentration, confirming that a part of the solvent self-dissociation, namely the ionic self-dehydration, is not appreciably repressed by metal hydrogen sulphates. From the data they were able to obtain the values

$$K_{\mathrm{ap}} = 3 \cdot 4 \times 10^{-4} \text{ mole}^2 \text{ kg}^{-2},$$
$$K_{\mathrm{id}} = 1 \cdot 8 \times 10^{-4} \text{ mole}^2 \text{ kg}^{-2},$$
$$\Delta H_{\mathrm{ap}} = 4800 \text{ cal mole}^{-1},$$

and $\qquad \Delta H_{\mathrm{id}} = 6200 \text{ cal mole}^{-1} \text{ at } 25°.$

Dacre and Wyatt (1961) measured directly the heat of the reaction

$$HB(HSO_4)_4 + KHSO_4 = KB(HSO_4)_4 + H_2SO_4 \tag{70}$$

and assuming that $HB(HSO_4)_4$ is a strong acid and correcting for the solvolysis of the $H_3SO_4^+$ ion they obtained a value of $5 \cdot 0 \pm 0 \cdot 2$ kcal mole^{-1} for ΔH_{ap}, in good agreement with the more indirectly determined value given above. It is our opinion that the cryoscopic data at 10° is the most accurate data available on the self-dissociation so this was used in conjunction with the above values of ΔH_{ap} and ΔH_{id} to obtain the self-dissociation constants at 25° and 40° given in Table III. The values (Gillespie and Robinson, 1964) do not however agree particularly well with the values given above for 25°.

The heat of infinite dilution of a saturated solution of 2,4,6-trinitrotoluene is less than 100 cal mole^{-1} and the heat of solution of the solid, 4·6 kcal mole^{-1}, is close to the heat of fusion (Kirkbride and Wyatt, 1958). These observations have been interpreted as indicating that the non-electrolyte probably exists in solution as simple molecules and not in a chemically solvated form, and that departures from ideality in these solutions are mainly due to entropy rather than thermal effects (Kirkbride and Wyatt, 1958). It is possible however that the heat required to break the solvent hydrogen bonds when the solute molecule is inserted is approximately equal to the heat evolved in the formation of hydrogen bonds between the nitro-groups of the solute and the solvent and that the agreement between the heat of solution and the heat of fusion is coincidental.

6. *Spectroscopy of Sulphuric Acid Solutions*

(a) *Infra-red and Raman Spectra.* There has been considerable interest in the Raman spectra of sulphuric acid solutions, particularly of the H_2O–SO_3 system, over many years, but the infra-red spectra of sulphuric acid and its solutions have only been studied quite recently. This was due to the impossibility of studying the infra-red spectrum of sulphuric acid using conventional cell material such as sodium chloride whereas for Raman spectra measurements a glass cell may be used. The recent infra-red work was done with thin films of sulphuric acid between silver chloride plates, or sodium chloride plates protected with a thin polythene film.

The constitution of oleum solutions has been examined by several workers using Raman spectroscopy and recently Giguere and Savoie (1960) have reported infra-red measurements. There has also been much work on the vibrational spectra of solutions of water in sulphuric acid. These results are discussed in a later section, (Section III A).

Only a very few other sulphuric acid solutions have been studied by infra-red and Raman spectroscopy. An important early application of Raman spectroscopy was the proof of the formation of the linear NO_2^+ ion in solutions of N_2O_5 and nitric acid in sulphuric acid (Ingold *et al.*, 1950), by the observation of the single line at 1400 cm^{-1} in the Raman spectrum which may be assigned to the nitronium ion and other lines, e.g. 1050 cm^{-1} attributable to the HSO_4^- ion.

(b) *Visible and Ultra-violet Spectroscopy.* Differences in the visible and ultra-violet absorption spectra of bases and their conjugate acids have been utilized in determining their degrees of ionization in sulphuric acid–water mixtures, particularly for acidity function measurements (Section II B, 7). Similar measurements have been carried out on solutions of nitro compounds in oleum. Other important applications of visible and ultra-violet spectroscopy to solutions of sulphur dioxide in oleum (Gold and Tye, 1952), and in support of the formation of acylium ions (Section IV H) and carbonium ions (Section IV, I) in sulphuric acid have also been reported.

(c) *Nuclear Magnetic Resonance Spectroscopy.* In solutions of metal hydrogen sulphates in sulphuric acid, because there is rapid proton exchange between the HSO_4^- ion and the solvent, the proton chemical shifts would be expected to be a linear function of the concentration expressed as a proton fraction, p, according to the expression

$$\delta = \delta_{H_2SO_4} + p(\delta_{HSO_4^-} + \delta_{H_2SO_4}). \tag{71}$$

Figure 12 shows that various metal hydrogen sulphates give linear but nevertheless different plots of δ against p (Gillespie and White, 1960; Birchall and Gillespie, 1964). It must be concluded that the metal ions cause a shift in the proton resonance by virtue of their interaction with the solvent. The largest down field shifts are produced by the ions that other measurements show to be the least solvated. The simplest interpretation of these

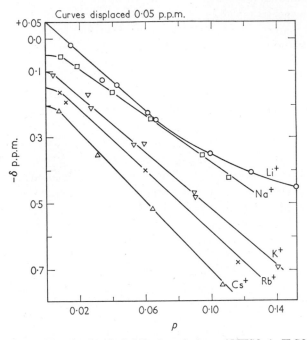

Fig. 12. Proton chemical shifts for solutions of $MHSO_4$ in H_2SO_4.

results is that the HSO_4^- ion produces a large down-field shift and that cation-solvent interaction produces a high-field shift. The observed order of the shifts then agrees with the extents of solvation determined by other methods. Since hydrogen-bonding is known to produce a low-field shift (Pople *et al.*, 1959) the high-field shift caused by solvated ions can presumably be attributed to there being fewer hydrogen bonds between the solvation layer and the bulk solvent than between the solvent molecules themselves. In other words there exists a region of disordered structure, containing relatively few hydrogen bonds, between the solvation layer and the normal structure of the bulk solvent.

The large shift to low field produced by HSO_4^- is of interest. The electron density around the proton in an isolated HSO_4^- would be expected to be greater than around the protons in a sulphuric acid molecule and therefore an isolated HSO_4^- ion would be expected to have a proton resonance at higher field than H_2SO_4. The shift to low field must be due to a strong interaction with the solvent. The negatively charged oxygen atoms of the HSO_4^- ion probably polarize OH bonds from surrounding sulphuric acid molecules and also form hydrogen bonds with them. This conclusion throws some doubt on the earlier assumption that the HSO_4^- ion is not solvated.

Proton chemical shifts have been used to estimate the degree of ionization of water in sulphuric acid (Hood and Reilly, 1959; Gillespie and White, 1960) and although the results obtained agree reasonably well with Raman spectral data (Young, 1951) the assumptions on which the method is based cannot be easily justified and the agreement may be fortuitous.

7. Hammett Acidity Function Measurements

Hammett and Deyrup (1932) showed that a convenient quantitative measure of acidity is the Hammett acidity function H_0 which is based on the relative degree of protonation of suitable neutral bases in very dilute solution in an acid medium. The acidity function is given by

$$H_0 = -\log a_{H^+}\left(\frac{f_B}{f_{BH^+}}\right) \tag{72}$$

where a_{H^+} is the activity of hydrogen ions, and f_B and f_{BH^+} are the activity coefficients of a suitable indicator base and its conjugate acid. The expression for H_0 may also be conveniently expressed in the form

$$H_0 = pK_{BH^+} - \log\frac{[BH^+]}{[B]} \tag{73}$$

when $[BH^+]/[B]$ is the indicator ratio (the ratio of the concentrations of protonated to unprotonated base).

Hammett and Deyrup (1932) were the first to evaluate H_0 for the water–sulphuric acid system and H_0 for oleums has been measured by Brand and co-workers (Brand, 1950; Brand et al., 1952). This work has been summarized by Paul and Long (1957).

Experimentally the indicator ratio, $[BH^+]/[B]$, in a particular medium has been measured spectrophotometrically by observing the extinction coefficient, ϵ, of very dilute solutions of the base in the medium and comparing it with the extinction coefficients of the fully ionized base, ϵ_{ion}, and unionized base, ϵ_b, at the same wavelength. Then

$$[BH^+]/[B] = \frac{\epsilon - \epsilon_b}{\epsilon_{ion} - \epsilon}. \tag{74}$$

When direct determination of pK_{BH^+} is not feasible it is evaluated by step-wise comparison of the indicator ratios of the base B in solutions of gradually increasing acidity, with those of another base C, for which the value of pK_{CH^+} is known, since for a particular acidity

$$H_0 = pK_{BH^+} - \log\frac{[BH^+]}{[B]} = pK_{CH^+} - \log\frac{[CH^+]}{[C]} \tag{75}$$

i.e.
$$pK_{BH^+} - pK_{CH^+} = \log \frac{[BH^+]}{[B]} - \log \frac{[CH^+]}{[C]}.$$
(76)

The underlying assumption is that

$$\frac{f_{BH^+} \times f_C}{f_B \times f_{CH^+}} = 1$$
(77)

where f_B and f_C are the activity coefficients of the bases and f_{BH^+} and f_{CH^+} those of their conjugate acids. An experimental test of the stepwise procedure is that

$$\log \frac{[BH^+]}{[B]} - \log \frac{[CH^+]}{[C]}$$

shall remain constant with variation of acidity. If this condition is satisfied then the H_0 scale has been assumed to be independent of the indicators

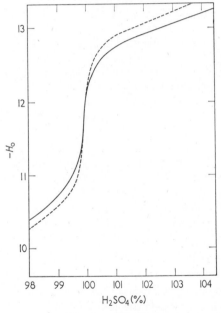

Fig. 13. H_0 for concentrated sulphuric acid and oleum. —, experimental curve; – – – –, calculated curve.

used for its measurement. However, Yates has recently shown that measurements of the H_0 scale for aqueous sulphuric acid, (5–80% H_2SO_4), using a series of overlapping substituted aromatic amides as indicators give different values from those obtained on the basis of substituted aromatic anilines (Yates *et al.*, 1964). The difference has been attributed to a difference in the extent of solvation of BH^+ by the medium.

In 1963, Jorgenson and Harrter re-evaluated the Hammett acidity function scale for water–sulphuric acid solutions more concentrated than

60% H_2SO_4. They showed that some of the previously measured pK values (Hammett and Deyrup, 1932) are in error and that the indicators used by previous workers do not form a suitable set for stepwise comparison. By using a uniform overlapping series of indicators consisting solely of primary anilines a new H_0 scale for sulphuric acid solutions has been established which is progressively more negative with increasing H_2SO_4 concentration than the Paul and Long scale. The weakest base used by Jorgenson and Harrter was picramide, (pK = $-10\cdot10$); this enabled the H_0 scale to be evaluated up to about 99% H_2SO_4.

TABLE XVII

H_0 Values for the H_2O–SO_3 System at Compositions Near to H_2SO_4

%H_2SO_4	H_0
96·0	$-10\cdot03$
97·0	$-10\cdot21$
98·0	$-10\cdot40$
99·0	$-10\cdot72$
99·5	$-11\cdot00$
100·0	$-12\cdot08$
100·5	$-12\cdot58$
101·0	$-12\cdot74$
101·5	$-12\cdot83$
102·0	$-12\cdot92$
103·0	$-13\cdot06$
104·0	$-13\cdot20$
105·0	$-13\cdot34$
106·0	$-13\cdot50$

Recently R. J. Gillespie and E. A. Robinson (unpublished results) have re-determined a number of indicator ratios in concentrated aqueous sulphuric acid and in oleum. Their measurements using picramide as the indicator are in good agreement with those of Jorgenson and Harrter. The other indicators used were substituted nitrobenzenes which appear to overlap successfully with the primary anilines. Some of the previous values for the extinction coefficients of fully ionized aromatic nitro compounds reported by Brand *et al.* (1952) were found to be in error. These errors can be attributed either to the difficulty of evaluating extinction coefficients in media where the indicator is undergoing slow sulphonation, or, in the case of very weak bases, such as 2 : 4 dinitrotoluene, to incomplete protonation of the base even in the most acidic solvent studied. By using highly acidic media such as fluorosulphuric acid, solutions of antimony pentafluoride in fluorosulphuric acid, and solutions of the strong acid $HB(HSO_4)_4$ in sulphuric acid it was possible to obtain what are believed to be more reliable values of ϵ_{ion} for some of the weaker bases. From these results a new H_0 scale was evaluated for concentrated aqueous sulphuric acid and oleums (Fig. 13, Table XVII).

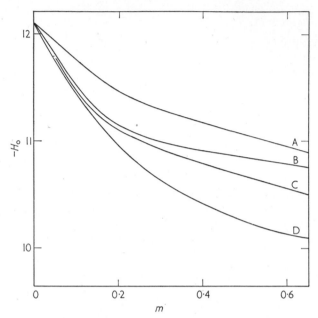

FIG. 14. H_0 for some electrolyte solutions in sulphuric acid: A, H_3O^+ . HSO_4^-; B, $C_6H_5COOH_2^+$. HSO_4^-; C, Na^+ . HSO_4^-; D, K^+ . HSO_4^-.

Various attempts have been made to justify theoretically the H_0 values for concentrated sulphuric acid solutions. These have recently been discussed by Jorgenson and Harrter (1963) who conclude that no simple explanation such as that given by Deno and Taft (1954), which was based on the supposed ideality of sulphuric acid solutions, suffices below 95% H_2SO_4. Even in 100% H_2SO_4, the H_0 functions of solutions of bases such as benzoic acid, $NaHSO_4$, $KHSO_4$ and water are not identical (Fig. 14), showing that activity effects cannot be neglected. Nevertheless the H_0 scale in the region of 100% H_2SO_4 in the H_2O–H_2SO_4–SO_3 system can be correlated reasonably well with the change in the concentration of $H_3SO_4^+$ ions (Fig. 13), since for the equilibrium between protons and solvated protons

$$H_2SO_4 + H^+ = H_3SO_4^+ \tag{78}$$

$$K = a_{H^+}\left(\frac{a_{H_2SO_4}}{a_{H_3SO_4^+}}\right) \tag{79}$$

which gives $$H_0 = -\log[H_3SO_4^+]\left(\frac{f_B}{f_{BH^+}}\right)f_{H_3SO^+} + \frac{K}{a_{H_2SO_4}} \tag{80}$$

where the a's refer to activities, the f's to activity coefficients, and $[H_3SO_4^+]$ is the concentration of $H_3SO_4^+$ ions. For dilute solutions in sulphuric acid it is reasonable to assume that $a_{H_2SO_4}$ is constant and if the activity coefficient terms can be neglected.

$$H_0 = -\log[H_3SO_4^+] + k \qquad (81)$$

where k is a constant. At the composition H_2SO_4 and at 25° $[H_3SO_4^+] = 0.135$ m, and the change in $[H_3SO_4^+]$ with composition is most readily compared with the observed H_0 scale by calculating H_0 relative to the observed value of -12.08 for 100% H_2SO_4, i.e.

$$[H_0]_{calc.} = -\log[H_3SO_4^+] - 13.95. \qquad (82)$$

The calculated values are compared with the experimental values in Fig. 13. The calculated values are slightly too low in aqueous acid and slightly too high in oleum although the two curves have a similar shape. It has been shown that in aqueous sulphuric acid aromatic nitro compounds give larger depressions of freezing point than in 100% sulphuric acid (Gillespie and Robinson, 1957a). Similarly it has been shown that in dilute oleum solutions the

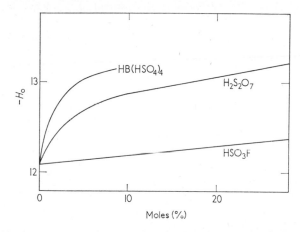

FIG. 15. The Hamett acidity function for solutions of some acids in sulphuric acid.

depressions that are produced by polynitro-compounds which behave as non-electrolytes are smaller than would be expected (Brayford and Wyatt, 1955). In aqueous acid the electrolyte $H_3O^+.HSO_4^-$ causes a salting-out effect, while in oleum there is a salting-in effect. This is consistent with the difference between the calculated and observed H_0 values.

The variation of H_0 with composition in the H_2SO_4–$HB(HSO_4)_4$, H_2SO_4–HSO_3F and H_2SO_4–$H_2S_2O_7$ systems are shown in Fig. 15 (Barr *et al.*, 1965). H_0 measurements have also been reported for the H_2SO_4–HSO_3Cl system by Palm (1956.)

III. Inorganic Solutes

A. THE SOLUTES WATER AND SULPHUR TRIOXIDE

The existence of a number of compounds in the $H_2O–SO_3$ system has long been recognized. For example phase diagram studies show congruent melting points for the following compounds: $H_2SO_4.4H_2O$ ($-28.366°$); $H_2SO_4.2H_2O$ ($-39.51°$); $H_2SO_4.H_2O$ ($8.56°$); H_2SO_4 ($10.37°$); and $H_2S_2O_7$ ($35.15°$), and the compounds $H_2SO_4.6H_2O$ and $H_2SO_4.3H_2O$ melt incongruently and are transformed into the four-hydrate at $-53.73°$ and $-36.56°$, respectively (Gable et al., 1950; Giauque et al., 1952; Kunzler and Giauque, 1952a). The numerous and extensive studies of aqueous sulphuric acid will not be considered further here: the discussion will be limited to dilute solutions of water in sulphuric acid. Freezing point measurements (Gillespie, 1950a; Bass et al., 1960) have shown that water is apparently incompletely ionized in sulphuric acid and a dissociation constant $K_{H_2O} = 1$ mole kg^{-1}, has been obtained. However there is no indication of incomplete dissociation in the electrical conductivities of solutions of water in sulphuric acid (Gillespie et al., 1960). This observation is most easily explained by assuming that the incompleteness of the ionization of water is due to the formation of ion-pairs, $H_3O^+.HSO_4^-$, and that the life-time of an $H_3O^+.HSO_4^-$ ion-pair is less than the average time taken for proton transfer in the conduction by HSO_4^- ions. Recent spectroscopic work by E. A. Robinson (unpublished results) appears to support the formation of $H_3O^+.HSO_4^-$ ion-pairs and frequencies of 1140 and 1300 cm^{-1} can be assigned to the SO stretching vibrations of this species.

Recently Giguere and Savoie (1960) have investigated the infra-red spectra of solutions of water in sulphuric acid and similar measurements have been reported by Walrafen and Dodd (1961). Many workers have studied the Raman spectra of aqueous sulphuric acid solutions and Young (1959) claimed that for sulphuric acid solutions having compositions between H_2SO_4 and $H_2SO_4.H_2O$, the species $H_5SO_5^+$ is present in addition to H_2SO_4, HSO_4^-, and $H_3O.^+$ Presumably $H_5SO_5^+$ is the monosolvated H_3O^+ ion, ($H_3O^+.H_2SO_4$). Cryoscopic measurements also indicate that the H_3O^+ ion is solvated, probably with two H_2SO_4 molecules (Bass et al., 1960) and Wyatt (1960) found it necessary to assume the formation of $H_3O^+(H_2SO_4)$ in order to account for the partial molar heat content of water in sulphuric acid.

Lehmann (1953) has summarized data on the phase diagram of the $H_2SO_4–SO_3$ system and claims the existence of $H_2S_2O_7$, $H_2S_3O_{10}$, $H_2S_4O_{13}$, and $H_2S_8O_{25}$. Cryoscopic studies showed that a weak acid, presumably $H_2S_2O_7$, is present in dilute solutions of SO_3 in sulphuric acid (Gillespie, 1950b). The dissociation constant was found to be $K_{H_2S_2O_7} = 0.014$ moles kg^{-1}, (Bass et al., 1960). Conductivity measurements at 10° and 25° are consistent with the degree of ionization of $H_2S_2O_7$ expected on the basis of this constant (Gillespie *et al.*, 1960) and the position of the conductivity minimum in conductimetric titration of dilute oleum with a strong base has also been shown (Flowers *et al.*, 1960b) to be consistent with $K_{H_2S_2O_7} = 0·014$. The freezing point depressions obtained when small amounts of ammonium sulphate were added to dilute oleum could be interpreted only if higher polysulphuric acids and their ions were assumed to be present in the system in addition to $H_2S_2O_7$, $HS_2O_7^-$, and $S_2O_7^{2-}$. In particular $H_2S_3O_{10}$ was shown to be present even at concentrates as low as 0·15 molal and the initial decrease in the freezing point depression of an 0·4 molal solution when $(NH_4)_2SO_4$ was added could be explained only if $H_2S_4O_{13}$ was assumed to be present (Gillespie, 1950b).

The constitution of oleum solutions has been examined by several workers using Raman spectroscopy (Millen, 1950c; Walrafen and Young, 1960; Gillespie and Robinson, 1962b) and Giguere and Savoie (1960) have measured the infra-red spectra. All the workers are in agreement that the spectra give evidence for the formation of $H_2S_2O_7$ and the spectra have been analysed by comparison with the spectrum of $S_2O_5F_2$ which is isoelectronic with $H_2S_2O_7$ (Gillespie and Robinson, 1962b). There has been, however, some controversy concerning the spectral evidence for the formation of $H_2S_3O_{10}$. In 1960 Walrafen and Young claimed that the spectra could be accounted for without having to take into account any polysulphuric acid more complex than $H_2S_2O_7$. However the presence of $H_2S_3O_{10}$, as well as $H_2S_2O_7$ in oleum solutions more concentrated than 12% SO_3 has been proved unambiguously by comparison of the spectra of oleums with those of $S_2O_5F_2$ and $S_3O_8F_2$ (Gillespie and Robinson, 1962b). It was shown that a diagnostic feature of the vibrational spectrum of a trisulphuryl compound is the appearance of two frequencies near to 700 cm^{-1}, whereas in the case of a disulphuryl compound there is only one frequency in this part of the spectrum. In relatively dilute oleums there is a single vibrational frequency near to 730 cm^{-1}, ($S_2O_5F_2$ 733 cm^{-1}), while in more concentrated oleums there are two lines at approximately 690 and 735 cm^{-1}, ($S_3O_8F_2$ 699 and 724 cm^{-1}). Other details of the spectra also confirm the occurrence of $H_2S_3O_{10}$ in oleum solutions. Very recently Walrafen (1964) has accepted the evidence for the occurrence of $H_2S_3O_{10}$ and has confirmed it by observations on the intensities of certain spectral lines. Unfortunately the spectrum of $S_4O_{11}F_2$ shows no definite diagnostic features compared to that of $S_3O_8F_2$ and so it was not possible to confirm the presence of $H_2S_4O_{13}$ conclusively by comparison of oleum spectra with that of $S_4O_{11}F_2$. However the SO_2 symmetric stretch, which has a frequency of 1195 cm^{-1} in H_2SO_4, 1224 cm^{-1} in oleum of the composition $H_2S_2O_7$, and 1230 cm^{-1} at the composition $H_2S_3O_{10}$, gradually moves to even higher frequencies as the concentration of SO_3 in oleum increases, until at 92·2% SO_3 it is near to 1260 cm^{-1}. This continuous shift in the frequencies attributed to SO_2 symmetric stretches has been interpreted as indicating that increasing amounts of polysulphuric acids such as $H_2S_4O_{13}$, and even higher polyacids, are formed in very strong oleums (Gillespie and Robinson, 1962b). The SO_2 symmetric stretching frequency in the acyclic SO_3 polymer, which is presumably a very high molecular weight polysulphuric acid, since its formation from the liquid trimer is catalysed by traces of water, is also at 1260 cm^{-1}. In moderately strong oleums the monomer SO_3 is also found to be present and in very strong oleums both the monomer and the trimer $(SO_3)_3$ are present. The Raman spectra of solutions of SO_3 in D_2SO_4 have also been investigated and can be interpreted in a similar way to the H_2SO_4–SO_3 system (Gillespie and Robinson, 1962b).

B. BORON

Boric acid is very soluble in sulphuric acid, and various compounds of boric acid and boric oxide with sulphuric acid have been reported. One of these compounds has the composition $H_3BO_3 . 3SO_3$ (d'Arcy, 1889), and it may be regarded as boron tri(hydrogen sulphate), $B(HSO_4)_3$. On the basis of his measurements of freezing point depressions Hantzsch suggested that this compound is formed when boric oxide is dissolved in sulphuric acid (Hantzsch, 1907). More recent freezing point measurements (Flowers et al., 1956b) have shown that $\nu = 6$ for solutions of both H_3BO_3 and B_2O_3, whereas the formation of $B(HSO_4)_3$ would give $\nu = 7$ and $\nu = 8$ for boric acid and boric oxide, respectively,

$$H_3BO_3 + 6H_2SO_4 = B(HSO_4)_3 + 3H_3O^+ + 3HSO_4^- \tag{83}$$
$$B_2O_3 + 9H_2SO_4 = 2B(HSO_4)_3 + 3H_3O^+ + 3HSO_4^-. \tag{84}$$

Conductivity measurements show that for boric acid $\gamma = 2$ and for boric oxide $\gamma = 1$, which again is not in agreement with equations (83) and (84) which require $\gamma = 3$ in both cases. If boron tri(hydrogen sulphate) combines with a hydrogen sulphate ion to form the boron tetra(hydrogen sulphate) ion

$$B(HSO_4)_3 + HSO_4^- = B(HSO_4)_4^- \tag{85}$$

by analogy with

$$BF_3 + F^- = BF_4^- \tag{86}$$

and $$B(OH)_3 + OH^- = B(OH)_4^- \tag{87}$$

equations (83) and (84) can be rewritten as follows

$$H_3BO_3 + 6H_2SO_4 = B(HSO_4)_4^- + 3H_3O^+ + 2HSO_4^- \tag{88}$$

and $$B_2O_3 + 9H_2SO_4 = 2B(HSO_4)_4^- + 3H_3O^+ + HSO_4^-. \tag{89}$$

Now $\nu = 6$ and $\gamma = 2$ for boric acid, and $\nu = 6$ and $\gamma = 1$ for boric oxide in agreement with the experimental results.

The conclusion that the boron tetra(hydrogen sulphate) ion is formed in these solutions is of great interest since, as it apparently does not undergo solvolysis, the corresponding acid $HB(HSO_4)_4$ must be a relatively strong acid of the sulphuric acid solvent system. Solutions of the free acid can be prepared by dissolving boric acid or boric oxide in oleum instead of sulphuric acid in which case the H_3O^+ ion is removed by the reaction

$$H_3O^+ + SO_3 = H_3SO_4^+ \qquad (90)$$

and the overall equations are

$$H_3BO_3 + 3H_2S_2O_7 = H_3SO_4^+ + B(HSO_4)_4^- + H_2SO_4 \qquad (91)$$

and $\quad B_2O_3 + 3H_2S_2O_7 + 4H_2SO_4 = 2H_3SO_4^+ + 2B(HSO_4)_4^-. \qquad (92)$

Cryoscopic and conductimetric measurements confirm these reactions and show that the acid $HB(HSO_4)_4$ is extensively ionized, $K_b = 0.4$ moles kg^{-1} (Flowers et al., 1956b). A solution of $HB(HSO_4)_4$ can be titrated conductimetrically with a strong base, such as $KHSO_4$ (Flowers et al., 1960b).

$$KHSO_4 + HB(HSO_4)_4 = KB(HSO_4)_4 + H_2SO_4. \qquad (93)$$
$$\text{base} \qquad \text{acid} \qquad\qquad \text{salt} \qquad\quad \text{solvent}$$

The conductivity minimum occurs at

$$\frac{n_{KHSO_4}}{n^i_{HB(HSO_4)_4}} = 0.98,$$

where n_{KHSO_4} is the number of moles of base added to a solution of acid containing initially $n^i_{HB(HSO_4)_4}$ moles of tetra(hydrogen sulphato) boric acid. The freezing point of the solution hardly changes as $KHSO_4$ is added up to the composition

$$\frac{n_{KHSO_4}}{n^i_{HB(HSO_4)_4}} = 1.0.$$

This is because the $H_3SO_4^+$ ion is replaced by an equal concentration of K^+ ions and the concentration of $B(HSO_4)_4^-$ ions remains constant; hence the total number of solute particles remains unchanged. After the composition of minimum conductivity the conductivity increases and the freezing point of the solution decreases as a consequence of the addition of excess $KHSO_4$.

Concentrated solutions of $HB(HSO_4)_4$ have been investigated by means of Raman spectroscopy (Gillespie and Robinson, 1962c). The spectra of these solutions are rather complex but apart from the frequencies that can be reasonably assigned to the species $H_3SO_4^+$, H_2SO_4, and $B(HSO_4)_4^-$ there are other bands which are due to $H_2S_2O_7$ and $H_2S_3O_{10}$. These polysulphuric acids are presumably formed in condensation processes between $B(HSO_4)_4^-$ ions giving polymeric ions containing B—O—B bonds, e.g.

$$2B(HSO_4)_4^- = \begin{bmatrix} & O & \\ & \diagup\diagdown & \\ (HSO_4)_2B & & B(SO_4H)_2 \\ & O \quad\ O & \\ & \diagdown\ \diagup & \\ & S & \\ & \diagup\diagdown & \\ & O \quad O & \end{bmatrix}^{2-} + H_2S_2O_7 + H_2SO_4 \qquad (94)$$

$$\text{II}$$

Thompson and Greenwood (1959) claim to have obtained the acid $HB(HSO_4)_4$ as a wet solid by the reaction of BCl_3 with sulphuric acid:

$$BCl_3 + 4H_2SO_4 = HB(HSO_4)_4 + 3HCl. \tag{95}$$

In view of the evidence from the Raman spectra of concentrated solutions of this acid that elimination of $H_2S_2O_7$ occurs to give B—O—B links (Gillespie and Robinson, 1962c), and in view of the complex structures of the salts it seems unlikely that the wet solid was in fact pure $HB(HSO_4)_4$. It is more likely that the product of the reaction is a mixture of polysulphatoboric acids with sulphuric acid and disulphuric acid having the overall composition $HB(HSO_4)_4$.

Salts of tetra(hydrogen sulphato) boric acid of the general composition $M^IB(SO_4)_2$, $M^{II}[B(SO_4)_2]_2$, and $M^{III}[B_2O(SO_4)_3]$ have been prepared by the reaction between the corresponding sulphates, boric acid and sulphur trioxide (Schott and Kibbel, 1962), e.g.

$$(NH_4)_2SO_4 + 2B(OH)_3 + 6SO_3 = 2NH_4[B(SO_4)_2] + 3H_2SO_4. \tag{96}$$

On heating the calcium, strontium, or barium salt elimination of SO_3 gave the compound $M^{II}[B_2O(SO_4)_3]$. $NH_4[B(SO_4)_2]$ was also prepared by the reaction of boron nitride with sulphuric acid

$$BN + 2H_2SO_4 = NH_4[B(SO_4)_2]. \tag{97}$$

All the compounds are very hygroscopic and sensitive to hydrolysis; they are believed to contain highly polymeric anions.

Attempts to obtain salts, such as $KB(HSO_4)_4$ by the neutralization of solutions of $HB(HSO_4)_4$ in sulphuric acid have not been successful. In order to obtain a crystalline product it was necessary to prepare considerably more concentrated solutions of the complex boric acid than those used in the physical measurements, and under these conditions the solid sodium, potassium, ammonium, and strontium salts that were obtained had a ratio of sulphate to boron of less than four (Gillespie and Robinson, 1962d). This behaviour is analogous to the behaviour of the borate ion in aqueous solution, which has the formula $B(OH)_4^-$ in dilute solution (Edwards *et al.*, 1955) although many borates which separate from concentrated solution contain complex ions such as $B_4O_7^{2-}$ and $B_6O_{11}^{4-}$ formed by polymerization of $B(OH)_4^-$ and $B(OH)_3$ through the elimination of water.

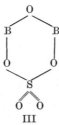

III

It was found (Gillespie and Robinson, 1962d) that the compositions of the salts and the results of cryoscopic and conductimetric measurements on the salts could be satisfactorily explained by assuming that they contain anions with structures based on the six-membered ring III, such as IV and V.

IV

V

C. SILICON

The experimental values of ν and γ for hexamethyldisiloxane (Rice, 1948; Newman *et al.*, 1949; Flowers *et al.*, 1963), indicate that it ionizes according to the equation

$$[(CH_3)_3Si]_2O + 3H_2SO_4 = 2(CH_3)_3Si.SO_4H + H_3O^+ + HSO_4^-. \tag{98}$$

Price (1948) suggested that trimethylsilicon hydrogen sulphate ionizes further to give the trimethylsiliconium ion

$$(CH_3)_3Si.SO_4H = (CH_3)_3Si^+ + HSO_4^- \tag{99}$$

but there is no evidence from the cryoscopic or conductimetric measurements that this occurs to any appreciable extent (Flowers *et al.*, 1963). The results of measurements on solutions of trimethylethoxysilane, triethylethoxysilane and trimethylsilanol (Newman *et al.*, 1949) show that they also react to give the corresponding trialkylsilicon hydrogen sulphates.

$$R_3SiOEt + 3H_2SO_4 = R_3Si.SO_4H + EtSO_4H + H_3O^+ + HSO_4^- \tag{100}$$

$$R_3Si.OH + 2H_2SO_4 = R_3Si.SO_4H + H_3O^+ + HSO_4^-. \tag{101}$$

Trimethylsilyl sulphate has been prepared by the reaction of oleum on hexamethyldisiloxane (Sommer et al., 1946).

Recently Reavill (1964) has commented on the unsuitability of tetramethylsilane when used in nuclear magnetic resonance spectroscopy as an internal reference standard for sulphuric acid solutions. He has shown that $(CH_3)_4Si$ is immiscible with sulphuric acid but on shaking at room temperature forms methane and trimethylsilyl sulphate.

The experimental results for dimethyldiethoxysilane (Flowers et al., 1963) are in good agreement with the formation of the corresponding di(hydrogen sulphate)

$$(CH_3)_2Si(OEt)_2 + 5H_2SO_4 = (CH_3)_3Si(HSO_4)_2 + 2EtSO_4H + 2H_3O^+ + 2HSO_4^- \tag{102}$$

and results for the compound $[(CH_3)_2SiO]_4$ are also consistent with the formation of dimethylsilicon di(hydrogen sulphate) (Price, 1948)

$$(CH_3)_2SiO_4 + 12H_2SO_4 = 4(CH_3)_2Si(SO_4H)_2 + 4H_3O^+ + 4HSO_4^-. \tag{103}$$

Methyltriethoxysilane differs from the compounds discussed above in that both ν and γ show a definite concentration dependence: ν decreases from 8·4–7·7 while γ decreases from 2·8–2·2 over the concentration range 0·01–0·06 molal (Flowers et al., 1963). Presumably the low observed values of ν and γ, and their concentration dependence are due to polymerization of the methylsilicon trihydrogen sulphate. The general equation for the formation of linear polymers may be written

$$CH_3Si(OEt)_3 + (6+3/n)H_2SO_4 = \frac{1}{n}\left[HSO_4 - \underset{\underset{SO_4H}{|}}{\overset{\overset{CH_3}{|}}{Si}} - O - \left(\underset{\underset{SO_4H}{|}}{\overset{\overset{CH_3}{|}}{Si}} - O \right)_{n-2} - \underset{\underset{SO_4H}{|}}{\overset{\overset{CH_3}{|}}{Si}} - SO_4H \right]$$

$$+ 3EtHSO_4 + \left(2+\frac{1}{n}\right)H_3O^+ + \left(2+\frac{1}{n}\right)HSO_4^- \tag{104}$$

n	$\nu = 7+\dfrac{3}{n}$	$\gamma = 2+\dfrac{1}{n}$
dimer	2	8·5	2·5
trimer	3	8·0	2·3
tetramer	4	7·75	2·25

It is possible that these polymers are better formulated as containing six-membered rings with bridging sulphate groups formed by the elimination of sulphuric acid from the linear polymer VI:

$$\text{HSO}_4-\underset{\underset{\text{O}}{|}}{\overset{\overset{\text{CH}_3}{|}}{\text{Si}}}\overset{\text{O}}{\diagdown}\underset{\underset{\text{O}}{|}}{\overset{\overset{\text{CH}_3}{|}}{\text{Si}}}\overset{\text{O}}{\diagup}\underset{\underset{\text{O}}{|}}{\overset{\overset{\text{CH}_3}{|}}{\text{Si}}}\overset{\text{O}}{\diagdown}\underset{\underset{\text{O}}{|}}{\overset{\overset{\text{CH}_3}{|}}{\text{Si}}}\overset{\text{O}}{\diagup}\underset{\underset{\text{O}}{|}}{\overset{\overset{\text{CH}_3}{|}}{\text{Si}}}\overset{\text{O}}{\diagdown}\underset{\underset{\text{O}}{|}}{\overset{\overset{\text{CH}_3}{|}}{\text{Si}}}-\text{SO}_4\text{H}$$

VI

This is consistent with the proposed structures for complex sulphato compounds of boron and arsenic eg. III and XV. The formation of a mixture of these polymers would account satisfactorily for the experimental observations.

The results of a cryoscopic study of tetraphenylsilane, tetrabenzylsilane and hexaphenyldisilane (Szmant *et al.*, 1951) can only be interpreted if it is assumed that complete cleavage of all the Si—C bonds occurs with the formation of the corresponding aryl sulphonic acids, which were isolated from the solutions. The cleavage of Si—C bonds is well known to be caused by a variety of acidic and basic reagents and kinetic studies have been made of the rate of the cleavage of phenyltrimethylsilane by sulphuric acid (Deans and Eaborn, 1959). However, the formation of $Si(HSO_4)_4$ or of the anions $Si(HSO_4)_5^-$ or $Si(HSO_4)_6^{2-}$

$$Ph_4Si + 12H_2SO_4 = Si(HSO_4)_4 + 4PhSO_3H + 4H_3O^+ + 4HSO_4^- \qquad (105)$$

$$Ph_4Si + 12H_2SO_4 = Si(HSO_4)_5^- + 4PhSO_3H + 4H_3O^+ + 3HSO_4^- \qquad (106)$$

$$Ph_4Si + 12H_2SO_4 = Si(HSO_4)_6^{2-} + 4PhSO_3H + 4H_3O^+ + 2HSO_4^- \qquad (107)$$

is not in agreement with the cryoscopic results. It was found that v decreases from 10·8–10·3, and γ from 2·7–2·5 over the concentration range 0·005–0·03 molal. Thus it appears likely that polymerization occurs and the cryoscopic and conductimetric results for Ph_4Si (Flowers *et al.*, 1963), and the cryoscopic results for tetrabenzylsilane and hexaphenyldisilane (Szmant *et al.*, 1951), and for $[(CH_3)_3SiO]_4Si$ (Price, 1948) can be reasonably accounted for in terms of the formation a three-dimensional oxy(hydrogen sulphate)polymer, e.g.

$$SiPh_4 \rightarrow 4PhSO_3H + \frac{1}{2}n[Si_2O_3(HSO_4)_2]_{\frac{n}{2}} + 2\cdot 5H_3O^+ + 2\cdot 5HSO_4^-$$

$$(108)$$

$$Si[OSi(OCH_3)_3]_4 \rightarrow 4(CH_3)_3Si \cdot SO_4H + \frac{1}{2}n[Si_2O_3(HSO_4)_2]_{\frac{n}{2}} + 2\cdot 5H_3O^+ +$$

$$2\cdot 5HSO_4^-.$$

$$(109)$$

The compounds $Si(OEt)_4$, $Ph_3Si.OH$, $Ph_2Si(OH)_2$, $Si(OAC)_4$, and (naphthyl)$_3$Si.OH appear to react with sulphuric acid to give insoluble polymers.

D. TIN AND LEAD

Stannic acid and stannic sulphate are almost insoluble in sulphuric acid, but a number of salts of sulphostannic acid, $H_2Sn(HSO_4)_6$, have been prepared by evaporating mixtures of stannic oxide, a metal sulphate, and sulphuric acid (Weinlaud and Kuhl, 1907; Druce, 1924), e.g. $Rb_2Sn(SO_4)_3$, $K_2Sn(SO_4)_3$, $Ag_2Sn(SO_4)_3.3H_2O$, $CaSn(SO_4)_3.3H_2O$, $PbSn(SO_4)_3.3H_2O$. All the hydrated salts contain three molecules of water, and they may reasonably be formulated as salts of tri(hydrogen sulphato)stannic acid, $H_2Sn(OH)_3(HSO_4)_3$, e.g. $Ag_2Sn(OH)_3(HSO_4)_3$. Evidence for the existence of hexa(hydrogen sulphato)stannic acid, $H_2Sn(HSO_4)_6$, in solution in sulphuric acid has been obtained (R. J. Gillespie and E. A. Robinson, 1965) from a study of the freezing points and conductivities of solutions of tetraphenyltin, triphenyltin hydroxide, and tin tetra-acetate in sulphuric acid. The results of these measurements are consistent with the following modes of ionization:

$$Ph_4Sn + 14H_2SO_4 = H_2Sn(HSO_4)_6 + 4PhSO_3H + 4H_3O^+ + 4HSO_4^- \quad (110)$$

$$Ph_3Sn.OH + 13H_2SO_4 = H_2Sn(HSO_4)_6 + 3PhSO_3H + 4H_3O^+ + 4HSO_4^- \quad (111)$$

$$Sn(OAc)_4 + 10H_2SO_4 = H_2Sn(HSO_4)_6 + 4AcOH_2^+ + 4HSO_4^-. \quad (112)$$

The values of ν and γ which decrease with increasing concentration are consistent with an equilibrium between the free acid and its anions.

$$H_2Sn(HSO_4)_6 + HSO_4^- = HSn(HSO_4)_6^- + H_2SO_4 \quad (113)$$

$$HSn(HSO_4)_6^- + HSO_4^- = Sn(HSO_4)_6^{2-} + H_2SO_4. \quad (114)$$

Brubaker (1955) has investigated solutions of Sn^{IV} in aqueous solutions of sulphuric acid of various strengths by means of spectrophotometric and electromigration studies and by studying the equilibrium between hydrous stannic oxide and aqueous sulphuric acid solutions. He concludes that in dilute solution, hydrous stannic oxide is in equilibrium with $Sn(SO_4)^{2+}$ while in concentrated solutions there is an equilibrium between $Sn(SO_4)^{2+}$, $Sn(SO_4)_2$ and $H_2Sn(SO_4)_3$.

Tetramethyltin dissolves rapidly in sulphuric acid with evolution of methane, according to the equation

$$(CH_3)_4Sn + H_2SO_4 = (CH_3)_3Sn.HSO_4 + CH_4. \quad (115)$$

A similar reaction has been observed between tetramethyltin and concentrated solutions of hydrogen halides (Coates, 1960). Cryoscopic and conductimetric measurements indicate that the trimethyltin hydrogen sulphate thus formed is substantially ionized to give a trimethyltin cation

$$(CH_3)_3Sn.HSO_4 = (CH_3)_3Sn^+ + HSO_4^-. \quad (116)$$

This reaction may also be written as

$$(CH_3)_3Sn.HSO_4 + H_2SO_4 = (CH_3)_3Sn.SO_4H_2^+ + HSO_4^- \qquad (117)$$

and it is not possible to distinguish between these two possibilities by cryoscopic and conductimetric measurements. A study of the infra-red spectra of concentrated solutions has been made (E. A. Robinson, unpublished results), and although it is difficult to interpret the spectra in detail, they are more complex than would be expected for the trimethyltin cation $(CH_3)_3Sn^+$. Recent infra-red studies of solid trimethyltin salts such as the perchlorate, nitrate, carbonate, and tetrafluoroborate have led to the conclusion that these compounds do not contain $(CH_3)_3Sn^+$ cations, but that the anions are covalently bound to tin in a five co-ordinated trigonal bipyramidal structure (Clark and O'Brien, 1963; Hathaway and Webster, 1963; Okawara et al., 1963). X-Ray studies of $(CH_3)_3SnF$ show that there is trigonal bipyramidal co-ordination of the tin in a structure involving fluorine bridges (Clark et al., 1963). In aqueous solution trialkyltin cations probably exist in solvated forms, e.g. $R_3SnOH_2^+$, rather than the planar ion R_3Sn^+ (Coates, 1960). It is therefore likely that the cation present in sulphuric acid is $[(CH_3)_3Sn.SO_4H_2]^+$ or $[(CH_3)_3Sn(SO_4H_2)_2]^+$. Trimethyltin sulphate gives $\nu = 4$ and $\gamma = 2$ in accord with the ionization

$$[(CH_3)_3Sn]_2SO_4 + 4H_2SO_4 = 2(CH_3)_3Sn.SO_4H_2^+ + 2HSO_4^- \qquad (118)$$

and is thus a strong base although the corresponding hydroxide is only a weak base in water.

Di-n-butyltin diacetate reacts with sulphuric acid to give three hydrogen-sulphate ions per solute molecule ($\gamma = 3$) (R. J. Gillespie and E. A. Robinson, unpublished results). For the reaction

$$(n-Bu)_2Sn(OAc)_2 + 4H_2SO_4 = (n-Bu)_2Sn(HSO_4)_2 + 2AcOH_2^+ + 2HSO_4^- \quad (119)$$

which might be expected by analogy with the behaviour of dialkylsilicon compounds, $\gamma = 2$; the observed γ-value is consistent only with the formation of a singly charged tin cation, e.g.

$$(n-Bu)_2Sn(OAc)_2 + 5H_2SO_4 = (n-Bu)_2Sn(HSO_4)_2H^+ + 2AcOH_2^+ + 3HSO_4^-.$$
$$(120)$$

Di-n-butyltin di(hydrogen sulphate) appears to behave as a strong base.

Methylstannonic acid is only slowly soluble in sulphuric acid, doubtless as a consequence of its polymeric nature. The observed values of ν and γ vary from 6 to 5 and from 3 to 2, respectively, with increasing concentration, and are consistent with the reaction

$$CH_3Sn.O.OH + 5H_2SO_4 = CH_2Sn(HSO_4)_2 + 2H_3O^+ + 2HSO_4^- \qquad (121)$$

followed by ionization of $CH_3.Sn(HSO_4)_3$ as a weak base

$$CH_3.Sn(HSO_4)_3 + H_2SO_4 = CH_3.Sn(HSO_4)_3H^+ + HSO_4^-. \qquad (122)$$

In contrast to the behaviour of silicon, all the tin compounds investigated are completely converted to the corresponding sulphato compounds, which is consistent with the smaller electronegativity of tin. The basicity of the tin hydrogen sulphates decreases as the number of hydrogen sulphate groups attached to the tin atom increases. Thus R_3SnSO_4H, and $R_2Sn(SO_4H)_2$ are strong bases, while $RSn(SO_4H)_3$ is a weak base, and $Sn(HSO_4)_4$ is an acid.

It has been suggested that the solutions of lead tetra-acetate in sulphuric acid from which $Pb(SO_4)_2$ is obtained, and the greenish yellow solutions obtained by the electrolysis of sulphuric acid using lead electrodes, contain the acid $H_2Pb(SO_4)_3$, since the potassium and ammonium salts, $K_2Pb(SO_4)_3$ and $(NH_4)_2Pb(SO_4)_3$ can be obtained from the solutions (Dolezalek and Finkh, 1906; Esch, 1903). The insoluble salts $(NH_4)_2Pb(SO_4)_3$, $K_2Pb(SO_4)_3$, $Rb_2Pb(SO_4)_3$, and $Cs_2Pb(SO_4)_3$ have also been prepared by treating an acid solution of $Pb(SO_4)_2$ with a solution of metal sulphate in sulphuric acid (Elbs and Fischer, 1901).

Cryoscopic and conductimetric measurements show that lead tetra-acetate, like tin tetra-acetate, is fully converted to the tetra(hydrogen sulphate) (Gillespie and Robinson, 1957b and unpublished results). Since this behaves as an acid it may be regarded as hexa(hydrogen sulphato) plumbic acid

$$Pb(OAc)_4 + 10H_2SO_4 = H_2Pb(HSO_4)_6 + 4AcOH_2^+ + 4HSO_4^-. \quad (123)$$

From the variation of the values of ν and γ with concentration, (ν varies from 8·2—7·5 and γ from 3·4—2·5, over the concentration range 0·005—0·55 molal), it was possible to deduce values for the two dissociation constants of this acid at 25°:

$$H_2Pb(HSO_4)_6 + H_2SO_4 = H_3SO_4^+ + HPb(HSO_4)_6^- \quad K_1 = 1·2 \times 10^{-2} \text{ moles kg}^{-1} \quad (124)$$

$$HPb(HSO_4)_6^- + H_2SO_4 = H_3SO_4^+ + Pb(HSO_4)_6^{2-} \quad K_2 = 1·8 \times 10^{-3} \text{ moles kg}^{-1}. \quad (125)$$

On gently warming below 100°, the yellow solution of lead tetra-acetate in sulphuric acid deposits bright yellow plumbic sulphate, $Pb(SO_4)_2$; above 100° decomposition occurs to give oxygen and a precipitate of plumbous sulphate. Plumbic sulphate has also been prepared from PbF_4 and concentrated sulphuric acid (Brauner, 1894). Like $Sn(SO_4)_2$ it is insoluble in sulphuric acid. It seems reasonable to suppose that the insolubility of $Pb(SO_4)_2$ and the salts $M_2Pb(SO_4)_3$ is due to their being polymerized by sulphate bridges, although their structures are not known.

E. NITROGEN AND PHOSPHORUS

Solutions of nitric acid, metallic nitrates and dinitrogen pentoxide in sulphuric acid have long been known to be efficient reagents in aromatic nitration (Gillespie and Millen, 1948). The idea that the nitrating species under certain conditions might be the nitronium ion was suggested by several workers but no good evidence for the existence of NO_2^+ as a stable entity was available until Ingold and co-workers (Gillespie *et al.*, 1950; Goddard *et al.*, 1950; Ingold *et al.*, 1950) studied by means of cryoscopy and Raman spectroscopy, solutions of nitric acid and some oxides of nitrogen in sulphuric acid and other acids, and also prepared stable salts of NO_2^+. The quantitative formation of NO_2^+ in solutions of nitric acid in sulphuric acid has also been confirmed by conductimetric measurements (Gillespie and Wasif, 1953c). In the case of nitric acid solutions in sulphuric acid the cryoscopic ν-value is close to 4 and electrical conductivity measurements give $\gamma = 2$, as required by the equation,

$$HNO_3 + 2H_2SO_4 = NO_2^+ + H_3O^+ + 2HSO_4^-. \tag{126}$$

The Raman spectrum of these solutions contains two strong lines at 1050 cm^{-1} and 1400 cm^{-1} which cannot be attributed to the solvent or solute molecules. The former is diagnostic of the HSO_4^- ion and the latter, which is polarized, is readily assigned to the linear NO_2^+ ion, for which just one polarized line is expected in the Raman spectrum. This interpretation of the spectrum has been confirmed by an investigation of the Raman spectra of mixtures of nitric acid with other strong acids and of the salts $NO_2^+.ClO_4^-$ and $NO_2^+.HS_2O_7^-$ (Millen, 1950b). The Raman spectrum of HNO_3 in oleum consists of the spectrum of oleum with the addition of two other lines, one at 1400 cm^{-1} the symmetric stretching frequency of the NO_2^+ ion, and another at 1075–1095 cm^{-1} which is due to the $HS_2O_7^-$ ion (Chedin, 1936, 1937; Millen, 1950a). Cryoscopic measurements show that nitric acid ionizes in excess dilute oleum to produce the NO_2^+ ion (Gillespie and Graham, 1950) according to the equation

$$HNO_3 + 2H_2S_2O_7 = NO_2^+ + HS_2O_7^- + 2H_2SO_4. \tag{127}$$

Ogg and Ray (1956) have investigated the ^{14}N n.m.r. spectrum of solutions of nitric acid in oleum and have observed the nitrogen resonance of the NO_2^+ ion as a single broad peak, the breadth reflecting the effect of a large quadrupole interaction due to the unsymmetrical environment. Comparison with the similar broad spectrum of the linear azide ion provides further evidence that the nitronium ion is linear. The infra-red spectra of solutions of nitric acid in sulphuric acid have been investigated by Marcus and Fresco (1957) who observed the strong asymmetric stretching frequency of the NO_2^+ ion at 2360 cm^{-1}.

Metal nitrates and dinitrogen pentoxide have similarly been shown to give the nitronium ion according to the equations (Gillespie *et al.*, 1950; Millen, 1950b):

$$KNO_3 + 3H_2SO_4 = NO_2^+ + K^+ + H_3O^+ + 3HSO_4^- \tag{128}$$

$$N_2O_5 + 3H_2SO_4 = 2NO_2^+ + H_3O^+ + 3HSO_4^-. \tag{129}$$

Dinitrogen trioxide and metal nitrites react with sulphuric acid to give fully ionized nitrosonium hydrogen sulphate

$$N_2O_3 + 3H_2SO_4 = 2NO^+ + H_3O^+ + 3HSO_4^-$$ (130)

$$NaNO_2 + 3H_2SO_4 = NO^+ + Na^+ + H_3O^+ + 3HSO_4^-$$ (131)

and dinitrogen tetroxide behaves as nitrosyl nitrate since it gives a mixture of nitronium and nitrosonium hydrogen sulphate (Gillespie et al., 1950; Millen, 1950b):

$$N_2O_4 + 3H_2SO_4 = NO_2^+ + NO^+ + H_3O^+ + 3HSO_4^-.$$ (132)

Like triphenylamine, triphenylphosphine is a strong base, being fully protonated according to the equation

$$Ph_3P + H_2SO_4 = Ph_3PH^+ + HSO_4^-.$$ (133)

In addition it undergoes rather slow sulphonation and/or oxidation.

Phosphoric acid behaves as a strong base, as is shown, for example, by cryoscopic and conductimetric measurements on KH_2PO_4 (Gillespie et al., 1965), which give $\nu = 4$ and $\gamma = 2$, in agreement with ionization according to the equation

$$KH_2PO_4 + 2H_2SO_4 = K^+ + H_4PO_4^+ + 2HSO_4^-.$$ (134)

For potassium diphosphate $\nu = 12$ and $\gamma = 5$ indicating that diphosphoric acid dehydrates sulphuric acid to give the $P(OH)_4^+$ ion (Gillespie et al., 1965)

$$K_4P_2O_7 + 7H_2SO_4 = 4K^+ + 2P(OH)_4^+ + HS_2O_7^- + 5HSO_4^-.$$ (135)

Cryoscopic and conductimetric measurements have shown that trimeric phosphonitrilic chloride $(PNCl_2)_3$ accepts 1·2 protons in sulphuric acid while the tetramer is more extensively protonated accepting approximately 2·0 protons (Paddock, 1964).

F. ARSENIC, ANTIMONY, AND BISMUTH

Arsenic pentoxide is insoluble in sulphuric acid at room temperature, and only dissolves to a very small extent at temperatures near the boiling point of the acid. Arsenious oxide, on the other hand, is moderately if rather slowly soluble in sulphuric acid. Cryoscopic and conductimetric measurements (Gillespie and Robinson, 1963a) have shown that it ionizes in an analogous manner to N_2O_3, forming $AsO.HSO_4$,

$$As_2O_3 + 3H_2SO_4 = 2AsO.HSO_4 + H_3O^+ + HSO_4^-.$$ (136)

Whereas the ionization of $NO.HSO_4$ is complete however, that of $AsO.HSO_4$ is only approximately 50% complete in a 0·05 molal solution of As_2O_3. If As_2O_3 behaved like N_2O_3, values of $\nu = 6$ and $\gamma = 3$ would be expected and at very low concentrations the observed values of ν and γ are indeed reasonably consistent with the formation of fully ionized $AsO.HSO_4$. The simplest explanation of the observed decrease in ν from 6·0–4·8 and in γ from 2·6–2·1 as the concentration of As_2O_3 increases from $0.01-0.07$ molal is that $AsO.HSO_4$ is incompletely ionized

$$AsO.SO_4H \rightleftharpoons AsO^+ + HSO_4^-. \tag{137}$$

Values of ν and γ decreasing towards 4 and 1, respectively, as the concentration of As_2O_3 increases, would then be expected. The experimental observations are reasonably consistent with this mode of reaction and an approximately constant value of the dissociation constant of $AsO.HSO_4$ ($K = 12$ moles kg^{-1}), may be calculated. However the decrease in ν is more rapid than that for γ. This may be explained by assuming that $AsO.HSO_4$ polymerizes at higher concentrations, for example, by the formation of a dimer,

$$As_2O_3 + 3H_2SO_4 = (AsO.HSO_4)_2 + H_3O^+ + HSO_4^-. \tag{138}$$

The ready formation of a white precipitate having the composition $As_2O_3.SO_3$ even from quite dilute solutions is also consistent with the formation of polymers for which structures VII or VIII seem reasonable

VII   VIII

An additional sulphuric acid molecule is needed to terminate such a chain, giving an –OH group at one end and a –HSO$_4$ group at the other end:

IX

The first two members of this series of polymers then represent solvated forms of $AsO.HSO_4$ and $(AsO.HSO_4)_2$, i.e. $HOAs(HSO_4)_2$ and $(HO)(SO_4H)AsOAs(SO_4H)_2$.

Similarly the species written above as AsO^+ is probably more correctly written in one of the solvated forms X or XI, which can be derived from $HOAs(HSO_4)_2$ by loss of HSO_4^- or by proton addition; similar dimeric ions XII and XIII are also possible.

X   XI

XII   XIII

It is unfortunate that the cryoscopic and conductimetric measurements do not enable one to distinguish between AsO^+ and the solvated forms X and XI. Raman spectroscopy, which established that NO^+ and NO_2^+ exist in solution in sulphuric acid in the unsolvated forms (Ingold *et al.*, 1950) cannot be used because solutions of sufficient concentration to give satisfactory spectra of the dissolved species cannot be obtained.

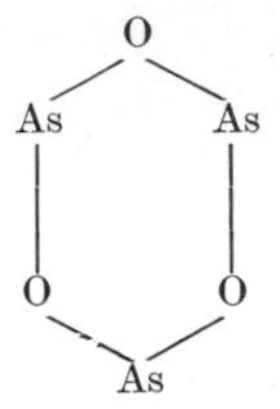

XIV 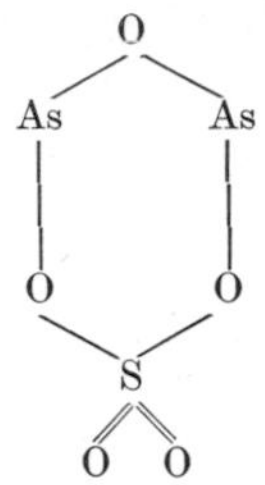   XV

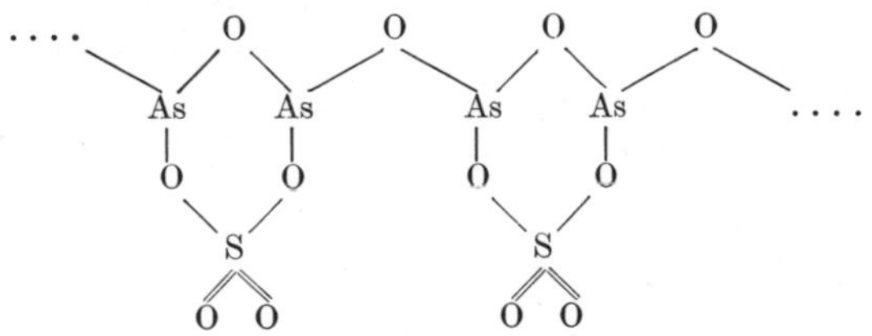

XVI

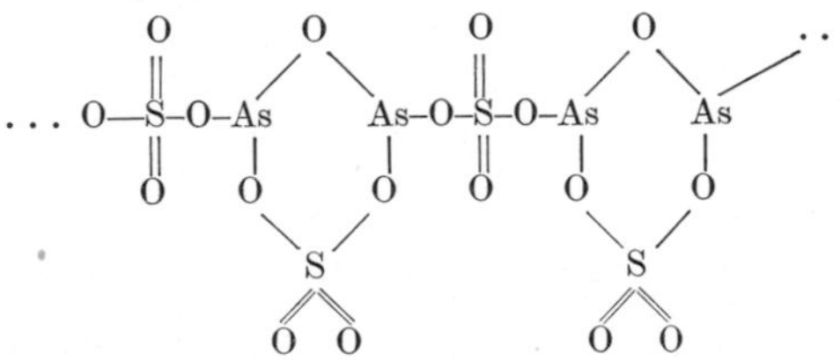

XVII

Early workers reported the preparation of several sulphato compounds of arsenic (III), e.g. $As_2O_3.SO_3$; $As_2O_3.2SO_3$; $As_2O_3.3SO_3$ (Adie, 1890; Stavenhagen, 1893; Mellor, 1922a) which are closely related to the species that have been found to occur in 100% H_2SO_4 and in oleum. In general oxygen compounds of arsenic (III) are found to have only single bonds to oxygen and As_4O_6 contains the six-membered ring XIV. Therefore it is postulated that the ring (XV) is an important structural unit in the sulphato compounds of arsenic (III). The ring (XV) is analogous to the ring (III) proposed for the sulphato compounds of boron. On this basis $As_2O_3.SO_3$ may be formulated as XVI and $As_2O_3.2SO_3$ as XVII.

Antimony trioxide is sparingly soluble in 100% sulphuric acid at its boiling point. On cooling white prisms of $Sb_2O_3.3SO_3$, i.e. $Sb_2(SO_4)_3$, are deposited (Mellor, 1922b). Other complexes obtained from aqueous sulphuric acid are $Sb_2O_3.2SO_3$ and $Sb_2O_3.SO_3$. Several workers have shown that these compounds are not fully hydrolysed by water and compounds such as $SbO.SO_4H$ and $(SbO)_2SO_4$ can be obtained. Clearly the behaviour of Sb_2O_3 in sulphuric acid is analogous to that of As_2O_3 but fully sulphated forms are preferentially formed under milder sulphating conditions. This reflects the lower electronegativity of Sb(III) compared to As(III). A number of salts of the acid $HSb(SO_4)_2$ have been prepared (Mellor, 1922b). They are insoluble in sulphuric acid at room temperature. It has been suggested that these salts contain discrete $Sb(SO_4)_2^-$ anions in which the two sulphate groups are chelated to antimony. However their insolubility in sulphuric acid makes it more probable that they contain polymeric anions in which sulphate groups bridge between antimony atoms.

Bismuth(III) sulphate is formed by evaporating Bi_2O_3 with sulphuric acid or from the nitrate and sulphuric acid. It is slowly hydrolysed in hot water to the bismuthyl compound $(BiO)_2SO_4$. Both the oxide and sulphate are very sparingly soluble in sulphuric acid at normal temperatures. Alkali metal salts, $MBi(SO_4)_2$, are formed when a metal sulphate is added to a boiling solution of Bi_2O_3 in concentrated sulphuric acid. These salts are very sparingly soluble in sulphuric acid and are similar in nature to the corresponding compounds of antimony (Mellor, 1922c).

G. VANADIUM, CHROMIUM, AND MANGANESE

Mishra and Symons (1962) have proposed on the basis of conductimetric measurements that V_2O_5 dissolves in 100% H_2SO_4 to give an equilibrium mixture of $VO(HSO_4)_3$ and $HOVO(HSO_4)_2$. A more extensive cryoscopic and conductimetric investigation has shown that in very dilute solution both V_2O_5 and NH_4VO_3 ionize to give only $VO(HSO_4)_3$ according to the equations

$$V_2O_5+9H_2SO_4 = 2VO(HSO_4)_3+3H_3O^++3HSO_4^- \qquad (139a)$$

$$NH_4VO_3+6H_2SO_4 = VO(HSO_4)_3+2H_3O^++NH_4^++3HSO_4^- \qquad (139b)$$

and that with increasing concentration polymeric species such as $[VO(HSO_4)_2]_2O$ are formed (Gillespie *et al.*, 1965).

Mishra and Symons (1962) have studied solutions of K_2CrO_4 in sulphuric acid and dilute oleum. They found that the solutions were relatively stable and that the conductimetric γ-value $\simeq 3$. This is consistent with the reaction

$$K_2CrO_4+4H_2SO_4 = \underset{\underset{O}{\overset{\|}{\|}}}{HO-Cr-O-} \underset{\underset{O}{\overset{\|}{\|}}}{S-OH} +2K^++H_3O^++3HSO_4^-. \qquad (140)$$

Chromatosulphuric acid H_2CrSO_7 has been previously described by Gilbert *et al.* (1922).

Potassium permanganate dissolves in slightly aqueous sulphuric acid to give green solutions. Solutions less concentrated than 0·01 molal were found to be stable for 24–36 hours in the absence of reducing agents but eventually deposited MnO_2 (Royer, 1961). More concentrated solutions quickly became turbid and precipitated a green solid which decomposed to MnO_2. Even for dilute solutions the decomposition was quite rapid when the solvent was anhydrous H_2SO_4 or oleum. Royer (1961) found that the cryoscopic ν-value varies with concentration from approximately six for a 0·00358 molal solution to approximately 4·2 for an 0·0145 molal solution, which was turbid. The cryoscopic ν-value also decreased with time to give a limiting value of approximately four after 3–12 hours. The conductimetric γ-value was found to decrease with time from approximately 2·6–2·0 in about 20 minutes at 25°. By extrapolation to zero time an initial γ-value of approximately 3·0 was obtained. Royer interpreted these results in terms of the formation of the permanganyl ion according to the following equation

$$KMnO_4 + 3H_2SO_4 = K^+ + H_3O^+ + MnO_3^+ + 3HSO_4^- \qquad (141)$$

and he attributed the decrease in ν and γ with time and with increasing concentration to the precipitation of insoluble permanganyl hydrogen sulphate

$$KMnO_4 + 3H_2SO_4 = K^+ + H_3O^+ + 2HSO_4^- + (MnO_3SO_4H)_{solid}. \qquad (142)$$

Mishra and Symons (1962) found that $KMnO_4$ decomposes slowly in 100% sulphuric acid and rapidly in dilute oleum to give oxygen and manganese dioxide or tervalent manganese. They found a γ-value of 2·0–2·2 but they do not mention any variation of this value with time. They also prefer to take the average of Royers ν-values, which is approximately 5, and to ignore the variation with time; consequently they favour the reaction

$$KMnO_4 + 3H_2SO_4 = K^+ + H_3O^+ + MnO_3SO_4H + 2HSO_4^-. \qquad (143)$$

These authors also carried out a conductimetric titration in which $KMnO_4$ was added to dilute oleum. They found the conductivity minimum at approximately half the r value for a similar titration with $KHSO_4$ (r = moles of solute/ moles of $H_2S_2O_7$). Since the latter minimum is at $r = 0·56$ the minimum with $KMnO_4$ is at approximately 0·28. They propose that the reaction

$$KMnO_4 + 2H_2S_2O_7 = MnO_3SO_4H + K^+ + H_2S_2O_7^- + H_2SO_4 \qquad (144)$$

would explain their results, but this would in fact give a conductivity minimum at $r = 0·36$. Provided the decomposition to give oxygen and MnO_2 may be justifiably ignored the conductimetric titration may be best explained by assuming the occurrence of further sulphation to give $MnO_2(SO_4H)_3$ according to the equation

$$KMnO_4 + 3H_2S_2O_7 = MnO_2(SO_4H)_3 + K^+ + HS_2O_7^- + H_2SO_4 \qquad (145)$$

which would give a conductivity minimum at $r = 0.26$ in close agreement with the observed value.

Unfortunately one must conclude that on the basis of the inadequate experimental evidence presented above no firm conclusions can be drawn concerning the behaviour of $KMnO_4$ in sulphuric acid.

H. SULPHUR, SELENIUM, AND TELLURIUM

Sulphur dioxide is moderately soluble in sulphuric acid (Miles and Carson, 1946) and gives a solution which has an electrical conductivity which is very slightly greater than that of the solvent (R. J. Gillespie and E. A. Robinson, unpublished results). This appears to be due to a very slight ionization according to the equation

$$SO_2 + H_2SO_4 = HSO_2^+ + HSO_4^- \qquad (146)$$

although Gold and Tye (1950) found very little change in the absorption spectrum of sulphur dioxide and oleum, and they concluded that there was very little interaction with the solvent and no evidence for any appreciable protonation. The solubility of sulphur dioxide is greater in oleum and increases rapidly with increase in the SO_3 concentration, i.e. with increasing acidity of the solvent (Miles and Carson, 1946). This suggests that the basicity of sulphur dioxide is essentially responsible for its solubility in sulphuric acid and oleum, presumably because of the formation of a hydrogen-bonded complex which precedes the proton transfer accompanying ionization

$$H_2SO_4 + SO_2 \rightarrow HSO_3.OH \cdots O{=}S{=}O \rightarrow HSO_4^- + {}^+HO{=}S{=}O. \quad (147)$$

It has been known for many years that selenium dioxide is soluble in sulphuric acid to give a bright yellow solution (Meyer and Langer, 1927). More recently it has been shown (Flowers et al., 1959) that in dilute solutions it behaves as a weak base

$$SeO_2 + H_2SO_4 \rightleftharpoons HSeO_2^+ + HSO_4^- \quad K_b = 4.4 \times 10^{-3} \qquad (148)$$

forming the $SeO.OH^+$ ion. It is probable that the unionized portion of the selenium dioxide is present as the hydrogen sulphate, $SeO(OH)(SO_4H)$. The reaction of selenium dioxide with sulphuric acid would then be more correctly written

$$SeO_2 + H_2SO_4 \rightarrow SeO(OH).HSO_4 \rightleftharpoons SeO.OH^+ + HSO_4^-. \qquad (149)$$

Small amounts of the ion $HSe_2O_4^+$ (XVIII) are also present in dilute solution of SeO_2 in sulphuric acid, together with unionized diselenious hydrogen sulphate, $Se_2O_3(OH)(HSO_4)$(XIX).

Relatively large amounts of this dimeric ion and probably higher polymeric ions are formed with increasing concentration of SeO_2.

When selenium dioxide is added to an oleum (Flowers et al., 1959) the conductivity decreases and passes through a minimum when one mole of SeO_2 has been added to each mole of disulphuric acid originally present in the oleum. The simplest interpretation of this result is that a largely union-ized complex $SeO_2.H_2S_2O_7$ is formed. This can probably be formulated as $SeO(HSO_4)_2$. Confirmation of such an unionized species is obtained from freezing point measurements which show that at the composition of minimum conductivity $\nu = 1.3$ for an initially 0·1 M solution of $H_2S_2O_7$. There is also some evidence for the existence of the corresponding derivative of diselenious acid, i.e. $Se_2O_3(HSO_4)_2$.

It is somewhat surprising that tellurium dioxide is insoluble in sulphuric acid (Mellor, 1922d) since compounds such as $2TeO_2.SO_3$ (Brauner, 1889) have been described and since it is soluble in acids such as HNO_3, $HClO_4$, and HSO_3F, from which solutions compounds such as $2TeO_2.HNO_3$ (Kon and Blois, 1958) and $2TeO_2.HClO_4$ (Fichter and Scmid, 1916) have been isolated. All these compounds can be regarded as derivatives of ditellurous acid, e.g. $Te_2O_3(OH)(NO_3)$, $Te_2O_3(OH)(ClO_4)$, and $Te_2O_3(SO_4)$. It seems likely that TeO_2 does form a sulphate when treated with sulphuric acid but that being highly polymeric it is insoluble.

I. HALOGENS

Recent measurements (R. J. Gillespie and E. K. Robinson, unpublished results) have shown that hydrogen chloride reacts quantitatively at low concentrations with sulphuric acid to give chlorosulphuric acid.

$$HCl + H_2SO_4 = HClSO_3 + H_3O^+ + HSO_4^-.$$

Many chlorides also react in a similar manner, e.g.

$$(CH_3)_3C_6H_2COCl + H_2SO_4 = (CH_3)_3C_6H_2CO^+ + HClSO_3 + H_3O^+ + 2HSO_4^-.$$
$$(150)$$

Perchloric acid and chlorosulphuric acid behave as very weak acids (Barr et al., 1961).

Solutions of iodic acid in sulphuric acid have been studied by the cryoscopic and conductimetric techniques by Arotsky et al. (1962) and by Gillespie and Senior (1964). The more extensive experiments of the latter authors show that iodic acid is not simply protonated as proposed by Arotsky et al.,

$$HIO_3 + H_2SO_4 = H_2IO_3^+ + HSO_4^- \tag{151}$$

but reacts to form unionized iodyl hydrogen sulphate $IO_2.HSO_4$

$$HIO_3 + 2H_2SO_4 = IO_2.HSO_4 + H_3O^+ + HSO_4^- \tag{152}$$

which is probably present in solution in solvated and polymerized forms such as **XX** and **XXI**. A white solid that separates from the solution on standing is probably a long-chain or three-dimensional polymer such as **XXII** or **XXIII**. There is no evidence that either of the simple ions IO_2^+ or $H_2IO_3^+$ exist in appreciable concentrations in sulphuric acid.

$$
\begin{array}{c}
SO_4H \\
| \\
I{<}^{O}_{OH} \\
| \\
SO_4H
\end{array}
$$

XX

$$
HSO_4\ \underset{O}{\overset{SO_4H}{I}}\ O\ \underset{O}{\overset{SO_4H}{I}}\ O\ \underset{OH}{\overset{SO_4H}{I}}
$$

XXI

$$
HSO_4\ \underset{O}{\overset{SO_4H}{I}}\ O\ \underset{O}{\overset{SO_4H}{I}}\ O\ \underset{O}{\overset{SO_4H}{I}}\ O\ \cdots\cdots\cdots\ \underset{O}{\overset{SO_4H}{I}}\ O\ \underset{OH}{\overset{SO_4H}{I{-}OH}}
$$

XXII

$$
\begin{array}{c}
\overset{O}{\underset{}{}}\ \ \overset{O}{}\ \ \overset{O}{} \\
-O-I-O-I-O-I- \\
| \quad | \quad | \\
SO_4 \ SO_4 \ SO_4 \\
| \quad | \quad | \\
-O-I-O-I-O-I-O \\
\overset{}{\underset{O}{}}\ \ \overset{}{\underset{O}{}}\ \ \overset{}{\underset{O-}{}}
\end{array}
\qquad
\begin{array}{c}
O \quad O \\
\| \quad \| \\
O-I-O-I-O \\
| \quad | \\
SO_4 \ SO_4 \\
| \quad | \\
O-I-O-I-O \\
\| \quad \| \\
O \quad O
\end{array}
$$

XXIII

Yellow iodous sulphate $(IO)_2SO_4$, "Chretiens sulphate", is obtained by reacting iodine with iodic acid in sulphuric acid (Chretien, 1895, 1896). Infra-red studies have shown that this compound and the related $(IO)_2SeO_4$ and $IO.IO_3$ are probably ionic and contain the polymeric iodyl ion $(IO^+)_n$ (Dasent and Waddington, 1960). In solution in sulphuric acid iodosyl sulphate reacts with nitrobenzene to give m-iodosonitrobenzene suggesting that the simple iodosyl cation is present in the sulphuric acid solutions. More reactive substrates such as benzene and chlorobenzene give a quantitative yield of the diaryliodonium sulphate. Masson and Hanby (1938) suggested that this latter product arises from I^{3+} ions present in small concentration in equilibrium with the IO^+,

$$IO^+ + 2H^+ = I^{3+} + H_2O \tag{153}$$

the formation of the diaryl iodonium sulphate taking place in the following manner

$$I^{3+} + RH = H^+ + RI^{2+} \tag{154}$$
$$RI^{2+} + RH = H^+ + R_2I^+. \tag{155}$$

The above equilibrium should shift to the right with the removal of water and indeed the yellow sulphate is transformed to a white compound in oleum

7

(Masson and Argument, 1938). This compound has the composition $I_2(SO_4)_3.H_2SO_4$; it may be regarded as a partially desolvated form of $I(HSO_4)_3$. Cryoscopic and conductimetric measurements on solutions of iodosyl sulphate in sulphuric acid show (R. J. Gillespie and J. B. Senior, unpublished results) that it is not a non-electrolyte as claimed by Arotsky *et al.* (1962) but is converted to the hydrogen sulphate, which is about 50% ionized in the dilute solutions studied

$$(IO)_2SO_4 + H_2SO_4 \leftrightharpoons IO^+ + 2HSO_4^-. \qquad (156)$$

In dilute oleum $IO.HSO_4$ forms the more sulphated dimer $I_2O(HSO_4)_4$ and with excess oleum the fully sulphated iodine tri(hydrogen sulphate), $I(HSO_4)_3$. The white solid that results from the action of oleum on iodosyl sulphate is the partially desolvated form $I(SO_4)(HSO_4)$ which possibly has the linear polymeric structure XXIV or is the similar ionic compound $[I(SO_4)^+]_n HSO_4^-$ while the normal sulphate $I_2(SO_4)_3$ is no doubt a three-dimensional polymer such as XXV.

XXIV

XXV

Iodine dioxide, $(IO_2)_n$, behaves as expected as a compound of I(III) and I(V) and dissolves in sulphuric acid to give $IO_2.HSO_4$ and $IO.HSO_4$ (R. J. Gillespie and J. B. Senior, unpublished results).

Masson (1938) showed that iodine dissolves in solutions of iodosyl sulphate in concentrated sulphuric acid giving brown solutions, which react smoothly with chlorobenzene to give a mixture of chlorotriiodobenzenes and a precipitate of elementary iodine. The rapidity of the reaction and the fact that the brown solute is stable only in strongly acid media, led to the conclusion that the iodine was present in a cationic form. From the stoichiometry of the reactions with chlorobenzene of solutions containing different ratios of iodine to iodosyl sulphate, Masson deduced the existence of the ions I^+, I_3^+, and I_5^+.

The freezing points and conductivities of sulphuric acid solutions containing iodine and iodic acid have been studied. At the mole ratio $I_2/HIO_3 = 7.0$ the observed values of ν and γ are in excellent agreement with the formation I_3^+ according to the equation

$$HIO_3 + 7I_2 + 8H_2SO_4 = 5I_3^+ + 3H_3O^+ + 8HSO_4^-. \qquad (157)$$

Although more iodine can be dissolved in such solutions to give mole ratios $I_2/HIO_3 > 7.0$, the freezing points and conductivities of the solutions remain constant and independent of the amount of iodine added. This can only be due to the formation of I_5^+

$$I_3^+ + I_2 = I_5^+. \tag{158}$$

At the mole ratio $I_2/HIO_3 = 2.0$ the formation of I^+ would be represented by the equation

$$HIO_3 + 2I_2 + 8H_2SO_4 = 5I^+ + 3H_3O^+ + 8HSO_4^- \tag{159}$$

for which $\nu = 16$, $\gamma = 8$ and $\nu - \gamma = 8$. If $IHSO_4$ were a non-electrolyte the corresponding equation would be

$$HIO_3 + 2I_2 + 8H_2SO_4 = 5IHSO_4 + 3H_3O^+ + 3HSO_4^- \tag{160}$$

$$\nu = 11, \qquad \gamma = 3 \text{ and } \nu - \gamma = 8.$$

It was found that ν decreased from 8·5–7·7, γ from 3·5–3·3 and $\nu - \gamma$ from 5·0–4·4 with increasing concentration. These results are not in agreement with the quantitative formation of either I^+ or $I.HSO_4$. Much better agreement with the observed values is given by the equation

$$4IHO_3 + 8I_2 + 17H_2SO_4 = 5I_3^+ + 7H_3O^+ + 5IO.HSO_4 \tag{161}$$

$$\nu = 8.5 - 7.25, \ \gamma = 4.25 - 3, \ \nu - \gamma = 4.25.$$

As $IO.HSO_4$ is known to be partially ionized, the values for ν and γ quoted above represent extreme values corresponding to degrees of dissociation of 0 and 100% respectively. The observed values of ν and γ are a little higher than would be expected in the most dilute solutions studied and this may indicate that at these concentrations a small amount of I^+ or $I.HSO_4$ is present. The disproportionation of I^+ can be written

$$4I^+ + H_2O + 2HSO_4^- = IO^+ + I_3^+ + 2HSO_4^- \tag{162}$$

and it is clear that the equilibrium will be shifted in favour of an increasing amount of disproportionation with increasing concentration.

It has been claimed that the deep blue solutions formed by dissolving iodine in oleum contain I^+ and that absorption bands observed at 640, 500 and 410 mμ may be attributed to this species (Symons, 1957). The brown solutions containing I_3^+ have absorption maxima at 290 and 460 mμ. Solutions containing the solutes in the mole ratio $I_2/HIO_3 = 2.0$, corresponding to the stoichiometric formation of I^+, have the strong absorption band at 640 mμ characteristic of I^+ and also a strong band at 460 mμ overlapping with the 500 and 410 mμ bands of I^+. The relative intensities of the absorptions indicate that in the particular solutions studied about one-third of the iodine was present as I^+, the rest having undergone disproportionation (Symons, 1957). As the solutions were much more dilute than those used in the cryoscopic studies the smaller extent of disproportionation is not surprising.

Addition of ICl or IBr to a solution containing iodine and iodic acid in the mole ratio $I_2/HIO_3 = 2$ gave results very similar to those obtained on adding iodine and it was concluded that the I_2Cl^+ and I_2Br^+ ions are formed respectively.

J. TRANSITION METAL COMPLEXES

It has been shown, by observing the appearance of the characteristic high-field resonance in the n.m.r. spectrum due to hydrogen bonded to a transition metal, that a number of metal, carbonyl and cyclopentadienyl complexes protonate on the metal in sulphuric acid (Davison *et al.*, 1962a). For example the triphenylphosphine and triphenylarsine iron carbonyls $PPh_3Fe(CO)_4$, $AsPh_3Fe(CO)_4$, $(PPh_3)_2Fe(CO)_3$ and $(AsPh_3)_2Fe(CO)_3$ all give stable yellow solutions in 98% sulphuric acid. The proton resonance spectra of these solutions show high-field proton resonances attributable to Fe–H at $\tau \sim 18$. The relative intensities of the high-field lines and the phenyl groups show that the carbonyls function as monoacid bases, e.g.

$$Fe(CO)_4PPh_3 + H_2SO_4 = HFe(CO)_4PPh_3^+ + HSO_4^-. \tag{163}$$

A number of tricarbonyl arenes of chromium dissolve readily in sulphuric acid solution to give yellow solutions which may contain the corresponding conjugate acids, but they decompose rather rapidly.

The purple-red binuclear compounds $[\pi-C_5H_5Mo(CO)_3]_2$ and $[\pi-C_5H_5W(CO)_3]_2$ give red-brown solutions in sulphuric acid which decompose only slowly in the absence of air and which contain the protonated complexes. The chemical shifts in the n.m.r. spectrum of the proton bound to the metal are exceptionally large, $\tau = 30-40$. Additional evidence that the hydrogen is directly associated with the metal atom comes from the observation of satellite peaks in the spectra of the tungsten compounds which may be attributed to spin-coupling of the proton with the ^{183}W tungsten isotope. The satellite spectrum shows that the proton is in some way associated with both metal atoms in these complexes and from a detailed consideration of the spectrum it was concluded that the proton undergoes rapid intramolecular exchange between the two tungsten atoms.

The binuclear iron complex $[\pi-C_5H_5Fe(CO)_2]_2$ is soluble in sulphuric acid and gives a high-field line in the n.m.r. spectrum with a relative area to the $\pi-C_5H_5$ line of 1 : 10 clearly showing that $[\pi-C_5H_5Fe(CO)_2]_2$ is monobasic. Cryoscopic studies have given slightly high ν-values of 2·3 and 2·4. The reason for this is not known and unfortunately there appear to have been no other cryoscopic studies of compounds of this type with which comparison might be made. The neutral compound has a band in the infra-red spectrum at 1785 cm^{-1} which has been attributed to a bridging carbonyl group. This band is absent in the spectrum of the sulphuric acid solution. It is also absent in the mull spectrum of the hexafluorophosphate salt obtained by treating a solution of the compound in HF with phosphorus pentachloride. The protonated species therefore appears to have two $—C_5H_5Fe(CO)_2$ units linked by a metal–metal bond and the proton can be considered to be in a position comparable to that in the tungsten and molybdenum species and undergoing rapid intramolecular exchange.

Carbonyl–olefin–metal complexes behave differently on protonation in sulphuric acid (Davison *et al.*, 1962b). No transition metal–hydrogen bond is formed; instead the proton adds to the olefin ligand to give what can be regarded as "carbonium ions" bound to and stabilized by the carbonyl metal portion. Tricarbonylcyclo-octatetrane iron is readily soluble in sulphuric acid to give a red solution. The proton n.m.r. spectrum does not contain any high-field line characteristic of a metal–hydrogen bond and the spectrum is consistent with protonation on the ring to give the tricarbonylbicyclo(5,10) octadieniumiron cation

164

Somewhat surprisingly, however, the spectrum differs substantially from that of the free bicyclo(5,10)octadienium cation (Section IV I, 1).

Tricarbonylcycloheptatriene ion is protonated in sulphuric acid to give the $C_7H_9Fe(CO)_3^+$ cation.

165

A number of cyano complexes have been investigated in acid solution and it has been shown that they protonate on the cyano groups and not on the metal atom (Schilt, 1963). For example $H[Fe(phen)(CN)_4]$ gives a bright yellow solution in concentrated sulphuric acid. From the changes in the visible spectrum that occur on dilution of the solution with water it was concluded that the $[Fe(phen)(CNH)_4]^{3+}$ ion is formed. Contrary to earlier reports it was found that tris-(1,10 phenanthroline)iron(II) and the analogous 2,2-bipyridine complex do not possess any measurable affinity for acids. The gradual change in colour that occurs in solutions of these complexes in concentrated sulphuric acid is due to oxidation.

K. CHELATION BY THE SULPHATE GROUP

We have formulated various sulphato compounds as containing bridging sulphate groups as in **XXVI** rather than bidentate sulphate groups as in **XXVII**

XXVI   XXVII

as there appears to be no direct evidence that the sulphate group behaves as a dichelate group whereas several compounds are known where it apparently functions as a bridging group.

In the case of the sulphato-boron compounds, it is of interest to compare the proposed structures with that of methylene sulphate which has been shown (Baker and Field, 1932) to be dimeric in benzene and therefore presumably has structure **XXVIII** rather than **XXIX**

XXVIII   XXIX

Since boron has nearly the same radius as carbon, it is reasonable that sulphato-boron compounds should have similar structures. Comparison with trimethylene sulphate is also appropriate. This compound is monomeric in benzene (Baker and Field, 1932) and can therefore be formulated as in **XXX** containing a six membered ring.

XXX

Chelation by the sulphate group seems possible in many compounds e.g. $H_3Fe(SO_4)(C_2O_4)_2$, $H_3Fe(SO_4)_2.C_2O_4$, $M_2Pb(SO_4)_3$, $K_3Ce(SO_4)_3.H_2O$, $Sb_2(SO_4)_3$, etc. However in all of these cases there is no direct evidence to support this kind of bonding and it is possible that the structures are more complex than the simple molecular formula implies and contain bridging sulphate groups. There are several compounds in which the presence of a bridging sulphate group appears to be established. For example, the compound diethyl germanium sulphate has been shown by cryoscopy to be dimeric in acetone (Anderson, 1950) and therefore presumably has structure XXXI and structures such as XXXII have been suggested for the salts formed by the reaction of chelating diamines with bis(tetraethyl digold sulphate) (Evans and Gibson, 1941).

$$
\begin{array}{ccc}
Et & SO_4 & Et \\
\diagdown\,\diagup & & \diagdown\,\diagup \\
Ge & & Ge \\
\diagup\,\diagdown & & \diagup\,\diagdown \\
Et & SO_4 & Et
\end{array}
$$

XXXI

$$
(Et_2Au\ dipy)_2^+ \qquad \left[\begin{array}{ccc}
Et & SO_4 & Et \\
\diagdown\,\diagup & & \diagdown\,\diagup \\
Au & & Au \\
\diagup\,\diagdown & & \diagup\,\diagdown \\
Et & SO_4 & Et
\end{array} \right]^{2-}
$$

XXXII

Several cases are known where the sulphate group behaves as a bridging group between two metal atoms which are also joined by some other bridging group such as NH_2, OH, or H_2O. Nakamoto and co-workers (1957) have examined the infra-red spectrum of XXXIII and have concluded that the sulphate group has C_{2v} symmetry and is therefore a bridging group. However Barraclough and Tobe (1961) claim that it is not easy to distinguish between a bridging sulphate group and a chelate sulphate group on the basis of the infra-red spectrum.

$$
\left[\begin{array}{c}
NH_2 \\
(NH_3)_4CO \diagup \diagdown Co(NH_3)_4 \\
\diagdown \diagup \\
SO_4
\end{array} \right] (NO_3)_3
$$

XXXIII

IV. ORGANIC SOLUTES

A. SIMPLE BASES

Many ketones, aldehydes, carboxylic acids, anhydrides, ethers, amines, amides, nitriles, nitro compounds, sulphoxides, sulphones, and some ethylenic and aromatic hydrocarbons are simply converted to their conjugate acids (Gillespie and Leisten, 1954). In cases where ionization is incomplete relative basicities have been measured by cryoscopic, conductimetric and spectroscopic methods. Results of such measurements are given in Table XVIII.

TABLE XVIII

Dissociation Constants for Weak Bases

Base	Conductimetric	Cryoscopic	Spectroscopic	Titration*
p-Butylnitrobenzene	—	$0 \cdot 10^d$	$0 \cdot 10^h$	—
p-Nitrotoluene	$0 \cdot 095^a$ $0 \cdot 105^g$	$0 \cdot 094^d$	$0 \cdot 080^e$ $0 \cdot 090^h$	—
o-Nitrotoluene	$0 \cdot 067^a$ $0 \cdot 073^g$	$0 \cdot 062^d$	—	—
m-Nitrotoluene	$0 \cdot 023^a$ $0 \cdot 028^g$	$0 \cdot 020^d$	$0 \cdot 021^e$ $0 \cdot 025^h$	$0 \cdot 024^f$
Nitrobenzene	$0 \cdot 010^a$ $0 \cdot 013^g$	$0 \cdot 011^d$	$0 \cdot 007^e$ $0 \cdot 0096^h$	$0 \cdot 013^f$
p-Chloronitrobenzene	$0 \cdot 004^a$ $0 \cdot 0057^g$	$0 \cdot 003^a$	$0 \cdot 005^e$ $0 \cdot 0042^h$	—
o-Chlorobenzene	$0 \cdot 0024^g$	—	—	—
m-Chlorobenzene	$0 \cdot 0013^g$	—	$0 \cdot 0011^h$	—
Nitromethane	$0 \cdot 0025^a$	$0 \cdot 004†$	—	—
Acetonitrile	$0 \cdot 16^b$	—	—	—
Benzonitrile	$0 \cdot 07^b$	—	—	—
Dimethylsulphone	$0 \cdot 0148^c$	$0 \cdot 0150^c$	—	$0 \cdot 0145^c$
Diethylsulphone	$0 \cdot 0119^c$	$0 \cdot 0120^c$	—	$0 \cdot 0123^c$
Di-n-propylsulphone	$0 \cdot 0051^c$	$0 \cdot 0048^c$	—	$0 \cdot 0052^c$
Di-n-butylsulphone	$0 \cdot 0039^c$	$0 \cdot 0041^c$	—	$0 \cdot 0040^c$
Tetramethylenesulphone	$0 \cdot 0039^c$	$0 \cdot 0036^c$	—	$0 \cdot 0036^c$
2,4-Dinitrotoluene	$0 \cdot 0005^g$	—	$0 \cdot 0006^e$	
1,2-Dinitrobenzene	$0 \cdot 0003^g$	—	—	
1,3-Dinitrobenzene	$0 \cdot 0003^g$	—	—	
1,4-Dinitrobenzene	$0 \cdot 0003^g$	—	—	

* Titration of base against solution of $H_2S_2O_7$ in H_2SO_4.
† Measured in slightly aqueous H_2SO_4.
[a] Gillespie and Solomons (1957).
[b] Liler and Kosanovic (1958).
[c] Hall and Robinson (1964).
[d] Gillespie and Robinson (1957).
[e] R. J. Gillespie and E. A. Robinson, unpublished experiments.
[f] Flowers et al. (1960).
[g] Liler (1962).
[h] Brand et al. (1952).

B. POLYBASIC COMPOUNDS

The position and extent of protonation of a polybasic compound depends on the intrinsic basicity of each group, their spatial separation and the mesomeric interaction between them.

The intrinsic basicity of an amino group is such that, generally, in a polyamine the amino groups are all protonated regardless of their position in the molecule. Thus o-phenylene diamine produces a threefold depression of the freezing point indicating diprotonation (Leisten, 1964) and it has been shown by conductivity measurements that all four of the nitrogen atoms of

evidence for the now generally accepted view that amides protonate on oxygen rather than on nitrogen. It has been shown, for example, that the relative areas of the nitrogen proton resonance and the methyl group resonance of acetamide in sulphuric acid are in the ratio 2 : 3 (Bunton *et al.*, 1962). If protonation was on nitrogen, the two peaks of equal area would be obtained. It has also been shown that spin–spin coupling between the nitrogen protons and the methyl-protons of N-methyl acetamide in 100% sulphuric acid produces a doublet spectrum for the methyl group, whereas N-protonation would have produced a triplet spectrum (Berger *et al.*, 1959). In sulphuric acid at room temperature it is not possible to observe a separate signal in the n.m.r. spectrum for the protonated carbonyl group because of rapid exchange with the solvent. However in fluorosulphuric acid at low temperatures exchange with the solvent is slowed down sufficiently that a signal from the $C=OH^+$ group is observed at very low field (Birchall and Gillespie, 1963; Gillespie and Birchall, 1963).

Leisten has studied the rate of hydrolysis of a number of amides in 100% H_2SO_4 (Leisten, 1960)

$$R.C(OH^+)NHR + HSO_4^- + 2H_2SO_4 \rightarrow RCO_2H_2^+ + RNH_3^+ + HSO_4^- + HS_2O_7^-.$$

$$(166)$$

He finds that as the composition of the medium is changed from aqueous sulphuric acid towards 100% H_2SO_4 the usual A2 mechanism, involving a bimolecular attack of a water molecule on the amide conjugate acid, is replaced by the A1 mechanism in which the rate determining step is the unimolecular heterolysis of the N-protonated amide

(167a)

$$RCONH_2R^+ \xrightarrow{\text{Slow}} RCO^+ + RNH_2 \qquad (167b)$$

$$RNH_2 + H^+ \xrightarrow{\text{Fast}} RNH_3^+ \qquad (167c)$$

$$RCO + H_2O \xrightarrow{\text{Fast}} RCO_2H^+. \qquad (167d)$$

In order to explain the observation that addition of an acid such as $H_2S_2O_7$ or HSO_3Cl increases the rate while addition of a base such as water decreases the rate Leisten proposed that the reaction is subject to general acid catalysis as a consequence of the fact that step (c) occurs synchronously with step (a).

It has been shown by means of cryoscopic measurements that urea, urethane and N-methylurethane are monoprotonated in sulphuric acid (Holstead *et al.*, 1953). This conclusion has been confirmed in the case of urea by conductimetric measurements and it has also been shown that tetramethylurea is completely monoprotonated and is probably diprotonated to the extent of about 10% in a 0·05 M solution (T. Birchall, J. Gauldie and R. J. Gillespie, unpublished work).

D. ESTERS

The esters of carboxylic acids generally undergo hydrolysis in sulphuric acid. However a number of esters such as methyl and ethyl benzoate and ethyl acetate react only slowly at room temperature and freezing point measurements show that initially they are simply protonated. On pouring the sulphuric acid solutions onto ice the ester is recovered in good yield (Kothner, 1901; Hantzsch, 1907; Oddo and Scandola, 1910). It is generally assumed, but has not been proved, that protonation occurs on the carbonyl oxygen.

Graham (1943) showed that the hydrolysis of methyl benzoate is of zero order with respect to water in 98–100% sulphuric acid. He concluded that the reaction is unimolecular. Leisten (1956) has measured the rate cyroscopically in aqueous H_2SO_4, 100% H_2SO_4 and in dilute oleum. He showed that the first-order rate constant is independent of the initial concentration of the ester and therefore of the concentration of hydrogen sulphate ion, since methyl benzoate is ionized as a strong base. These results therefore eliminate the possibility of a rate-determining attack by hydrogen sulphate ion on the conjugate acid. The rates are similar in slightly aqueous acid and in 100% acid and a little greater in oleum, clearly indicating that water is not involved in the rate-determining step. Unimolecular heterolysis can proceed by either acyl–oxygen fission ($A_{AC}1$) or alkyl–oxygen fission ($A_{AL}1$).

$$A_{ac} \qquad\qquad A_{al}$$

Electron-donating substituents in R' should aid, and in R retard $A_{AC}1$ heterolysis but have the opposite effects on $A_{AL}1$ heterolysis. Conversely electron-attracting substituents in R' should retard and in R aid the $A_{AC}1$ heterolysis but have contrary effects in the $A_{AL}1$ case. Graham (1943) found that the rate of hydrolysis of methyl p-toluate was four times that of methyl benzoate and concluded that the mechanism was $A_{AC}1$. Qualitative comparisons of rate have been made for a large number of esters by Kuhn and Corwin (1948) and by Bradley and Hill (1955) and all their results show the effects predicted for the $A_{AC}1$ mechanism. The rate of hydrolysis of alkyl benzoates varies in the following manner $Me > Et < i-Pr < t-Bu$

indicating a change in mechanism between Et and i–Pr. Leisten showed that the introduction of a p-nitro group into ethyl benzoate leads to a sixtyfold decrease in rate whereas in the case of isopropyl benzoate it leads to a two hundredfold increase. Thus the change in mechanism in the hydrolysis of this series of esters is from $A_{AC}1$ in the case of methyl and ethyl benzoate to $A_{AL}1$ in the cases of isopropyl and tertbutyl benzoate. These esters give an initial ν value of 2·0 which increases as hydrolysis proceeds to a limiting value of 3·0. Thus the overall equation for the hydrolysis may be written

$$PhCO_2Me + 2H_2SO_4 = PhCO_2H_2^+ + HSO_4^- + MeHSO_4. \tag{168}$$

By introducing sufficiently electron-attracting substituents in R it is possible to cause even the ethyl esters to hydrolyse by alkyl–oxygen fission. Thus it has been found that the rate of hydrolysis of their ethyl esters increases in the series p-nitro < 4-chloro-3-nitro < 3,5-dinitrobenzoic acid (Kershaw and Leisten, 1960)

Methyl mesitoate gives a constant ν-value of 5 (Treffers and Hammett, 1937) indicating that it undergoes rapid and complete hydrolysis, presumably by acyl–oxygen fission, to give a stable acyl ion.

$$C_6H_2Me_3CO_2Me + 2H_2SO_4 = C_6H_2Me_3CO^+ + H_3O^+ + MeHSO_4 + 2HSO_4^-. \tag{169}$$

It is noteworthy that esters of mesitoic acid are hydrolysed only with great difficulty in aqueous solution. Their ionization in sulphuric acid consequently provides a useful method of hydrolysing such esters; the free acid is easily recovered by pouring the solution onto ice. The reverse process, the esterification of mesitoic and related acids which is difficult by normal methods can also be carried out conveniently by pouring a sulphuric acid solution into the required alcohol (Newman, 1940).

E. CARBOXYLIC ANHYDRIDES

Acetic and benzoic anhydrides give fourfold depressions of the freezing point of 100% sulphuric acid (Gillespie, 1950c), but in slightly aqueous sulphuric acid $\nu = 2$ (Leisten, 1955). Conductivity measurements indicate the formation of one hydrogen sulphate ion from each molecule of anhydride (Flowers et al., 1956). These results provide strong evidence for the following mode of ionization

$$(RCO)_2O + 3H_2SO_4 = 2RCO_2H_2^+ + HS_2O_7^- + HSO_4^- \tag{170}$$

in 100% H_2SO_4 and

$$(RCO)_2O + H_2SO_4 + H_3O^+ = 2RCO_2H_2^+ + HSO_4^- \tag{171}$$

in aqueous sulphuric acid.

Phthalic anhydride gives a freezing point depression in 100% sulphuric acid that is only 10–15% greater than for a non-electrolyte (Hantzsch, 1907; Oddo and Casalino, 1917a; Leisten, 1960) and conductivity measurements show that it gives 1·14–1·18 hydrogen sulphate ions (Flowers *et al.*, 1956a). This is very probably due to incomplete protonation. However in slightly aqueous sulphuric acid it produces a much smaller freezing point depression because of conversion to protonated phthalic acid (Leisten, 1961).

$$
\begin{array}{c}
\text{CO} \\
\text{CO}
\end{array}\!\!\!O + H_3O^+ = \begin{array}{c}
CO_2H_2^+ \\
C_2OH
\end{array} \tag{172}
$$

Complete conversion to the conjugate acid of phthalic acid would give $\nu = 0$. Phthalic acid gives a slightly greater than twofold depression of the freezing point of slightly aqueous sulphuric acid as a consequence of the formation of its conjugate acid

$$
\begin{array}{c}
CO_2H \\
CO_2H
\end{array} + H_2SO_4 \rightarrow \begin{array}{c}
CO_2H_2^+ \\
CO_2H
\end{array} + HSO_4^- \tag{173}
$$

and possibly some further slight protonation on the second carboxyl group. However in sulphuric acid containing HSO_4^- and $HS_2O_7^-$ phthalic acid gives ν-values of only slightly greater than unity (Leisten, 1961) because $HS_2O_7^-$ dehydrates the acid to give the anhydride,

$$
\begin{array}{c}
CO_2H \\
CO_2H
\end{array} + HS_2O_7^- = \begin{array}{c}
CO \\
CO
\end{array}\!\!\!O + HSO_4^- + H_2SO_4 \tag{174}
$$

for which $\nu = 1$ if no further protonation occurs. Clearly the equilibrium between the acid and the anhydride is critically balanced in the region of 100% sulphuric acid and a slight excess of water shifts the equilibrium to the acid side while a slight excess of sulphur trioxide shifts it to the anhydride side. Maleic acid and anhydride behave in a similar manner. Succinic acid also behaves similarly except that the second stage of protonation of the acid is about 50% complete and the anhydride is also about 50% converted to its conjugate acid in sulphuric acid containing small amounts of HSO_4^- (Leisten, 1961).

F. ETHERS

Aliphatic ethers behave as strong or moderately strong bases in sulphuric acid giving initial ν-values of two or less (Oddo and Scandola, 1910; Gillespie and Leisten, 1954; Jaques and Leisten, 1961). Such solutions are however not generally stable and the freezing point of the solution decreases. In the case of diethyl and certain other aliphatic ethers Oddo and Scandola (1910) were able to isolate small quantities of the corresponding alkyl hydrogen sulphates after the ethers had stood for a short time in solution in sulphuric acid. This result and the fact that the ν-value eventually reaches a constant limiting value of approximately four indicates that complete solvolysis occurs according to the equation

$$RR'O + 3H_2SO_4 = RHSO_4 + R'HSO_4 + H_3O^+ + HSO_4^-. \qquad (175)$$

From the rate of variation of ν with time rates of solvolysis have been obtained for a number of ethers (Jaques and Leisten, 1961). The results are consistent with a mechanism in which the rate-determining step is a unimolecular fission of the conjugate acid or of some other ether–solvent complex to produce the more stable of the two possible carbonium ions. Somewhat surprisingly the rate of solvolysis is reduced by added hydrogen sulphate and even more by added water. If the complex undergoing unimolecular fission were the conjugate acid, hydrogen sulphates and water should both have the same effect. Therefore the following pre-equilibrium has been postulated (Jaques and Leisten, 1961) in order to account for the solvent effects

$$RR'OH^+ + SO_3 \rightleftharpoons RR'SO_4H^+ \qquad (176)$$

followed by

$$R\overset{\frown}{\underset{\underset{\displaystyle SO_3H}{|}}{-}O-R'} \rightarrow R^+ + R'SO_4H \qquad (177)$$

The carbonium ion formed by the heterolysis unites rapidly with a hydrogen sulphate ion. The observed solvent effects would be expected for this mechanism because the solvent-self-dissociation in which SO_3 is formed

$$2H_2SO_4 = SO_3 + HSO_4^- + H_3O^+ \qquad (178)$$

is repressed more strongly by water than by hydrogen sulphate ion alone. Preliminary experiments on aryl alkyl ethers have indicated that in some cases at least the mechanism is different and it is the conjugate acid that undergoes heterolysis (Jaques and Leisten, 1961). However, in view of the fact that at low temperatures in fluorosulphuric acid anisole has been shown to protonate on an aromatic carbon rather than on oxygen, further studies are clearly needed before the nature and mechanism of the reaction of aromatic ethers with sulphuric acid are established with certainty.

G. NITRILES

Hantzsch (1908) found by means of cryoscopic measurement that nitriles are not completely ionized in sulphuric acid. This conclusion has recently been confirmed by conductometric measurements and dissociation constants of 0·16 and 0·07 have been obtained for acetonitrile and benzonitrile respectively (Liler and Kosanovic, 1958). However solutions of these nitriles are not stable and hydrolysis to the corresponding amide occurs

$$RCN + 2H_2SO_4 = RCONH_2 + H_2S_2O_7. \qquad (179)$$

The rates of the reactions were followed by measuring the change in the conductivity of the solutions (Liler and Kosanovic, 1958). In both cases the hydrolysis was found to be second order and it was concluded that the rate determining step in the reaction is the attack of HSO_4^- ions on the conjugate acid of the nitrile

$$RCNH^+ + HSO_4^- = RCONH_2 + SO_3. \qquad (180)$$

H. CARBOXYLIC ACIDS

Most aliphatic and many aromatic carboxylic acids behave as fully ionized simple bases (Hantzsch, 1907; Oddo and Casalino, 1917b; Gillespie and Leisten, 1954). However electron-withdrawing substituents can reduce the basicity so that ionization is incomplete. Thus although acetic acid is a strong base, dichloracetic acid is a weak electrolyte and trichloracetic acid is a non-electrolyte (Gillespie and Wasif, 1953c).

Some substituted benzoic acids, e.g. mesitoic acid, undergo a complex ionization involving the elimination of water and the formation of a stable acyl ion (Treffers and Hammett, 1937)

$$Me_3C_6H_2CO_2H + 2H_2SO_4 = Me_3C_6H_2CO^+ + H_3O^+ + 2HSO_4^-. \qquad (181)$$

Mesitoic acid has $\nu = 4$, and $\gamma = 2$ (Treffers and Hammett, 1937; R. J. Gillespie and E. A. Robinson, unpublished results); on dilution of the sulphuric acid solution with water the acid is obtained and on dilution with methanol the methyl ester is obtained. Other acids, for example, 2,3,5,6-tetramethyl- and pentamethylbenzoic acids, behave in the same way (Newman and Deno, 1951a). 2,6-Dimethylbenzoic acid and 3,5-dibromo-2,4,6-trimethylbenzoic acid, which give $\nu = 3.5$ and 2.4 respectively, are believed to ionize partly in the above "complex" manner and partly as simple bases. A very similar type of ionization has been observed for certain aromatic keto-acids. For example, o-benzoylbenzoic acid has a ν-value of 4, which has been considered to indicate the following ionization (Newman et al., 1945):

$$(182)$$

Other acids which appear to behave in a similar manner are o-mesitoylbenzoic, 1,8-naphthaldehydic, and 4,5-phenanthaldehydic acid (Newman et al., 1945).

A number of carboxylic acids are unstable in sulphuric acid and decompose to give carbon monoxide

$$RCO_2H + 2H_2SO_4 = R^+ + CO + H_3O^+ + 2HSO_4^- \qquad (183)$$

e.g. formic acid

$$HCO_2H + H_2SO_4 = CO + H_3O^+ + HSO_4^- \qquad (184)$$

oxalic acid

$$(CO_2H)_2 + 2H_2SO_4 = CO + CO_2 + H_3O^+ + HSO_4^- \qquad (185)$$

α-keto acids

$$PhCO.CO_2H + 2H_2SO_4 = PhCO_2H_2^+ + CO + HSO_4^- \qquad (186)$$

α-hydroxy-acids

$$\begin{array}{c} CH_2CO_2H \\ | \\ CH(OH)CO_2H \end{array} + 2H_2SO_4 = \begin{array}{c} CH_2CO_2H \\ | \\ CH(OH)^+ \end{array} + H_3O^+ + CO + 2HSO_4^-$$

$$\begin{array}{c} \downarrow -H^+ \\ CH_2CO_2H \\ | \\ CHO \end{array} \qquad (187)$$

and triphenylacetic acid, diphenyl acetic acid, and bis-(p-chlorophenyl)-acetic acid (Welch and Smith, 1953; Gillespie and Leisten, 1954). Dicyclohexylacetic acid and 2,4,6-trimethylcyclohexane carboxylic acid also evolve carbon monoxide but the other products of the reactions have not been identified (Welch and Smith, 1953). The kinetics of the decompositions have been studied in the case of formic (de Right, 1933), oxalic (Lichty, 1907; Wiig, 1930; Liler, 1963), citric (Wiig, 1930), benzoylformic (Elliot and Hammick, 1951), triphenylacetic (Dittmar, 1929), and malic acids (Whitford, 1925). In each case the reaction is first order with respect to the organic compound and the rate decreases with increasing water content of the solvent. Liler (1963) has studied the decomposition of oxalic acid by means of conductimetric measurements. The initial conductivities enabled the degree of ionization of oxalic acid to be determined and the results agree well with previous cryoscopic measurements which showed that oxalic acid is only about 30% protonated (Oddo and Casalino, 1917b; Wiles, 1953). The decomposition rates obtained by Liler agree well with those found earlier by using a permanganate titration to follow the reaction (Lichty, 1907). She found that the rate of decomposition is proportional to the concentration diprotonated oxalic acid rather than proportional to the concentration of the monoprotonated species. Hence she concluded that the reaction occurs by a unimolecular decomposition of the diprotonated species which is present at very low concentration. On the basis of his observation that the slope of the plot of the logarithm of the rate constant against H_0 was approximately equal to two, Hammett had previously come to the same conclusion (Hammett, 1940).

I. CARBONIUM IONS

1. *Aromatic Hydrocarbon Conjugate Acids and Positive Ions*

Carbonium ions have been obtained by protonation and by oxidation of aromatic hydrocarbons in sulphuric acid although other reactions such as sulphonation and dealkylation also often occur. Thus mesitylene is sulphonated (Deno *et al.*, 1959) and hexamethylbenzene (Leisten, 1964b) undergoes simultaneous demethylation and sulphonation; they both give the same product, namely mesitylene trisulphonic acid. However anthracene and 3,4-benzpyrene give the stable conjugate acids XXXIV and XXXV (Gold and Tye, 1952). More extensive studies of the protonation of aromatic hydrocarbons have been carried out in other acidic solvents such as HF and HSO_3F under conditions where more stable solutions can be obtained than in sulphuric acid (McCauley and Lier, 1951; Reid, 1954; Dallinga *et al.*, 1958; Mackor *et al.*, 1958; MacClean and Mackor, 1961, 1962; Birchall and Gillespie, 1964).

XXXIV   XXXV   XXXVI

Cyclo-octatetraene dissolves in 98% sulphuric acid to give the bicyclo-(5,10)-octadienyl cation (von Rosenberg *et al.*, 1962). The n.m.r. spectrum suggests that the cation has the structure XXXVI as the H_{2-6} signals occur in the aromatic region, the H_1 and H_7 signals are at abnormally low field and H_{8a} is highly shielded, presumably, in view of its position above the ring, by the ring current effect.

Electron spin resonance measurements have shown that radical cations are formed in dilute solutions by oxidation of hydrocarbons such as anthracene, napthacene, and perylene in sulphuric acid (Weissman *et al.*, 1956; Carrington *et al.*, 1959). 9-Methyl and 9,10-dimethyl anthracene are oxidized to the corresponding cations by persulphate in sulphuric acid but xylene is oxidized to 2,5-dimethylbenzosemiquinone (Bolton and Carrington, 1961; Brivati *et al.*, 1961). This latter radical can also be prepared by the reduction of a sulphuric acid solution of the quinone with sodium dithionate (Bolton and Carrington, 1961). The relation of these results to the spectroscopic results which show that anthracene is converted to its conjugate acid is not clear. Possibly the major product is the conjugate acid and only a rather small amount of this is converted to the radical ion. It has indeed been pointed out that the ability of a hydrocarbon to form a positive ion in sulphuric acid follows the ease of protonation (Kon and Blois, 1958) and it has been suggested that this can be understood in terms of the following sequence of reactions

$$A + H_2SO_4 = AH^+ + HSO_4^- \tag{188a}$$

$$AH^+ + A = AH + A^+ \tag{188b}$$

$$AH + 2H_2SO_4 = A^+ + 2H_2O + SO_2 + HSO_4^-. \tag{188c}$$

However there is no real evidence in support of this mechanism.

2. Tri-aryl Carbonium Ions

It has long been known that when triphenyl methanol is dissolved in sulphuric acid it ionizes according to the equation

$$Ph_3COH + 2H_2SO_4 = Ph_3C^+ + H_3O^+ + 2HSO_4^- \tag{189}$$

to give a stable yellow solution. This mode of ionization is demonstrated by the absorption spectrum of the solution which is very similar to that of the electrically conducting solution of triphenyl methyl chloride in sulphur dioxide (Hantzsch, 1921; Gold and Hawes, 1951), by freezing point depression measurements which give $\nu = 4$ (Hantzsch, 1908; Oddo and Scandola, 1909b), and by the reaction of the sulphuric acid solution with alcohols to form ethers

$$Ph_3C^+ + ROH = Ph_3C.OR + H^+. \tag{190}$$

The tri-p-methyl, tri-p-chloro and tri-p-nitro derivatives of triphenyl-methanol have also been shown to ionize in the same manner (Newman and Deno, 1951b). In the case of the tri-amino and tris-p-dimethylamino derivatives it was found that the carbonium ion is formed but only two of the three amino groups are protonated (Newman and Deno, 1951b). It appears therefore that in these cases the carbonium ion is best represented by the quinonoid structure XXXVII.

XXXVII

3. Di-aryl Carbonium Ions

A number of stable carbonium ions of this type can be prepared by dissolving the corresponding alcohol or olefin in sulphuric acid. For example

$$Ph_2C{=}CH_2 + H_2SO_4 = Ph_2\overset{+}{C}.CH_3 + HSO_4^- \tag{191}$$

$$Ph_2C\overset{OH}{\underset{CH_3}{<}} + H_2SO_4 = Ph_2\overset{+}{C}.CH_3 + H_3O^+ + 2HSO_4^-. \quad (192)$$

Thus 1,1-diphenyl ethylene gives an initial twofold depression of the freezing point of sulphuric acid and diphenylmethyl carbinol gives an initial fourfold depression (Gold and Tye, 1952). The cations are not completely stable as the freezing points of the solutions decrease somewhat with time. The ultraviolet spectra of the sulphuric acid solutions of 1,1-diphenylethylene and triphenylethylene, and anthracene were found to be very similar with peaks at 2050–3150 and at 4250–4350Å. This similarity is easily understood if the species obtained in the three cases are protonated at those positions which simple-molecular orbital calculations predict would yield the most stable classical ion, i.e.

Di-p-chlorophenylmethylcarbinol and di-p-chlorophenylcarbinol and dimesityl carbinol all give $\nu = 4$, and hence form the corresponding carbonium ions although in the latter case the solution is not completely stable; probably sulphonation occurs (Newman and Deno, 1951b). Diphenyl carbinol also gives an initial ν-value of somewhat greater than four, indicating carbonium ion formation, but rather rapid reaction with the solvent, presumably sulphonation, occurs (Welch and Smith, 1950). Somewhat more stable solutions may be prepared by dissolving the benzhydrol in carbon tetrachloride and extracting with sulphuric acid. Solutions prepared in this way, on pouring into water, methanol, and glacial acetic acid, give dibenzhydryl ether, methylbenzyhdryl ether and benzhydryl acetate respectively (Welch and Smith, 1950).

4. Mono-aryl Carbonium Ions

Benzyl alcohol was first shown by Cannizzaro (1854) to yield a pink insoluble polymer in sulphuric acid. p-Chlorobenzyl alcohol similarly gives a red polymer. Heptamethyl benzyl alcohol and $\alpha,\alpha,2,4,6$-pentamethylbenzylalcohol give ν-values which vary rapidly with time but, by extrapolation to zero time, initial values of approximately four have been obtained (Newman and Deno, 1951b). On dilution, a sulphuric acid solution of $\alpha,\alpha,2,4,6$-pentamethylbenzyl alcohol gives 2-mesitylpropylene in a yield which decreases with the time of solution. There is evidence that sulphonation occurs to give water-soluble products. The mesityldimethyl carbonium ion that is formed in this way is also obtained when α,2,4,6-tetramethylstyrene is dissolved in sulphuric acid. In this case extrapolation to zero time gave the expected ν-value of approximately two. Although cryoscopic work indicates that all mono-aryl carbonium ions and most di-aryl carbonium ions are unstable in sulphuric acid solution, and undergo sulphonation or polymerization, several workers have claimed that stable solutions of a wide variety of di-aryl and mono-aryl carbonium ions can be prepared by suitable procedures which keep the concentrations of all species with which the carbonium ion might react to a minimum. The best procedure appears to be to dilute an acetic acid solution of the appropriate alcohol with excess sulphuric acid or to extract a cyclohexane solution with a large excess of sulphuric acid (Grace and Symons, 1959; Williams, 1962). Unfortunately the solutions prepared in this way are too dilute to enable confirmatory cryoscopic or conductimetric measurements to be made. The only evidence that carbonium ions are in fact formed in these solutions is the observation that all the solutions have an absorption band in the visible ultra-violet spectrum at approximately 400 mμ. Grace and Symons (1959) obtained rather high extinction coefficients of approximately 10^4 but Williams (1962) has pointed out that the extinction coefficient is not independent of concentration and he gives values for most carbonium ions that are much smaller than those obtained by Grace and Symons.

Deno et al. (1959, 1960) attempted to obtain solutions in aqueous sulphuric acid of a number of mono-aryl carbonium ions. They observed the characteristic absorption at 400 mμ but none of the solutions were stable and this absorption disappeared rather rapidly in many cases. They found that pentamethyl benzyl alcohol disproportionates to hexamethylbenzene and pentamethylbenzaldehyde.

5. Dipositive Carbonium Ions

Cryoscopic measurements on sulphuric acid solutions of tetraphenyl-p-xylene glycol and tetraphenylphthalein are consistent with their ionization to form dipositive carbonium ions (Hart et al., 1963).

$$(C_6H_5)_2C\!\!-\!\!\langle\ \rangle\!\!-\!\!C(C_6H_5)_2 + 4H_2SO_4 = (C_6H_5)_2\overset{+}{C}\!\!-\!\!\langle\ \rangle\!\!-\!\!\overset{+}{C}(C_6H_5)_2$$
$$\underset{OH}{\mid}\qquad\underset{OH}{\mid}\qquad\qquad\qquad +2H_3O^+ + 4HSO_4^- \qquad (193)$$

$$\qquad\qquad (194)$$

On dilution of the sulphuric acid solutions with water the original compounds are recovered. Solutions of tetraphenyl-o-xylene glycol and the *meta* compound have absorption spectra that are very similar to that of the *para* compound and the solutions of the *meta* compound gives the glycol on dilution while the solution of the *ortho* compound gives tetraphenylphthalein. It is therefore concluded that these compounds also give the corresponding dipositive carbonium ions.

Hart and Fish (1958, 1960, 1961) have claimed that another type of dipositive carbonium ion, which they call an extraordinary dipositive carbonium ion, is obtained when trichloromethylpolymethylbenzenes are dissolved in sulphuric acid. For example in the case of trichloromethyl-mesitylene they obtained a ν-factor of five and other evidence which they interpreted as indicating ionization according to the equation

$$(CH_3)_3C_6H_2CCl_3 + 2H_2SO_4 = CH_3^+\!\!\left\langle\begin{array}{c}CH_3\\ \\CH_3\end{array}\right\rangle\!\!=\!\overset{+}{C}\text{-}Cl + 2HCl + 2HSO_4^-. \quad (195)$$

However this interpretation ignores the reaction of HCl with sulphuric acid to give chlorosulphuric acid (Section III I)

$$HCl + 2H_2SO_4 = HClSO_3 + H_3O^+ + HSO_4^-. \quad (196)$$

Re-investigation (Gillespie and Robinson, 1964, and unpublished results) has shown that a monopositive and not a dipositive carbonium ion is in fact formed.

$$(CH_3)_3C_6H_2CCl_3 + 3H_2SO_4 = CH_3\!\!\left\langle\begin{array}{c}CH_3\\ \\CH_3\end{array}\right\rangle\!\!\text{-}\overset{+}{C}Cl_2 + HClSO_3 + H_3O^+ + 2HSO_4^-$$

$$\quad (197)$$

6. *Aliphatic Carbonium Ions*

The allylic cation **XXXVIII** is formed by adding a mixture of the dienes **XXXIXa** and **XXXIXb** to concentrated sulphuric acid. This is shown by the twofold depression of the freezing point and the n.m.r. spectrum of the solutions which has four bands with chemical shifts from tetramethyl silane of 1·98, 6·67, 6·93 and 9·79 p.p.m. and relative areas of $1 : 4 : 6 : 6$ (Deno *et al.*, 1962a).

Tricyclopropylcarbinol gives an initial ν-value of four in sulphuric acid and the alcohol is recovered in 63% yield on dilution with ice (Deno *et al.*, 1962b). It has been suggested that these results indicate the formation of the tri-cyclopropylcarbonium ion. It is somewhat surprising however that the n.m.r.

spectrum consists of a single line only. The solution has a maximum ultra-violet absorption at 270 mμ (Deno *et al.*, 1962b).

But-1-ene, but-2-ene, pent-1-ene and pent-2-ene all dissolve in concentrated sulphuric acid ($>75\%$) and on dilution secondary hydrogen sulphates are obtained (Norris and Jouber, 1927). Isobutylene, trimethylethylene and 2-methyl but-1-ene dissolve readily in acid as dilute as 60% and dilution with water produces tertiary alcohols, although this may be due to rapid hydrolysis of the tertiary hydrogen sulphate originally formed. It seems likely therefore that in 100% sulphuric acid, olefins in general dissolve initially to form alkyl hydrogen sulphates. In all cases except that of ethylene, which gives the stable ethyl hydrogen sulphate, subsequent oxidation and polymerization reactions occur. However these polymerization reactions, and the alkylation of paraffins and aromatic hydrocarbons by olefins that takes place in the presence of sulphuric acid, strongly suggest that alkyl carbonium ions are formed by the ionization of alkyl hydrogen sulphates in sulphuric acid but there is no evidence to indicate that the degree of ioniza-tion is large.

XXXVIII   XXXIXa   XXXIXb

Ethanol gives a constant ν-value of 3 and $\gamma = 1$, indicating the formation of ethyl hydrogen sulphate, (Oddo and Scandola, 1909b; Gillespie, 1950b; Gillespie and Wasif, 1953c). n-Propyl and other straight chain primary alcohols give initially pale yellow solutions and an approximately threefold depression of the freezing point, indicating the formation of the alkyl hyd-rogen sulphate (Hantzsch, 1908). The ν-values however increase markedly with time and obvious subsequent reactions occur leading to a deepening of the colour of the solutions to a dark red or brown, the evolution of sulphur dioxide, and the separation of a colourless hydrocarbon layer. Some branched chain alcohols give initial ν-values between 2 and 3 which increase rapidly with time because of similar reactions to those that occur with most of the straight chain alcohols. Tertiary alcohols give initial ν-values of approxi-mately two (Hantzsch, 1908; Oddo and Scandola, 1909b; Newman *et al.*, 1949). This has generally in the past been attributed to oxonium ion formation. However recent work (Leisten, 1964a), which showed that in an H_2SO_4–$HS_2O_7^-$–HSO_4^- solvent the initial freezing point depression is very small, confirms a different interpretation that was first suggested by the results of studies in methanesulphonic acid (Craig *et al.*, 1950) namely that t-butanol is immediately dehydrated and polymerized

$$C_4H_9OH + H_2SO_4 = 1/n(C_4H_8)_n + H_3O^+ + HSO_4^-. \qquad (198)$$

By preparing very dilute solutions of olefins or alcohols by the method that was originally used for arylolefins and alcohols Rosenbaum and Symons (1960) have claimed that stable solutions of tertiary alkyl carbonium ions can be formed. Their evidence is that for alcohols and halides an intense absorption band at 293 mμ develops over a period of up to seven days, and that the same band develops very rapidly for most olefins. They attribute this band to the alkylcarbonium ion as they were unable to detect the formation of any sulphur dioxide or of any of a large number of possible oxidation products. Deno *et al.* (1959), claim that the species formed are alkenyl cations.

7. *Polyenes*

The higher polyenes dissolve in sulphuric acid to give coloured solutions, the intensity of the colour increasing with increasing chain length (Kuhn and Winterstein, 1928). It has recently been claimed that 1,6-diphenyl-hexatriene is immediately oxidized in 100% H_2SO_4 to the corresponding dipositive ion (M^{2+}) (de Boer and van der Meij, 1962). However Leisten and Walton (1963) have shown by means of cryoscopic experiments that sulphur dioxide is not an important product of the reaction and that two moles of water are formed per mole of hexatriene. They therefore conclude that the product is a protonated hexatriene disulphonic acid formed according to the equation

$$C_6H_5.CH=CH.CH=CH=CH.C_6H_5+3H_2SO_4$$
$$\rightarrow [SO_3H.C_6H_4.(CH)_6C_6H_4.SO_3H]H^+. \qquad (199)$$

The site of protonation was not established.

J. AROMATIC SULPHONATION

Ingold (1953b) has discussed work on aromatic sulphonation prior to 1953 and has concluded that the kinetics in slightly aqueous sulphuric acid are consistent with SO_3 as the reactive species, rather than $H_3SO_4^+$, HSO_3^+, or S_2O_6, since the rate of sulphonation varies as the first power of the concentration of the aromatic compound and as the inverse square of the concentration of water. Brand and co-workers (Brand, 1950; Brand and Horning, 1952; Brand *et al.*, 1959) have studied aromatic sulphonation by sulphuric acid over a wide range of solvent composition from aqueous acid to oleum and have shown that for a number of solutes the variation of the first order rate constant with solvent composition varies almost linearly with $-H_0+\log a_{SO_3}$, where H_0 is the Hammett acidity function of the solvent and a_{SO_3} is the activity of sulphur trioxide. The possibility that the reactive species is HSO_3^+ was eliminated on the grounds of a slower rate of sulphonation in deuterated solvent than in proto-solvent, because their spectrometric measurements led to the conclusion that DSO_3^+ should be more abundant in D_2SO_4 than HSO_3^+ would be in H_2SO_4. However it has been shown conductimetrically that m-nitrotoluene is less ionized in D_2SO_4 than in H_2SO_4 (Flowers et al., 1958) and it has been shown recently that D_2SO_4 is probably a weaker acid and a weaker base than H_2SO_4 (Hall and Robinson, 1964), so that their argument may not be sound. However their conclusion that HSO_3^+ is not the reactive species is probably correct as SO_3 is a very weak base. For example, SO_3 gives a non-conducting solution in fluorosulphuric acid, which is a considerably stronger acid than sulphuric acid (Barr et al., 1964). Thus the concentration of the protonated species must be exceedingly small in slightly aqueous sulphuric acid or dilute oleum so that it is improbable that it is the reagent involved in sulphonation in these media. The mechanism of the reaction may be written as follows:

$$ArH + SO_3 \rightarrow Ar\!\!\begin{array}{c} \diagup H \\ \diagdown SO_3 \end{array} \qquad \text{(200a)}$$

$$Ar\!\!\begin{array}{c} \diagup H \\ \diagdown SO_3 \end{array} + H^+ \rightleftharpoons Ar\!\!\begin{array}{c} \diagup H \\ \diagdown SO_3H^+ \end{array} \qquad \text{(200b)}$$

$$Ar\!\!\begin{array}{c} \diagup H \\ \diagdown SO_3H^+ \end{array} \rightarrow ArSO_3H + H^+ \qquad \text{(200c)}$$

REFERENCES

Adie, R. H. (1890) J. chem. Soc. **57**, 450.
Anderson, H. H. (1950) J. Amer. chem. Soc. **72**, 194.
Arotsky, J., Mishra, H. C. and Symons, M. C. R. (1962) J. chem. Soc., 2582.
Baker, W. and Field, F. B. (1932) J. chem. Soc. 86.
Barr, J., Gillespie, R. J. and Robinson, E. A. (1961) Can. J. Chem. **39**, 1266.
Barr, J., Gillespie, R. J. and Thompson, R. C. (1964) Inorg. Chem. (in the press).
Barraclough, C. G., and Tobe, M. L. (1961) J. chem. Soc. 1993.
Bass, S. J. and Gillespie, R. J. (1960) J. chem. Soc. 814.
Bass, S. J., Gillespie, R. J. and Oubridge, J. V. (1960b) J. chem. Soc. 837.
Bass, S. J., Gillespie, R. J. and Robinson, E. A. (1960c) J. chem. Soc. 821.
Bass, S. J., Flowers, R. H., Gillespie, R. J., Robinson, E. A. and Solomons, S. (1960a) J. chem. Soc. 4315.
Berger, A., Lowenstein, A. and Meirboum, S. (1959) J. Amer. chem. Soc. **81**, 62.
Bergius, F. (1910) Z. physikal. chem. **72**, 338.
Birchall, T. and Gillespie, R. J. (1963) Canad. J. Chem. **41**, 2642.
Birchall, T. and Gillespie, R. J. (1964) Canad. J. Chem. **42**, 502.
Bolton, J. R. and Carrington, A. (1961) Proc. chem. Soc. 385.
Bradley, A. and Hill, M. E. (1955) J. Amer. chem. Soc. **77**, 1575.
Brand, J. C. D. (1946) J. chem. Soc. 585.
Brand, J. C. D. (1950a) J. chem. Soc. 997.
Brand, J. C. D. (1950b) J. chem. Soc. 1004.

Brand, J. C. D. and Horning, W. C. (1952) *J. chem. Soc.* 3922.

Brand, J. C. D., Horning, W. C. and Thornley, M. B. (1952) *J. chem. Soc.* 1374.

Brand, J. C. D., James, J. C. and Rutherford, A. (1953) *J. chem. Soc.* 2447.

Brand, J. C. D., Jarvie, A. W. P. and Horning, W. C. (1959) *J. chem. Soc.* 3844.

Brauner, B. (1889) *J. chem. Soc.* **55**, 382.

Brauner, B. (1894) *Z. anorg. chem.* **7**, 11.

Brayford, J. R. and Wyatt, P. A. H. (1955) *J. chem. Soc.* 2453.

Brivati, J. A., Hulme, R. and Symons, M. C. R. (1961) *Proc. chem. Soc.* 384.

Brubaker, C. H. (1955) *J. Amer. chem. Soc.* **77**, 3265.

Bunton, C. A., Figgis, B. N. and Nayak, B. (1962) *In* "Advances in Molecular Spectro-scopy", Vol. I, p. 209. Pergamon Press, Oxford.

Cannizzaro, S., von (1854) *Ann. der Chem.* **92**, 113.

Carrington, A., Dravieko, F. and Symons, M. C. R. (1959) *J. chem. Soc.* 947.

Chedin, J. (1936) *C. R. Acad. Sci., Paris* **292**, 220.

Chedin, J. (1937) *Ann. Chim.* **8**, 243.

Chretien, P. (1895) *Ann. chim. Phys.* **15**, 367.

Chretien, P. (1896) *C. R. Acad. Sci., Paris* **123**, 814.

Clark, H. C. and O'Brien, R. J. (1963) *Inorg. Chem.* **2**, 1020.

Clark, H. C., O'Brien, R. J. and Trotter, J. (1963) *Proc. chem. Soc.* 85.

Coates, G. E. (1960) *In* "Organometallic Compounds", p. 184. Wiley, New York.

Couture, A. M. and Laidler, K. J. (1956) *Canad. J. Chem.* **34**, 1209.

Craig, R. A., Garrett, A. B. and Newman, M. S. (1950) *J. Amer. chem. Soc.* **72**, 163.

Dacre, B. and Wyatt, P. A. H. (1961) *J. chem. Soc.* 568.

Dallinga, G., Mackor, E. L. and Verrigin Stuart, A. A. (1958) *Mol. Phys.* **1**, 123.

d'Arcy, R. H. (1889) *J. chem. Soc.* **55**, 159.

Dasent, W. E. and Waddington, T. C. (1960) *J. chem. Soc.* 3350.

Davison, A., McFarlane, W., Pratt, L. and Wilkinson, G. (1962a) *J. chem. Soc.* 3653.

Davison, A., McFarlane, W., Pratt, L. and Wilkinson, G. (1962b) *J. chem. Soc.* 4821.

Deans, F. B. and Eaborn, C. (1959) *J. chem. Soc.* 2299, 2303.

de Boer, E. and van der Meij, P. H. (1962) *J. chem. Soc.* 139.

Deno, N. C. and Taft, R. W. (1954) *J. Amer. chem. Soc.* **76**, 244.

Deno, N. C., Groves, P. T. and Saires, G. (1959) *J. Amer. chem. Soc.* **81**, 5790.

Deno, N. C., Groves, P. T., Jarvzelski, J. J. and Lugash, M. N. (1960) *J. Amer. chem. Soc.* **82**, 4719.

Deno, N. C., Richey, H. G., Hodge, J. D. and Wisotsky, M. J. (1962a) *J. Amer. chem. Soc.* **84**, 1498.

Deno, N. C., Richey, H. G., Lia, J. S., Hodge, J. D., Houser, J. J. and Wisotsky, M. J. (1962b) *J. Amer. chem. Soc.* **84**, 2016.

de Right, R. E. (1933) *J. Amer. chem. Soc.* **55**, 4761.

Dittmar, H. R. (1929) *J. Phys. chem.* **33**, 533.

Dolezalek, F. and Finkh, K. (1960a) *Z. anorg. chem.* **50**, 82.

Dolezalek, F. and Finkh, K. (1906b) *Z. anorg. chem.* **51**, 320.

Druce, J. G. F. (1924) *Chem. News.* **128**, 33. *C.A.* **18**, 976.

Edwards, J. O. Morrison, G. C., Ross, V. F. and Schultz, J. W. (1955) *J. Amer. chem. Soc.* **77**, 166.

Elbs, K. and Fischer, F. (1901) *Z. elektrochem.* **7**, 343.

Elliott, W. W. and Hammick, D. L. (1951) *J. chem. Soc.*, 3402.

Esch, W. (1903) *Chem. Ztg.* **27**, 297.

Evans, R. V. G. and Gibson, C. S. (1941) *J. chem. Soc.* 109.

Flexser, L. A. and Hammett, L. P. (1938) *J. Amer. chem. Soc.* **60**, 885.

Flexser, L. A., Hammett, L. P. and Dingwall, A. (1935) *J. Amer. chem. Soc.* **57**, 2103.

Flowers, R. H., Gillespie, R. J., and Oubridge J. V. (1956a) *J. chem. Soc.* 607.

Flowers, R. H., Gillespie, R. J. and Oubridge, J. V. (1956b) *J. chem. Soc.* 1925.

Flowers, R. H., Gillespie, R. J. and Robinson, E. A. (1959) *J. inorg. and nuclear Chem.* **9,** 155.

Flowers, R. H., Gillespie, R. J. and Robinson, E. A. (1960a) *J. chem. Soc.* 845.

Flowers, R. H., Gillespie, R. J. and Robinson, E. A. (1960b) *Canad. J. Chem.* **58,** 1363.

Flowers, R. H., Gillespie, R. J., Oubridge, J. V. and Solomons, S. (1958) *J. chem. Soc.* 667.

Flowers, R. H., Gillespie, R. J. and Robinson, E. A. (1963) *Canad. J. Chem.* **41,** 2464.

Flowers, R. H., Gillespie, R. J. and Wasif, S. (1956) *J. chem. Soc.* 607.

Flowers, R. H., Gillespie, R. J., Robinson, E. A. and Solomons, C. (1960c) *J. chem. Soc.* 4327.

Gable, C. M., Betz, H. F. and Marron, S. H. (1950) *J. Amer. chem. Soc.* **72,** 1445.

Giauque, W. F., Horning, E. E., Kunzler, J. E. and Rubin, T. R. (1952) *J. Amer. chem. Soc.* **74,** 62.

Giguere, P. A. and Savoie, R. (1960) *Canad. J. Chem.* **38,** 2467.

Giguere, P. A. and Savoie, R. (1963) *J. Amer. chem. Soc.* **85,** 287.

Gilbert, L. F., Buckley, H. and Masson, I. (1922) *J. chem. Soc.,* 1934.

Gillespie, R. J. (1950a) *J. chem. Soc.* 2493.

Gillespie, R. J. (1950b) *J. chem. Soc.* 2516.

Gillespie, R. J. (1950c) *J. chem. Soc.* 2542.

Gillespie, R. J. (1950d) *J. chem. Soc.* 2997.

Gillespie, R. J. (1959) *Rev. Pure and Applied Chem. (Australia),* **9,** 1.

Gillespie, R. J. (1960) *J. chem. Soc.* 2516.

Gillespie, R. J. and Birchall, T. (1963) *Canad. J. Chem.* **41,** 148.

Gillespie, R. J. and Cole, R. H. (1956) *Trans Faraday Soc.* **52,** 1325.

Gillespie, R. J. and Graham, J. (1950) *J. chem. Soc.* 2532.

Gillespie, R. J. and Leisten, J. A. (1954) *Quart. Rev. (London),* **8,** 40.

Gillespie, R. J. and Millen, D. J. (1948) *Quart. Rev. (London),* **2,** 277.

Gillespie, R. J. and Oubridge, J. V. (1956) *J. chem. Soc.* 80.

Gillespie, R. J. and Robinson, E. A. (1957a) *J. chem. Soc.* 4233.

Gillespie, R. J. and Robinson, E. A. (1957b) *Proc. chem. Soc.* 145.

Gillespie, R. J. and Robinson, E. A. (1959) "The Sulfuric Acid Solvent System". *In* "Advances in Inorganic Chemistry and Radiochemistry", Vol. I, p. 385. Academic Press, New York.

Gillespie, R. J. and Robinson, E. A. (1962a) *Canad. J. Chem.* **40,** 644.

Gillespie, R. J. and Robinson, E. A. (1962b) *Canad. J. Chem.* **40,** 658.

Gillespie, R. J. and Robinson, E. A. (1962c) *Canad. J. Chem.* **40,** 784.

Gillespie, R. J. and Robinson, E. A. (1962d) *Canad. J. Chem.* **40,** 1009.

Gillespie, R. J. and Robinson, E. A. (1963a) *Canad. J. Chem.* **41,** 450.

Gillespie, R. J. and Robinson, E. A. (1963b) *Canad. J. Chem.* **41,** 2074.

Gillespie, R. J. and Senior, J. B. (1964) *Inorg. Chem.* **3,** 440.

Gillespie, R. J. and Solomons, C. (1957) *J. chem. Soc.* 1796.

Gillespie, R. J. and Wasif, S. (1953a) *J. chem. Soc.* 209.

Gillespie, R. J. and Wasif, S. (1953b) *J. chem. Soc.* 215.

Gillespie, R. J. and Wasif, S. (1953c) *J. chem. Soc.* 221.

Gillespie, R. J. and White, R. F. M. (1958) *Trans. Faraday Soc.* **54,** 1846.

Gillespie, R. J. and White, R. F. M. (1960) *Canad. J. Chem.* **38,** 1371.

Gillespie, R. J., Hughes, E. D. and Ingold, C. K. (1950b) *J. chem. Soc.* 2473.

Gillespie, R. J., Oubridge, J. V. and Solomons, C. (1956) *J. chem. Soc.* 1804.

Gillespie, R. J., Robinson, E. A. and Solomons, C. (1960) *J. chem. Soc.,* 4320.

Gillespie, R. J., Graham, J., Hughes, E. D., Ingold, C. K. and Peeling, E. R. A. (1950a) *J. chem. Soc.* 2504.

Gluekauf, E. (1955) *Trans. Faraday Soc.* **51**, 1235.

Goddard, D. R., Hughes, E. D. and Ingold, C. K. (1950) *J. chem. Soc.* 2559.

Gold, V. and Hawes, B. M. W. (1951) *J. chem. Soc.* 2102.

Gold, V. and Tye, F. L. (1950) *J. chem. Soc.* 2932.

Gold, V. and Tye, F. L. (1952) *J. chem. Soc.* 2172.

Grace, J. A. and Symons, M. C. R. (1959) *J. chem. Soc.* 958.

Graham, J. (1943) Ph.D., Thesis (London).

Greenwood, N. N. and Thompson, A. (1959) *J. chem. Soc.* 3474.

Gurney, R. W. (1953) *In* "Ionic Processes in Solution". McGraw-Hill, London.

Hall, S. K. and Robinson, E. A. (1964) *Canad. J. Chem.* **42**, 1113.

Hammett, L. P. (1940) *In* "Physical Organic Chemistry", p. 284. McGraw-Hill, New York.

Hammett, L. P. and Deyrup, A. J. (1932) *J. Amer. chem. Soc.* **54**, 2721.

Hammett, L. P. and Deyrup, A. J. (1933) *J. Amer. chem. Soc.* **55**, 1900.

Hantzsch, A. (1907) *Z. physikal. chem.* **61**, 257.

Hantzsch, A. (1908) *Z. physikal. chem.* **65**, 41.

Hantzsch, A. (1921) *Ber. dtsch. chem. Ges.* **54B**, 2573.

Hart, H. and Fish, R. W. (1958) *J. Amer. chem. Soc.* **80**, 5894.

Hart, H. and Fish, R. W. (1960) *J. Amer. chem. Soc.* **82**, 5419.

Hart, H. and Fish, R. W. (1961) *J. Amer. chem. Soc.* **83**, 4460.

Hart, H., Sulzberg, J. and Rafos, R. R. (1963) *J. Amer. chem. Soc.* **85**, 1800.

Hathaway, B. J., and Webster, D. E. (1963) *Proc. chem. Soc.* 14.

Holstead, C., Lamberton, A. H. and Wyatt, P. A. H. (1953) *J. chem. Soc.* 3341.

Hood, G. C. and Reilly, C. A. (1957) *J. chem. Phys.* **27**, 1126.

Ingold, C. K. (1953a) *In* "Structure and Mechanism in Organic Chemistry", p. 400. G. Bell, London.

Ingold, C. K., Millen, D. J. and Poole, H. G. (1950) *J. chem. Soc.* 2576.

Jaques, C. and Leisten, J. A. (1961) *J. chem. Soc.* 4963.

Jones, G. and Dole, M. (1929) *J. Amer. chem. Soc.* **51**, 2590.

Jorgenson, M. J. and Harrter, D. R. (1963) *J. Amer. chem. Soc.* **85**, 878.

Kendall, J., Adler, J. H. and Davidson, A. W. (1921) *J. Amer. chem. Soc.* **43**, 979.

Kershaw, D. N. and Leisten, J. A. (1960) *Proc. chem. Soc.* 84.

Kirkbride, B. J. and Wyatt, P. A. H. (1957) *Trans. Faraday Soc.* **54**, 483.

Kirkbride, B. J. and Wyatt, P. A. H. (1958) *J. chem. Soc.* 2100.

Kon, H. and Blois, M. S. (1958) *J. chem. Phys.* **28**, 743.

Kothner, von P. (1901) *Ann. der chem.* **319**, 1.

Kuhn, L. P. and Corwin, A. H. (1948) *J. Amer. chem. Soc.* **70**, 3370.

Kuhn, L. P. and Winterstein, A. (1928) *Helv. chim. acta* **11**, 87.

Kunzler, J. E. (1953) *Anal. Chem.* **25**, 93.

Kunzler, J. E. and Giauque, W. F. (1952a) *J. Amer. chem. Soc.* **74**, 804.

Kunzler, J. E. and Giauque, W. F. (1952b) *J. Amer. chem. Soc.* **74**, 3472.

Kunzler, J. E. and Giauque, W. F. (1952c) *J. Amer. chem. Soc.* **74**, 5271.

Lehmann, H. A. (1953) *Ber. dtsch. chem. Ges.* **21**, 17.

Leisten, J. A. (1955) *J. chem. Soc.* 298.

Leisten, J. A. (1956) *J. chem. Soc.* 1572.

Leisten, J. A. (1960) *J. chem. Soc.* 545.

Leisten, J. A. (1961) *J. chem. Soc.* 2191.

Leisten, J. A. (1964a) *J. chem. Soc.* (in the press).

Leisten, J. A. (1964b) *J. chem. Soc.* (in the press).

Leisten, J. A. and Walton, P. R. (1963). *Proc. chem. Soc.*, 60.

Leisten, J. A. and Walton, P. R. (1964). *J. chem. Soc.* (in the press).

Lichty, D. M. (1907) *J. Phys. Chem.* **11**, 225.

Liler, M. (1962). *J. chem. Soc.* 4272.

Liler, M. (1963) *J. chem. Soc.* 3106.

Liler, M. and Kosanovic, Dj. (1958). *J. chem. Soc.* 1084.

Mackor, E. L., Hofstra, A. and van der Waals, J. H. (1958) *Trans. Faraday Soc.* **54**, 66, 187.

MacClean, C. and Mackor, E. L. (1961) *Mol. Phys.* **4**, 241.

MacClean, C. and Mackor, E. L. (1962) *Disc. Faraday Soc.* **34**, 165.

Marcus, R. A. and Fresco, J. M. (1957) *J. chem. Phys.* **26**, 1665.

Masson, I. (1938) *J. chem. Soc.* 1708.

Masson, I. and Argument, C. (1938) *J. chem. Soc.*, 1702.

Masson, I. and Hanby, W. E. (1938) *J. chem. Soc.* 1699.

McCauley, D. A. and Lier, A. P. (1951) *J. Amer. chem. Soc.* **73**, 2013.

Mellor, J. W. (1922a) "A Comprehensive Treatise on Inorganic and Theoretical Chemistry," Vol. 9, p. 332. Longmans Green, London.

Mellor, J. W. (1922b) "A Comprehensive Treatise on Inorganic and Theoretical Chemistry", Vol. 9, p. 580. Longmans Green, London.

Mellor, J. W. (1922c) "A Comprehensive Treatise on Inorganic and Theoretical Chemistry", Vol. 9, p. 698. Longmans Green, London.

Mellor, J. W. (1922d) "A Comprehensive Treatise on Inorganic and Theoretical Chemistry", Vol. 11, p. 117. Longmans Green, London.

Meyer, J. and Langer, M. (1927) *Ber. dtsch. chem. Ges.* **60**, 285.

Miles, F. D. and Carson, T. (1946) *J. chem. Soc.* 786.

Millen, D. J. (1950a) *J. chem. Soc.* 2589.

Millen, D. J. (1950b) *J. chem. Soc.* 2600.

Millen, D. J. (1950c) *J. chem. Soc.* 2606.

Mishra, H. C. and Symons, M. C. R. (1962) *J. chem. Soc.* 4411.

Mountford, G. A. and Wyatt, P. A. H. (1964) *J. chem. Soc.* 518.

Nakomoto, K., Fujita, J., Tanaka, S. and Kobayashi, M. (1957) *J. Amer. chem. Soc.* **79**, 4904.

Newman, M. S. (1940) *J. Amer. chem. Soc.* **63**, 2431.

Newman, M. S. and Deno, N. C. (1951a) *J. Amer. chem. Soc.* **73**, 3651.

Newman, M. S. and Deno, N. C. (1951b) *J. Amer. chem. Soc.* **73**, 3644.

Newman, M. S., Craig, R. A. and Garrett, A. B. (1949) *J. Amer. chem. Soc.* **71**, 869.

Newman, M. S., Kuivila, H. and Garrett, A. B. (1945) *J. Amer. chem. Soc.* **67**, 704.

Norris, J. F. and Jouber, J. M. (1927) *J. Amer. chem. Soc.* **49**, 873.

Oddo, G. and Casalino, A. (1917a) *Gazzetta.* **47**(ii), 232.

Oddo, G. and Casalino, A. (1917b) *Gazzetta.* **47**(ii), 200.

Oddo, G. and Scandola, E. (1908) *Gazzetta.* **38**, 603.

Oddo, G. and Scandola, E. (1909a) *Gazzetta.* **39**(i), 569.

Oddo, G. and Scandola, E. (1909b) *Gazzetta.* **39**(ii), 1.

Oddo, G. and Scandola, E. (1910) *Gazzetta.* **40**(ii), 163.

Ogg, R. A. and Ray, J. D. (1956) *J. chem. Phys.* **25**, 1285.

Okawara, R., Hathaway, B. J. and Webster, D. E. (1963) *Proc. chem. Soc.* 13.

Paddock, N. (1964) *Quart. Rev. (London)* **18**, 168.

Palm, V. A. (1956) *Proc. Russ. Acad. Sci. (Chemistry)* **108**, 249.

Pascard, R. (1955) *C. R. Acad. Sci., Paris,* **240**, 2162.

Paul, M. A. and Long, F. A. (1957) *Chem. Revs.* **58**, 935.

Pople, J. A., Schneider, W. G. and Bernstein, H. J. (1959) "High Resolution Nuclear Magnetic Resonance". McGraw-Hill, New York.

Price, F. P. (1948) *J. Amer. Soc.* **70**, 871.

Reavill, R. E. (1964) *J. chem. Soc.* 519.

Reid, C. (1954) *J. Amer. chem. Soc.* **76**, 3264.

Robinson, E. A. (1964) Unpublished experiments.

Robinson, R. A. and Stokes, R. H. (1948) "Electrolyte Solutions", p. 223. Butterworths, London.

Rosenbaum, J. and Symons, M. C. R. (1960) *Mol. Phys.* **3**, 205.

Royer, J. L. (1961) *J. inorg. and nuclear Chem.* **17**, 159.

Schilt, A. A. (1963) *J. Amer. chem. Soc.* **85**, 904.

Schott, G. and Kibbel, H. U. (1962) *Z. anorg. chem.* **314**, 104.

Somiya, T. (1927) *Proc. Imp. Acad. (Japan)* **3**, 76.

Sommer, L. H., Petruska, E. W., Kerr, G. T. and Whitmore, F. C. (1946) *J. Amer. chem. Soc.* **68**, 156.

Stavenhagen, A. (1893) *Z. anorg. chem.* **6**, 284.

Stewart, R. and Yates, K. (1958) *J. Amer. chem. Soc.* **80**, 6355.

Stewart, R. and Yates, K. (1960) *J. Amer. chem. Soc.* **82**, 4059.

Symons, M. C. R. (1957) *J. chem. Soc.* 387.

Szmant, H. H., Devlin, O. M. and Brost, G. A. (1951) *J. Amer. chem. Soc.* **73**, 3059.

Thompson, A. and Greenwood, N. N. (1959) *J. chem. Soc.* 736.

Treffers, H. P. and Hammett, L. P. (1937) *J. Amer. chem. Soc.* **59**, 1708.

von Rosenberg, J. L., Mahler, J. E. and Pettit, R. (1962) *J. Amer. chem. Soc.* **84**, 2842.

Walrafen, G. E. (1964) *J. chem. Phys.* **40**, 2326.

Walrafen, G. E. and Dodd, D. M. (1961) *Trans. Faraday. Soc.* **57**, 1286.

Walrafen, G. E. and Young, T. F. (1960) *Trans. Faraday Soc.* **56**, 1419.

Weinland, R. F. and Kuhl, H. (1907) *Z. anorg. chem.* **54**, 244.

Weissman, S. I., de Boer, E., and Conradi, J. J. (1956) *J. chem. Phys.* **26**, 963.

Welch, C. M. and Smith, H. A. (1950) *J. Amer. chem. Soc.* **72**, 4748.

Welch, C. M. and Smith, H. A. (1953) *J. Amer. chem. Soc.* **75**, 1412.

Whitford, E. L. (1925) *J. Amer. chem. Soc.* **47**, 953.

Wicke, Von E. and Eigen, M. (1953) *Z. Elektrochem.* **57**, 319.

Wiig, E. O. (1930) *J. Amer. chem. Soc.* **52**, 4729, 4737, 4742.

Wiles, L. A. (1953) *J. chem. Soc.* 996.

Wiles, L. A. and Baughan, E. C. (1953) *J. chem. Soc.* 933.

Williams, G. and Hardy, M. L. (1953) *J. chem. Soc.*, 2560.

Williams, J. F. A. (1962) *Tetrahedron* **18**, 1487.

Wyatt, P. A. H. (1953) *J. chem. Soc.* 1175.

Wyatt, P. A. H. (1960) *Trans. Faraday Soc.* **56**, 490.

Wyatt, P. A. H. (1961) *Trans. Faraday Soc.* **57**, 773.

Yates, K., Stevens, J. B. and Katriskey, A. R. (1964). To be published.

Young, T. F. (1951) *Record of chem. Progress* **12**, 81.

Young, T. F. (1959). *In* "The Structure of Electrolytic Solutions" (Hamer, ed.) Chapter 4. Wiley, New York.

CHAPTER 5

Co-ordinating Solvents

RUSSELL S. DRAGO AND K. F. PURCELL

Chemistry Department, University of Illinois, Urbana, Illinois, U.S.A.

I. Introduction... 211
II. Criteria for Establishing Co-ordination...................... 215
    A. Ultra-violet and Visible Spectroscopy.................. 215
    B. Infra-red Spectroscopy................................ 216
    C. Nuclear Magnetic Resonance Spectroscopy............... 217
    D. Cryoscopy.. 219
    E. Conductivity... 219
III. Energetics of the Co-ordination Process 220
    A. Statement of the Problem.............................. 220
    B. Evaluation of the Energy Terms....................... 222
IV. Solute Behaviour in Selected Solvents...................... 226
    A. NN-Dimethylacetamide (DMA)........................ 228
    B. N-Methylacetamide (NMA)............................ 230
    C. Dimethyl sulphoxide (DMSO).......................... 230
    D. Nitromethane and Nitrobenzene (NM,NB)............... 234
    E. Acetone (Ac).. 237
    F. Methanol and Ethanol (MeOH,EtOH).................... 239
    G. Pyridine (Py)....................................... 241
    H. Acetonitrile (MeCN) 243
    I. Tetramethylene Sulphone (Sulpholane–TMSO$_2$)....... 245
V. Generalizations... 247
References... 249

I. INTRODUCTION

Solvent co-ordination of solutes and its ramifications are very important in non-aqueous solvent chemistry. If an inorganic solute dissolves in a solvent, solution is nearly always accompanied by solvent co-ordination. This co-ordination involves a specific interaction of the Lewis acid–base type between the solvent and solute. In the absence of significant interactions in "non-co-ordinating solvents", such as saturated hydrocarbons, CCl$_4$, fluoro-carbons etc., very few inorganic materials dissolve. Consequently, the majority of investigations in inorganic chemistry have been carried out in co-ordinating solvents. It is our feeling that the considerations outlined in this chapter are pertinent to the description of non-aqueous solvent chemistry in co-ordinating media.

In the past, explanations of solute behaviour in many solvents have ignored solvent co-ordination and emphasized the self-ionization of the solvent. For example, the behaviour of solutions of Lewis acids and bases in the solvent POCl$_3$ is correlated by considerations involving the self-ionization of this solvent

$$POCl_3 \leftrightharpoons POCl_2^+ + Cl^-. \tag{1}$$

An acid is defined as a solute capable of increasing the concentration of the cationic species, $POCl_2^+$, and a base as a solute capable of increasing the concentration of the anion, Cl^-. Addition of $FeCl_3$ to $POCl_3$ produces $FeCl_4^-$ and supposedly $POCl_2^+$, hence $FeCl_3$ is an acid. This model for non-aqueous solvent behaviour is referred to as the Solvent Systems Concept (Gutmann, 1959). In order to illustrate the application of this concept and in order to establish an alternate model of solute–solvent interactions based on the premise of solvent co-ordination, the systems $POCl_3$–$FeCl_3$ and $PO(OEt)_3$–$FeCl_3$ will be discussed.

The ultra-violet absorption spectra of dilute solutions of ferric chloride ($\sim 10^{-4}$ M) in phosphorus oxychloride demonstrate that the tetrachloro-ferrate(III) ion, $FeCl_4^-$, is one of the principal absorbing species present (Baaz et al., 1960). No conclusive evidence is available to establish the presence of $POCl_2^+$, in this solution. At higher concentrations of $FeCl_3$ (about 0·1 M) in the absence of sufficient chloride ion from the solvent to convert all the $FeCl_3$ to $FeCl_4^-$, the existence of a red addition compound $FeCl_3(POCl_3)_x$ is proposed. The essential equilibria are represented by the Solvent Systems Concept as:

$$FeCl_3 + POCl_3 \leftrightharpoons Cl_3FeClPOCl_2 \rightleftharpoons POCl_2^+ + FeCl_4^-. \tag{2}$$

The colour transformation from red to yellow is completely reversible upon dilution or concentration. Addition of a source of chloride ion to red $FeCl_3$ solutions converts the colour to the characteristic yellow colour of $FeCl_4^-$.

Conductimetric titrations of ferric chloride solutions in phosphorus oxychloride (Gutmann and Baaz, 1959) with soluble chlorides give sharp inflections at a mole ratio of one chloride ion to one $FeCl_3$ molecule. According to the Solvent Systems Concept, the net ionic equation describing this titration is

$$POCl_2^+ + Cl^- \rightleftharpoons POCl_3. \tag{3}$$

The complete equation for the titration of ferric chloride is then represented by

$$R_4N^+Cl^- + POCl_2^+FeCl_4^- \rightleftharpoons R_4N^+FeCl_4^- + POCl_3. \tag{4}$$

Contrary to the Solvent System formulation of a chlorine co-ordinated addition compound (equation (2)), X-ray structure determinations and Raman and infra-red investigations indicate that the oxygen is the co-ordination position in several adducts of the $POCl_3$ molecule. X-Ray single crystal studies (Lindquist and Branden, 1959; Branden and Lindquist, 1960) on the addition compounds $SbCl_5 . OPCl_3$ and $(TiCl_4 . OPCl_3)_2$ show that both metals are octahedrally co-ordinated and bonded to the oxygen atom of the $POCl_3$ molecule. The Raman spectra of the compounds $AlCl_3 . OPCl_3$ and $GaCl_3 . OPCl_3$ indicate that co-ordination occurs through the oxygen (Gerding et al., 1960). The infra-red spectra of phosphoryl halide addition compounds with $TiCl_4$, $SnCl_4$ and $TiBr_4$, also support the assignment of oxygen as the co-ordinating atom (Sheldon and Tyree, 1958).

Proponents of the solvent system concept (Lindquist, 1958; Baaz and Gutmann, 1959) argue that although the oxygen co-ordinated species exist in the solid, or under conditions of the Raman and infra-red spectral studies, two competitive equilibria (oxygen co-ordination at high solute concentration and solvent ionization to produce chloride at low solute concentration) occur in $POCl_3$ solutions and are responsible for the observed phenomena. Thus the problem of the species present in dilute solutions of $FeCl_3$ in $POCl_3$ remains unresolved.

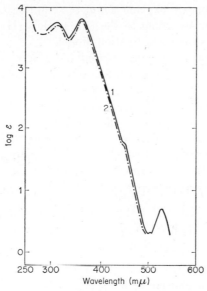

FIG. 1. Absorption spectra of $FeCl_3$ solutions in $POCl_3$ and $PO(OEt)_3$. $[FeCl_3] = 10^{-4}$ M, (1) $POCl_3$; (2) $PO(OEt)_3$.

In an attempt to demonstrate that the behaviour and reactions of $FeCl_3$ in $POCl_3$ could be accounted for without invoking removal of chloride ion from the solvent, i.e. solvent ionization, the behaviour of $FeCl_3$ in a non-chlorine containing solvent was studied (Meek and Drago, 1961). Triethyl phosphate was selected because of its structural similarity to $POCl_3$. Triethyl phosphate is expected to be a slightly better donor than $POCl_3$ but the similarity is such that vastly different co-ordination behaviour would not be expected. The similarity of dilute solutions of $FeCl_3$ in $POCl_3$ and $PO(OEt)_3$ is illustrated in Fig. 1. Absorption bands characteristic of $FeCl_4^-$ are observed in both solvents.

Use of triethyl phosphate as a solvent excludes the possibility of the tetrachloroferrate ion being formed from a chloride ion liberated by a

8

self-ionization of the solvent, as has been postulated for $POCl_3$. The following set of equilibria (5) is suggested to explain the formation of $FeCl_4^-$ in both $PO(OEt)_3$ and $POCl_3$ and to account for the principal species present.

$$FeCl_3 + Y_3PO \rightleftharpoons (FeCl_3OPY_3) \rightleftharpoons FeCl_{3-x}(OPY_3)_{1+x}^{x+} + xFeCl_4^-. \qquad (5)$$

This representation of the equilibria is in agreement with the experimental evidence that demonstrates oxygen co-ordination in the $POCl_3$ addition compounds. The infra-red spectra of $PO(OEt)_3$ co-ordinated to iron species also indicate that co-ordination of the solvent molecule occurs via the phosphoryl oxygen atom (Meek and Drago, 1961). Comparison of equations (2) and (5) demonstrates the essential difference between the Solvent System Concept and our proposed explanation of the equilibria. The species present at equilibrium differ according to the two models. This latter explanation will be referred to as the Co-ordination Model.

Conductimetric titrations were carried out (Meek and Drago, 1961) in triethyl phosphate to demonstrate further the similarity in behaviour of $PO(OEt)_3$ and $POCl_3$. Sharp breaks in the conductivity curves were obtained at a 1 : 1 molar ratio for the titration of both $FeCl_3$ and $SbCl_3$ with chloride ion. These breaks correspond to the formation of $FeCl_4^-$ and $SbCl_4^-$ ions. Analogous behaviour, noted above, has been reported to occur in $POCl_3$. According to our scheme, the equations for the titration involve the conversion of all iron(III) species to the $FeCl_4^-$ ion:

$$f_1\,FeCl_2(OPY_3)_4^+ + 2f_1\,Cl^- \rightarrow f_1\,FeCl_4^- \qquad (6a)$$

$$f_2\,FeCl(OPY_3)_5^+ + 3f_2\,Cl^- \rightarrow f_2\,FeCl_4^- \qquad (6b)$$

$$f_3\,Fe(OPY_3)_6^{3+} + 4f_3\,Cl^- \rightarrow f_3\,FeCl_4^- \qquad (6c)$$

$$f_4\,FeCl_3(OPY_3) + f_4\,Cl^- \rightarrow f_4\,FeCl_4^-, \qquad (6d)$$

where f_i is the fraction of total Fe present as the ith species. Since the iron to chlorine ratio in a solution of $FeCl_3$ is 1 : 3, one mole of chloride ion per mole of $FeCl_3$ will be required to convert all the iron to $FeCl_4^-$. That this is so is substantiated by the spectrophotometric data. These equations should be contrasted with those proposed according to the Solvent System Concept (equations (3) and (4)).

All of the properties of ferric chloride solutions in phosphorus oxychloride which have been used to support the Solvent System Concept have been reproduced in triethyl phosphate. This indicates that solvent ionization is not a requirement to explain the equilibria and chemical reactions that occur when Lewis acids are dissolved in phosphorus oxychloride. When one compares equilibria in different solvents, the Co-ordination Model focuses attention on the donor or acceptor properties of the solvent and the solvating ability of the solvent. Consequently, the behaviour of acidic solutes in donor organic solvents is in many respects similar to the behaviour of these materials in many oxyhalide and oxide solvents. Although the main concern in this chapter will be with "organic" solvents, the above discussion of $POCl_3$ and $PO(OEt)_3$ is presented to emphasize the fact that the concepts developed here may very well apply in most solvents.

In this chapter our interest will be with developing general concepts suggested by the Co-ordination Model and applying these considerations to non-aqueous solvent behaviour. We shall deal first with methods of establishing co-ordination and determining the species present in solution. This will be followed by a description of the energetics of the solvent–solute interactions and a formulation of the species in solution in different solvents. Both of these considerations are a direct outgrowth of the Co-ordination Model. Finally we shall discuss solute behaviour in a series of typical co-ordinating solvents from the standpoint of qualitatively correlating the species formed with the principal solvent properties. As far as possible, data will be presented that are pertinent to the problem of estimating the essential solvent parameters. A limited number of typical solvents will be discussed.

II. CRITERIA FOR ESTABLISHING CO-ORDINATION

One of the first concerns in discussing solvent co-ordination is the criteria for determining whether or not solvent co-ordination occurs. Whatever experiment is selected, the criteria must invariably rely on a difference in physical properties of the free donor or acceptor and the co-ordinated species. Since changes in electronic structure are expected when co-ordination of the Lewis acid–base type occurs, various spectroscopic techniques can be employed. Cryoscopic and conductimetric techniques have also been employed to advantage. In this section we shall briefly describe the results of some selected studies which establish co-ordination.

A. ULTRA-VIOLET AND VISIBLE SPECTROSCOPY

A very early application of this technique involved the spectroscopic study of iodine in different solvents. The wavelength of the $\pi^* \rightarrow \sigma^*$ transition of I_2 is shorter in solvents in which co-ordination occurs than in non-coordinating solvents. The transition occurs at 520 mμ in the gas phase, 517 mμ in CCl_4, 520 mμ in heptane, and 500 mμ in benzene where co-ordination occurs and at shorter wavelengths in more basic solvents (Benesi and Hildebrand, 1949). In donor solvents, co-ordination to iodine is also accompanied by the appearance of a new charge-transfer band in the ultra-violet spectrum (Andrews and Keefer, 1961).

The electronic spectra of transition metal ions are especially valuable not only for establishing solvent co-ordination but also for determining the co-ordination number and structure of these ions dissolved in solvents. When a complex that exists in solution can be isolated as a solid, the stoichiometry of the complex can be determined by analysis and it becomes a simple matter to determine the co-ordination number and structure of the ion. A solution structure can often be inferred from electronic spectra of the complex. The generalized spectra of the first transition series ions with their various structures have been reported (Dunn, 1960).

The solution species which result when $FeCl_3$ is dissolved in certain solvents represent examples for which the isolatable solids are not the same as the species in solution (Drago et al., 1965a,b). In the $FeCl_3$–DMA system (DMA is dimethylacetamide), the spectrum of the various chloro-species had to be determined by examination of the spectroscopic changes in $Fe(DMA)_6(ClO_4)_3$ solutions as a function of added chloride ion. The species present were inferred from the existence of isobestic points and from the spectroscopic changes over different concentration ranges.

The system $CoCl_2$–pyridine was examined by Katzin and Gebert (1950 a, b, c) in the solvent acetone by visible spectroscopy. The method of Job (Job, 1928) was employed to obtain the stoichiometry of the $CoCl_2$–pyridine complexes. It has been explicitly pointed out by Woldbye (1955) that this method, unless used cautiously, can be unreliable. In the case at hand, the method appears valid and yields the result that complexes with pyridine to cobalt ratios of $1:1$ and $2:1$ can exist in acetone. A Job's study of the effect of pyridine on the spectrum of $CoCl_4^{2-}$ in acetone also showed the existence of a $1:1$ complex formulated as $CoCl_3py^-$ (py is pyridine). Similarly, Fine (1962) has recently studied the formation of CoX^+, CoX_2, CoX_3^- and CoX_4^{2-} in acetone ($X = Cl, Br, I$). The unfilled co-ordination positions are occupied by acetone molecules e.g. CoX_3ac^- (ac is acetone).

Another example of an application of spectrophotometry to the general problem of solvent co-ordination involves the $(Co(acac)_2)_n$–pyridine system in benzene as the "inert" medium (acac is acetonylacetone) (Fackler, 1963). Equilibrium constants for the formation of the several $Co(acac)_2$–pyridine species were obtained, i.e. $(Co(acac)_2)_2.py$; $Co(acac)_2.py$; and $Co(acac)_2.2py$.

A general discussion of the study of complex formation by spectrophotometry and the mathematical treatment of the data is given by Newman and Hume (1957).

B. INFRA-RED SPECTROSCOPY

Since co-ordination affects the electron distribution in a molecule, changes in the force constants of various bonds and hence changes in their vibrational frequency occur upon complex formation. Consequently, the infra-red spectrum of the solute and/or the solvent can be used as a criterion for co-ordination but the absence of a shift is not always a reliable criterion for the absence of co-ordination. It is essential that such studies be carried out in solution, for it is well known that a change in the spectrum of a compound occurs on change of state (liquid to solid). For example, the spectrum of a solvent molecule trapped in a solid lattice may differ appreciably from the spectrum of the solvent in the liquid or gaseous state. A difference detected when the spectrum of the proposed adduct is examined as a solid cannot be utilized rigorously to establish co-ordination.

In addition to indicating co-ordination, changes in the infra-red spectrum of a donor molecule can often be employed to indicate the position of co-ordination in the donor. For example, it has been shown that $CH_3CON(CH_3)_2$ co-ordinates through oxygen with the Lewis acids I_2, C_6H_5OH (Schmulbach and Drago, 1960; Joesten and Drago, 1962a,b), and several metal ions (Bull et al., 1963; Drago et al., 1963b). Toward many first row transition metal ions it has been shown that the oxygen atom of dimethylsulphoxide is the donor (Cotton and Francis, 1960; Meek et al., 1960; Cotton and Francis, 1961; Drago and Meek, 1961), but sulphur is the donor atom in the $Pd((CH_3)_2SO)_4^{2+}$ complex (Cotton and Francis, 1960). In both $CH_3CON(CH_3)_2$ and $(CH_3)_2SO$, co-ordination through oxygen drains electron density out of the oxo-bond, lowering the bond order, and decreasing the force constant and frequency of the oxo stretching vibration.

A complication which is sometimes encountered with the infra-red technique should be mentioned. Co-ordination gives rise to another effect which instead of decreasing actually increases the vibration frequency of the bond under examination. This is called the *kinematic effect* and arises from the formation of the new bond (i.e. the co-ordination bond). For example, when acetonitrile co-ordinates to an acceptor the C—N stretching motion must now occur at the expense of changes in the acceptor-nitrogen bond distance, in effect coupling these two vibrations. This push-pull effect acts to increase the frequency of the C—N vibration. Another effect, which acts to increase the C—N force constant, results from the hybridization change of nitrogen upon complexation. According to isovalent hybridization arguments (Bent, 1961), co-ordination by nitrogen increases the *s* character in the C—N bond (the N hybrid orbital). Since the drain of σ-electron density from the C—N group is small in many complexes, co-ordination to the nitrogen of nitriles often results in an increased frequency for the C—N vibration. It is to be emphasized that the above effects and the drain of electron density out of the π- and σ-bonds work simultaneously and only the net effect is measured by the direction of the frequency shift.

Another effect which seems to be of importance for ligands with low lying π^*-orbitals (empty) is that of back bonding. If the acid possesses electrons in π-type orbitals which are of the same symmetry and nearly the same energy as the empty ligand π^*-orbitals, π-bonding involving these orbitals can occur (Orgel, 1960). This brings about a decrease in force constant of the donor multiple bond.

C. NUCLEAR MAGNETIC RESONANCE SPECTROSCOPY

This method has tremendous potential for demonstrating co-ordination. For example, when a hydrogen bonding interaction occurs, the chemical shift of the proton involved in the interaction usually moves to lower field. This shift is evidence for "co-ordination" of the proton (Shoolery et al., 1955; Korinek and Schneider, 1957). In a very interesting experiment Schneider and Reeves (1957) have shown that in benzene solution the proton in $CHCl_3$ undergoes a pronounced shift to high field amounting to $1\cdot40$ p.p.m. at infinite dilution. This shift was employed to establish the existence of a hydrogen-bonding interaction between the chloroform proton and benzene as a donor. The shift to high field suggests that the chloroform proton is directed at approximately right angles to the plane of the aromatic ring and in the vicinity of the six-fold rotation axis. In this position, the proton shift to high field arises from the magnetic anisotropy of the ring current in benzene.

The thallium-proton coupling constant of $(CH_3)_2TlClO_4$ has been found to be very sensitive to the solvent (Shier and Drago, 1965). In those solvents where the thallium co-ordination number is 6 and the CH_3TlCH_3 moiety linear, coupling constants in the range 410–475 c/s were found and the magnitude of the coupling constant paralleled solvent donor properties.

It has also been found (Onak et al., 1959; Landesman and Williams, 1961) that co-ordination of donor molecules to many boron compounds causes a shift of the ^{11}B resonance to higher field in the adduct. For example, δ in BCl_3 is at about 35 p.p.m. lower field than in BCl_4^-, $BCl_3O(C_2H_5)_2$ and $BCl_3C_5H_5N$. Similar shifts in the ^{11}B resonance have been employed to determine whether or not co-ordination has occurred to the weak Lewis acid $B(OEt)_3$.

An n.m.r. technique for establishing the co-ordination number of certain solutes has been recently described (Jackson et al., 1960). The essentials of the technique are illustrated by considering one of the reported systems. The ^{17}O nuclear magnetic resonance spectra of aqueous solutions ($H_2{}^{17}O$) of Al^{3+} show a single ^{17}O resonance including both bulk and co-ordinated water. Upon addition of Co^{2+}, two separate resonances are observed—one for H_2O bound to Al^{3+} and the other for solvent water exchanging rapidly with water bound to the paramagnetic Co^{2+} ion. The paramagnetic Co^{2+} ion gives rise to a large contact shift which is averaged over all water molecules not firmly bound to Al^{3+}. This causes a shift in the bulk water resonance and the two separate peaks due to bulk water and water co-ordinated to Al^{3+} can be distinguished. The same result was obtained when Be^{2+} and Ga^{3+} were substituted for Al^{3+} but not when Mg^{2+}, Sn^{2+}, Ba^{2+}, Hg^{2+} or Bi^{3+} solutions were examined. The sensitivity of these experiments was limited by the ^{17}O enrichment available and co-ordination numbers could not be accurately obtained. Connick and Fiat (1963), using H_2O enriched to 12% in ^{17}O and a more sensitive measuring technique, performed essentially the same experiments and found co-ordination numbers 6 and 4 for Al(III) and Be(II), respectively. This appears to be a very promising technique for non-aqueous solvent work.

In another experiment Swinehart and Taube (1962) used proton n.m.r. to establish the co-ordination number of Mg^{2+}. Using various mixed $MeOH-H_2O$ (mole ratio $\sim 10:1$) solutions of $Mg(ClO_4)_2$ and cooling the samples to $-75°C$ they observed separate resonances for MeOH and H_2O both bound and free. Their calculations give a solvation number for MeOH of 5·0 and of H_2O of 0·7, yielding a total co-ordination number for magnesium(II) (solvent) of 5·7. The deviation from 6·0 is attributed to perchlorate co-ordination.

D. CRYOSCOPY

Although of limited use in studying more complex solutes in solution, simple 1 : 1 association can be convincingly demonstrated with this technique. A case in point is the studies of Voitovich and Barabanova (1961) who examined, by the method of continuous variations, $POCl_3-MX_n$ interactions in nitrobenzene. By plotting δt, the deviation of $C_6H_5NO_2$ freezing point from the additive value for the solutes, against mole % MX_n, they observed a maximum at 1 : 1 $POCl_3 : MX_n$ for $FeCl_3$ and $AlCl_3$ (the conductivities of solutions of 1 : 1 composition were shown to be negligible).

E. CONDUCTIVITY

In the general case, this method is too involved to yield a great deal of information, yet in certain instances this method is of great value. Conductivity measurements were used by de Maine and Koubek (1959) to establish ionization of $FeCl_3$ when it is dissolved in $MeNO_2$ or $MeNO_2$ solutions in CCl_4. The Onsager equation holds for $FeCl_3$ concentrations from $2·5 \times 10^{-2}$ M to $8·5 \times 10^{-2}$ M. In studying $FeCl_3-MeNO_2$ solutions spectrophotometrically (visible region), they also find that the "effective molar extinction coefficient" (optical density$\div$total iron concentration) is a linear function of the iron concentration. The linear conductivity and spectrophotometric relationships are reported to be consistent only with equations (7) or (8):

$$2FeCl_3(sol) \overset{K_1}{\rightleftharpoons} Fe_2Cl_6(sol) \tag{7a}$$

$$Fe_2Cl_6(sol) \overset{K_2}{\rightleftharpoons} FeCl_2^+(sol) + FeCl_4^-(sol) \tag{7b}$$

or

$$2FeCl_3(sol) \overset{K_1}{\rightleftharpoons} Fe_2Cl_6(sol) \tag{8a}$$

$$Fe_2Cl_6(sol) \overset{K_3}{\rightleftharpoons} Fe_2Cl_5^+(sol) + Cl^-(sol). \tag{8b}$$

It is necessary that K_1 be very small and K_2 (or K_3) be large. The species $FeCl_3(sol)$ is probably $MeNO_2FeCl_3$ and equations (7) are most probably correct.

III. Energetics of the Co-ordination Process

In applying the Co-ordination Model, the first step involves formation of the initial adduct between the Lewis acid (a dative acceptor of electron density) and the Lewis base (a dative donor of electron density). Next one considers the subsequent reactions that this adduct can undergo. Very frequently ionization occurs in these subsequent steps. In many instances the subsequent reaction may occur to such an extent that the initial adduct may not exist in significant concentrations at equilibrium.

A. STATEMENT OF THE PROBLEM

The essential properties of a solvent that determine the extent of solute ionization can be most simply described by considering the hypothetical solute MX dissolved in a solvent. Assuming that all MX molecules have at least p molecules of solute attached, the equilibrium in solution can be formulated as:

$$MXS_{p(sol)} + S_{(sol)} \leftrightharpoons MS^+_{p+1(sol)} + X^-_{(sol)}. \tag{9}$$

This formulation represents a simple case in that it assumes only a fixed co-ordination number for M equal to $p+1$. The thermochemical cycle in Fig. 2(a) can then be written to describe the important enthalpy contributions

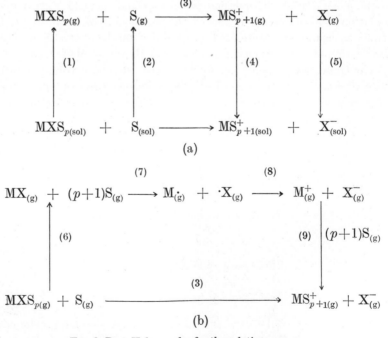

Fig. 2. Born-Haber cycles for the solution process.

to the equilibria. The contribution of enthalpy effects to the position of equilibrium in solution is determined by the difference in the heats of solvation of MXS_p and MS_{p+1}^+, the solvation of X^-, the latent enthalpy of evaporation of S and the difference in donor strength of X^- and the solvent as measured by the difference in the gaseous heats of formation of $MXS_p + S$ and $MS_{p+1}^+ + X^-$. In a donor solvent, specific interaction occurs, i.e. co-ordination, with the solute as indicated by step (3), and non-specific interactions as indicated by steps (1), (4), and (5). The term non-specific solvation will be employed to describe dipolar solvent interaction where co-ordination cannot occur, e.g. dipolar interactions of the solvent outside the first co-ordination sphere with certain metal complexes. As will be seen shortly, it is possible in certain circumstances to have contributions to steps (1), (4), and (5) from specific interactions of the hydrogen-bonding type between the solvent and an anion or a fully co-ordinated complex.

For some purposes it may be more convenient to break up step (3) into the steps in Fig. 2(b). In Fig. 2(b), (6) is the heat of dissociation of MXS_p into p molecules of S and gaseous MX, (7) the heat of dissociation of MX, (8) the ionization potential and electron affinity of M and X, and (9) the heat of co-ordination of M^+ with $p+1$ molecules of S. This cycle is equivalent to step (3) in Fig. 2(a) but provides a different path for determining the energy associated with

$$MXS_{p(g)} + S_{(g)} \rightleftharpoons MS_{p+1}^+ + X_{(g)}^-. \tag{10}$$

In addition to all the above effects, there are three additional important considerations.

(1) In order that the position of equilibrium parallel the net enthalpy change of all the steps in the cycle for different solvents and solutes, the net entropy change in these solvents must be constant or linearly related to the net enthalpy change.

(2) When extensive ion-pairing occurs, additional species must be added to the cycle and contributions to the energetics from this effect must be considered. The term ion-pairing will be employed to mean cation–anion association in which the anion is not in the first co-ordination sphere of the cation. The extent of ion-pairing can be estimated from the solvent dielectric constant or more accurately from conductivity studies of non-acidic ionic solutes in the solvent. The energy from this type of interaction is very significant in low dielectric solvents and is a very important factor in explaining why dissociation of solutes into ions occurs in these solvents.

(3) When different solutes are compared in a given solvent, differences in solute co-ordination number will be very important. The energies of the steps will be greatly influenced by entropy effects and hybridization changes.

For a more complex system than MX, e.g. $FeCl_3$, a large number of species must be considered:

$$FeCl_3S + Cl^- \rightleftharpoons FeCl_4^- + S \qquad (11a)$$

$$FeCl_3S + 3S \rightleftharpoons FeCl_2S_4^+ + Cl^- \qquad (11b)$$

$$FeCl_2S_4^+ + S \rightleftharpoons FeClS_5^{2+} + Cl^- \qquad (11c)$$

$$FeClS_5^{2+} + S \rightleftharpoons FeS_6^{3+} + Cl^-. \qquad (11d)$$

In this case, each equilibrium can be represented by a cycle similar to that for MX and the resulting species at equilibrium will depend on the competitive equilibria for each step. When solid phases are present in the system, the problem is further complicated by the lattice energies of the solid phases.

If the entropy and extent of ion-pairing are considered, a knowledge of the enthalpies corresponding to all the steps in the energy cycle for different solutes and solvents would produce a clear understanding of the important factors which affect the position of equilibrium for various solutes dissolved in different solvents. Unfortunately, for most systems, direct measurement of the energies corresponding to all these steps is not possible. The approach we shall employ in this chapter will consequently be one of indirect estimate of the relative magnitudes of these effects towards different solutes in different solvents.

B. EVALUATION OF ENERGY TERMS

The energy of step (3) of Fig. 2 can be qualitatively estimated from a knowledge of the co-ordination behaviour of the donor solvent. For this purpose it is necessary to study donor properties towards a variety of acids and to take care to employ criteria which actually measure donor strength. Stability constants and pK_B data do not provide this information, for these constants describe the complex free energy changes that can be represented by a cycle similar to that for MX. The term *donor strength* will be employed to indicate the relative co-ordinating ability of a donor measured in the absence of solvation as indicated by the enthalpy of adduct formation. *Basicity* will be employed to indicate the relative position of a donor–acceptor equilibrium in a solvent. Reliable data on donor properties can be obtained by measuring donor–acceptor interactions in the gas phase or in a non-coordinating solvent (such as CCl_4, hexane, etc.) where the difference in enthalpy of solvation of the donor plus acceptor and the adduct is small. In order to understand solvent donor properties, enthalpies should also be investigated over a wide range of different acid types for a given solvent. This is to be done so that intelligent predictions of interaction energies can be made for systems for which the enthalpies corresponding to donor–acceptor interactions cannot be directly measured. Some significant reversals in donor properties are observed. For example, it was found (Niedzielski *et al.*, 1965) that Et_2O is a stronger donor towards phenol (enthalpy of adduct formation, $\Delta H = -5.0 \text{ kcal mole}^{-1}$) than Et_2S ($\Delta H = -4.6 \text{ kcal mole}^{-1}$) but Et_2S is a better donor towards iodine ($\Delta H = -7.8 \text{ kcal mole}^{-1}$) than

$Et_2O(\Delta H = -4.2$ kcal mole^{-1}). A similar reversal in donor strength towards these two acids was found for the donors $CH_3CON(CH_3)_2$ and $CH_3CSN(CH_3)_2$ (Niedzielski et al., 1965). For these systems it is proposed that the distortable sulphur donor interacts more strongly with the distortable acid iodine than the mole polar oxygen donor but the oxygen donor interacts more strongly with the polar acid phenol. The term distortability refers to the ease with which electron density at the bonding site in the acceptor or donor can be polarized when these molecules have the electronic configurations that they have in the adduct. This phenomenon should be general.

There have been many attempts to infer the magnitude (enthalpy) of the donor–acceptor interaction from the shift upon co-ordination of a donor or acceptor vibration frequency. It has been shown that the difference in the —OH stretching frequency of phenol in free phenol and in a hydrogen-bonded adduct is linearly related to the enthalpy of adduct formation (Joesten and Drago, 1962a,b). There have been many other literature articles in which the magnitude of a frequency shift has been assumed to indicate the magnitude of donor–acceptor interaction. For example, the decrease in carbonyl stretching frequency of acetophenone upon complex formation with the following acids has been reported (Susz and Chaladon, 1958): (parentheses contain the decrease in absorption maximum in cm^{-1}) $HgCl_2$ (18), $ZnCl_2$ (47), BF_3 (107), $TiCl_4$ (118), $AlCl_3$ (120), $FeCl_3$ (130), $AlBr_3$ (130). It should be emphasized that the phenol relationship is the only frequency shift–enthalpy relationship that has been established at the present time. Indeed, in a dramatic illustration, it has been shown (Meek et al., 1962) that even though $(CH_3)_2SO$ and $(CH_2CH_2)_2SO$ interact to the same extent with cobalt in $Co(R_2SO)_6^{2+}CoCl_4^{2-}$ (as evidenced by identical positions in the spectrochemical series toward Ni^{2+}) the frequency shifts of the oxo-bond vibrations are 51 cm^{-1} and 88 cm^{-1}, respectively. An incorrect conclusion regarding the magnitude of the interaction would result from the use of infra-red data. Complications arise in this example and frequently in other systems because of coupling of ligand vibrational modes.

Although there is no definite experimental confirmation, it may be possible, for certain systems, to infer solvent donor strengths toward certain cationic Lewis acids from the spectrochemical series. For example, the following Dq values have been reported (Drago et al., 1963b) for six co-ordinate Ni^{2+} complexes: NH_3 (1080 cm^{-1}), H_2O (860 cm^{-1}), $(CH_3)_2SO$ (773 cm^{-1}), $CH_3CON(CH_3)^2$ (769 cm^{-1}). These results parallel the expected donor order. The need of defining the acid in formulating a donor order is essential not only because of differences in the importance of distortability and electrostatic interactions for different acids but also because of steric effects. For example, it was found (Joesten and Drago, 1965) that the donor order of amides of general formula $R_1CONR_2R_3$ (where R_i is CH_3 or H) towards iodine and phenol increases as the number of methyl groups is increased.

However, the Dq values (Drago *et al.*, 1963b) (for NiS_6^{+2}) are in the order

$$HCON(CH_3)_2 > HCON(CH_3)H > CH_3CONH_2 \gg CH_3CON(CH_3)_2 >$$
$$CH_3CON(CH_3)H.$$

When the amides are co-ordinated to metal ions, a steric repulsion arises between co-ordinated ligands if R_1 and R_3 are both alkyl. Figure 3 illustrates

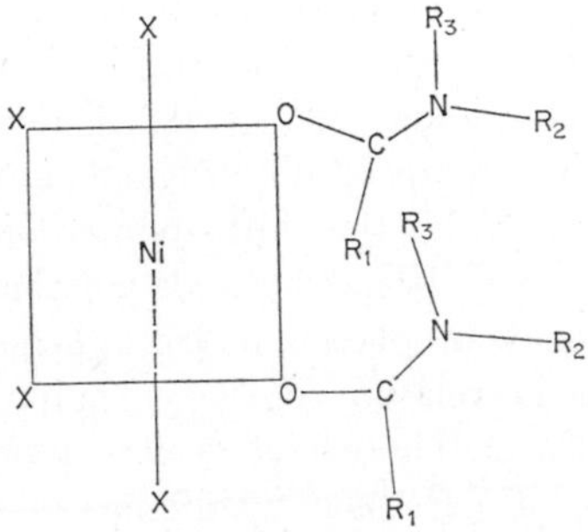

FIG. 3. Illustration of steric interactions between amide ligands in $Ni(amide)_6^{2+}$. Reproduced with permission from the *Journal of the Chemical Society*.

the nature of this steric effect. Only two ligands are illustrated and the concept is simplified to describe the effect. When R_1 is H there is a pronounced decrease in steric repulsion, a stronger interaction of the metal ion with the ligand results, and Dq is large compared to the case where R_1, R_2, and R_3 are methyl groups. This steric effect also is reduced in acetamide where both R_2 and R_3 are hydrogen and only R_1 is methyl. An appreciable steric effect is encountered when R_1 and R_3 are methyl, and also when all R_i groups are alkyl. When R_1 and R_3 are methyl the stable rotamer is the one in which the methyl groups are trans to each other because of steric interactions between R_1 and R_2 when they are both alkyl. Within a given main category, slight inductive effects can be detected as evidenced by the order listed above. A similar steric effect is operative in the six co-ordinate chromium(III) complexes.

When there is considerable metal to ligand π-bonding, Dq is much greater than anticipated from the measured donor strength with non-π-bonding acids. In a π-bonded complex, of which $Ni(CH_3CN)_6^{2+}$ is an example, Dq is a poor criterion of the donor strength of the ligand toward the metal ion.

In summary then, in the course of interpretation of the behaviour of solutes in various solvents, solvent donor properties should be estimated by examining all quantitative data available. Most weight should be given to those results obtained with acids that are most like the solute under consideration.

The problem of estimating the energies associated with steps (1), (4), and (5) of Fig. 2 is even more difficult. In the absence of specific interactions, the solvation will be predominately of the charge-dipole type. And when the solvent dielectric constant is related primarily to the dipole moment of the solvent, non-specific solvation energies should parallel the dielectric constant. Polar solvent molecules will interact most strongly with the most highly charged species and shift the equilibrium in the direction of these species.

It is known that the extent of ion-pairing will also depend on the solvent dielectric constant. The force, F, of attraction or repulsion between two charged species is given by:

$$F = \frac{q_1 q_2}{\epsilon r^2} \tag{12}$$

where q_1 and q_2 are the charges on the two species separated by a distance r in a *homogeneous* medium of dielectric constant ϵ. If the medium is a solvent, the charge-dipole interactions of the solvent with the ions will result in partial charge distribution over the solvent layers about the ions. As a result charge is dispersed, the ions' electric fields are rapidly attenuated, and ion-pairing will decrease. A high dielectric constant solvent attentuates the electric field of an ion more rapidly than a solvent with a low dielectric constant. In the absence of specific interactions, the $K_{assoc.}$ of a tetra-alkyl ammonium halide, measured from conductivity data, and the energy of solvation should parallel the dielectric constant of the solvent. Since co-ordination does not occur to the tetra-alkyl ammonium halides, the solvent donor properties should not affect this interaction.

The dielectric constant is a poor criterion of solvation if specific interactions of the Lewis acid–base type are possible between the co-ordinated solute and the solvent, for these effects usually are energetically more important than the non-specific dielectric effects. Examples of these specific interactions are the hydrogen bonding of certain solvents with the anion, e.g. Cl^-, and the hydrogen-bonding interaction of a donor solvent molecule with co-ordinated protonic ligands, e.g. $Co(NH_3)_6^{3+}$. In the current absence of better criteria, the salt association constant, $K_{assoc.}$, for alkylammonium salts and the Z-values of Kosower (1958a,b,c) can be utilized to estimate solvation energies. The Z-value is obtained from the solvent dependence of the charge transfer transition which the ion-pair 1-ethyl, 4-carbomethoxy pyridinium iodide undergoes. The wavelength of the band maximum for a given solvent is reported as a transition energy (in kcal mole^{-1}) and is referred to as the Z-value for that solvent. Since the ground state of the ion-pair is ionic, its energy is lowered by a highly solvating solvent while the energy of the neutral excited state is raised, for its dipole is oriented in a different direction from that of the ion-pair. Consequently the energy of the transition or Z-value will be higher for a polar or distortable solvent. Hydrogen-bonding solvents undergo specific interaction with the anion and consequently lead to appreciable stabilization of the ground state. This gives rise to very large Z-values. Referring to the cycle for MX, this is equivalent to saying that the Z-value will contain an energy contribution from an interaction like step (5) of Fig. 2. It is interesting to point out that although the dielectric constants of methanol and formamide are 32·6 and 109·5, respectively, the respective Z-values are 83·6 kcal mole^{-1} and 83·3 kcal mole^{-1} because of the effect just described. The values of $K_{assoc.}$ for alkylammonium halides in various solvents can also be employed to provide evidence regarding solvation. Dielectric constant and anion solvation both affect $K_{assoc.}$. We feel that this criterion, $K_{assoc.}$, is one of the best measures we have of the solvating properties of solvents.

IV. Solute Behaviour in Selected Solvents

Very few investigations of solute behaviour in non-aqueous solvents have been carried out in enough detail to provide information regarding the

Table I

Physical Properties of NN-Dimethylacetamide

M.p. (°C)	20^a
B.p. (°C)	$165\cdot0^{\circ a}$
Specific conductivity (ohm^{-1} cm^{-1})	$0\cdot8$–$2\cdot0\times10^{-7}$ ^{b}
Density (g/cm^3) at 25°C	$0\cdot9366^b$
Dielectric constant at 25°C	$37\cdot8^b$
Viscosity (centipoise) at 25°C	$0\cdot919^b$
Z–Value (kcal mole^{-1})	$66\cdot9^c$
Dq toward Ni(II) (cm^{-1})	769^d
Data for formation of the I_2 adduct	
$\quad-\varDelta H$ (kcal mole^{-1})	$4\cdot0^e$
$\quad K$ (l mole^{-1})	$6\cdot9$
Data for formation of the phenol adduct	
$\quad-\varDelta H$ (kcal mole^{-1})	$6\cdot4^f$
$\quad K$ (l mole^{-1})	134

^{a} Beilstein, 1962.
^{b} Lester et al., 1956.
^{c} D. Hart, personal communication.
^{d} Drago et al., 1963b.
^{e} Drago et al., 1961.
^{f} Joesten and Drago, 1962a,b.

structure of the species present in solution. Consequently a knowledge of the effect of a solvent on many solutes is unknown and a complete understanding of the relative importance of the essential solvent properties is lacking. Because of this lack of information, only a somewhat sketchy synopsis of this important subject can be given at present. It is not our purpose to give

TABLE II

Conductance Data for NN-Dimethylacetamide[a]

Electrolyte	Λ_0	$K_{assoc.}$	Electrolyte	Λ_0	$K_{assoc.}$
KNO_3	71·6	25	Et_4NBr	75·9	20
$NaNO_3$	71·2	50	Pr_4NBr	69·4	20
$NaBr$	69·0	17	Me_3NPhSO_3Ph	59·3	25
$NaSO_3Ph$	56·8	33			

[a] Lester *et al.*, 1956.

an exhaustive review of the data which is available and only a few characteristic solvents will be discussed to demonstrate the line of reasoning which is suggested by the Co-ordination Model. After a discussion of the properties and behaviour of certain solutes in some solvents, a brief general discussion

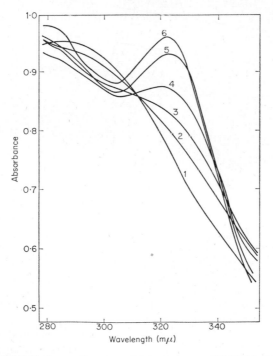

FIG. 4. Effect of chloride ion on the ultra-violet spectrum of $Fe(ClO_4)_3$ in NN-Dimethylacetamide. $[Fe(ClO_4)_3] = 1·28 \times 10^{-4}$ M; $[Cl^-]$: (1) $= 0$, (2) $= 0·36 \times 10^{-4}$ M, (3) $= 0·73 \times 10^{-4}$ M, (4) $= 1·09 \times 10^{-4}$ M, (5) $= 1·46 \times 10^{-4}$ M, (6) $= 2·19 \times 10^{-4}$ M. Reproduced with permission from the *Journal of the Chemical Society*.

will be presented in which an attempt will be made to correlate the existing data with the main properties of the different solvents. In view of the limited information available some of the interpretations in this latter section should be regarded as tentative. We hope this discussion will indicate an approach which can unify solute behaviour in non-aqueous solvents and will stimulate further research in this area.

A. NN-DIMETHYLACETAMIDE (DMA)

The physical properties of DMA are given in Table I. The limiting conductances, Λ_0, for several $1:1$ electrolytes in DMA at 25°C are contained

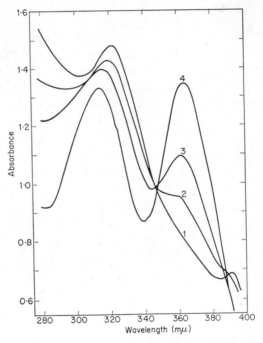

FIG. 5. Effect of chloride ion on the ultra-violet spectrum of $Fe(ClO_4)_3$ in NN-dimethyl-acetamide. $[Fe(ClO_4)_3] = 2\ 0 \times 10^{-4}$ M; $[Cl^-]$: (1) $= 4·54 \times 10^{-4}$ M, (2) $= 5·66 \times 10^{-4}$ M, (3) $= 6·79 \times 10^{-4}$ M, (4) $= 9·05 \times 10^{-4}$ M. Reproduced with permission from the *Journal of the Chemical Society*.

in Table II. Lithium salts are completely dissociated at concentrations up to 0·02 M and $\lambda_{0Li^+} < \lambda_{0Na^+}$ (Lester *et al.*, 1958).

An extensive study of the iron-chloro species formed in dilute solutions of ferric chloride in DMA has been carried out (Drago *et al.*, 1965a,b). The ultra-violet absorption spectra of $Fe(DMA)_6(ClO_4)_3$ as a function of added chloride is presented in Figs. 4 and 5. Addition of Cl^- up to a mole ratio of 1·8 to 1 results in the loss of the maximum at 287 which is attributed to

$Fe(DMA)_6^{3+}$. Absorbance increases in the 320 mμ region achieving a maximum at 323 mμ at a Cl^- to Fe^{3+} ratio of 1·8 to 1. This peak is attributed to $FeCl_2^+$. At wavelengths longer than 340 the absorbance is seen to increase initially (Cl^- : Fe^{3+} ratio of 0·6 to 1) and then decrease. Concurrently, *one* isobestic point is observed at Cl^- : Fe^{3+} ratios up to and including 0·9 to 1. Over this range the absorbances at wavelengths around 290 mμ decrease (up to and including 0·9 to 1) and then increase, and decrease again at the higher (>2) Cl^- ratios. At a Cl^- to Fe^{3+} ratio exceeding 2 to 1, the spectrum characteristic of $FeCl_4^-$ appears with two isobestic points and maxima at 314 mμ and 364 mμ. The spectra in Fig. 4 are consistent with the formation of $FeCl^{2+}$ and $FeCl_2^+$ with the latter beginning to form at 0·9 to 1 Cl^- to Fe^{3+}. The presence of three species at Cl^- ratios from 0·9–1·8 to 1 is certain from the loss of the isobestic point at 316mμ. Figure 5 illustrates the formation of $FeCl_4^-$ from $FeCl_2(DMA)_4^{2+}$ without detectable amounts of $FeCl_3(sol)$. Figure 5 also demonstrates that when ferric chloride (curve 3) is dissolved in DMA the principle species present in dilute solutions are $FeCl_2(DMA)_4^+$ and $FeCl_4^-$. Though exact values were not measured for the formation constants, K_n, of species $FeCl_n^{3-n}$, the following order accounts for the above behaviour.

$$K_3 \ll K_1 < K_2 \lesssim K_4.$$

By means of the following equations, the behaviour of $FeCl_3$ in DMA is seen to be adequately described by the Co-ordination Model:

$$DMA + FeCl_3 \rightleftharpoons FeCl_3.DMA \quad \text{(initial adduct)} \qquad (13a)$$

$$FeCl_3.DMA + 3DMA \rightleftharpoons FeCl_2(DMA)_4^+ + Cl^- \qquad (13b)$$

$$Cl^- + FeCl_3.DMA \rightleftharpoons FeCl_4^- + DMA. \qquad (13c)$$

Since the structure of the initial adduct is not known, the following set of equations could also describe the behaviour of $FeCl_3$ in DMA:

$$2FeCl_3 + DMA \rightleftharpoons Fe_2Cl_6.DMA \qquad (14a)$$

$$Fe_2Cl_6.DMA + 3DMA \rightleftharpoons FeCl_2(DMA)_4^+ + FeCl_4^-. \qquad (14b)$$

This latter reaction gives rise to a simple mechanism for forming $FeCl_4^-$ by attack of DMA on $Fe_2Cl_6.DMA$:

Buffagni and Dunn (1961) have carried out a very thorough study of the system $CoCl_2$–DMA. The spectra (visible region) can be interpreted in terms of the existence of the species $CoCl_4^{2-}$, $Co(DMA)_6^{2+}$, $CoCl_3(DMA)^-$ and $CoCl(DMA)_5^+$. Apparently the neutral species, $CoCl_2(DMA)_2$ or $CoCl_2(DMA)_4$, exists in very low concentration as was found for the species

FeCl$_3$.DMA. The behaviour of the CoCl$_2$–DMA system is also seen to be readily interpreted by the Co-ordination Model by writing equations similar to those above for FeCl$_3$.

B. N-METHYLACETAMIDE (NMA)

The physical properties and conductance data obtained for this solvent are presented in Tables III and IV.

TABLE III

Physical Properties of N-Methylacetamide

M.p. (°C)	29·5[a]
B.p. (°C)	206[c]
Specific conductivity (ohm^{-1} cm^{-1}) at 40°C	1–3 × 10^{-7} [a]
Density (g/cm^3) at 40°C	0·9420[a]
Dielectric constant at 40°C	165·5[a]
Viscosity (centipoise) at 40°C	3·019[a]
Z–Value (kcal mole^{-1})	77·9[b]
Dq toward Ni(II) (cm^{-1})	752[c]
Data for formation of the phenol adduct	
−ΔH (kcal mole^{-1})	4·7 ± 3[d]

[a] Dawson et al., 1957.
[b] D. Hart, personal communication.
[c] Drago et al., 1963b.
[d] Joesten, 1962.

An interesting trend in anion solvation is obvious from the λ_0^- of Cl$^-$, Br$^-$, and I$^-$. In hydrogen bonding solvents (those with an acidic proton) like NMA, it is to be expected that anion solvation would be high. This solvation energy consists, to a large extent, of the energy from the specific interaction

$$|\overline{X}| \ldots H \ldots N\text{—}COCH_3$$
$$\underset{\displaystyle CH_3}{|}$$

Limiting anionic conductance should inversely parallel the extent of hydrogen bonding and this is the order observed for NMA, i.e. λ_0^- increases Cl$^-$ < Br$^-$ < I$^-$.

The studies of Drago et al. (1965a,b) are also consistent with extensive anion solvation. The ultra-violet spectrum of FeCl$_3$ in NMA indicates the presence of only FeS$_6^{3+}$ and Cl$^-$. This strikingly demonstrates the importance of anion solvation and dielectric constant (or Z-value) for this solvent since the donor strength of NMA is nearly the same as that of DMA.

C. DIMETHYL SULPHOXIDE (DMSO)

The physical properties of DMSO are tabulated in Table V and the limiting conductances of several 1 : 1 electrolytes are presented in Table VI. These salts are completely dissociated in DMSO at least up to concentrations of 10^{-3} M. Dimethyl sulphoxide appears to be a better solvating solvent than DMA.

TABLE IV

Conductance Data for N-Methylacetamide

Electrolyte	Λ_0	$K_{assoc.}$
KCl[a]	17·9	
NaCl[a]	17·8	
KBr[a]	19·0	
NaBr[a]	18·9	
KI[a]	20·7	
NaI[a]	20·1	
CsBr[a]	20·1	
Et$_4$NBr[a]	22·1	
Et$_4$NPi[a]	21·3	
HCl[b]	20·7[b]	
HPi[b]	20·9	0
NH$_4$ClO$_4$[b]	26·5	0
NH$_4$NO$_3$[b]	26·5	0
NH$_4$NO$_3$[b]	24·2	0
KClO$_4$[b]	25·2	0
KSCN[b]	24·5	0
KNO$_3$[b]	22·9	0
KPi[b]	20·2	0
NaClO$_4$[b]	25·0	0
NaSCN[b]	24·2	0
NaNO$_3$[b]	22·7	0
NaPi[b]	20·2	0

[a] French and Glover, 1955.
[b] Dawson et al., 1957.

Preliminary investigations (Drago et al., 1965a,b) indicate that $FeCl_4^-$ is unstable in DMSO and ionizes to produce cationic Fe(III) species. These species are most probably $Fe(DMSO)_6^{3+}$ and cationic iron chloro species.

The behaviour of $CoCl_2$ in DMSO and in solutions of Cl^- in DMSO has been studied by P. Van Der Voorn (unpublished results) and by Buffagni and Dunn (1961). The spectra of these solutions are given in Fig. 6. Comparing these spectra with the molar extinction curves of $CoCl_2$, $CoCl_3^-$ and $CoCl_4^{2-}$ reported by Fine (1962) one may make a few qualitative statements about the solution species which exist under the conditions of these experiments. The solution of $CoCl_2$ most certainly contains the tetrahedral species $CoCl_2(DMSO)_2$ and

TABLE V

Physical Properties of Dimethylsulphoxide

M.p. (°C)	$18{\cdot}4^a$
B.p. (°C)	$189{\cdot}0^a$
Specific conductivity (ohm^{-1} cm^{-1})	$3 \times 10^{-8\,a}$
Density (g/cm^3) at 25°C	$1{\cdot}096^a$
Dielectric constant at 25°C	$46{\cdot}6^a$
Viscosity (centipoise) at 25°C	$1{\cdot}96^a$
Z–Value (kcal mole^{-1})	$71{\cdot}1^b$
Dq towards Ni(II) (cm^{-1})	773^c
Data for formation of the I$_2$ adduct	
$\quad -\Delta H$ (kcal mole^{-1})	$4{\cdot}4^d$
$\quad K$ (l mole^{-1})	$11{\cdot}6$
Data for formation of the phenol adduct	
$\quad -\Delta H$ (kcal mole^{-1})	$6{\cdot}5^d$
$\quad K$ (l mole^{-1})	182

[a] Sears et al., 1956a.
[b] Kosower, 1958a.
[c] Meek et al., 1962.
[d] Drago et al., 1963a.

CoCl$_3$(DMSO)$^-$; the formation of the anionic complex is accompanied by the formation of octahedral Co^{2+} species and absorption due to these species is observed below 550 mμ. As the concentration of Cl$^-$(Ph$_3$NMeCl) is increased the spectra indicate progressive formation of CoCl$_3$(DMSO)$^-$ and CoCl$_4^{2-}$.

TABLE VI

Conductance Data for Dimethylsulphoxide^a

Electrolyte	Λ_0	Electrolyte	Λ_0
KI	38·2	NaNO$_3$	40·8
NaI	37·6	KClO$_4$	39·1
KBr	38·4	NaClO$_4$	38·3
NaBr	38·0	KPi	31·7
KSCN	43·5	NaPi	31·1
NaSCN	43·0	Bu$_4$NI	35·0
KNO$_3$	41·5	Me$_3$NPhI	37·8

[a] Sears et al., 1956a.

Buffagni and Dunn (1961) reported that a solution of $CoCl_4^{2-}$ in DMSO contains approximately 20% tetrahedral species ($CoCl_4^{2-}$ and $CoCl_3(DMSO)^-$; the remainder of the Co^{2+} is present as the various octahedral forms.

An interesting effect is observed (Meek, 1962) in $NiCl_2$–DMSO solutions. At room temperature such solutions possess the light green colour of 6 co-ordinate Ni(II) complexes (visible spectra indicate octahedral Ni(II))

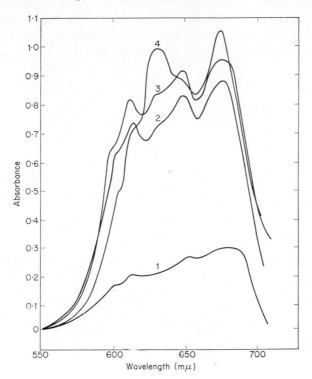

Fig. 6. Effect of chloride ion on visible spectrum of $CoCl_2$ in dimethylsulphoxide. (1) $[CoCl_2] = 0\cdot002$ M; (2) $[Co^{2+}] = 0\cdot003$ M, $[Cl^-] = 0\cdot012$ M; (3) $[Co^{2+}] = 0\cdot003$ M, $[Cl^-] = 0\cdot024$ M; (4) $[Co^{2+}] = 0\cdot003$ M, $[Cl^-]$ = large excess. Reproduced with permission from the *Journal of the Chemical Society.*

which are probably $Ni(DMSO)_6^{2+}$ and $NiCl(DMSO)_5^+$. Upon heating to approximately 50°C, the originally green solution turns to an intense deep blue characteristic of tetrahedral nickel. This colour change is completely reversible and upon heating a solution at 50°C for 6 hours, large blue crystals deposit. Analysis of these crystals is consistent with the formation of the mixed complex $Ni(DMSO)_6^{2+}NiCl_4^{2-}$. This is the same compound obtained from DMSO solutions of $NiCl_2$ upon addition of C_6H_6 at room temperature. This latter case is an example of a situation where the solid isolated and that in solution at room temperature are quite different.

D. NITROMETHANE AND NITROBENZENE (NM, NB)

The physical properties of nitromethane and nitrobenzene are presented together in Table VII.

It is very difficult to interpret the results obtained in the solvent nitromethane because of the difficulty in purifying this material. Two purification procedures are noted by Buffagni and Dunn (1961). It is probably safe to assume that unless purification is specified in an article, impure material was employed. Purification by distillation can be hazardous. Conductances for some electrolytes are given in the succeeding table.

TABLE VII

Physical Properties of Nitromethane and Nitrobenzene

	CH_3NO_2	$C_6H_5NO_2$
M.p. (°C)	$-28\cdot5^a$	$5\cdot8^a$
B.p. (°C)	$101\cdot3^a$	$210\cdot8^a$
Specific conductivity (ohm^{-1} cm^{-1}) at 25°C	$6\cdot56\times10^{-7}$ ^{a}	$9\cdot1\times10^{-7}$ ^{a}
Density (g/cm^3) at 25°C	$1\cdot1312^a$	$1\cdot193^a$
Dielectric constant at 30°C	$35\cdot9^a$	$34\cdot8^a$
Viscosity (centipoise) at 30°C	$0\cdot595^a$	$1\cdot634^a$
Z–Value (kcal mole^{-1})	—	—
Dq toward Ni(II)	—	—
$-\varDelta H$ (kcal mole^{-1})(from $\varDelta\nu_{OH}$ towards phenol)	$1\cdot9^b$	$2\cdot04^b$

[a] Weissberger et al., 1955.
[b] Joesten, 1962.

Interesting behaviour of solutions in these solvents has been noted and studied by several authors. They are fairly good solvating solvents (in the non-specific sense) and dissolve many electrolytes. Dissociation of molecular species into ions is often observed. The $K_{assoc.}$ for Bu$_4$NBr in $C_6H_5NO_2$ at 25°C is 46 (Sodek and Fuoss, 1950). As co-ordinating solvents they occupy positions at the weak end of the scale but they can and do act as Lewis bases.

The donor strength of CH_3NO_2 and $C_6H_5NO_2$ are unknown at present. It is reported (Drago et al., 1963a) that the —O—H frequency shift of phenol cannot be used to measure the donor strength of sulpholane, $(CH_2CH_2)_2SO_2$, because the phenol interacts with both oxygens. A similar effect is expected with nitro compounds so the enthalpies in Table VII represent lower limits and the actual values will have to be measured directly. The crystal field parameter Dq has not been reported but there are indications that nitromethane displaces certain ligands from the co-ordination sphere of metal ions. This could occur through a hydrogen-bonding inter-action of the donor ligand with CH_3NO_2 and does not necessarily imply nitromethane co-ordination. However, there is more direct evidence for nitromethane co-ordination. A most interesting study is the one of de Maine

TABLE VIII

Molar Conductance Data for Nitromethane

Salt	Λ_{molar}	Concentration
$Fe(HMPA)_6(ClO_4)_3{}^a$	236	0·0005
$Cr(HMPA)_6(ClO_4)_3{}^a$	253	0·005
$Al(HMPA)_6(ClO_4)_3{}^a$	241	0·0005
$Fe(HMPA)_4(ClO_4)_2{}^a$	185	0·002
$Mg(HMPA)_4(ClO_4)_2{}^a$	153	0·001
$Co(HMPA)_4(ClO_4)_2{}^b$	178	0·0105
$Ni(HMPA)_4(ClO_4)_2{}^b$	184	0·005
$Zn(HMPA)_4(ClO_4)_2{}^b$	180	0·002
$(Ph_3AsMe)_2NiCl_4{}^c$	173	0·0005
$(Ph_3AsMe)_2CoI_4{}^c$	151	0·0005
$(Et_4N)_2MnCl_4{}^c$	200	0·0005
$(Ph_3AsMe)I{}^c$	85	0·0005
$(Et_4N)I{}^c$	97	0·0005
$Co(diars)_2(ClO_4)_2{}^c$	177	0·0005
$Co(diars)_3(ClO_4)_3{}^c$	262	0·0005

[a] Donoghue and Drago, 1963.
[b] Donoghue and Drago, 1962.
[c] Gill and Nyholm, 1959.

and Koubek (1959) on the system $FeCl_3$–CH_3NO_2 and the ternary system $FeCl_3$–CH_3NO_2–CCl_4. Beer's Law is not obeyed by solutions of $FeCl_3$ in CH_3NO_2 but on the other hand, for a given solvent composition, a linear relationship is found at all wavelengths when the ratio of optical density to total $FeCl_3$ is plotted against total $FeCl_3$. Conductivity measurements made on these solutions revealed normal behaviour in that the Onsager equation described the equivalent conductance as a function of $FeCl_3$ concentration, $[\Lambda = \Lambda_0 - (\alpha + \beta\Lambda_0)\sqrt{C}]$. Reference should be made to the original paper for details but these phenomena reportedly are only consistent with either one or the other of the following equilibria

$$FeCl_3 {}_{(sol)} + FeCl_3 {}_{(sol)} \rightleftharpoons \text{``complex''} \rightleftharpoons FeCl_4^- {}_{(sol)} + FeCl_2^+ {}_{(sol)} \tag{15a}$$

$$FeCl_3 {}_{sol)} + FeCl_3 {}_{sol)} \rightleftharpoons \text{``complex''} \rightleftharpoons Fe_2Cl_5^+ {}_{(sol)} + Cl_{(sol)}^-. \tag{15b}$$

In these equilibria, the concentration of the "complex" (probably Fe_2Cl_6) must be extremely small to account for the linear relationships mentioned above. By analogy with other solvents described herein, the equilibria in (15a) are preferred.

Buffagni and Dunn (1961) have made a thorough spectrophotometric study of solutions of $CoCl_2$ in nitromethane. The spectroscopic properties of these solutions as a function of Cl^- concentration are satisfactorily ration-

TABLE IX

Physical Properties of Acetone

M.p. (°C)	$-95\cdot4^a$
B.p. (°C)	$56\cdot2^a$
Specific conductivity (ohm^{-1} cm^{-1}) at 25°C	$5\cdot8\times10^{-8}$ ^{a}
Density (g/cm^3) at 25°C	$0\cdot7851^a$
Dielectric constant at 25°C	$20\cdot7^a$
Viscosity (centipoise) at 30°C	$0\cdot2954^a$
Z–Value (kcal mole^{-1})	$65\cdot7^b$
Data for formation of I_2 adduct	
$-\Delta H$ (kcal mole^{-1})	$2\cdot5^c$
K (l mole^{-1})	$0\cdot85$
Data for formation of phenol adduct	
$-\Delta H$ (kcal mole^{-1})	$3\cdot3^c$
K (l mole^{-1})	$13\cdot5$

[a] Weissberger et al., 1955.
[b] Kosower, 1958a.
[c] Drago et al., 1963b.

alized on the basis of the following equilibria in which NM symbolizes CH_3NO_2

$$CoCl_2 + 2NM \rightleftharpoons CoCl_2(NM)_2 \tag{16a}$$

$$CoCl_2(NM)_2 + Cl^- \rightleftharpoons CoCl_3(NM)^- + NM \tag{16b}$$

$$CoCl_3(NM)^- + Cl^- \rightleftharpoons CoCl_4^{2-} + NM. \tag{16c}$$

The existence of the first equilibrium described above is supported by the conductance of a solution of $CoCl_2$ in CH_3NO_2. No ionic species can be detected by this technique. In addition, careful examination of all the spectra revealed the absence of any "octahedral" complexes.

Gagnoux et al. (1958) interpreted the infra-red spectra of

$$p\text{-}RC_6N_4NO_2\text{-}MX_n \quad \text{and} \quad CH_3NO_2\text{-}MX_n$$

to indicate co-ordination by the nitro compounds; for the expected lowering of the $-N{<}^O_O$ asymmetric stretching frequency is observed. However, this work must be viewed with caution as spectra were obtained on solids. It is obvious that there is need for more definitive work with this solvent.

E. ACETONE (Ac)

The physical properties and some conductance data for acetone are presented in Tables IX and X.

TABLE X

Conductance Data for Acetone

Electrolyte	Λ_0	$K_{assoc.}$
Bu_4NI[a]	180·2	164
$KSCN$[a]	202·2	294
KI[b]	193·0	
NaI[b]	191·0	
KBr[b]	196·0	
$NaBr$[b]	194·0	
$KSCN$[b]	208·0	
$NaSCN$[b]	200·0	
KNO_3[b]	202·0	
$NaNO_3$[b]	200·0	
$KClO_4$[b]	196·0	
$NaClO_4$[b]	194·0	
KPi[b]	166·0	
$NaPi$[b]	159·0	

[a] Sears et al., 1956a.
[b] Sears et al., 1956b.

Very recently Fine (1962) has studied the formation of CoX_n^{2-n} complexes ($X = Cl^-$, Br^-, I^-) in acetone. He established the presence of CoX_2, CoX_3^-, and CoX_4^{2-} complexes in solution. Their spectra indicate that they are all of tetrahedral symmetry. In this study it was *assumed* that acetone occupies the co-ordination positions unoccupied by X^-. Using the concept of average ligand field (Jorgensen, 1956; Cotton et al., 1961) (apparently valid for ligands near one another in the spectrochemical series), a value of Dq' (where Dq' is the ligand field splitting parameter for a tetrahedral complex) for acetone was calculated using known values of Dq' for the halides. The value $(4·3 \pm 0·4) \times 10^3$ cm^{-1}, which when multiplied by 9/4 to convert to an approximate 10 Dq for an octahedral field of acetone molecules about Co(II), produces a surprisingly high value of 9700 cm^{-1}. Fine also calculates equilibrium quotients for the formation of these complexes. This data is presented in Table XI.

A conductivity study (Dawson and Belcher, 1951) of $FeCl_3$ in acetone indicates the solute is incompletely dissociated. The ions are apparently univalent. This system may parallel that of nitromethane discussed above. More work is required on this system.

Friedman and Plane (1963) have published an interesting study of Cu(II) solvation in water–acetone mixtures. The absorption spectra of these solutions as a function of mole % H_2O are adequately explained by the equilibria

$$Cu(H_2O)_6^{2+} + ac \rightleftharpoons Cu(H_2O)_5ac^{2+} + H_2O \tag{17a}$$

and

$$Cu(H_2O)_5ac^{2+} + ac \rightleftharpoons Cu(H_2O)_4ac_2^{2+} + H_2O. \tag{17b}$$

These authors conclude that the ligand field strengths for water, acetone, and ethanol are qualitatively

$$water \geq acetone \geq ethanol.$$

TABLE XI

Equilibrium Quotients for CoX_n^{2-n} Species

Quotient	Cl^-	Br^-	I^-
$\dfrac{[CoX_2]}{[Co^{2+}][X^-]^2}$	3×10^9	2×10^9	$> 10^9$
$\dfrac{[CoX_3^-]}{[CoX_2][X^-]}$	$> 10^5$	$> 10^5$	$2 \cdot 2 \times 10^4$
$\dfrac{[CoX_4^{2-}]}{[CoX_3^-][X^-]}$	$5 \cdot 4 \times 10^2$	42	16

Katzin and Gebert (1950a,b,c) have studied several Co(II) salts in acetone and found behaviour paralleling that already discussed. The salts $Co(SCN)_2$, $CoCl_2$, and $Co(NO_3)_2$ all form anion complexes of the type CoX_3^- and CoX_4^{2-} with increasing X^- concentration. Unfortunately for our purpose, anhydrous salts were not used in this work and the complexes most certainly contain co-ordinated H_2O. The existence of aquo complexes is suggested by a ternary phase diagram published by Katzin and Ferraro (1950) showing the solid complexes $Co(NO_3)_2 \cdot 6H_2O$, $Co(NO_3)_2 \cdot 4H_2O$, $Co(NO_3)_2 \cdot 3H_2O$, $Co(NO_3)_2 \cdot 2H_2O$, and *probably* $Co(NO_3)_2 \cdot 2ac$.

Koch (1950) has proposed the existence of an unusual species in acetone solutions of KI and AgI. Although AgI is insoluble in acetone, three moles of AgI reportedly dissolve per mole of KI in this solvent and the conductance of KI solutions is much lower when AgI is present. The formation of $I(AgI)_3^-$ was proposed to account for this. The same behaviour is observed for HgI_2. Further verification and/or study of this system would be interesting.

Studies of 1 : 1 adduct formation between various Lewis acids and aldehydes and aromatic or aliphatic ketones have been carried out by Susz (1959), by Gagnoux et al. (1958) and by Susz and Chalandon (1958). The only conclusion that can be drawn from these studies is that co-ordination occurs.

F. METHANOL AND ETHANOL (MeOH, EtOH)

The physical properties of these solvents are given in Table XII. A few conductance values are given in Table XIII.

TABLE XII

Physical Properties of Methanol and Ethanol

	MeOH	EtOH
M.p. (°C)	$-97 \cdot 5^a$	$-114 \cdot 5^a$
B.p. (°C)	$64 \cdot 51^a$	$78 \cdot 3^a$
Specific conductivity (ohm^{-1} cm^{-1}) at 25°C	$1 \cdot 50 \times 10^{-9 \, a}$	$1 \cdot 35 \times 10^{-9 \, a}$
Density (g/cm^3) at 25°C	$0 \cdot 7868^a$	$0 \cdot 7851^a$
Dielectric constant at 25°C	$32 \cdot 6^a$	$24 \cdot 3^a$
Viscosity (centipoise) at 25°C	$0 \cdot 5445^a$	$1 \cdot 078^a$
Z–Value (kcal mole^{-1})	$83 \cdot 6^b$	$79 \cdot 6^b$
Dq toward Ni(II) (cm^{-1})	850^c	—
Data for formation of I_2 adduct		
$-\Delta H$ (kcal mole^{-1})	$1 \cdot 90^d$	$2 \cdot 10^d$
K (l mole^{-1})	$0 \cdot 47$	$0 \cdot 45$

[a] Weissberger et al., 1955.
[b] Kosower, 1958a.
[c] V. Imhof, unpublished results.
[d] Tsubomura and Lang, 1961.

When dilute solutions of ferric chloride in methanol are examined spectrophotometrically (Drago et al., 1965a,b) only cationic iron-chloro species are found—no tetrachloroferrate. This is predicted if one considers that methanol is a strong base toward first row transition metal cations ($Dq = 850$ cm^{-1}) and is a good solvating solvent as evidenced by the Z–Value and $K_{assoc.}$ for Bu$_4$NBr. Its dielectric constant is misleading with respect to its ionizing ability. The specific hydrogen-bonding interaction with anions probably is responsible for the high Z–Value and the dissociation of the anionic iron–chloro species.

One might question the $K_{assoc.}$ values for MgX^+ contained in Table XIII. If anion solvation were large, $K_{assoc.}$ would be expected to increase $K_{Cl^-} < K_{Br^-} < K_{I^-}$. If $Cl^- > Br^- > I^-$ is the order of anion donor strength toward the divalent cation Mg^{2+} and one considers that methanol is required to displace or extract the anion from the metal ion, the results can be accounted for. The magnitude of the $K_{assoc.}$ demonstrate strikingly the effect of a divalent cation on ion association relative to monovalent cations.

TABLE XIII

Conductance Data for MeOH and EtOH

Electrolyte	Λ_0	K_{as}	Solvent
LiBr[a]	89·1	—	MeOH
AgNO$_3$[c]	—	73·8	MeOH
KSCN[e]	115·7	11·0	MeOH
MgCl$_2$[b]	41·8	600·0	EtOH
MgBr$_2$[b]	44·6	215·0	EtOH
MgI$_2$[b]	47·2	180·0	EtOH
Bu$_4$NBr[d]	96·7	26·0	MeOH

[a] Sears *et al.*, 1955a.
[b] Dawson and Golben, 1952.
[c] Busby and Griffiths, 1963.
[d] Sodek and Fuoss, 1950.
[e] Sears *et al.*, 1955b.

Katzin (1952) has published spectrophotometric data which further support the above described solvent properties for alcohols. Spectra of $Ni(SCN)_2$ solutions in iso-C_3H_7OH indicate the existence, in significant amounts, of only $Ni(SCN)^+$ and $Ni(SCN)_2$ up to ratios of 4 to 1 of SCN^- to Ni^{2+}. Up to a ten-fold excess of chloride ion to cobalt, only $CoCl^+$ and $CoCl_2$ are detected. Much larger concentrations of Cl^- are needed to form $CoCl_3^-$. The same spectrum is obtained when either $CoCl_2$ or $CoCl_4^{2-}$ is added to this alcohol. The same is true for cobalt(II) bromide. At greater than a four-fold excess of SCN^- to cobalt, the species $Co(SCN)_2$ and $Co(SCN)_3^-$ are claimed but no $Co(SCN)_4^{2-}$ is reported in the solvents iso-C_3H_7OH and C_4H_9OH.

Several workers have carried out investigations in mixed alcohol–water mixtures but, as mentioned above, it is often difficult to interpret results from mixed solvents. In an interesting study, Mackor (1951) has investigated the stability of the AgI_2^- complex in mixed acetone–water and methanol–water solvents. Stability increases on going from water to acetone–water but not on going to methanol–water. Also, K_{form} for AgI_2^- is the same in methanol–acetone as it is in acetone–water mixtures. This study illustrates the similarities between alcohols (particularly methanol) and water. This work is consistent with the hydrogen-bonding propensity of alcohols.

G. PYRIDINE (Py)

The physical properties of this compound are presented in Table XIV and conductance data are given in Table XV.

TABLE XIV

Physical Properties of Pyridine

M.p. (°C)	$-41 \cdot 8^a$
B.p. (°C)	$115 \cdot 6^a$
Specific conductivity (ohm^{-1} cm^{-1}) at 25°C	$4 \cdot 0 \times 10^{-8}$ ^{a}
Density (g/cm^3) at 30°C	$0 \cdot 97281^a$
Dielectric constant at 25°C	$12 \cdot 3^a$
Viscosity (centipoise) at 30°C	$0 \cdot 829^a$
Z–Value (kcal mole^{-1})	$64 \cdot 0^b$
Dq toward Ni(II) (cm^{-1})	$\sim 1000^c$
Data for formation of I_2 adduct	
$\quad -\varDelta H$ (kcal mole^{-1})	$7 \cdot 8^d$
$\quad K$ (l mole^{-1})	269
Data for formation of phenol adduct	
$\quad -\varDelta H$ (kcal mole^{-1})	$8 \cdot 07^e$
$\quad K$ (l mole^{-1})	—

[a] Weissberger et al., 1955.
[b] Kosower, 1958a.
[c] Rosenthal and Drago, 1965.
[d] Tsubomura and Lang, 1961.
[e] Joesten, 1962.

Preliminary experiments (D. Hart, personal communication) on the stability of $FeCl_3$ and $FeCl_4^-$ in pyridine reveal that $FeCl_4^-$ is not formed from $FeCl_3$ in pyridine. The species are probably Fe_2Cl_6 and py→$FeCl_3$. However, $FeCl_4^-$ has some stability in pyridine. Since addition of Cl^- to a pyridine solution of $FeCl_4^-$ results in an increase in absorbance at 316 and 365 mμ there is some dissociation of $FeCl_4^-$. The nature of the other species has not been ascertained.

A study of adducts of pyridine and substituted pyridines with $SbCl_5$ and phosphorus acids of the type PX_nF_{5-n} has been reported by Holmes et al. (1963). Molecular weights and conductivity measurements were interpreted to indicate that ionization does not occur and only 1 : 1 adducts are formed in nitrobenzene solution. They report enthalpies of adduct formation which were determined calorimetrically in nitrobenzene but which were not corrected for differences in non-specific solvation of the base and adduct.

As mentioned in Section II, Katzin (1950b) has studied the formation of pyridine complexes of $CoCl_2$ in various solvents. The existence of 1:1 and 2:1 py-$CoCl_2$ complexes in acetone has been established. The ion $pyCoCl_3^-$ can be obtained when excess Cl^- is added to this system. These authors claim to have isolated $Co(py)_6Cl_2$, but Rosenthal and Drago (1965) have not been able to isolate this complex.

TABLE XV

Conductance Data for Pyridine

Electrolyte	Λ_0	$K_{assoc.}$
NH_4Pi^a	80·5	3580
KPi^a	65·7	10,000
$NaPi^a$	60·5	23,200
$LiPi^a$	58·6	12,000
$AgClO_4{}^a$	81·9	524
$AgNO_3{}^a$	86·9	1070
$PyHNO_3{}^a$	102·2	19,600
Bu_4NOAc^a	76·0	5880
$Bu_4NNO_3{}^a$	76·6	2700
Bu_4NI^a	73·1	2440
Bu_4NBr^a	75·3	4000
Bu_4NPi^a	57·7	780
KI^b	80·2	—
NaI^b	75·2	—
KBr^b	82·9	—
$NaBr^b$	77·9	—
$KNO_3{}^b$	84·7	—
$NaNO_3{}^b$	79·6	—

[a] Audrieth and Kleinberg, 1953.
[b] Sears et al., 1956b.

An interesting study by Fackler, mentioned under Section II, illustrates nicely the effect of a co-ordinating solvent on solute species. A similar study of the system $(Ni(acac)_2)_3$–C_6H_6–py was also carried out by Fackler (1962). The absorption spectra of benzene solutions of $(Ni(acac)_2)_3$ as a function of pyridine concentration indicate the following behaviour:

$$2(Ni(acac)_2)_3 + 3py \rightleftharpoons 3(Ni(acac)_2)_2 \cdot py \qquad (18a)$$

$$(Ni(acac)_2)_2 \cdot py + 3py \rightleftharpoons 2Ni(acac)_2 \cdot 2py. \qquad (18b)$$

These studies are of interest in that they dramatically illustrate solute aggregation in weakly co-ordinating solvents and the effect of a co-ordinating solvent on these aggregates.

The conductance data in Table XV indicate that electrolytes are extensively associated in pyridine. This is most certainly a result of the low dielectric constant of pyridine. Anion solvation through specific interaction does not occur in pyridine but the cation Li^+ is co-ordinated and solvated more than Na^+ and K^+ as shown by Λ_0 and $K_{assoc.}$ for common anion salts of these cations. Apparently, Na^+ and K^+ possess smaller solvodynamic units.

H. ACETONITRILE (MeCN)

Acetonitrile is the most common of the nitrile solvents and we have chosen to discuss solute behaviour in this solvent. Its physical properties are presented in Table XVI and some conductance data are given in Table XVII.

TABLE XVI

Physical Properties of Acetonitrile

M.p. (°C)	$-45 \cdot 7^a$
B.p. (°C)	$81 \cdot 6^a$
Specific conductivity (ohm^{-1} cm^{-1}) 25°C	$5 \cdot 9 \times 10^{-8\ a}$
Density (g/cm³) 25°	$0 \cdot 7768^a$
Dielectric constant at 25°C	$36 \cdot 2^a$
Viscosity (centipoise) at 30°C	$0 \cdot 325^a$
Z–Value (kcal mole^{-1})	$71 \cdot 3^b$
Dq toward Ni(II) (cm^{-1})	1026^c
Data for formation of I_2 adduct	
$-\Delta H$ (kcal mole^{-1})	$2 \cdot 3^d$
K (l mole^{-1})	$0 \cdot 40$
Data for formation of phenol adduct	
$-\Delta H$ (kcal mole^{-1})	$3 \cdot 3^d$
K (l mole^{-1})	$5 \cdot 0$

[a] Weissberger et al., 1955.
[b] Kosower, 1958a.
[c] Joesten, 1962.
[d] Drago et al., 1963a.

The conductance data for the alkali metal perchlorates seem to follow the expected trend of increasing solvation: $Cs < Rb < K < Na < Li$. The $K_{assoc.}$ values change inversely to this sequence. From the data on the Me_4N^+ salts it appears that I^- and NO_3^- behave similarly in CH_3CN. The $K_{assoc.}$ values for the halides verify the anticipated sequence of ion solvation $(I^- < Br^- < Cl^-)$.

Marcinkowski (1961) has studied, spectrophotometrically and conducti-metrically, solutions of $CoCl_2$ in CH_3CN. It is claimed that the following equilibria account for the observed properties of the solutions:

$$2CoCl_2 + 6MeCN \rightarrow Co(MeCN)_6^{2+}CoCl_4^{2-} \tag{19a}$$

$$CoCl_4^{2-} + 2MeCN \rightleftharpoons CoCl_4(MeCN)_2^{2-}. \tag{19b}$$

The solute iron(III) chloride dissociates in CH_3CN into cationic and anionic species (Drago and Carlson, 1964):

$$FeCl_3 \rightleftharpoons (MeCN)FeCl_3 \rightleftharpoons FeCl_2(MeCN)_4^+ + Cl^- \tag{20a}$$

$$Cl^- + FeCl_3(MeCN) \rightleftharpoons FeCl_4^- + MeCN. \tag{20b}$$

TABLE XVII

Conductance Data for Acetonitrile

Electrolyte	Λ_0	$K_{assoc.}$
KI^a	186·7	—
$LiClO_4{}^b$	183·4	68·4
$NaClO_4{}^b$	192·3	70·9
$KClO_4{}^b$	208·2	97·7
$RbClO_4{}^b$	203·0	103·7
$CsClO_4{}^b$	207·6	144·6
$Me_4NNO_3{}^c$	200·5	23·0
$Bu_4NNO_3{}^c$	168·2	7·0
Me_4NCl^d	193·1	77·5
Me_4NBr^d	192·7	41·4
Me_4NI^d	195·3	27·5

[a] Marcinkowski, 1961.
[b] Minc and Werblan, 1962.
[c] Berns and Fuoss, 1961.
[d] Popov and Skelly, 1954.

Barnes and Hume (1963) have studied the complexes formed by copper(II) and bromide ion in acetonitrile. They find $CuBr_4^-$ is stable in this solvent as a "tetrahedral" complex. The complex $CuBr_3^-$ has been formulated, not as a tetrahedral ion, but rather as a five co-ordinate trigonal bypyramidal complex

Beattie and Webster (1963) have studied solutions of PCl_5 and $SbCl_5$ in

CH_3CN by infra-red spectroscopy. They conclude from spectroscopic studies that PCl_5 ionizes as

$$2PCl_5 \rightleftharpoons PCl_4^+ + PCl_6^- \tag{21}$$

while $SbCl_5$ dissociates *and* co-ordinates MeCN:

$$2SbCl_5 \rightleftharpoons SbCl_4(MeCN)_2^+ + SbCl_6^-. \tag{22}$$

Ellendt and Cruse (1952) have published their findings on conductance studies of HgX_2 solutions. They observe formation of the complexes HgX_3^-,

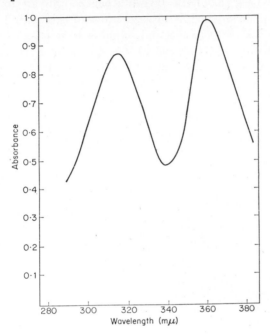

FIG. 7. Absorption spectrum of $FeCl_3$ in tetramethylene sulphone. $[FeCl_3] = 2 \cdot 0 \times 10^{-4}$ M. Reproduced with permission from the *Journal of the Chemical Society*.

HgX_4^{2-}, and $Hg_2X_5^-$. Free energies (in kcal mole^{-1}) of formation of the complexes $Hg_2X_5^-$ and HgX_4^{2-} have been reported for the following reactions in water and acetronitrile:

$$2HgX_2 + R_4NX \rightleftharpoons R_4NHg_2X_5 \tag{23a}$$

and

$$R_4NHgX_3 + R_4NX \rightleftharpoons (R_4N)_2HgX_4. \tag{23b}$$

1. TETRAMETHYLENE SULPHONE (SULPHOLANE–TMSO₂)

Sulpholane represents a very interesting non-aqueous solvent, the physical properties of which are listed in Table XVIII. Limiting conductances and $K_{assoc.}$ for a few salts are given in Table XIX.

9

Some inconvenience is encountered in working with sulpholane because of its high melting point (around room temperature). Solutions are more readily handled because of the large molal freezing point depression constant. The solvent 3-methylsulpholane has a somewhat lower melting point.

Many inorganic substances are found to be miscible and soluble in sulpholane. The limited data available indicate a resemblance, as far as solubilities are concerned, to SO_2. The donor properties of sulpholane are very interesting. Toward iodine, the donor strength is comparable to that of benzene. Toward phenol it is proposed that both oxygen atoms co-ordinate to the hydrogen and a greater donor strength is observed toward this acid. The donor properties of sulphones, sulphoxides and sulphites have been reported and the trends interpreted (Drago et al., 1963a). The spectrum of $FeCl_3$ in this solvent is shown in Fig. 7. It appears that $FeCl_4^-$ is stable in this solvent.

TABLE XVIII

Physical Properties of Sulpholane

M.p. (°C)	$28 \cdot 86^a$
B.p. (°C) at 760 mm	283^a
Specific conductivity (ohm^{-1} cm^{-1}) at 25°C	2×10^{-8} ^{a}
Dielectric constant (30°C)	44^a
Density (g/cm^3) 30°C	$1 \cdot 2615^a$
Viscosity (centipoise) (30°C)	$9 \cdot 87^a$
Molal freezing point depression constant	$66 \cdot 2^a$
Z-Value (kcal mole^{-1})	$77 \cdot 5^c$
Dq toward Ni^{2+}	—
Data for iodine adduct	
$-\Delta H$ (kcal mole^{-1})	$2 \cdot 2^b$
K (l mole^{-1})	$0 \cdot 73$
Data for phenol adduct	
$-\Delta H$ (kcal mole^{-1})	$5 \cdot 0^b$
K (l mole^{-1})	$17 \cdot 1$

[a] Burwell and Langford, 1959.
[b] Drago et al., 1963a.
[c] D. Hart, personal communication.

Langford and Langford (1962) have investigated the species present when $CoCl_2$ and $Co(ClO_4)_2$ are dissolved in sulpholane. Conductivity measurements of $CoCl_2$ solutions prove the absence of appreciable ionization and a blue solid can be isolated from the blue solutions. This solid possesses the stoichiometry $CoCl_2 \cdot TMSO_2$. From the shape of the visible absorption bands and their intensities, the structure of the complex is proposed to be tetrahedral.

Dissolution of $Co(ClO_4)_2$ in $TMSO_2$ produces a red solution and the complex $Co(TMSO_2)_3(ClO_4)_2$ can be isolated. This complex possesses an absorption spectrum similar to $Co(H_2O)_6^{2+}$. The $\Lambda_{equiv.}$ at a concentration of $1\cdot1 \times 10^{-3}$ M is $18\cdot4$ ohms^{-1} cm^{-2} (cf. with values for 1 : 1 electrolytes as given in the table). Both of these complexes are highly unstable with respect to hydrolysis.

TABLE XIX

Conductance Data for Sulpholane[a]

Salt	Λ_0	$K_{assoc.}$
NaSCN	~13·5	48
MeN⬡O$^+$I$^-$	~12·5	77
LiNO$_3$	~10·5	91
Ph$_4$AsCl	~10·5	0
MeNPh$_3$I	—	0

[a] Burwell and Langford, 1959.

V. SOME GENERALIZATIONS

The solute ferric chloride has been investigated in all the solvents discussed in the previous section and this enables some interesting solvent comparisons to be made. It should be emphasized at the start that solutes for which the donor order of the solvents varies from that for ferric chloride will behave differently. Acetonitrile, tetramethylenesulphone, nitromethane and nitro-benzene represent a class of compounds the dielectric constant and solvating ability of which are appreciable ($K_{assoc.}$ for R_4NBr in CH_3CN and $C_6H_5NO_2$ are 41 and 46, respectively; the dielectric constants are in the range 36–40, the Z-values are $71\cdot3$ kcal mole^{-1} and 67 kcal mole^{-1}) but the donor strengths are weak towards cationic iron(III). Triethylphosphate and acetone have donor properties that are probably equivalent to the above solvents but are poorer solvating solvents. In all six of these solvents the solute $FeCl_4^-$ is stable and the principle species formed when $FeCl_3$ is added in small amounts are $FeCl_2S_4^+$ and $FeCl_4^-$, i.e. only steps a and b occur in equation (11). The solvent DMA is a better donor toward iron(III) than the above solvents and also a better solvating solvent as evidenced by $K_{assoc.}$ for R_4NBr but the essential species present are still $FeCl_2S_4^+$ and $FeCl_4^-$ when $FeCl_3$ is dissolved and the solute $FeCl_4^-$ is not appreciably dissociated. In DMA as in most of the above mentioned solvents there is probably also some $FeCl_3S$ present but the amount has not been determined. N-Methylacetamide is a solvent whose donor properties are slightly less than DMA but whose solvating ability is greater, because of hydrogen-bonding to chloride and its high dielectric constant. In this solvent $FeCl_4^-$ is not stable and the principle species in dilute $FeCl_3$ solutions at equilibrium are cationic iron complexes and Cl^-. The equilibrium in equation (11) is displaced toward more chloride dissociation than in the case of DMA because of the greater solvating ability of N-methylacetamide.

A comparison of DMA and DMSO is interesting. In the latter solvent the principal species are cationic iron complexes and chloride ion. Tetrachloroferrate is dissociated in this solvent. The donor properties of DMA and DMSO are similar, though the latter solvent is probably a slightly better donor. The $K_{assoc.}$ for R_4NBr, the Z-value and the dielectric constant all indicate that DMSO is a better solvating solvent than DMA. These two effects (especially the solvating ability) account for the behaviour of $FeCl_3$ and $FeCl_4^-$ in DMSO relative to DMA.

Methanol is a good solvating solvent when specific interactions are possible but only fair when these effects are minor. It is a strong donor toward some acids, e.g. Ni^{2+}, but a weak donor towards distortable (soft) acids, e.g. I_2, Et_3PbCl, etc. Consequently, its behaviour as a solvent will be variable. Towards ferric chloride, strong co-ordination to cationic iron(III) and solvation of chloride ion cause $FeCl_4^-$ to be unstable. Cationic iron species and chloride ion are the principal species in dilute solutions of ferric chloride in methanol.

Pyridine is an interesting solvent for it has strong donor properties especially toward distortable acids but is a poor solvating solvent. The principle species present when $FeCl_4^-$ and $FeCl_3$ are dissolved in pyridine are $FeCl_3 \cdot py$ and $FeCl_4^-$ in the former instance and $FeCl_3 \cdot py$ in the latter.

The results of the experiments with the solute $(Ph_3AsCH_3)_2CoCl_4$ can be similarly interpreted. The species in CH_3NO_2 is reported to be predominantly $CoCl_3S^-$. The structure of the species $CoCl_3S^-$ is not known other than that the symmetry about Co^{2+} is roughly tetrahedral. Addition of $CoCl_2$ to $MeNO_2$ results in a non-conducting solution of $CoCl_2(MeNO_2)_2$.

The two amides and dimethylsulphoxide are sufficiently good bases and possess sufficiently high dielectric constants to displace Cl^- from the metal co-ordination sphere, resulting in the formation of the cationic species CoS_6^{2+}, $CoClS_5^+$ in addition to some $CoCl_3S^-$, $CoCl_4^{2-}$ and Cl^-. The order of stability of $CoCl_4^{2-}$ in these solvents is: $CH_2Cl_2 > CH_3NO_2 > DMA > DMF > DMSO$. For those solvents which have been investigated with both solutes, $CoCl_4^{2-}$ and $FeCl_4^-$, the order is seen to be similar.

In conclusion, we have been able to account for a large amount of non-aqueous solvent chemistry with the Co-ordination Model. In view of the complex nature of the processes being discussed (see Section III) the agreement between predicted and observed behaviour is remarkable. This is undoubtedly due to the fact that the comparisons have involved similar systems where drastic entropy differences are not encountered. The general use of the term "solvating solvent" has also been in the general distinction that there is decreased ion-pairing with increased solvation. Furthermore the spectroscopic techniques employed to examine dissociation of the systems selected are not sensitive to the extent of ion-pairing but mainly depend upon the number and type of the groups in the co-ordination sphere of the metal. The success of the Co-ordination Model in correlating the chemistry discussed above is the strongest argument in support of this model. It is hoped that this limited success will encourage further experimentation so that the limits of this general approach can be ascertained.

REFERENCES

Andrews, L. J. and Keefer, R. M. (1961) "Advances in Inorganic Chemistry and Radiochemistry" (H. J. Emeleus and A. G. Sharpe, eds.) Vol. 3, p. 91. Academic Press, New York.

Audrieth, L. F. and Kleinberg, J. (1953) "Non-Aqueous Solvents", p. 125. Wiley, New York.

Baaz, M. and Gutmann, V. (1959) *Mh. Chem.* **90**, 426.

Baaz, M., Gutmann, V. and Hübner, L. (1960) *Mh. Chem.* **91**, 537.

Barnes, J. C. and Hume, D. N. (1963) *Inorg. Chem.* **2**, 444.

Beattie, I. R. and Webster, M. (1963) *J. chem. Soc.* 38.

Beilstein (1962) "Bielsteins Handbuch Der Organishen Chemie" (H.-G. Boit, ed.), p. 124. Vierte Auflage, Vierter Band, Erstes Teil.

Benesi, H. A. and Hildebrand, J. H. (1949) *J. Amer. chem. Soc.* **71**, 2703.

Bent, H. A. (1961) *Chem. Rev.* **61**, 275.

Berns, D. S. and Fuoss, R. M. (1961) *J. Amer. chem. Soc.* **83**, 1321.

Bränden, C. and Lindquist, I. (1960) *Acta chem. Scand.* **14**, 726.

Buffagni, S. and Dunn, T. M. (1961) *J. chem. Soc.* 5105.

Bull, W. E., Madan, S. K. and Willis, J. E. (1963) *Inorg. Chem.* **2**, 303.

Burwell, R. L. and Langford, C. H. (1959) *J. Amer. chem. Soc.* **81**, 3799.

Busby, R. E. and Griffiths, U. S. (1963) *J. chem. Soc.* 902.

Connick, R. E. and Fiat, D. N. (1963) *J. chem. Phys.* **39**, 1349.

Cotton, F. A. and Francis, R. (1960) *J. Amer. chem. Soc.* **82**, 2986.

Cotton, F. A. and Francis, R. (1961) *J. inorg. nucl. Chem.* **17**, 62.

Cotton, F. A., Goodgame, D. M. L. and Goodgame, M. (1961) *J. Amer. chem. Soc.* **83**, 4690.

Dawson, K. R. and Belcher, R. L. (1951) *Trans. Ky. Acad. Sci.* **13**, 129; *Chem. Abstr.* **45**: 10005 g.

Dawson, L. R. and Golben, M. (1952) *J. Amer. chem. Soc.* **74**, 4134.

Dawson, L. R., Wilhoit, E. D., Holmes, R. R. and Sears, P. G. (1957) *J. Amer. chem. Soc.* **79**, 3004.

Donoghue, J. T. and Drago, R. S. (1962) *Inorg. Chem.* **1**, 866.

Donoghue, J. T. and Drago, R. S. (1963) *Inorg. Chem.* **2**, 1158.

Drago, R. S. and Meek, D. W. (1961) *J. phys. Chem.* **65**, 1446.

Drago, R. S., Carlson, R. L. and Hart, D. (1965a) (in the press).

Drago, R. S., Carlson, R. L. and Purcell, K. F. (1965b) (in the press).

Drago, R. S., Wayland, B. and Carlson, R. L. (1963a) *J. Amer. chem. Soc.* **85**, 3125.

Drago, R. S., Carlson, R. L., Rose, N. J. and Wenz, D. A. (1961) *J. Amer. chem. Soc.* **83**, 3572.

Drago, R. S., Meek, D. W., Joesten, M. D. and LaRoche, L. (1963b) *Inorg. Chem.* **2**, 124.

Dunn, T. M. (1960) In "Modern Coordination Chemistry" (J. Lewis and R. Wilkins, eds.), p. 229. Interscience, New York.

Ellendt, G. and Cruse, K. (1952) *Z. phys. Chem.* **201**, 130.

Fackler, J. P., Jr. (1962) *J. Amer. chem. Soc.* **84**, 24.

Fackler, J. P., Jr. (1963) *Inorg. Chem.* **2**, 266.

Fine, D. A. (1962) *J. Amer. chem. Soc.* **84**, 1139.

French, C. M. and Glover, K. H. (1955) *Trans. Faraday Soc.* **51**, 1418, 1427.

Friedman, N. J. and Plane, R. A. (1963) *Inorg. Chem.* **2**, 11.

Gagnaux, P., Janjic, D. and Susz, B. P. (1958) *Helv. chim. Acta*, **41**, 1322.

Gerding, H., Königstein, J. A. and van der Worm, E. R. (1960) *Spectrochim. Acta* **16**, 1881.

Gill, N. S. and Nyholm, R. S. (1959) *J. chem. Soc.* 3997.

Gutmann, V. (1959) *J. Phys. Chem.* **63**, 378.

Gutmann, V. and Baaz, M. (1959) *Mh. Chem.* **90**, 729.

Holmes, R. R., Gallagher, W. P. and Carter, Jr., R. P. (1963) *Inorg. Chem.* **2**, 437.

Jackson, J. H., Lemons, J. F. and Taube, H. (1960) *J. chem. Phys.* **32**, 553.

Job, P. (1928) *Annls. Chim.* [10], **9**, 113.

Joesten, M. D. (1962) Thesis, University of Illinois.

Joesten, M. D. and Drago, R. S. (1962a) *J. Amer. chem. Soc.* **84**, 2037.

Joesten, M. D. and Drago, R. S. (1962b) *J. Amer. chem. Soc.* **84**, 3817.

Joesten, M. D. and Drago, R. S. (1965) (in the press).

Jørgensen, C. K. (1956) *Acta chem. Scand.* **10**, 887.

Katzin, L. I. (1952) *J. chem. Phys.* **20**, 1165.

Katzin, L. I. and Ferraro, J. R. (1950) *J. Amer. chem. Soc.* **72**, 5451.

Katzin, L. I. and Gebert, E. (1950a) *J. Amer. chem. Soc.* **72**, 5455.

Katzin, L. I. and Gebert, E. (1950b) *J. Amer. chem. Soc.* **72**, 5464.

Katzin, L. I. and Gebert, E. (1950c) *J. Amer. chem. Soc.* **72**, 5659.

Koch, F. K. V. (1930) *J. chem. Soc.* 2385.

Korinek, G. J. and Schneider, W. G. (1957) *Canad. J. Chem.* **35**, 1157.

Kosower, E. M. (1958a) *J. Amer. chem. Soc.* **80**, 3253.

Kosower, E. M. (1958b) *J. Amer. chem. Soc.* **80**, 3261.

Kosower, E. M. (1958c) *J. Amer. chem. Soc.* **80**, 3267.

Landesman, H. and Williams, R. E. (1961) *J. Amer. chem. Soc.* **83**, 2663.

Langford, C. H. and Langford, P. O. (1962) *Inorg. Chem.* **1**, 184.

Lester, G. R., Gover, T. A. and Sears, P. G. (1956) *J. phys. Chem.* **60**, 1076.

Lester, G. R., Vaughan, J. W. and Sears, P. G. (1958) *Trans. Ky. Acad. Sci.* **19**, 28.

Lindquist, I. (1958) *Acta chem. Scand.* **12**, 135.

Lindquist, I. and Brändén, C. I. (1959) *Acta crystallogr.* **12**, 692.

Mackor, E. L. (1951) *Rec. Trav. chim.* **70**, 457.

de Maine, P. A. D. and Koubek, E. (1959) *J. inorg. nucl. Chem.* **11**, 329.

Marcinkowski, A. E. (1961) *Dissertation Abstrs.* **22**, 97.

Meek, D. W. (1962) Thesis, University of Illinois, p. 60.

Meek, D. W. and Drago, R. S. (1961) *J. Amer. chem. Soc.* **83**, 4322.

Meek, D. W., Drago, R. S. and Piper, T. S. (1962) *Inorg. Chem.* **1**, 285.

Meek, D. W., Straub, D. K. and Drago, R. S. (1960) *J. Amer. chem. Soc.* **82**, 6013.

Minc, S. and Werblan, L. (1962) *Electrochim. Acta*, **7**, 256.

Newman, L. and Hume, D. N. (1957) *J. Amer. chem. Soc.* **79**, 4571.

Niedzielski, R. J., Drago, R. S. and Middaugh, R. L. (1965) (in the press).

Onak, T. P., Landesman, H., Williams, R. E. and Shapiro, I. (1959) *J. phys. Chem.* **67**, 1533.

Orgel, L. E. (1960) "An Introduction to Transition Metal Chemistry", p. 133. Methuen, London.

Popov, A. I. and Skelly, N. E. (1954) *J. Amer. chem. Soc.* **76**, 5309.

Rosenthal, M. and Drago, R. S. (1965) (in the press).

Schmulbach, C. D. and Drago, R. S. (1960) *J. Amer. chem. Soc.* **82**, 4484.

Schneider, W. G. and Reeves, L. W. (1957) *Canad. J. Chem.* **35**, 251.

Sears, P. G., Holmes, R. R. and Dawson, L. R. (1955b) *Trans. electrochem. Soc.* **102**, 145.

Sears, P. G., Lester, G. R. and Dawson, L. R. (1956b) *J. Phys. Chem.* **60**, 1433.

Sears, P. G., McNeer, R. L. and Dawson, L. R. (1955a) *Trans. electrochem. Soc.* **102**, 269.

Sears, P. G., Wilhoit, E. D. and Dawson, L. R. (1956a) *J. phys. Chem.* **60**, 169.

Sheldon, J. C. and Tyree, S. Y. (1958) *J. Amer. chem. Soc.* **80**, 4775.

Shier, G. D. and Drago, R. S. (1965) (in the press).

Shoolery, J. N., Pimentel, G. C. and Huggins, C. M. (1955) *J. chem. Phys.* **23**, 1244.

Sodek, H. and Fuoss, R. M. (1950) *J. Amer. chem. Soc.* **72**, 301.

Susz, B. P. and Chalandon, P. (1958) *Helv. chim. Acta*, **61**, 1332.

Susz, B. (1959) *C.R. Acad. Sci., Paris* **248**, 2569.

Swinehart, J. H. and Taube, H. (1962) *J. chem. Phys.* **37**, 1579.

Tsubomura, H. and Lang, R. (1961) *J. Amer. chem. Soc.* **83**, 2085.

Voitovich, B. A. and Barabonova, A. S. (1961) *Zh. neorg. Khim.* **6**, 2098; Eng. translation, **6**, 1073.

Weissberger, A., Proskauer, E. S., Riddich, J. A., Toops, E. E. Jr. (1955) "Techniques of Organic Chemistry", Vol. VII. Interscience, New York.

Woldbye, F. (1955) *Acta chem. Scand.* **9**, 299.

CHAPTER 6

Liquid Sulphur Dioxide

T. C. WADDINGTON

School of Molecular Sciences, University of Warwick, Coventry, England

I. Introduction.. 253
II. Solubilities in Liquid Sulphur Dioxide..................................... 254
III. Solvate Formation with Sulphur Dioxide................................. 256
IV. Electrical Conductivity and Ionization in Liquid Sulphur Dioxide Solutions.... 260
V. Electrochemical Studies in Solutions in Liquid Sulphur Dioxide.............. 264
    A. Electrolysis... 264
    B. Electrode Potentials.. 264
VI. Chemical Reactions in Liquid Sulphur Dioxide 266
    A. Solvolysis... 266
    B. Metathetical Reactions.. 267
    C. Amphoteric Reactions... 268
    D. Oxidation–reduction Reactions.................................. 271
    E. Complex Formation 272
VII. Isotopic Exchange Reactions in Liquid Sulphur Dioxide.................... 273
VIII. Conclusion and Summary.. 280
    References.. 282

I. INTRODUCTION

The behaviour of liquid sulphur dioxide as an ionizing solvent has been a subject of extensive study since the work of Walden (1902) and Walden and Centnerszwer (1899, 1902a,b,c, 1903) at the turn of the century. Much of the work in the solvent before 1945 has been summarized by Jander (1949) and by Audrieth and Kleinberg (1953). There has been a fairly recent short review by Elving and Markowitz (1960), and more recently Lichtin (1963) has reviewed the physical chemistry and physical organic chemistry of solutions of electrolytes in the solvent. There seems little point in re-reviewing at length the topics covered in earlier reviews, and these topics will only be dealt with cursorily except where previous interpretations have been in doubt. However, no review has done more than briefly mention the investigations of isotopic exchange in the solvent, so vital to a proper understanding of its mode of action, and these will be discussed at length.

The relevant physical properties of liquid sulphur dioxide are given in Table I. The melting to boiling point range makes sulphur dioxide a very useful solvent, and its vapour pressure is sufficiently low at 0°C that it can be safely handled under its own vapour in sealed glass vessels without special precautions. This is an important consideration, as contamination by water and oxygen must be avoided to prevent complicating side reactions.

TABLE I

Some Physical Constants of Sulphur Dioxide

Property	Value	Temperature (°K)
Melting point (°K)	197·64	—[a]
Boiling point (°K)	263·08	—[a]
Liquid range	65°	
Enthalpy of fusion (kcal mole^{-1})	1·9691	197·64[a]
Enthalpy of vapourization (kcal mole^{-1})	5·96	263·08[a]
Vapour pressure (cm Hg)*	28·48	243[a]
	53·06	253[a]
	115·96	273[a]
	171·4	283[a]
	2456·0	293[a]
Viscosity of liquid (millipoise)	$n = 4·03 - 0·0363T(°C)$	—[b, c] —
Dielectric constant of liquid	$D = 95·12 \exp\{-6·676 \times 10^3 T(°K)\}$	—[c, d, e]
	$D = 15·4$	273·4
Dipole moment (Debye)	1·62	256·9[f]
S—O Bond Length (Å)	1·43	—[g]
O—S—O Bond Angle	119·5°	—[g]
Density (g cm^{-3})	1·46	263·1[h]
Specific conductivity (ohm^{-1} cm^{-1})	$3-4 \times 10^{-8}$	—[i, j]
Molar ebullioscopic constant (deg mole^{-1})	1·48	
Molar cryoscopic constant (deg mole^{-1})	0·0393	

* Calculated from

$$\log = -\frac{1867·52}{T} - 0·015865T + 0·000015574T^2 + 13·07540$$

[a] Giauque and Stephenson (1938).
[b] Luchinskii (1938).
[c] Lichtin and Leftin (1956).
[d] Vierk (1950).
[e] Nickerson and McIntosh (1957).

[f] Le Fevre (1953)
[g] Kivelson (1954).
[h] Lichtin and Glazer (1951).
[i] Franklin (1911).
[j] Lichtin (1963).

II. SOLUBILITIES IN LIQUID SULPHUR DIOXIDE

In general, covalent substances are considerably more soluble in liquid sulphur dioxide than ionic compounds. Table II below lists the solubilities in liquid sulphur dioxide of salts of monovalent inorganic cations. It will be seen that only the alkali metal iodides are soluble to the extent of more than a mole per thousand grams of solvent, and that the solubility of most of the others is only a few millimoles. All the tetramethylammonium halides are freely soluble in liquid sulphur dioxide, probably because of their low lattice energies. The solubilities of some salts of divalent and trivalent cations are given in Table III. It will be seen that, with the exceptions of aluminium chloride and antimony trichloride, which are covalent, solubilities are at most

TABLE II

Solubilities in Liquid Sulphur Dioxide of Alkali Metal and other Monovalent Salts [a, b]

Ion	SO_3^{2-}	SO_4^{2-}	F^-	Cl^-	Br^-	I^-	SCN^-	CN^-	ClO_4^-	$CH_3CO_2^-$
Li^+	—	1·55	23·0	2·82	6·0	1490·0	—	—	—	3·48
Na^+	1·37	insol.	6·9	insol.	1·36	1000·0	80·5	3·67	—	8·90
K^+	1·58	insol.	3·1	5·5	40·0	2490·0	502·0	2·62	—	0·61
Rb^+	1·27	—	—	27·2	sol.	sol.	—	—	—	—
Cs^+	—	—	—	—	—	—	—	—	—	—
NH_4^+	2·67	5·07	less than 27 at 50°C	1·67	6·0	580·0	6160·0	—	2·14	141·0
Tl^+	4·96	0·417	insol.	0·292	0·60	1·81	0·915	0·522	0·43	285·0
Ag^+	insol.	insol.	insol.	20·07	0·159	0·68	0·845	1·42	—	1·02

Data refer to 0°C unless otherwise stated. Solubilities are in millimoles per 1000 g sulphur dioxide.

[a] Jander (1949).
[b] Gmelin (1953).

only a few millimoles per thousand grams of solvent. In general, covalent substances are very soluble. Such substances as bromine, iodine monochloride, thionyl chloride, thionyl bromide, boron trichloride, carbon disulphide, phosphorous trichloride, arsenic trichloride and phosphorous oxychloride are miscible with liquid sulphur dioxide in all proportions. Carbon tetrachloride, silicon tetrachloride and the other group IV tetrahalogenides are completely miscible with liquid sulphur dioxide above a critical miscibility temperature which varies from compound to compound (Bond and Beach, 1926; Bond and Stephens, 1929; Bond and Crone, 1934; Bond and Belton, 1945).

The pioneer work of Walden and Centnerszwer (1899, 1902a,b,c, 1903) showed that, with a few exceptions, liquid sulphur dioxide is an excellent solvent for organic compounds. Amines, ethers, esters, alcohols, sulphides, mercaptans and acids, both aliphatic and aromatic, are readily soluble. Aromatic hydrocarbons dissolve readily and so do olefins, but paraffins possess only limited solubility. Halogenated and nitrated aromatic compounds are very soluble. The selective solubility of aromatic hydrocarbons in liquid sulphur dioxide is the basis of the Edeleanu process for refining kerosene. Water is not completely

TABLE III

Solubilities in Liquid Sulphur Dioxide of Divalent and Other Metal Salts [a, b]

Ion	SO_3^{2-}	SO_4^{2-}	F^-	Cl^-	Br^-	I^-	SCN^-	CN^-	ClO_4^-	$CH_3CO_2^-$
Be^{2+}	—	—	—	5·8	—	—	—	—	—	—
Mg^{2+}	—	—	—	1·47	1·3	0·50	—	—	—	—
Ca^{2+}	—	—	—	—	—	—	—	—	—	—
Sr^{2+}	—	—	—	—	—	—	—	—	—	—
Ba^{2+}	insol.	—	—	insol.	insol.	18·15	insol.	—	—	—
Zn^{2+}	—	—	—	11·75	—	3·45	40·4	—	—	—
Cu^{2+}	—	—	—	insol.	—	1·17	—	—	—	—
Hg^{2+}	—	0·338	—	3·8	2·06	0·265	0·632	0·556	—	2·98
Pb^{2+}	—	insol.	2·16	0·69	0·328	0·195	0·371	0·386	—	2·46
Co^{2+}	—	—	—	1·00	—	12·2	insol.	—	—	—
Ni^{2+}	—	—	—	insol.	—	—	insol.	—	—	0·08
Al^{3+}	—	—	—	v. sol.	0·60	5·64	—	—	—	—
Sb^{3+}	—	—	0·56	575·0	21·8	0·26	—	—	—	—
Bi^{3+}	—	—	—	0·60	3·44	—	—	—	—	—

Data refer to 0°C unless otherwise stated. Solubilities are in millimoles per 1000 g SO_2

[a] Jander (1949).
[b] Gmelin (1953).

miscible with liquid sulphur dioxide, but the extent of its solubility at various temperatures has never been accurately determined. Wickert (1938a,b) has reported the existence of a compound $SO_2.H_2O$ which remains as a stable residue upon evaporation of a solution of water in sulphur dioxide at 0°C. He has also reported that the solubility of water in liquid sulphur dioxide at 22°C is 2·3 g per 100 g of SO_2. Conductivity measurements indicate a fair solubility at temperatures below 0°C.

III. Solvate Formation with Sulphur Dioxide

Sulphur dioxide forms stable solvates with many alkali metal halides and other substances, similar to the crystalline hydrates and ammoniates formed with water and ammonia. These solvates have been studied in detail by

Jander and Mesech (1938a,b), by Foote and Fleischer (1931, 1932, 1934), by Ephraim and Kornblum (1916) and by Ephraim and Aellig (1923). In many cases the heat of formation of the adducts has been determined from vapour pressure measurements. The molar ratio of sulphur dioxide to adduct generally varies from one to four, but much higher ratios are sometimes encountered. The information on the alkali metal salts is summarized in Table IV below.

The early workers did not in fact obtain complete phase diagrams of the systems MX—SO_2, and in consequence there is probably still a large number of undetected solvate phases in these systems. The mono-adducts with the tetramethylammonium halides are probably best regarded as halosulphinates,

with ions of structure $X—S{\overset{O^-}{\underset{O}{\diagup\diagdown}}}$, by comparison with the halosulphonates.

Their stability decreases in the order $F>Cl>Br>I$. In the alkali metal halide polysolvates one cannot be sure whether the sulphur dioxide is co-ordinated to the cation, the anion or both. But the apparent increase in stability of the iodides over the bromides, and the lack of existence of alkali metal chloride solvates, the reverse of the position with the tetramethyl-ammonium halide mono-solvates, leads one to suspect that the bonding is best regarded as due to charge transfer interactions between the anion and the sulphur dioxide molecules. This is supported by the spectroscopic work of Lippincott and Welch (1961) on the compounds $KI.4SO_2$ and $KNCS.4SO_2$, where the shifts in the vibration frequencies of the sulphur dioxide indicate charge transfer from the negative ion.

With covalent compounds sulphur dioxide forms many solvates, acting in most cases as an electron acceptor through sulphur and only in a few as an electron donor through oxygen. Thus the phase diagram of the boron trifluoride–sulphur dioxide system shows clearly the formation of an $SO_2.BF_3$ adduct (Booth and Martin, 1942). Curiously, the boron trichloride–sulphur dioxide system differs in its behaviour and shows the formation of two immiscible solutions at low temperature, becoming miscible at room temperature (Satenstejn and Viktorov, 1937; Martin, 1945). An adduct with antimony pentachloride, $SO_2.SbF_5$ has also been reported (Aynsley et al., 1951). $SnBr_4$ and $TiCl_4$ both form adducts with SO_2, the formulae reported being $SnBr_4.SO_2$ and $2TiCl_4.SO_2$ (Bond and Belton, 1945). Zirconium tetrachloride also forms a 1 : 1 adduct (Bond and Stephens, 1929).

There is an early report of an adduct $(AlCl_3)_2SO_2$ as well as of $AlCl_3.SO_2$ (Baude, 1904), but subsequent workers appear only to have isolated $AlCl_3.SO_2$ (Silberrad, 1922; Burg and Bickerton, 1945); this compound appears to be dimeric.

Most organic mono-amines form stable mono-adducts with sulphur dioxide. These compounds are usually highly coloured and soluble in liquid

TABLE IV

Solvate Formation with Alkali Metal and Tetramethyl Ammonium Salts and Sulphur Dioxide

Cation	Anion						
	F^-	Cl^-	Br^-	I^-	NCS^-	SO_4^{2-}	$CH_3.CO_2^-$
Li^+	—	—	—	2, −1°, 9·4 [c]	—	—	None
Na^+	—	—	—	2, +15°, 10·01 [c] 4, +5°, 9·63 [c]	2, —, 10·5 [a]	—	1, >80° [a]
K^+	1, [a]	None [b]	4, −1°, 8·38 [b]	4, +6°, 9·67 [c]	0·5, −49°, 11·3 [a] 1, +12·5°, 9·9 [b] 2, —, 9·75 [a]	—	1, >80° [e]
Rb^+	1, [a]	—	—		0·5, +31·5°, 10·64 [c]	—	1, >50° [e]
Cs^+	—	—	—	3, +15·3°, 10·5 [b] 4, +15·5°, 10·9 [c]	0·5, +19°, 10·14 [c]	—	1, >80° [e]
Me_4N^+	1, +150° [a]	1, +88°, 11·1 [b] 2, +35°, 10·6 [b]	1, +41°, 8·99 [b] 2, +16°, 10·3 [b]	3, —, 10·25 [a] 4, +17°, 10·89 [c] 1, +20°, —[a]	—	3, +28°, 11·7 [b] 6, −2·6°, 8·53 [b]	— —

The first figure given represents the number of sulphur dioxide molecules in the solvate per mole of salt; the second, the decomposition temperatures under atmospheric pressure in degrees centigrade; and the third, the heat of decomposition to gaseous sulphur dioxide in kcal mole⁻¹.

[a] Seel and Riehl (1955a,b).
[b] Jander and Mesech (1938a,b).
[c] Ephraim and Kornblum (1916)
[d] Foote and Fleischer (1931, 1932, 1934)
[e] Ephraim and Aellig (1923).

sulphur dioxide (Michaelis, 1891; Andre, 1900; Korezynski and Gleboka, 1920; Hill, 1931; Foote and Fleischer, 1934; Hill and Fitzgerald, 1935; Mesech, 1938; Bright and Jasper, 1941; Bright and Fernelius, 1943; Burg, 1943; Bateman et al., 1944; Jander, 1949; Moede and Curran, 1949; Byrd, 1962). Co-ordination would appear to be through the nitrogen to the sulphur. Diamines may take up two molecules of sulphur dioxide, thus p-phenylenedi-amine gives $p\text{-}C_6H_4(NH_2)_2 . 2SO_2$ (Hill and Fitzgerald, 1935; Mesech, 1938) and N,N,N',N'-tetramethyl-p-phenylenediamine gives $p\text{-}C_6H_4(NME_2)_2.2SO_2$ (Bryd, 1962). The claim of Jander and Wickert (Jander and Wickert, 1936; Wickert and Jander, 1937) that a further reaction takes place:

$$2(C_2H_5)_3N + 2SO_2 \rightarrow 2\overset{\text{red}}{(C_2H_5)_3N.SO_2} \rightarrow \{(C_2H_5)_3N.SO_2\}_2 \rightarrow$$
$$\underset{(I)}{}$$

$$\underset{(II)}{\{(C_2H_5)_3N\}_2\overset{\text{white}}{SO^{2+}SO_3^{2-}}} \tag{1}$$

has been strongly criticized by Bateman et al. (1944). They reported that the compound (II), claimed to have been isolated by Jander and Wicker, is in fact $(C_2H_5)_3NH^+.HSO_3^-$, triethylammonium hydrogen sulphite, produced by the action of moisture on the red compound (I), and that the melting point of the hydrogen sulphite (74°–75°) agrees closely with that reported by Jander for compound (II). The conclusions of Bateman et al. (1944) are supported by the work of Burg (1943), Hill and Fitzgerald (1931, 1935) and others. Jander et al. (1937), report that ammonia itself similarly forms a compound $(H_3N)_2SO^+SO_3^{2-}$ in liquid sulphur dioxide but it seems likely that here again they are observing either the formation of $NH_4^+HSO_3^-$ from moisture in their sulphur dioxide or the formation of HSO_2NH_2, amidosulphonous acid. Triethylamine oxide also forms a stable adduct $Et_3NO.SO_2$ with liquid sulphur dioxide (Lecher and Hardy, 1948). Its structure appears to be

$$Et\text{---}N\text{---}O\text{---}S\diagup^{O}_{\diagdown O}$$

with Et groups above and below on the N.

Though from their solubility in liquid sulphur dioxide there is obviously an interaction between alcohols and phenols and sulphur dioxide, the phase diagrams of these systems do not appear to have been studied, and there is only the isolated report of an unstable adduct between phenol and sulphur dioxide (Kashtanov and Sokolova, 1951). Ultra-violet spectroscopic studies have shown that the interaction of sulphur dioxide with ethers and alcohols (de Maine, 1957) is due to the formation of charge transfer complexes and also that charge transfer complexes are formed between sulphur dioxide and a wide variety of aromatic molecules (Andrews and Keefer, 1951; Lichtin et al., 1952; Andrews, 1954).

IV. ELECTRICAL CONDUCTIVITY AND IONIZATION IN LIQUID SULPHUR DIOXIDE SOLUTIONS

Much of the work on electrolytic solutions in liquid sulphur dioxide has been summarized relatively recently (Jander, 1949; Audrieth and Kleinberg, 1953; Elving and Markowitz, 1960). Very recently Lichtin (1963) has thoroughly reviewed the work of the last dozen or so years on conductivity measurements in liquid sulphur dioxide. Nearly all the experimental evidence

TABLE V

Data for Salts Composed of Spherical and Tetrahedral Ions at 0°C

Ion-pair	Limiting molar conductance ($cm^2\ ohm^{-1}\ mole^{-1}$)	K (mole litre$^{-1} \times 10^4$)	a_0 (Å)	$r_+ + r_-$ (Å)
LiBr	189	0·27	2·70	2·55[a]
NaBr	265	0·48	2·87	2·91[b]
KCl	243	0·74	2·96	3·14[c]
KBr	249	1·43	3·28	3·28[c]
KI	244	3·0	3·58	3·50[c]
Me$_4$NCl	243	10·3	4·96	5·11[d]
Me$_4$NBr	236	11·8	5·25	5·25[c]
Me$_4$NI	234	13·9	5·54	5·47[e]
Me$_4$NClO$_4$	218	8·4	4·63	6·3[e]
Me$_4$NBF$_4$	215	7·9	4·56	6·1[e]
Et$_4$NBr	215	21	6·8	6·6[e]
Et$_4$NI	197	39	10·0	8·1[e]

Reproduced with permission from "Progress in Physical Organic Chemistry," Vol. I, Wiley, New York.

[a] Lichtin and Rao (1960).
[b] Lichtin and Kliman (1965)
[c] Lichtin and Leftin (1956).
[d] Lichtin (1963).
[e] Lichtin and Pappas (1957).

on liquid sulphur dioxide is limited to uni-univalent electrolytes. Liquid sulphur dioxide is a solvent of low dielectric constant, so behaviour of the type first described by Kraus and Fuoss (1933) occurs, and a plot of equivalent conductance against concentration shows a minimum. At concentrations above about 10^{-1} M the conductivity is largely due to ion triplets; a minimum is found in the conductivity at about 10^{-1} M, and below this the conductivity increases with decreasing concentration, obeying Ostwald's dilution law. Electrical conductivity at concentrations of less than 10^{-2} M is not significantly complicated by triplet ion formation, and in this region association constants for ion-pair formation may be evaluated. Lichtin (1963) has made extensive use of Shedlovsky's equation (Fuoss and Shedlovsky, 1949) to obtain degrees of dissociation of ion-pairs in liquid sulphur dioxide. Readers are referred to Lichtin's (1963) chapter on "Ionization and Dissociation Equilibria in Solution in Liquid Sulphur Dioxide" for a detailed account of the methods of calculation. Here it is sufficient to say that, by a suitable rearrangement (Daggett, 1951) of Shedlovsky's equation, the conductivity data can be plotted to yield $1/\Lambda_0$ as intercept and $1/K\Lambda_0^2$ as slope, where K is the ion-pair dissociation constant and Λ_0 is the equivalent conductance at infinite dilution. Table V is reproduced from Lichtin's article. Lichtin has also used Bjerrum's theory (Bjerrum, 1926a,b) of ionic association to calculate the distances of closet approach, a_0, in ion-pairs, and these are compared with the sum of the crystal radii, $r_+ + r_-$ of the ions.

TABLE VI

Temperature Dependence of K, Λ_0 and a_0 for KBr

T	Λ_0	$K \times 10^4$	a_0
−24·99	188	3·62	$3·41 \pm 0·03$[a]
−20·58	202	2·88	$3·34 \pm 0·02$[a]
−15·56	212	2·51	$3·33 \pm 0·03$[a]
−10·71	224	2·11	$3·31 \pm 0·03$[a]
− 8·93	228	1·99	$3·28$[b]
− 5·25	233	1·80	$3·31 \pm 0·02$[a]
+ 0·12	249	1·43	$3·28$[b]
+ 6·23	274	1·04	$3·23 \pm 0·02$[c]

Reproduced with permission from "Progress in Physical Organic Chemistry", Vol. I, Wiley, New York.

[a] Lichtin and Pappas (1957).
[b] Lichtin and Leftin (1956).
[c] Lichtin and Rao (1961).

The limiting conductances of the salts reported in the table show that, as in water and many other solvents, there must be considerable hydrodynamic transport of solvent associated with the lithium ion. It is interesting, however, that the association behaviour of the lithium ion with bromide, as reflected in the Bjerrum distance, a_0, indicates that there can be little or no "solvent separation" of paired ions. Lichtin reports that in only one case, that of potassium bromide, (Lichtin and Leftin, 1956; Lichtin and Pappas, 1957; Lichtin and Rao, 1961) is there sufficient data for calculation of the dissociation constant for ion-pairs over a range of temperature. Table VI is taken from Lichtin's article. The Bjerrum distance, a_0, changes very little over the range of temperatures from $-24°C$ to $+6°C$ and is in good agreement with the sum of the ionic radii. A plot of log K against $1/T$ gives a straight line, from which we find $\Delta H_\alpha^\circ = 5\cdot25$ kcal mole^{-1} and $\Delta S_\alpha^\circ = -36\cdot8$ kcal degree^{-1} mole $^{-1}$ at $0°C$. The decrease of K with increasing temperature follows from the temperature dependence of the dielectic constant. The large negative value of ΔS_α° indicates the much greater interaction of the free ions with the solvent than of the ion pair. The increase in the limiting equivalent conductance with increase in temperature is probably due to the hydrodynamic effect of the decrease in viscosity of the solvent.

The conductivity data recorded by earlier workers and their interpretations of it are certainly not as reliable as that of Lichtin and co-workers; however, using a simple Ostwald dilution law, Dutoit and Gyr (1909) obtained values of K of the same order of magnitude as those obtained by Lichtin with the more sophisticated Shedlovsky equation. Some of their results are given in Tables VII and VIII below.

TABLE VII

Dissociation Constants at $-15°C$ in Liquid Sulphur Dioxide Obtained Using the Ostwald Dilution Law

	$K \times 10^3$		$K \times 10^3$
RbBr	0·34	RbI	0·50
KBr	0·35	KI	0·57
NH_4Br	0·16	NH_4I	0·47
Me_4NBr	1·37	Me_4NI	1·66

TABLE VIII

Limiting Equivalent Conductances at $-15°C$ in Liquid Sulphur Dioxide

Anion	Cation			
	$Me_4N_4^+$	Rb^+	NH_4^+	K^+
I^-	199	215	208	207
Br	194	211	208	203
SCN^-		~ 174		

The above data refer to the dissociation in liquid sulphur dioxide of ion-pairs of compounds which are essentially ionic in the solid. On the other hand, there are a wide variety of materials, such as triphenylmethylchloride (Walden, 1902), which are covalent in the solid and in many common solvents, but which give conducting solutions in liquid sulphur dioxide.

The van't Hoff i factor has been measured by the ebullioscopic method for variety of solutes (Jander and Mesech, 1939; Jander, 1949) in liquid sulphur dioxide. The factor was defined as the theoretical molecular weight divided by the observed molecular weight, using a molal ebullioscopic constant of 1·45°C per mole. The observations are of necessity confined to fairly concentrated solutions, in which, in the case of electrolytes, one would expect considerable triple ion formation. Some values are given in Table IX below. For all non-electrolytes except water, the mole number is unity within the limits of experimental error. Binary electrolytes give i-values ranging from about 0·4 in very concentrated solutions to greater than unity in more dilute solutions, thus indicating a wide range of associated species.

TABLE IX

Vant' Hoff i-values for a Number of Electrolytes and Non-electrolytes in Liquid Sulphur Dioxide, as a Function of Concentration

Compound	i-Values at dilutions in litres per mole					
	1	2	4	8	16	32
Toluene	—	1·07	—	—	—	—
Napthalene	—	0·99	—	1·03	—	1·01
Acetanilide	—	0·99	—	1·00	—	1·03
ω-Chloro-acetophenone	—	1·05	—	1·03	—	0·89
Tetra-ethyl urea	—	1·08	—	1·01	—	0·90
Acetyl chloride	—	0·83	—	0·75	—	—
$SbCl_3$	—	—	—	1·09	—	1·11
$SbCl_5$	—	0·91	—	0·88	—	—
$SnCl_4$	—	—	—	1·00	—	—
H_2O	—	0·62	—	0·64	—	—
KSCN	0·43	0·50	0·61	0·70	0·78	—
KBr	—	0·55	0·67	0·85	0·95	1·01
KI	0·54	0·63	0·77	0·95	1·08	1·17
$KSbCl_6$	—	1·23	1·25	1·28	1·36	1·42
Me_4NCl	—	1·14	1·05	1·03	1·06	1·22
Me_4NClO_4	—	1·04	1·04	1·10	1·26	1·33
$(Me_4N)_2SO_4$	—	1·03	1·02	1·05	1·27	1·47
Ph_3CCl	—	0·99	1·14	1·26	1·30	—

V. Electrochemical Studies in Solutions in Liquid Sulphur Dioxide

A. ELECTROLYSIS

The nature of the products obtained during the electrolysis of salts in liquid sulphur dioxide has been the subject of conflicting reports. Steele (1907) first investigated the products of electrolysis in liquid sulphur dioxide and reported that sulphur was deposited at the cathode during the electrolysis of potassium or sodium iodide between platinum electrodes in the solvent. He also observed that the current fell quickly from an initially high value to a much lower one. Bagster and Steele (1912a,b) extended this work. They found that, on the electrolysis of a wide range of iodides, both elemental sulphur and sulphite salts were found at the cathode; at a platinum anode free iodide was liberated. Anodes of metals such as zinc and iron passed into solution as the iodides. Centnerszwer and Drucker (1923) obtained results differing from Bagster and Steele on electrolysis of iodides in sulphur dioxide between platinum electrodes. They obtained a cathodic deposit with strongly reducing properties, which careful analysis showed to be a mixture of thio-sulphites and pyrosulphites; no elemental sulphur was found. This was confirmed by Cady and Toft (1925), who electrolysed solutions of potassium iodide, thiocyanate, iodate, chlorate and ferricyanide in liquid sulphur dioxide and found that the cathode products were thiosulphites, pyrosulphites, salts of thionic acids, etc. They attributed the cathodic sulphur found by Bagster and Steele to the presence of some water in the sulphur dioxide. When, however, triphenylmethyl bromide is electrolysed in liquid sulphur dioxide (Schlenk et al., 1910), triphenylmethyl is deposited at the cathode. Since Ph_3CBr is ionized in liquid sulphur dioxide to Ph_3C^+ and Br^-, it seems that here we have a simple cation discharge reaction taking place.

Evidence for the existence of the hydroxonium ion was obtained by Bagster and Cooling (1920) from the electrolysis of a mixture of water and hydrogen bromide in liquid sulphur dioxide. Although neither water nor hydrogen bromide is a conductor in sulphur dioxide, a mixture of the two gives a conducting solution. On electrolysis the cathodic products were water and hydrogen, and the anodic product was bromine. In addition, the quantity of water deposited at the cathode was in agreement with that calculated on the the basis of Faraday's Laws. Electrolysis of bromine, iodine monobromide and iodine trichloride between silver electrodes in liquid sulphur dioxide (Bruner and Bekier, 1913) leads respectively to the deposition of silver bromide, silver iodide and silver chloride at the anode. The cathodic processes were not elucidated.

B. ELECTRODE POTENTIALS

Bagster and Steele (1912a,b) made the earliest measurements of electrode potentials in liquid sulphur dioxide. They found reproducible potentials for cells such as the following:

$$Zn/ZnBr_2(sat), SO_2, Hg_2Cl_2/Hg.$$

Salts with a common ion affected these potentials in the same way as those of the corresponding aqueous cells. They measured potentials with a quandrant electrometer, since they found that the electrodes polarized extremely easily. They also measured the potentials of the three metals zinc, cadmium and lead in saturated solutions of their salts against a mercurous chloride–mercury electrode. Wickert (1938a,b) measured the potential of the hydrogen electrode ($E = 0\cdot3V$) and the oxygen electrode ($E = 0\cdot2V$) against a mercurous chloride–mercury electrode, using as the electrolyte a solution of hydrogen chloride, of unspecified concentration, in liquid sulphur dioxide. These potentials are of the same order of magnitude as those obtained later by Cruse (1940). Cruse (1940) has made what are certainly the most careful and detailed measurements of electrode potentials in liquid sulphur dioxide. He set up the cells

Pb, $PbCl_2/Cl^-$ in SO_2/Hg_2Cl_2, Hg,
Ag, $AgCl/Cl^-$ in SO_2/Hg_2Cl_2, Hg,
Ag, $AgBr/Br^-$ in SO_2/Hg_2Br_2, Hg,

and measured their e.m.f.'s. The reactions taking place in these cells are respectively as follows:

(a) $Pb(s) + Hg_2Cl_2(s) = PbCl_2(s) + 2Hg(l)$,
(b) $2Ag(s) + Hg_2Cl_2(s) = 2AgCl(s) + 2Hg(l)$,
(c) $2Ag(s) + Hg_2Br_2 = 2AgBr(s) + 2Hg(l)$.

These reactions are of course independent of concentration of halide ions in the sulphur dioxide and of the nature of the solvent, and the thermodynamic data should enable one to calculate the e.m.f.'s. Cruse found that in fact the e.m.f.'s he calculated were not in very good agreement with the measured values, though they were of the right order of magnitude, e.g.

cell (a) E^0 measured $= 0\cdot36V$; E^0 calculated $= 0\cdot55V$;
cell (b) E^0 measured was variable, but initially about $0\cdot04V$;
    E^0 calculated $= 0\cdot049V$;
cell (c) E^0 measured was very variable, but initially about $0\cdot06V$;
    E^0 calculated $0\cdot048V$.

He found in cells (b) and (c) that the e.m.f. tended to change steadily with time, though that of (a) was fairly steady. He also set up the cells

Ag, $AgBr/HBr$ in SO_2/H_2, Pt and
Ag, $AgCl/HCl$ in SO_2/H_2, Pt

and measured their e.m.f.'s at various hydrogen halide concentrations. As one would predict, there was a straight line relationship between e.m.f. and hydrogen halide concentration. However, the absolute values of the e.m.f.'s did not agree well with those he derived thermodynamically, the measured values being about 0·2V too high.

VI. Chemical Reactions in Liquid Sulphur Dioxide

Solvate and adduct formation with ionic species and covalent molecules in liquid sulphur dioxide have already been discussed. Chemical reactions are discussed below under the following headings: solvolysis, metathetical reactions, amphoteric reactions, oxidation–reduction reactions and complex formation.

A. SOLVOLYSIS

Zinc diethyl reacts in liquid sulphur dioxide even at −78°C to give diethylsulphoxide and zinc oxide (Wickert, 1938a,b):

$$Zn(C_2H_5)_2 + SO_2 \rightarrow ZnO + (C_2H_5)_2SO. \tag{2}$$

Jander (1949) reports that on prolonged standing both alkali metal bromides and iodides react slowly with liquid sulphur dioxide in a sealed tube at room temperature. The precipitate obtained from a solution of potassium iodide, on long standing, was shown by analysis to be an equimolecular mixture of potassium sulphate and sulphur. From a solution of potassium bromide only a precipitate of potassium sulphate was obtained. In the case of the iodide, iodine was formed in solution; whereas in the case of the bromide, bromine and sulphur monobromide were found. Jander suggested the following mechanism for the bromide solvolysis:

$$8KBr + 8SO_2 = 4K_2SO_3 + 4SOBr_2 \tag{3a}$$
$$4SOBr_2 = 2SO_2 + S_2Br_2 + 3Br_2 \tag{3b}$$
$$4K_2SO_3 + 2Br_2 = 2K_2SO_4 \downarrow + 4KBr + 2SO_2 \tag{3c}$$
$$4KBr + 4SO_2 = 2K_2SO_4 + S_2Br_2 + Br_2. \tag{3d}$$

Presumably the same reactions are supposed to take place in the case of the iodide, except that the S_2I_2 is unstable and breaks down to sulphur and iodine, so that the over-all equation is

$$4KI + 4SO_2 = 2K_2SO_4 \downarrow + 2S \downarrow + 2I_2. \tag{4}$$

Lichtin (1963) disputes Jander's results and reports that dilute solutions of bromides and iodides are quite stable when prepared in liquid SO_2 which has been degassed (i.e. oxygen removed), but that, at least for solutions of iodides, instability is associated with the presence of oxygen. Jander (1949) also reports that solutions of alkali metal acetates are also solvolysed in liquid sulphur, even at −50°C. The reaction appears to lead to the metal sulphite and to acetic anhydride, considered by Jander to be the decomposition product of an intermediate thionyl acetate. The behaviour of the volatile halides in liquid sulphur dioxide varies. Halides of group IV do not react. Phosphorous pentachloride is readily solvolysed, even at $-50°C$, with the production of phosphorous oxychloride and thionyl chloride:

$$PCl_5 + SO_2 = POCl_3 + SOCl_2. \tag{5}$$

Phosphorous pentabromide reacts in an analogous way:

$$PBr_5 + SO_2 = POBr_3 + SOBr_2. \tag{6}$$

Further solvolysis does not occur. Neither antimony trichloride nor antimony pentachloride are solvolysed by liquid sulphur dioxide, and Jander points out that whereas the reaction

$$PCl_5 + SO_2 = POCl_3 + SOCl_2 \tag{7}$$

is exothermic, both the further solvolysis of $POCl_3$

$$2PCl_5 + 5SO_2 = (P_2O_5) + 5SOCl_2 \tag{8}$$

and the solvolysis of $SbCl_3$

$$SbCl_3 + SO_2 = (SbOCl) + SOCl_2 \tag{9}$$

would represent endothermic reactions.

Solvolysis reactions which do occur are

$$NbCl_5 + SO_2 = NbOCl_3 + SOCl_2 \tag{10}$$
$$WCl_6 + SO_2 = WOCl_4 + SOCl_2 \tag{11}$$
and
$$2UCl_5 = UCl_6 + UCl_4 \tag{12a}$$
$$UCl_5 + 2SO_2 = UO_2Cl_2 \downarrow + 2SOCl_2. \tag{12b}$$

B. METATHETICAL REACTIONS

A large number of reactions, called in some cases by Jander (1949) "neutralization reactions", but probably better described as metathetical reactions, have been observed in liquid sulphur dioxide by Jander and co-workers Jander and Wickert, 1936; Jander and Ullman, 1937; (Jander, 1938). Thus, sulphites react with thionyl halides in the solvent to produce chlorides and sulphur dioxide:

$$Cs_2SO_3 + SOCl_2 = 2CsCl + 2SO_2 \tag{13}$$
$$(Me_4N)_2SO_3 + SOBr_2 = 2Me_4NBr + 2SO_2. \tag{14}$$

Acetates also react:

$$2Ag(CH_3CO_2) + SOCl_2 = 2AgCl \downarrow + SO(CH_3CO_2)_2 \tag{15}$$
$$2NH_4(CH_3CO_2) + SOCl_2 = 2NH_4Cl \downarrow + SO(CH_3CO_2)_2. \tag{16}$$

$SO(CH_3CO_2)_2$ does not appear to have been isolated; it probably breaks up to acetic anhydride and sulphur dioxide. But the compounds $(C_6H_5CH_2CO_2)_2SO$ and $(ClCH_2CO_2)_2SO$ have been isolated and analysed by Jander. Other metathetical reactions are

$$2NH_4SCN + SOCl_2 = 2NH_4Cl \downarrow + SO(SCN)_2 \tag{17}$$

and

$$4KI + 2SOCl_2 = 4KCl + 2(SOI_2) \qquad (18a)$$
$$= 4KCl \downarrow + 2I_2 + S \downarrow + SO_2. \qquad (18b)$$

The $(SO(SCN)_2)$ appears to be stable in dilute solution in liquid sulphur dioxide at $-15°C$, but, on concentrating the solution, amorphous poly-cyanogen is precipitated. Jander has, however, used solutions of $SO(SCN)_2$ to carry out such reactions as

$$K_2SO_3 + SO(SCN)_2 = 2KSCN + 2SO_2 \qquad (19)$$

and followed them conductimetrically, demonstrating 1 : 1 end-points (Fig. 1).

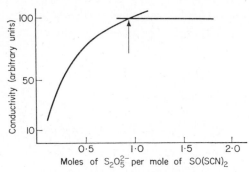

Fig. 1. Conductimetric titration of $SO(SCN)_2$ against $S_2O_5^{2-}$.

In a similar way the reaction between a sulphite and thionyl chloride can be followed conductimetrically (Fig. 2).

C. AMPHOTERIC REACTIONS

Jander (Jander and Immig, 1937; Jander, 1938; Jander and Hecht, 1943; Jander *et al.*, 1944) claims to have demonstrated amphoteric behaviour in liquid sulphur dioxide. When a solution of tetramethylammonium sulphite is added to a solution of aluminium chloride in liquid sulphur dioxide, a voluminous white precipitate of aluminium sulphite is formed. Presumably the metathetical reaction

$$2AlCl_3 + 3(Me_4N)_2SO_3 = Al_2(SO_3)_3 \downarrow + 6Me_4NCl \qquad (20)$$

has taken place. On further addition of tetramethylammonium sulphite, the precipitate redissolves, a complex anion presumably having been formed in solution:

$$Al_2(SO_3)_3 + 3(Me_4N)_2SO_3 = 2(Me_4N)_3Al(SO_3)_3. \qquad (21)$$

On addition of thionyl chloride to this solution the precipitate of aluminium sulphite is regenerated:

$$2(Me_4N)_3Al(SO_3)_3 + 3SOCl_2 = Al_2(SO_3)_3 \downarrow + 6Me_4NCl + 3SO_2. \qquad (22)$$

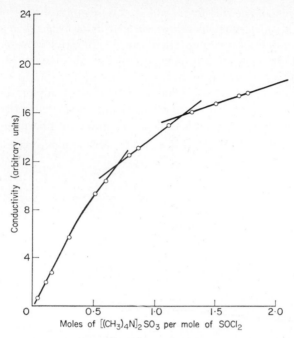

FIG. 2. Conductimetric titration of $S_2O_5^{2-}$ against $SOCl_2$ (Jander and Wickert, 1936).

Jander has followed both reactions conductimetrically and the curves obtained are shown in Figs. 3 and 4.

A similar reaction is observed with gallium trichloride. When tetramethyl-ammonium sulphite is added to a solution of gallium trichloride in liquid sulphur dioxide, a precipitate is formed:

$$2GaCl_3 + 3(Me_4N)_2SO_3 = 6Me_4NCl + Ga_2(SO_3)_2 + 2SO_2 \qquad (23a)$$
$$= 6Me_4NCl + Ga_2O_3.xSO_2. \qquad (23b)$$

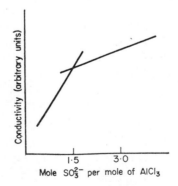

FIG. 3. Conductimetric titration of $(Me_4N)_2SO_3$ against $AlCl_3$ (Jander and Immig, 1937).

When an excess of the sulphite is added, the precipitate redissolves. Similar experiments with stannic chloride show that it too behaves in an analogous way to aluminium and gallium trichlorides. Tin oxide solvate, $SnO_2.xSO_2$, or stannic sulphite, is initially precipitated but dissolves in excess sulphite to give a solution of orthosulphitostannate, $(Me_4N)_4Sn(SO_3)_4$.

Jander also reports that a solution of PCl_3 in liquid sulphur dioxide, which is itself stable and colourless, gives, when a solution of tetramethylammonium sulphite is added at $-40°C$, a flocculent precipitate of phosphorous trioxide:

$$2PCl_3 + 3(Me_4N)_2SO_3 = P_2O_3 + 3SO_2 + 6Me_4NCl. \qquad (24)$$

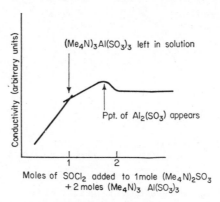

FIG. 4. Conductimetric titration of $SOCl_2$ against $(Me_4N)_2SO_3$ plus $(Me_4N)_3Al(SO_3)_3$ (Jander and Immig, 1937).

On addition of further sulphite the precipitate redissolves, and from this solution the compound $(Me_4N)PO_2SO_2$ has been isolated:

$$P_2O_3 + (Me_4N)_2SO_3 + SO_2 = 2(Me_4N)PO_2SO_2. \qquad (25)$$

The reaction has been followed conductimetrically, and Jander (1949) claims to have observed two end-points, the first at 3 moles of sulphite to 2 of PCl_3 and the second at 4 moles of sulphite to 2 of PCl_3 (see Fig. 5).

The solvates of antimony tri- and pentoxides also exhibit amphoretic behaviour in liquid sulphur dioxide. Many metals, whose oxides are amphoteric in water, dissolve in strong hydroxide solutions with the liberation of hydrogen. Jander and Hecht (1943) attempted to demonstrate an analogous situation in liquid sulphur dioxide. Metallic beryllium, aluminium, gallium, antimony and lead gave no reaction with tetramethylammonium sulphite in liquid sulphur dioxide. However, tin does react. With excess tetramethylammonium sulphite the following reaction takes place:

$$Sn + 2(Me_4N)_2SO_3 + 4SO_2 = (Me_4N)_2Sn(SO_3)_3 + (Me_4N)_2S_2O_3. \qquad (26)$$

When equimolar proportions of tin and tetramethylammonium sulphite are taken, tin oxide solvate is precipitated:

$$(Me_4N)_2SO_3 + xSO_2 + Sn = SnO_2.xSO_2 + (Me_4N)_2S_2O_3. \qquad (27)$$

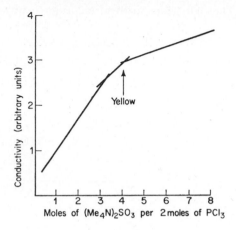

FIG. 5. Conductrimetric titration of SO_3^{2-} against PCl_3.

D. OXIDATION–REDUCTION REACTIONS

A number of oxidation-reduction reactions have been carried out in liquid sulphur dioxide. The sulphur dioxide usually acts merely as an inert carrier in the reactions. Tetramethylammonium sulphite is rapidly oxidized to the sulphate by iodine in the solvent (Jander and Immig, 1937c). A solution of ferric chloride will quantitatively oxidize potassium iodide to iodine:

$$2FeCl_3 + 2KI = 2FeCl_2 + 2KCl + I_2 \qquad (28)$$

and so will a solution of antimony pentachloride:

$$6KI + 3SbCl_5 = 3I_2 + 6KCl + 3SbCl_3. \qquad (29)$$

The $SbCl_3$ interacts with the potassium chloride to yield a precipitate of K_3SbCl_6:

$$6KCl + 2SbCl_3 = 2K_3SbCl_6. \qquad (30)$$

However, addition of excess antimony pentachloride causes this complex to dissolve with decomposition of the complex ion and formation of a hexa-chloroantimonate (V):

$$2K_3SbCl_6 + 6SbCl_5 = 6KSbCl_6 + 2SbCl_3. \qquad (31)$$

The conductimetric titration of $SbCl_5$ against KI in liquid sulphur dioxide is shown in Fig. 6 and shows breaks at mole ratios of $SbCl_5$ to KI of 1 : 2 (corresponding to equation (29)) and at 3 : 2 corresponding to

$$2KI + 3SbCl_5 = I_2 + 2KSbCl_6 + SbCl_3 \qquad (32)$$

the sum of equations (29), (20) and (31).

Seel *et al.* (1951a,b) have also recently studied the reactions of nitrosyl compounds with potassium and tetramethylammonium iodides in liquid sulphur dioxide. They all, from nitrosyl chloride to nitrosyl fluoroborate, react as follows:

$$2NOX + 2I^- = 2NO + I_2 + 2X^-.\tag{33}$$

The reaction of ethyl nitrite (nitrosyl ethoxide!) is as follows:

$$2ON.OEt + 2SO_2 + 2I^- = 2NO + I_2 + 2SO_2(OEt)^-.\tag{34}$$

With azides the corresponding reactions are

$$NOX + N_3^- = N_2O + N_2 + X^-\tag{35}$$

and

$$EtO.NO + N_3^- + SO_2 = N_2O + N_2 + SO_2(OEt)^-.\tag{36}$$

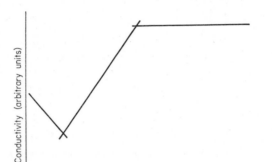

FIG. 6. Conductimetric titration of SbCl$_5$ against KI (Jander and Immig, 1937).

E. COMPLEX FORMATION

The formation of the complexes $K_3Sb(III)Cl_6$ and $KSb(V)Cl_6$ has been described in the previous section. Seel (1943a,b) and Seel and Bauer (1947) have described the preparation and characterization of a series of hexachloro-antimonates in liquid sulphur dioxide. When NOCl, CH_3COCl and PhCOCl are titrated against $SbCl_5$ in sulphur dioxide, the conductimetric curves show a sharp break at 1 : 1. The compounds $NO^+SbCl_6^-$, $CH_3CO^+SbCl_6^-$ and $PhCO^+SbCl_6^-$ respectively were isolated. The equivalent conductances of some of these solutions are shown in Table X.

The data on the mixed solution of $SOCl_2$ and $SbCl_5$ given in the table need some comment. Seel, following Jander (1943), formulated the solution of $SOCl_2$ and $SbCl_5$ as $SO^{2+}(SbCl_6^-)_2$. The conductivity data indicate that there is no justification for this. It is worthwhile noting that the only adduct reported between thionyl chloride and antimony pentachloride is $SOCl_2.SbCl_5$ (Lindquist and Einarsson, 1959). No structural data are available for this compound, but one's enthusiasm for formulating this as $SOCl^+SbCl_6^-$ must be considerably dampened both by the conductivity data quoted above and by the fact that the structure of the analogous compound $SeOCl_2.SbCl_5$, as determined by X-ray diffraction (Hermodsson, 1963), shows clearly that the selenium is covalently co-ordinated to antimony through the oxygen atom. Seel *et al.* (1952) have also prepared $NO_2^+SbCl_6^-$ in liquid sulphur dioxide from the reaction of nitryl chloride and antimony pentachloride. Solutions of the compound in liquid sulphur dioxide have conductivities of the same order as $NOSbCl_6$ and $KSbCl_6$. Other complexes that have been obtained in liquid sulphur dioxide are $PhCO^+AlCl_4^-$, from the reaction of aluminium trichloride and benzoyl chloride (Seel and Bauer, 1947), and acetyl fluoroborate, from acetyl fluoride and boron trifluoride (Seel, 1943a,b). A conductimetric titration of boron trichloride against potassium chloride gives a 1 : 1 end-point, indicating the formation of potassium tetrachlorborate in the solvent (Burge *et al.*, 1959).

TABLE X

The Molar Conductances of Some Complexes of $SbCl_5$ in Liquid Sulphur Dioxide [a, b]

	Λ cm^2 ohm^{-1} mole^{-1}	
	0°C	−70°C
$KSbCl_6$	92·8	49·0
$(MeCO)SbCl_6$	80·5	45·3
$(PhCO)SbCl_6$	71·5	37·8
$(NO)SbCl_6$	67·5	50·0
$SOCl_2 + 2SbCl_5$	0·4	0·7

Dilution = 50 litre mole^{-1}

[a] Seel and Bauer (1947).
[b] Seel (1943b).

As early as 1902, Walden and Centnerszwer (1902a,b, 1903) noted that added iodine increased the conductivity of potassium and rubidium iodides in liquid sulphur dioxide, and that the solubility of iodine itself was greatly increased by the presence of these electrolytes. These effects were a maximum at a ratio of iodide to iodine of 1 : 1, and they attributed them to the formation of metal tri-iodides, MI_3 in solution. They also obtained evidence for the formation of complex iodides of cadmium and mercury, from the increased solubility of cadmium and mercuric iodides in solutions of potassium and rubidium iodides in liquid sulphur dioxide (Walden and Centnerszwer, 1902c).

VII. Isotopic Exchange Reactions in Liquid Sulphur Dioxide

Perhaps the strongest argument against Jander's (1949) proposed ionization mechanism for liquid sulphur dioxide,

$$3SO_2 \rightleftharpoons SO^{2+} + S_2O_5^{2-} \tag{37}$$

and his explanation of the action of $SOCl_2$ as an acid in the solvent

$$SOCl_2 \rightleftharpoons SO^{2+} + 2Cl \tag{38}$$

comes from isotopic exchange studies in the solvent and in related systems, a comprehensive account of which is given by Norris (1959). The experimental results are summarized in Table XI.

TABLE XI

Summarized Results of Exchange Studies

Solvent	SO_2	$SOCl_2$
SO_2	Direct evidence for ^{18}O exchange [b]	SO_2 dissolved in excess $SOCl_2$ does not exchange *S [c, e]
$(Me_4N)_2S_2O_5$	Rapid *S exchange with solvent SO_2 [c]	
SO_3	Rapid ^{18}O exchange [d, a] No *S exchange [f]	
$SOCl_2$	No *S exchange [c, h] No ^{18}O exchange [i] *S exchange in presence of Cl^-, $SbCl_5$, $AlCl_3$ [c, j, k]	
$SOBr_2$	No *S exchange [c, h] No ^{18}O exchange [i] *S exchange in presence of Cl^-, Br^-, [c, j]	*S exchange between $SOCl_2$ and $SOBr_2$ dissolved in SO_2 [g] Also in mixture of $SOCl_2$ and $SOBr_2$ [g]
SCl_2	No *S exchange with SO_2 [e]	Measurable rate of *S exchange with $SOCl_2$. 45% in 2 h at 60°C [e]
Me_4NCl		Rapid *Cl exchange between $SOCl_2$ and Cl^- in SO_2 [l]

[a] Huston (1959).
[b] Lichtin et al. (1964).
[c] Johnson et al. (1951).
[d] Nakata (1943).
[e] Muxart (1950).
[f] Huston (1951).
[g] Johnson and Norris (1957).
[h] Masters and Norris (1955).
[i] Grigg and Lauder (1950).
[j] Herber et al. (1954).
[k] Burge and Norris (1959a, b).
[l] Masters et al. (1956).

Neither $SOCl_2$ or $SOBr_2$ exchange *S or ^{18}O with solvent SO_2 (Grigg and Lauder, 1950; Johnson et al., 1951; Masters and Norris, 1955), but pyrosulphite ion (sulphite dissolved in sulphur dioxide can only be recovered as pyrosulphite) does give rapid *S (Johnson et al., 1951), and presumably ^{18}O exchange, though the ^{18}O measurements do not seem to have been made. This suggests that the thionyl halides, if ionizing at all, are only ionizing as

$$SOX_2 = SOX^+ + X^- \qquad (39)$$

and this is supported (A) by the rapid radio-chlorine exchange between thionyl chloride and chloride ions in liquid sulphur dioxide, and (B) by the observation that thionyl chloride and thionyl bromide exchange radiosulphur rapidly and completely in liquid sulphur dioxide, even at $-50°C$. Observation (A) leads to the deduction that either the dissociation is occurring as in equation (39), or the exchange is occurring through an associative equilibrium

$$SOCl_2 + Cl^- \rightleftharpoons SOCl_3^-. \qquad (40)$$

Observation (B) leads to the deduction that either a simple dissociation is occurring, again as in equation (39), or there is a direct halide ion transfer, either by

$$SOCl_2 + SOBr_2 \rightleftharpoons SOCl^+ + SOBr_2Cl^- \qquad (41)$$

or through a transition complex

dissociating to uncharged SOClBr species. The exchange of ^{18}O between sulphur dioxide and dissolved sulphur trioxide indicates that the transfer of oxide ions to a really strong acceptor can take place (Nakata, 1959; Huston, 1943), and the failure of *S to exchange (Huston, 1951) confirms that the exchange reaction must either be

$$SO_2 + SO_3 \rightleftharpoons SO^{2+} + SO_4^{2-} \qquad (42)$$

or proceed through a transition complex such as

which maintains the nonequivalence of the sulphur atoms. It must be pointed out, however, that the conductivities of sulphur trioxide solutions in sulphur dioxide have only about the same low value as those of $SOCl_2$, i.e. Λ, the equivalent conductance, is $\sim 10^{-1}$ cm^2 ohm^{-1} mole^{-1} in 0.1 M solution (Jander, 1949).

Attempts have been made to measure the ^{18}O self exchange in liquid sulphur dioxide, but rapid heterogeneously catalysed exchange in the gas phase has made experiments difficult (Huston, 1959). Recently Lichtin et al. (1964), with $S^{16}O_2$ and $S^{18}O_2$ mixtures, have demonstrated by the use of infra-red spectroscopy that homogeneous exchange of oxygen takes place in the gas phase and in solutions of sulphur dioxide in carbon tetrachloride and cyclo-hexane. Exchange is complete within the time of a spectral measurement, i.e. within about ten minutes. They suggest that such exchange takes place via a cyclic intermediate, e.g. $O{=}S\overset{O}{\underset{O}{\diamondsuit}}S{=}O$, and point out that this is supported by the evidence that sulphur dioxide is slightly associated in both liquid and gas (Gmelin, 1953; Clusius et al., 1962).

In contrast to the negligible slow rate of the exchange of *S between thionyl halides and sulphur dioxide, the addition of halide ion is found to catalyse the reaction strongly (Herber et al., 1954; Masters and Norris, 1955). The thionyl bromide–sulphur dioxide *S exchange, studied in detail with tetra-methylammonium bromide (Herber et al., 1954) is independent of thionyl bromide concentration and obeys a rate law

$$\text{d[Exchange]}/dt = k[\text{Me}_4\text{NBr}] \tag{43}$$

k being found to be

$$4 \cdot 17 \times 10^6 \exp\left(-13{,}200/RT\right) \text{ sec}^{-1}.$$

A suggested mechanism is

$$\text{SOBr}_2 \underset{k_2}{\overset{k_1}{\rightleftharpoons}} \text{SOBr}^+ + \text{Br}^- \qquad \text{fast} \tag{44}$$

$$\text{*SO}_2 + \text{Br}^- \underset{k_4}{\overset{k_3}{\rightleftharpoons}} \text{*SO}_2\text{Br}^- \qquad \text{fast} \tag{45}$$

$$\text{*SO}_2\text{Br}^- + \text{SO}_2 \underset{k_6}{\overset{k_5}{\rightleftharpoons}} \text{SOBr}^+ + \text{SO}_3^{2-} \qquad \text{slow} \tag{46}$$

which gives a rate law

$$\text{d[Exchange]}/dt = k_3/k_4[\text{SO}_2]^2[\text{Br}^-]. \tag{47}$$

The chloride catalysed exchange of *S between thionyl chloride and solvent sulphur dioxide (Masters and Norris, 1955) obeys a different rate law

$$\text{d[Exchange]}/dt = k[\text{Me}_4\text{NCl}][\text{SOCl}_2][\text{SO}_2]. \tag{48}$$

This reaction has been studied throughout the solvent range from thionyl chloride in excess sulphur dioxide to sulphur dioxide in excess thionyl chloride, and the same rate law is obeyed, though there is a threefold increase in the rate constant in passing from excess sulphur dioxide to excess thionyl chloride. With tetramethylammonium chloride as catalyst in sulphur dioxide solutions, $k = 1 \cdot 08 \times 10^7 \exp\left(-14{,}700/RT\right)$ litre^2 mole^{-2} sec^{-1}; a suggested mechanism is

$$\text{*SO}_2 + \text{Cl}^- \underset{k_2}{\overset{k_1}{\rightleftharpoons}} \text{*SO}_2\text{Cl}^- \qquad \text{fast} \tag{49}$$

$$\text{*SO}_2\text{Cl}^- + \text{SOCl}_2 \underset{k_4}{\overset{k_3}{\rightleftharpoons}} \text{*SOCl}_2 + \text{SO}_2\text{Cl}^- \qquad \text{slow} \tag{50}$$

which gives the rate law of equation (48), with k equal to k_3k_1/k_2.

In the above no distinction has been made between "free" halide ion and total halide, i.e. between ion pairs and free halide ions. Conductivity data, of course, indicate that ion pairs predominate in halide solutions in liquid sulphur dioxide (Lichtin, 1963), and it is found that, in the thionyl chloride–sulphur dioxide exchange, tetramethylammonium chloride as catalyst gives rate values about twice those found with comparable concentrations of rubidium chloride. A similar effect was found with tetramethyl-ammonium and rubidium bromides in the exchange of sulphur between thionyl bromide and sulphur dioxide. The rate of thionyl chloride exchange is about seven times that of the thionyl bromide exchange at comparable concentrations, despite an apparently higher activation energy (14·7 kcal mole^{-1} for the chloride as against 13·2 kcal mole^{-1} for the bromide). It may be that the equilibrium in the reaction $SO_2 + X^- \rightleftharpoons SO_2X^-$ is further over to the right in the chloride than in the bromide; this would fall in line with the much higher stability of the SO_2F^- ion. This does not, however, explain the change in mechanism.

The $SOCl_2$–SO_2 exchange also seems to be subject to general catalysis by non-ionic bases. Recently the effect of triethylamine and acetone on the exchange rate has been investigated (Potter, 1962). For triethylamine the rate law

$$d[\text{Exchange}]/dt = k[SO_2][SOCl_2][Et_3N] \qquad (51)$$

was found to be followed over a wide range of reaction conditions, varying from thionyl chloride in liquid sulphur dioxide to sulphur dioxide in liquid thionyl chloride. There was, however, a consistent increase in the rate constant in going from solutions rich in sulphur dioxide to those rich in thionyl chloride. The rate constant was found to be $3·42 \times 10^6 \exp(-13,800/RT)$ litre^2 mole^{-2} sec^{-1} in excess thionyl chloride. In order to cover all conditions the rate law was modified to

$$d[\text{Exchange}]/dt = k[SOCl_2][SO_2.Et_3N] + k'[SO_2][SOCl_2.Et_3N] \qquad (52)$$

the first term dominating in dilute solution of sulphur dioxide in thionyl chloride. Acetone was found to exert only a weak catalytic effect on the exchange reaction, the rate law

$$d[\text{Exchange}]/dt = k[SO_2][SOCl_2][Me_2CO]^2 \qquad (53)$$

being obeyed over the range of concentrations employed. There was no readily apparent variation of k with any reactant concentration, and k was found to be

$$5·3 \times 10^{11} \exp(-24,000/RT) \text{ litre}^3 \text{ mole}^{-3} \text{ sec}^{-1}.$$

The thionyl chloride–sulphur dioxide exchange is also catalysed by antimony pentachloride and aluminium trichloride (Masters and Norris, 1955; Burge and Norris, 1959a,b). These give at comparable concentration about one

10

hundredth and one thousandth of the rates shown by tetramethylammonium chloride. The reaction obeys a rate law

$$d[\text{Exchange}]/dt = k[\text{SbCl}_5][\text{SOCl}_2][\text{SO}_2]. \tag{54}$$

This is consistent with the mechanism

$$*\text{SOCl}_2 + \text{SbCl}_5 \underset{k_2}{\overset{k_1}{\rightleftharpoons}} *\text{SOCl}_2.\text{SbCl}_5 \qquad \text{fast} \tag{55}$$

$$*\text{SOCl}_2.\text{SbCl}_5 + \text{SO}_2 \underset{k_4}{\overset{k_3}{\rightleftharpoons}} *\text{SO}_2 + \text{SOCl}_2.\text{SbCl}_5 \ \ \text{slow}. \tag{56}$$

The rate constants appear to be essentially constant over the whole range of composition from excess sulphur dioxide to excess thionyl chloride. $\text{SOCl}_2.\text{SO}_2$ has an equilibrium constant $K = 0.8$ at $0°\text{C}$ and the enthalpy of formation of the adduct is $\Delta H^0 = 3.6$ kcal mole^{-1}; k_3 is 0.875×10^2 exp $(-10,400/RT)$ litre^2 mole^{-2} sec^{-1}. The observed entropy of activation is -51.6 e.u. A comparison of the kinetic data for the various exchange reactions is given in Table XII.

Using mixtures of SbCl_5 and Me_4NCl, the catalytic effect was found to be a minimum at a $\text{Me}_4\text{NCl} : \text{SbCl}_5$ ratio of $1 : 1$ (Burge and Norris, 1959a,b). A similar minimum was found with Me_4NCl and AlCl_3 mixtures at $1 : 1$ by the same workers. The structure of the $\text{SOCl}_2.\text{SbCl}_5$ adduct, which can be isolated as a solid, would be of great help in solving the detailed mechanism of the reaction. The structure of the $\text{SeOCl}_2.\text{SbCl}_5$ adduct has been shown to be $\text{Cl}_2\text{SeO} \rightarrow \text{SbCl}_5$, and in view of the low conductivity of $\text{SOCl}_2.\text{SbCl}_5$ in liquid SO_2 it seems reasonable to conclude that the structure of the compound is $\text{Cl}_2\text{SO} \rightarrow \text{SbCl}_5$. The catalytic effect of mixtures of triethylamine and SbCl_5 has also been studied (Potter, 1962). Here again, at a mole ratio of $\text{SbCl}_5 : \text{Et}_3\text{N}$ of $1 : 1$, a minimum in catalytic activity is found; at this point catalytic behaviour is so weak that it is difficult to detect.

Perhaps the most interesting point that emerges from the exchange work is the suggested transition state species that the different inferred mechanisms involve. With thionyl bromide, catalysed by Br$^-$, the transition species is $\text{SO}_2\text{Br}^-.\text{SO}_2$, formulated as

with transfer of an oxide ion. With thionyl chloride catalysed by Cl$^-$ the transition species is $\text{SO}_2\text{Cl}^-.\text{SOCl}_2$, formulated as

TABLE XII

Summary and Comparison of Kinetic Data on the Catalysed Exchange of *S Exchange between Thionyl Halides and Sulphur Dioxide in Liquid Sulphur Dioxide

	$SOCl_2$ catalysed by Cl^-	$SOCl_2$ catalysed by $SbCl_5$	$SOCl_2$ catalysed by Et_3N	$SOCl_2$ catalysed by Me_2CO	$SOBr_2$ catalysed by Br^-
Rate law	$k[Cl^-][SOCl_2][SO_2]$	$k[SOCl_2, SbCl_5][SO_2]$	$k[SO_2][SOCl_2][Et_3N]$	$k[SO_2][SOCl_2][Me_2CO]^2$	$k[SO_2]^2[Br]$, only $k[Br^-]$ proved
Activation energy (kcal mole^{-1})	14·7	10·4	14·6 in excess SO_2 13·8 in excess $SOCl_2$	24·0	13·2
Pre-exponential factor	$1·08 \times 10^7$	$0·875 \times 10^2$	$3·42 \times 10^6$ in excess SO_2 $2·06 \times 10^6$ in excess $SOCl_2$	$5·3 \times 10^{11}$	$4·17 \times 10^6$
Entropy of activation (e.u.)	−29	−51·6	−30·7 in excess SO_2	−5·1	−30·4

involving a double bridge, an oxide ion transferring one way and a chloride ion the other. When the thionyl chloride–sulphur dioxide exchange is catalysed by Et_3N the transition species appears to be $(Et_3N.SO_2).SOCl_2$, possibly formulated as

in sulphur dioxide rich solutions and $(Et_3N.SOCl_2).SO_2$, possibly formulated as

in thionyl chloride rich solutions. The catalytic effect of Lewis acids on the exchange is much weaker, and the suggested mechanism for the exchange catalysed by $SbCl_5$ implies a transition species $(SOCl_2.SbCl_5).SO_2$. Certainly the entropy of activation for this exchange reaction is about twice as high as any of the others, -52 e.u., implying a more complex transition species.

VIII. Conclusion and Summary

In seeking to unify the results of their extensive investigations on the chemistry of liquid sulphur dioxide, Jander and Wickert (1936) adopted a suggestion of Cady and Elsey (1928) and proposed the "sulphito" concept of reactions in liquid sulphur dioxide. This theory is used as a guiding principle by Jander in his monograph in interpreting the reactions he has observed in liquid sulphur dioxide. Liquid sulphur dioxide is assumed to undergo an auto-ionization by the transfer of an oxide ion from one molecule of sulphur dioxide to another:

$$2SO_2 = SO^{2+} + SO_3^{2-} \tag{57}$$

The SO^{2+} and SO_3^{2-} ions are assumed to have a real existence and function similar to those of the hydroxonium, H_3O^+, and hydroxide, OH^-, ions formed during the auto-ionization of water. The reaction between thionyl chloride and a sulphite was considered by Jander to be a neutralization reaction:

$$Cs_2SO_3 + SOCl_2 = 2SO_2 + 2CsCl. \tag{58}$$

Many of the reactions discussed in earlier sections were studied by Jander and interpreted by him in terms of the "sulphito" concept. Of course, it is unnecessary to postulate the occurrence of intermediate ionic species or the involvement of the solvent to explain the metathetical reaction which occur in liquid sulphur dioxide. The reaction

$$(Me_4N)_2SO_3 + SOCl_2 = 2Me_4NCl + 2SO_2 \tag{59}$$

could presumably occur in any inert solvent and does not require SO^{2+}, or even $SOCl^+$ as an intermediate. The reaction can, and probably does, proceed by nucleophilic attack of SO_3^{2-}, or $S_2O_5^{2-}$ on $SOCl_2$, with expulsion of two chloride ions

$$SO_3^{2-} + SOCl_2 \rightleftharpoons (SO_3.SOCl_2^{2-}) \rightarrow (SO_3.SOCl^-) + Cl^- \rightarrow$$
$$(SO_3.SO) + 2Cl^- \rightarrow 2SO_2 + 2Cl^- \qquad (60)$$

and provided that the reaction is fast and the equilibrium

$$SO_3^{2-} + SOCl_2 \rightleftharpoons 2SO_2 + 2Cl^- \qquad (61)$$

sufficiently far over to the right, then a conductimetric titration will show a break at a ratio of $1 : 1$ of SO_3^{2-} to $SOCl_2$. Thus, there is no need to postulate any self-ionization of liquid SO_2. The evidence from studies on isotopic exchange in the solvent indicates in fact that no self-ionization seems to occur. It seems that liquid sulphur dioxide is not a self-ionizing solvent at all. What remains to be explained is the surprising solvent and ionizing powers of liquid sulphur dioxide. Lichtin (1963) has pointed out that once an ionic material has dissolved in liquid sulphur dioxide, its behaviour and conductivity can be rationalized by a theory in which the only solvent parameter is the dielectic constant, $15.36°$ at $0°$. On the other hand, many ionic materials of fairly high lattice energy are much more soluble in liquid sulphur dioxide than its comparatively low dielectic constant would suggest (see Section II). Liquid sulphur dioxide also seems to possess an unusual ionizing power. Thus triphenylmethyl chloride, a substance which is known to be covalent in the crystal and in many common solvents, is an extensively dissociated electrolyte in liquid sulphur dioxide.

The comparison of the ionization of triphenylmethyl chloride in nitrobenzene ($D = 24.5$) and in liquid sulphur dioxide ($D = 15.3$) is, as Lichtin (1963) points out, particularly interesting. Triphenylmethyl chloride is too weak an electrolyte in nitrobenzene for a dissociation constant to be found, whereas in liquid sulphur dioxide it is an electrolyte of much the same ionization as potassium chloride or bromide. This is rather like the behaviour of triphenylmethyl chloride in liquid hydrogen chloride ($D = 9.3$) (Waddington and Klanberg, 1960), where it is an electrolyte comparable in strength to tetramethylammonium chloride. This means that in both liquid sulphur dioxide and liquid hydrogen chloride there must be a specific interaction of the solvent with chloride ions above and beyond the electrostatic, for, both on the basis of its gross dielectic constant and dipole moment, nitrobenzene ($\mu = 4.24$, $D = 34.5$) should be a far better ionizing solvent than either sulphur dioxide ($\mu = 1.62$, $D = 15.4$) or hydrogen chloride ($\mu = 1.03$, $D = 9.3$). This specific interaction in liquid hydrogen chloride is due to hydrogen bonding; in liquid sulphur dioxide there is a good deal of evidence to suggest that it is due at least to charge transfer interactions (Lippincott and Welch, 1961; Lichtin, 1963), if not actual covalent bonding (see Section III).

Spectroscopic studies (Lichtin, 1963) of the complexes of sulphur dioxide with chloride, bromide and iodide ions show that all the halides intensify the electronic spectrum of sulphur dioxide and produce bathochromic shifts. Lippincott and Welch (1961) have identified the complexes of the iodide ion with sulphur dioxide as charge transfer complexes, and it seems reasonable to assume that all the halide ions can form charge transfer complexes with sulphur dioxide. A wide variety of complexes of sulphur dioxide are known and have been discussed in a previous section. It is interesting to note that most of the complexes are with potential electron donors; complexes of sulphur dioxide with electron acceptors are comparatively rare. Lichtin (1963) has calculated from the relative ionizations of substituted trimethyl chlorides that the complexing of chloride ion by sulphur dioxide reduces the free energy of ionization by more than 10 kcal mole^{-1}. Similar effects must occur with bromide and iodide ion and with other monovalent ions such as thiocyanate. Presumably, the free energies of solution of ionic halides and thiocyanates are affected in the same manner, due to specific complexing. Such an effect could produce solubilities $\sim 10^8$ times greater than those to be expected in an "inert" solvent of the same gross dielectic constant.

REFERENCES

Andre, S. (1900) *C. R. Acad. Sci., Paris,* **130,** 174.
Andrews, L. J. (1954) *Chem. Rev.* **54,** 713.
Andrews, L. J. and Keefer, R. M. (1951) *J. Amer. chem. Soc.* **73,** 4169.
Audrieth, L. F. and Kleinberg, J. (1953) "Non-Aqueous Solvents." Wiley, New York.
Aynsley, E. E., Peacock, R. D. and Robinson, P. L. (1951) *Chem. & Ind. (Rev.)* 1117.
Bagster, L. S. and Cooling, G. (1920) *J. chem. Soc.* **117,** 693.
Bagster, L. S. and Steele, B. O. (1912a) *Chem. News,* **105,** 157.
Bagster, L. S. and Steele, B. O. (1912b) *Trans. Faraday Soc.* 8, 51.
Bateman, L. C., Hughes, E. D. and Ingold, C. K. (1944) *J. chem. Soc.* 243.
Baude, E. (1904) *Ann. Chim. Phys.* **1,** 8.
Bjerrum, N. (1926a) *Ergebn. exakt. Naturw.* **6,** 125.
Bjerrum, N. (1926b) *K. danske vidensk. Selsk. Math.-fys. Medd.* **1,** No. 9, 1.
Bond, P. A. and Beach, H. T. (1926) *J. Amer. chem. Soc.* **48,** 348.
Bond, P. A. and Belton, W. E. (1945) *J. Amer. chem. Soc.* **67,** 1691.
Bond, P. A. and Crone, E. B. (1934) *J. Amer. chem. Soc.* **56,** 2028.
Bond, P. A. and Stephens, W. R. (1929) *J. Amer. chem. Soc.* **51,** 2910.
Booth, H. S. and Martin, D. R. (1942) *J. Amer. chem. Soc.* **64,** 2198.
Bright, J. R. and Fernelius, W. C. (1943) *J. Amer. chem. Soc.* **65,** 637.
Bright, J. R. and Jasper, J. J. (1941) *J. Amer. chem. Soc.* **63,** 3486.
Bruner, L. and Bekier, E. (1913) *Z. phys. Chem.* **84,** 570.
Burg, A. B. (1943) *J. Amer. chem. Soc.* **65,** 1629.
Burg, A. B. and Bickerton, J. H. (1945) *J. Amer. chem. Soc.* **67,** 2261.
Burge, D. E. and Norris, T. H. (1959a) *J. Amer. chem. Soc.* **81,** 2324.
Burge, D. E. and Norris, T. H. (1959b) *J. Amer. chem. Soc.* **81,** 2329.
Burge, D. E., Freund, H. and Norris, T. H. (1959) *J. phys. Chem.* **63,** 1969.

Byrd, W. E. (1962) *Inorg. Chem.* **1**, 762.

Cady, H. P. and Elsey, H. M. (1928) *J. chem. Educ.* **5**, 1425.

Cady, H. P. and Toft, R. (1925) *J. phys. Chem.* **29**, 1075.

Centnerszwer, M. and Drucker, J. (1923) *Z. Electrochem.* **29**, 210.

Clusius, K., Schleich, K. and Bernstein, R. B. (1962) *Helv. chim. acta,* **40**, 252.

Cruse, K. (1940) *Z. Electrochem.* **46**, 571.

Daggett, H. M. (1951) *J. Amer. chem. Soc.* **83**, 4977.

de Maine, P. A. D. (1957) *J. chem. Phys.* **26**, 1036.

Dutoit, P. and Gyr, E. (1909) *J. Chim. phys.* **7**, 189.

Elving, P. J. and Markowitz, J. M. (1960) *J. chem. Educ.* **37**, 75.

Ephraim, F. and Aellig, C. (1923) *Helv. chim. acta,* **6**, 37.

Ephraim, F. and Kornblum, J. (1916) *Ber. dtsch. chem. Ges.* **49**, 2007.

Foote, H. W. and Fleischer, J. (1931) *J. Amer. chem. Soc.* **53**, 1752.

Foote, H. W. and Fleischer, J. (1932) *J. Amer. chem. Soc.* **54**, 3902.

Foote, H. W. and Fleischer, J. (1934) *J. Amer. chem. Soc.* **56**, 870.

Franklin, E. C. (1911) *J. phys. Chem.* **15**, 675.

Fuoss, R. M. and Shedlovsky, T. (1949) *J. Amer. chem. Soc.* **71**, 1497.

Fuoss, R. M., and Kraus, C. A. (1933) *J. Amer. chem. Soc.,* **55**, 2387.

Giauque, W. F. and Stephenson, C. C. (1938) *J. Amer. chem. Soc.* **60**, 1389.

"Gmelin's Handbuch der Anorganische Chemie" System No. 9, Vol. B-1, p. 208. Verlag-Chemie, Weinheim (1953).

Grigg, E. C. M. and Lauder, I. (1950) *Trans. Faraday Soc.* **46**, 1039.

Herber, R. H., Norris, T. H. and Huston, J. L. (1954) *J. Amer. chem. Soc.* **76**, 2015.

Hermodsson, Y. (1963) Private Communication quoted by Lindquist, I., in "Inorganic Adduct Molecules of Oro-compounds", Springer-Verlag, Berlin.

Hill, A. E. (1931) *J. Amer. chem. Soc.* **53**, 2598.

Hill, A. E. and Fitzgerald, T. B. (1935) *J. Amer. chem. Soc.* **57**, 250.

Huston, J. L. (1951) *J. Amer. chem. Soc.* **73**, 3049.

Huston, J. L. (1959) *J. phys. Chem.* **63**, 389.

Jander, G. (1938) *Naturwissenschaften,* **26**, 779.

Jander G. (1949) "Die Chemie in Wasseränlichen Lösungmitteln". Springer-Verlag, Berlin.

Jander, G. and Hecht, H. (1943) *Z. anorg. Chem.* **250**, 287.

Jander, G. and Immig, H. (1937) *Z. anorg. Chem.* **233**, 295.

Jander, G. and Mesech, H. (1938a) *Z. phys. Chem.* A **183**, 121.

Jander, G. and Mesech, H. (1938b) *Z. phys. Chem.* A **183**, 137.

Jander, G. and Mesech, H. (1939) *Z. phys. Chem.* A **183**, 277.

Jander, G. Knöll, H. and Immig, H. (1937a) *Z. anorg. Chem.* **232**, 229.

Jander, G. and Ullman, D. (1937) *Z. anorg. Chem.* **230**, 405.

Jander, G. and Wickert, K. (1936) *Z. phys. Chem.* A **178**, 57.

Jander, G., Wendt, H. and Hecht, H. (1944) *Ber. dtsch. chem. Ges.* **77**, 698.

Johnson, L. F., Jr. and Norris, T. H. (1957) *J. Amer. chem. Soc.* **79**, 1584.

Johnson, R. E., Norris, T. H. and Huston, J. L. (1951) *J. Amer. chem. Soc.* **73**, 3052.

Kashtanov, L. I. and Sokolova, L. N. (1951) *Zh. Obsch. Khim.* **21**, 1484.

Kivelson, H. D. (1954) *J. chem. Phys.* **22**, 904.

Korezynski, A. and Glebocka, M. (1920) *Gazz. chim. ital.* **50**, I, 378.

Lecher, H. Z. and Hardy, W. B. (1948) *J. Amer. chem. Soc.* **70**, 3789.

Le Fevre, R. J. W. (1953) "Dipole Moments". Methuen, London.

Lichtin, N. N. (1963) "Progress in Physical Organic Chemistry", Vol. 1. Wiley, New York.

Lichtin, N. N. and Glazer, H. (1951) *J. Amer. chem. Soc.* **73**, 5537.

Lichtin, N. N. and Kliman, H. (1965) *J. Chem. and Eng. Data*, in the press.

Lichtin, N. N. and Leftin, H. P. (1956) *J. phys. Chem.* **60**, 160.

Lichtin, N. N. and Pappas, P. (1957) *Trans. N.Y. Acad. Sci.* **20**, 143.

Lichtin, N. N. and Rao, K. N. (1960) *J. phys. Chem.* **64**, 945.

Lichtin, N. N. and Rao, K. N. (1961) *J. Amer. chem. Soc.* **83**, 2417.

Lichtin, N. N., Laubicht, I. and Pincher, S. (1964) *Inorg. Chem.* **3**, 537.

Lichtin, N. N., Ullstern, R. E., Jr. and White, J. D. (1952) *J. Amer. chem. Soc.* **74**, 4715.

Lindquist, I. and Einarsson, P. (1959) *Acta chem. scand.* **13**, 420.

Lippincott, E. R. and Welch, F. E. (1961) *Spectrochim. Acta*, **17**, 123.

Luchinskii, G. P. (1938) *J. phys. Chem. Moscow*, **12**, 280.

Martin, D. R. (1945) *J. Amer. chem. Soc.* **67**, 1088.

Masters, B. J. and Norris, T. H. (1955) *J. Amer. chem. Soc.* **77**, 1346.

Masters, B. J., Potter, N. D., Asher, D. R. and Norris, T. H. (1956) *J. Amer. chem. Soc.* **78**, 4252.

Mesech, H. (1938) Dissertation, Greifswald.

Michaelis, A. (1891) *Ber. dtsch. chem. Ges.* **24**, 745.

Moede, J. A. and Curran, C. (1949) *J. Amer. chem. Soc.* **71**, 852.

Muxart, R. (1950) *C.R. Acad. Sci., Paris*, **231**, 1489.

Nakata, S. (1943) *J. chem. Soc., Japan*, **64**, 635.

Nickerson, J. D. and McIntosh, R. (1957) *Canad. J. Res. (Chem.)* **35**, 1325.

Norris, T. H. (1959). *J. phys. Chem.* **63**, 383.

Potter, N. D. (1962) *Diss. Abs.* **23**, 1919.

Satenstejn, A. I. and Viktorov, M. M. (1937) *Acta phys.-chim. URSS.* **1**, 883.

Schlenk, W., Weickel, T. and Herzenstein, A. (1910) *Ann.* **372**, 1.

Seel, F. (1943a) *Z. anorg. Chem.* **250**, 331.

Seel, F. (1943b) *Z. anorg. Chem.* **252**, 24.

Seel, F. and Bauer, H. (1947) *Z. Naturf.* **26**, 397.

Seel, F. and Riehl, L. (1955a) *Z. anorg. Chem.* **282**, 293.

Seel, F. and Riehl, L. (1953b) *Angew. Chem.* **67**, 32.

Seel, F., Boez, A. K. and Nogradi, J. (1951a) *Z. anorg. Chem.* **264**, 298.

Seel, F., Boez, A. K. and Nogradi, J. (1951b) *Z. anorg. Chem.* **264**, 311.

Seel, F., Nogradi, J and Rosse, R. (1952) *Z. anorg. Chem.* **269**, 197.

Silberrad, O. (1922) *J. chem. Soc.* **121**, 1015.

Steele, B. O. (1907) *Chem. News*, **96**, 224.

Vierk, A. L. (1950) *Z. anorg. Chem.* **261**, 279.

Waddington, T. C. and Klanberg, F. (1960) *J. chem. Soc.* 2332.

Walden, P. (1902) *Ber. dtsch. chem. Ges.* **35**, 2018.

Walden, P. and Centnerszwer, M. (1899) *Ber. dtsch. chem. Ges.* **32**, 2862.

Walden, P. and Centnerszwer, M. (1902a) *Z. phys. Chem.* **39**, 513.

Walden, P. and Centnerszwer, M. (1902b) *Z. anorg. Chem.* **30**, 145.

Walden, P. and Centnerszwer, M. (1902c) *Z. anorg. Chem.* **30**, 179.

Walden, P. and Centnerszwer, M. (1903) *Z. phys. Chem.* **42**, 432.

Wickert, K. (1938a) *Z. Electrochem.* **44**, 110.

Wickert, K. (1938b) *Naturwissenshaften*, **26**, 500.

Wickert, K. and Jander, G. (1937) *Ber. dtsch. chem. Ges.* **70** B, 251.

CHAPTER 7

The Halogens and Interhalogens as Solvents

A. G. SHARPE

University Chemical Laboratory, Cambridge, England

I. The Halogens	286
A. Chlorine	287
B. Bromine	287
C. Iodine	288
II. The Interhalogens	290
A. Compounds of Formula AB	290
B. Compounds of Formula AB_3	292
C. Compounds of Formula AB_5	295
D. Compounds of Formula AB_7	297
References	298

The halogens and interhalogens, because of their great reactivity, dissolve only a limited number of substances without causing them to undergo reactions more drastic than ion formation or solvation. Most work on these substances as solvents has been purely qualitative in nature, and even where quantitative data are available their interpretation is often obscure. It is scarcely surprising that this field of inorganic chemistry is one of the less exact areas of physical science: bromine trifluoride, the only one of the solvents to have the status of a reagent of some importance in preparative inorganic chemistry, explodes with water and most organic matter, reacts with asbestos with incandescence, and can be manipulated in quartz apparatus only because the reaction with silica in this form is very much slower than that with the finely-divided material; the iodine chlorides, though they are less violent in their reactions, nevertheless possess the property, inconvenient in electrochemical studies, of readily dissolving gold and platinum. The only technique which has been applied widely is that of measurement of electrical conductivity; this, however, though it provides some indication of the number and mobility of the ions present, gives little information as to their nature. Identification of products liberated at electrodes may throw some light on this problem, but too often the relationship between what carries the current and what is discharged at the electrodes is a subtle one. Even if, as is rarely the case, the structures of solid adducts containing the elements of the solvent are known, far-reaching changes may occur on dissolution, and halogen-exchange processes are often very rapid. Transport and e.m.f. measurements, which have provided so much of our knowledge of the nature of aqueous solutions, have not been made to any profitable extent in halogens and interhalogens. The picture which the following account presents is therefore not a very clear one, and much further work will be needed before the nature of solutions in these substances is well understood.

In this survey, solvents are considered according to formula type, first the halogens themselves and then, in turn, compounds of formula AB, AB_3, AB_5, and AB_7. There is a large literature on the interaction of bromine, iodine, iodine monochloride, or iodine bromide and donor molecules (especially organic bases), but most work on such systems relates to solid phases or to conditions in which the donor molecule is present in large excess; this subject has been reviewed elsewhere recently (Andrews and Keefer, 1961), and will receive only incidental mention here.

I. The Halogens

Little has yet been published concerning solutions in liquid fluorine (though it has been reported that chlorine is only sparingly soluble (Aoyama and Kanda, 1937)), but for the sake of completeness some of its properties Hu *et al.*, 1953) are included with those of chlorine (Giauque and Powell, 1939),

Table I

Physical Properties of the Liquid Halogens

	F_2	Cl_2	Br_2	I_2
M.p. (°C)	−220	−101	−7	114
B.p. (°C)	−188	−34	59	183
Specific gravity	1·51 (−190°)	1·57 (−35°)	3·12 (20°)	3·92 (133°)
Dielectric constant	1·52 (−190°)	2·0 (−35°)	3·1 (20°)	11·1 (118°)
Specific conductivity (ohm^{-1} cm^{-1})	—	7×10^{-8}	$1·1 \times 10^{-9}(25°)$	$5·2 \times 10^{-5}(114°)$
Heat of vapourization (kcal mole^{-1}) at b.p.	1·56	4·87	7·25	10·6
Entropy of vapourization (cal mole^{-1} deg^{-1})	18·5	20·4	22·0	23·1
Viscosity (millipoises)	—	4·9 (−34°)	10·3 (16°)	19·8 (116°)

bromine (Rabinowitsch, 1926), and iodine (Jander, 1949) in Table I. Attention may be directed to the fact that the specific conductivity of chlorine (McIntosh, 1922) appears to be appreciably greater than that of bromine; this value, however, was reported many years ago and should probably be regarded as an upper limit.

A. CHLORINE

Biltz and Meinecke (1923) reported that the chlorides of sodium, potassium, copper(II), cadmium, aluminium, lead(II), cerium(III) and zirconium(IV) are insoluble in liquid chlorine, and that tungsten(VI) chloride is only sparingly soluble. Carbon tetrachloride, silicon tetrachloride, titanium tetrachloride, arsenic trichloride, lead tetrachloride, phosphorus oxychloride, and disulphur dichloride dissolve readily. Biltz and Meinecke found no indication of compound formation in systems of the first four of these compounds and liquid chlorine, but Wheat and Browne (1938) have shown that compounds $CCl_4.nCl_2$, where $n = 0.5$ 1, 2, 3, or 4, exist, and that compound formation also occurs between chlorine and chloroform, methylene chloride, methyl chloride, and hydrogen chloride (Wheat and Browne, 1936a,b). The fact that chloroform and methylene chloride combine with, at most, three and two molecules of chlorine respectively, has been held to indicate that the chlorine atoms of the organic compound are acting as donors. If this is so, however, it is somewhat surprising that Wheat and Browne found no evidence for compound formation in the system carbon tetrachloride–bromine. The following values for the depression of the freezing-point of chlorine by 0.01 mole fraction of the solutes named have been given by Taylor and Hildebrand (1923), but the measurements are those of Waentig and McIntosh (1915).

	$-\Delta T(°C)$		$-\Delta T(°C)$
Acetone	0.190	Carbon tetrachloride	0.210
Ethyl acetate	0.190	Toluene	0.215
Diethyl ether	0.204	Chloroform	0.222
Stannic chloride	0.208		

The theoretical value calculated from the latent heat of fusion is, however, 0.27°. It therefore seems beyond doubt that there exists quite strong interaction between chlorine and the substances named, and the further study of these systems (and their comparison with, e.g. chlorine–hexane, in which interaction should be minimal), might be rewarding. In view of the evidence for the existence of the Cl_3^- ion in aqueous media, the action of liquid chlorine on chlorides of large organic cations also merits study: lattice energy considerations suggest that stable polychloride formation is most likely in such cases. The possibility of complexing with Lewis acids, especially antimony pentachloride, might also prove worth examination.

B. BROMINE

Many halides of non-metals are soluble in bromine, among them being carbon tetrachloride and tetrabromide, boron tribromide, silicon tetrabromide, titanium tetrabromide, stannic bromide, arsenic tribromide and antimony tribromide; there is up to the present time no evidence for compound formation (Biltz and Jeep, 1923; Wheat and Browne, 1936a). Phosphorus trichloride dissolves to form chlorobromides.

Bromine forms addition compounds with many organic bases such as pyridine, quinoline, acetamide, and benzamide; such compounds form conducting solutions in bromine, probably giving $Base_nBr^+$ and Br_3^- ions, but the conductivity is time-variable, suggesting that bromination of the organic molecule is taking place, and the interpretation of the data is obscure (Finkelstein, 1926; Plotnikov and Mikhailowskaya, 1940).

Alkali metal bromides do not dissolve to any appreciable extent in bromine, but bromides of large organic cations do so; a solution of tetrabutylammonium bromide, for example, has an equivalent conductivity of $15 \cdot 7$ ohm^{-1} cm^{-2} at $2 \cdot 01$ M concentration at $25°$. Since the solution is highly viscous, a very high degree of dissociation, presumably with formation of polybromide anions, is indicated (Moessen and Kraus, 1952). Phosphorus pentachloride also forms conducting solutions which appear to contain anionic chlorine; the variation of molar conductivity with concentration is complicated. Phosphorus pentabromide forms similar solutions (Plotnikov and Jakubson, 1928).

C. IODINE

Liquid iodine as a solvent has been investigated more extensively than the other halogens, though no new work has been reported during the last decade; the following account is based largely on a much more detailed one by G. Jander in 1949 (Jander, 1949).

Iodine itself is in some ways an abnormal substance. In the solid, the closest approach of what would usually be designated non-bonded atoms ($3 \cdot 56$ Å) is near enough to the interatomic distance in the molecule ($2 \cdot 68$ Å) to suggest that quite strong intermolecular attraction exists, and the rather high entropy of vapourization at the boiling point suggests that this attraction persists to some extent in the liquid phase. The dielectric constant of the liquid is remarkable in increasing with rise in temperature, from $11 \cdot 1$ at $118°$ to $13 \cdot 0$ at $168°$. The liquid is a much better conductor than the other halogens, but the conductivity, unlike that of the solid, falls with increase in temperature; these results are commonly interpreted as showing that the conductivity is partly metallic and partly electrolytic but the factor that the current-carrying ions are probably thermally unstable should also be borne in mind.

Sulphur, selenium, and tellurium are said to dissolve in liquid iodine without chemical change. Stannic iodide, zinc iodide, antimony tri-iodide, arsenic tri-iodide, mercuric iodide and iodoform also dissolve, and cryoscopic measurements suggest that they do so unchanged. The iodides of calcium, strontium and barium are insoluble, but those of the alkali metals are readily soluble; cryoscopic measurements, however, show that polymeric species are present, the degree of polymerization being greatest for lithium and least for caesium. Conductivities of solutions of alkali metal halides have been measured for the lithium, sodium, potassium, and rubidium salts; the specific conductivity of sodium iodide solutions is lower than those of the other compounds, and varies little with concentration; the specific conductivities of solutions of the other three iodides increase steeply with increasing concentration, reaching maxima at about 10 mole % of the salt. Furthermore, the temperature coefficient of the specific conductivity is reported to be negative for solutions of sodium iodide and positive for solutions of lithium, potassium, and rubidium iodides. It seems clear that triple ions and more complex species, as well as M^+ and I_3^-, are present in such solutions, but it appears profitless to speculate further until the anomalous position of sodium iodide has been confirmed and more detailed studies of all the solutions have been made.

The self-dissociation of liquid iodine has been represented by the equation

$$2I_2 \rightleftharpoons I^+ + I_3^-. \tag{1}$$

On this basis alkali metal iodides, which readily form tri-iodides, have been regarded as bases, and iodine monohalides as acids. Conductimetric titration, of e.g. KI and IBr in molten iodine shows a sharp break at a 1 : 1 molar ratio, which would correspond to the process

$$MI_3 + IX \rightleftharpoons MX + 2I_2. \tag{2}$$

Such a process can also be followed potentiometrically, though since the iodine monohalides are only weak electrolytes in iodine a symmetrical curve is not obtained. A rough estimate of the value for the ionic product $[I^+][I^-]$ has led to a value of 10^{-42}. Recently, however, the species I^+ has been identified beyond reasonable doubt in the blue solutions of iodine in oleum and iodine in iodine pentafluoride, and in each case it has been shown that it is paramagnetic with a moment of 1·7–2·0 Bohr magnetons (Arotsky and Symons, 1962; Aynsley et al., 1963). No measurements of the magnetic susceptibilities of solutions of iodine monohalides in liquid iodine have been reported, but it seems very doubtful whether free I^+ ions are present, and it can only be said that the simplest basis for the self-ionization of iodine appears to involve the formation of I_3^+ and I_3^- ions, and that more complex species may well be involved. Solvolytic reactions in liquid iodine, e.g.

$$KCN + I_2 \rightleftharpoons KI + ICN, \tag{3}$$

and amphoteric behaviour, e.g.

$$HgI_2 + 2KI \rightleftharpoons K_2HgI_4, \tag{4}$$

have also been described.

II. The Interhalogens

A. COMPOUNDS OF FORMULA AB

Of the compounds of this general formula, chlorine monofluoride (m.p. −156°, b.p. −100°), the unstable bromine monofluoride (m.p. about −33°, b.p. about 20°) and monochloride (m.p. about −66°, b.p. about 5°), and the recently reported iodine monofluoride have not been described as solvents, and only iodine monochloride and bromide will be discussed here. Their physical properties are given in Table II, which is based on reviews by Gutmann (1951a,b) and Greenwood (1951, 1956).

TABLE II

Physical Properties of Iodine Monochloride and Bromide

	ICl	IBr
M.p.(°C)	27·2(α), 13·9(β)	41°
B.p. (°C)	100	about 116
Specific gravity	3·13 (45°)	3·76 (42°)
Dielectric constant	—	
Specific conductivity (ohm^{-1} cm^{-1})	4·6×10^{-3}(35°)	3·0×10^{-4}(40°)
Heat of vapourization (kcal mole^{-1}) at b.p.	10·0	—
Entropy of vapourization (cal mole^{-1} deg^{-1})	26·7	—
Viscosity (millipoises)	41·9 (28°)	—

One special difficulty attends the interpretation of data on fused iodine monohalides: the compounds are dissociated into free halogens to an appreciable extent. For iodine monochloride the degree of dissociation is 0·4% at 25° and 1·1% at 100°; for iodine monobromide the corresponding figures are 8·8% and 13·4% (Greenwood, 1951).

The electrical conductivity of liquid iodine monochloride is increased considerably when potassium or ammonium chloride is dissolved in it, the equivalent conductances at 35° at infinite dilution being about 32 and 26 ohm^{-1} cm^2 respectively. Other compounds which are appreciably soluble to yield conducting solutions include RbCl, CsCl, KBr, KI, AlCl$_3$, AlBr$_3$, PCl$_5$, pyridine, acetamide, and benzamide. Lithium, sodium, silver, and barium chlorides are sparingly soluble; silicon tetrachloride, titanium tetrachloride, and niobium pentachloride dissolve but have very little effect on the conductivity; antimony pentachloride increases it, though to a much less extent than phosphorus pentachloride. Thionyl chloride, which is miscible in all proportions, acts merely as a diluent, and the conductivity decreases as more thionyl chloride is added. The interpretation of the conductivity data is complicated by the changes in density, viscosity and degree of dissociation which occur on dilution; further information has often been obtained by studies of systems involving iodine monochloride in nitrobenzene solution, but it should not be forgotten that addition of a third component may create further complications.

The self-ionization of iodine monochloride, which has generally been represented as

$$2ICl \rightleftharpoons I^+ + ICl_2^- \tag{5}$$

resembles that of iodine, and doubts about the presence of the free cation (as distinct from species such as I_2Cl^+) which were expressed earlier must be reiterated here. The existence of the ICl_2^- ion in e.g. solid alkali metal salts and $PCl_4^+ICl_2^-$ (Zelezny and Baenziger, 1952) is well established by X-ray methods, but there is no real evidence for the existence of the unsolvated cation; phase studies of the systems $AlCl_3$—ICl and $SbCl_5$—ICl reveal no 1 : 1 compounds, but only 1 : 2 and 1 : 2 and 1 : 3 adducts respectively. These presumably contain the I_2Cl^+ ion analogous to the ICl_2^+ ion present in $ICl_3.AlCl_3$ and $ICl_3.SbCl_5$, which are better represented as $ICl_2^+AlCl_4^-$ and $ICl_2^+SbCl_6^-$ (see later).

In solution in excess of iodine monochloride, the distinction between I^+ and its solvates is for many purposes of minor significance. Thus conductimetric titration of RbCl vs SbCl$_5$ or KCl vs NbCl$_5$ shows a break at 1 : 1 molar ratio, whilst NH_4Cl vs $SnCl_4$ shows a break at 2 : 1 molar ratio, indicating formation of the ion $SnCl_6^{2-}$. The compound $PCl_5.ICl$, which in the solid state is $PCl_4^+ICl_2^-$, behaves as an acid towards $KICl_2$ and as a base towards $SbCl_5$. Organic bases form 1 : 1 or 1 : 2 compounds; these are likely to be N-donor complexes and salts of the type (Base) $I^+ICl_2^-$ respectively. From the preparative viewpoint reactions in fused iodine monochloride are of very limited usefulness, pure products being seldom isolable; the reagent may, however, prove to be useful in stabilizing chloride complexes of elements in high oxidation states.

Fused iodine bromide as a solvent closely resembles iodine monochloride, but stable acids on this solvent system have not yet been isolated. Alkali metal bromides form polyhalides of formula $MIBr_2$, and phosphorus pentabromide gives the compound $IPBr_6$ which, by analogy with the chloro compound, is probably $PBr_4^+IBr_2^-$; in iodine bromide it behaves only as a base. Stannic bromide acts as an acid anhydride and, as may be shown by conductimetric titration, undergoes neutralization reactions such as

$$2RbIBr_2 + SnBr_4 \rightleftharpoons Rb_2SnBr_6 + 2IBr. \tag{6}$$

B. COMPOUNDS OF FORMULA AB₃

Excluding the recently discovered iodine trifluoride (Schmeisser and Scharf, 1960), concerning which very little is known, the compounds in this group are chlorine trifluoride, bromine trifluoride, and iodine trichloride. Their physical properties appear in Table III.

TABLE III*

Physical Properties of Liquid Interhalogens of Formula AB₃

	ClF_3	BrF_3	ICl_3
M.p. (°C)	−83	9	101
B.p. (°C)	12	126	—
Specific gravity	1·84 (12°)	2·80 (25°)	—
Dielectric constant	4·6 (12°)	—	—
Specific conductivity (ohm⁻¹ cm⁻¹)	$6·5 \times 10^{-9}(0°)$	$8·0 \times 10^{-3}(25°)$	$8·5 \times 10^{-3}(101°)$
Heat of vapourization (kcal mole⁻¹) at b.p.	6·6	10·2	—
Entropy of vapourization (cal mole⁻¹ deg⁻¹)	23·1	25·6	—
Viscosity (millipoises)	4·8 (12°)	22·2 (25°)	—

    * Banks, Davies and Rudge, 1953.
      Greenwood, 1951.
      Oliver and Grisand, 1952.
      Quarterman, Hyman and Katz, 1957.
      Rogers, Thompson and Speirs, 1954.
      Rogers, Speirs and Panish, 1957.
      Rogers and Garver, 1958.

Iodine trichloride in the molten state (in which there is appreciable dissociation into the monochloride and chlorine) has not been investigated as a solvent, but since the structure of solid iodine trichloride and those of its adducts with potassium chloride, aluminium chloride, and antimony pentachloride are all accurately known, some discussion of this compound is essential here. The solid contains planar dimeric molecules having the structure shown (Boswijk and Wiebenga, 1954).

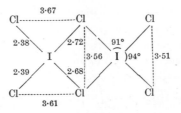

This might be described to a first approximation in terms of an ionic structure with resonance between the two forms ;

$$\left[\begin{array}{c}Cl\\I\\Cl\end{array}\right]^{+}\left[\begin{array}{c}Cl \quad Cl\\I\\Cl \quad Cl\end{array}\right]^{-} \text{and} \left[\begin{array}{c}Cl \quad Cl\\I\\Cl \quad Cl\end{array}\right]^{+}\left[\begin{array}{c}Cl\\I\\Cl\end{array}\right]^{-}$$

or the central chlorine atoms may be taking part in three-centre bonding. In the planar ion ICl_4^-, present in $KICl_4.H_2O$, the environment of the iodine atom is again unsymmetrical; all the angles are within 1° of 90°, but the I—Cl distances are as shown (Elma, de Boer and Vos, 1963):

$$Cl\underset{2\cdot53}{\overset{Cl}{\underset{}{\,\,\, \overset{\mid}{\underset{\mid}{I}}\,\, \overset{2\cdot47}{}\,Cl}}}\,Cl$$

(with $2\cdot42$ above, $2\cdot60$ below, Cl at top and bottom)

Finally, in the compounds $IAlCl_4$ and $ISbCl_6$ (Vonk and Wiebenga, 1959) the iodine atom has two chlorine atoms at distances of $2\cdot25$–$2\cdot33$ Å plus two more, completing a distorted square, at $2\cdot85$–$3\cdot00$ Å:

In $IAlCl_4$ In $ISbCl_6$

To a first approximation this indicates structures $ICl_2^{+}AlCl_4^-$ and $ICl_2^{+}SbCl_6^-$, but the shortness of the I—Cl (bonded to Sb or Al) distances shows there must be substantial cation–anion interaction. Nevertheless, this evidence for the ICl_2^+ and ICl_4^- ions is very important in interpreting the chemistry of adducts of other interhalogens for which no adequate structural data are available.

Although chlorine trifluoride has a very low conductivity and no studies of ionic reactions in it have been reported, it is noteworthy that compounds which may well contain ClF_4^- and ClF_2^+ ions, capable of reacting by the equation

$$ClF_2^{+}+ClF_4^{-} \rightleftharpoons 2ClF_3, \tag{7}$$

have recently been prepared. The action of fluorine on alkali metal chlorides, bromides, or iodides at 15°–250° results in the formation of the compound

$MClF_4$, where $M = K$, Rb, or Ca, and these must surely contain a ClF_4^- anion; whether they dissolve in liquid chlorine trifluoride does not appear to have been investigated (Asprey, Margrave and Silverthorn, 1961). Chlorine trifluoride forms $1 : 1$ complexes with antimony pentafluoride and boron trifluoride (Seel and Detmar, 1958; Selig and Shamir, 1964); both are good conductors and the infra-red spectrum of the second compound strongly suggests it has the structure $ClF_2^+BF_4^-$. There is also n.m.r. evidence which suggests that chlorine trifluoride, which consists of T-shaped molecules in the solid and gaseous states, may in the liquid state be in equilibrium with a low concentration of dimer (Muetterties and Phillips, 1957).

Bromine trifluoride is the only one of the interhalogens which has become a widely used laboratory reagent, chiefly for the preparation of complex fluorides. A number of reviews of its reactions have been given (Gutmann, 1950; Leech, 1956; Ryss, 1960); this account is restricted to instances in which it acts not only as a fluorinating agent but also as a solvent. Bromine trifluoride fluorinates everything which dissolves in it, and a discussion of solubilities is therefore restricted to those of soluble inorganic fluorides. These fall into two groups: alkali metal fluorides, silver(I) fluoride, and barium fluoride; and fluorides of gold(III), boron, titanium(IV), silicon, germanium(IV), vanadium(V), niobium(V), tantalum(V), phosphorus(V), arsenic(V), antimony(V), platinum(IV), ruthenium(V) and a few other metals. Members of both groups have been shown to be conductors in bromine trifluoride, and many form stable adducts, e.g. $AgBrF_4$, $SbBrF_8$, with the solvent. The fact that any member of the first group reacts with a member of the second group to yield a complex halide is easily understood if (by analogy with derivatives of iodine trichloride) derivatives containing BrF_4^- and BrF_2^+ ions are formed and these interact according to an equation such as

$$BrF_2^+SbF_6^- + Ag^+BrF_4^- \rightleftharpoons AgSbF_6 + 2BrF_3. \tag{8}$$

In a few instances, such as this one, it has been shown by measuring the conductivities of solutions containing different molar ratios of $AgBrF_4$ and $SbBrF_8$ that the conductivity is a minimum at $1 : 1$ molar ratio. Stannic fluoride forms a $1 : 2$ complex with bromine trifluoride and the reaction of this adduct with $KBrF_4$ can be represented by the equation (Woolf and Eméleus, 1949)

$$(BrF_2^+)_2SnF_6 + 2KBrF_4 \rightleftharpoons K_2SnF_6 + 4BrF_3. \tag{9}$$

Among a very large number of preparations of fluoro-complexes by means of this reagent the following must suffice to illustrate its scope (Eméleus and Gutmann, 1949; Sharpe, 1950; Woolf, 1950; Sharpe and Woolf, 1951; Sharpe, 1953; Hepworth et al., 1954):

$$Ag + Au \rightarrow AgBrF_4 + BrF_2AuF_4 \rightarrow AgAuF_4 \tag{10}$$

$$NOCl + SnF_4 \rightarrow (NO)_2SnF_6 \tag{11}$$

$$N_2O_4 + Sb_2O_3 \rightarrow (NO_2)SbF_6 \tag{12}$$

$$VF_5 + LiF \rightarrow LiVF_6 \tag{13}$$

$$Ru + KCl \rightarrow KRuF_6. \tag{14}$$

Removal of bromine trifluoride from the reaction product is not always easily completed, however; this has been attributed to solvolysis of the product or incomplete interaction of acid and base according to the neutralization equation

$$BrF_2^+ + BrF_4^- \rightleftharpoons 2BrF_3 \tag{15}$$

Stabilization of high oxidation states in bromine trifluoride sometimes occurs; thus although palladium tetrafluoride has not yet been isolated, salts such as K_2PdF_6 are readily obtained from alkali metal chloro-palladites and the reagent (Sharpe, 1953); complexes of chromium(V), e.g. $KCrOF_4$, have also been made in this solvent (Sharpe and Woolf, 1951). It should be pointed out that no acid or base in the bromine trifluoride system has yet been the subject of an adequate structural study; the anion in $KBrF_4$ has been variously reported to be tetrahedral (Siegel, 1956; 1957) or (what seems much more probable) planar (Sly and Marsh, 1957), and the BrF_2^+ ion has not so far been identified conclusively. Since BrF_2 and SbF_5 form a range of compounds (Fischer et al., 1955), it may be that more than one cationic species is involved. However, the analogy with adducts of iodine trichloride is a powerful one, and the value of the reagent in preparative work shows that even if the model for seld-ionization of the interhalogen is not established beyond doubt, it does nevertheless provide a basis on which useful studies can be made.

C. COMPOUNDS OF FORMULA AB_5

Since the recent preparation of chlorine pentafluoride (Smith, 1963) by the action of fluorine on the trifluoride at 350° and 250 atm, pentafluorides of chlorine, bromine, and iodine are all known, and some of their physical properties are given in Table IV. For the first two of these, however, nothing is known of their properties as solvents except that bromine trifluoride and hydrogen fluoride are miscible in all proportions with bromine pentafluoride, and the possibility of complex formation with alkali metal fluorides or, for example, tin(IV) and antimony(V) fluorides, does not seem to have been investigated. [A report of the existence of the compound K_2ClF_7 or $KClF_6 \cdot KF$ has been criticized (Emeléus and Sharpe, 1949), and appears to be without foundation.] The properties of iodine pentafluoride have been examined in more detail (Eméleus and Sharpe, 1949; Hargreaves and Peacock, 1960; Muetterties and Phillips, 1957; Rogers and Katz, 1952; Rogers, Thompson and Speirs, 1954; Rogers, Pruett and Speirs, 1955; Rogers, Speirs, Thompson and Panish, 1954; Rogers and Garver, 1958; Woolf, 1950).

A wide range of observations indicate that iodine pentafluoride is an associated liquid, and the observed dependence of the number, widths and positions of the ^{19}F resonances of the compound on temperature has been interpreted in terms of fluorine exchange through a dimeric intermediate (Muetterties and Phillips, 1957). The low specific conductivity of the liquid is greatly increased when potassium iodate or antimony(V) fluoride is dissolved in it; solutions of the former compound liberate iodine at the cathode on electrolysis, and the equivalent conductivity at infinite dilution is $35\cdot5$ ohm^{-1} cm^2. The nature of the ions present has not, however, been established.

TABLE IV

Physical Properties of Interhalogens of Formula AB$_5$

	ClF$_5$	BrF$_5$	IF$_5$
M.p. (°C)	−100	−61	9·4
B.p. (°C)	—	40·5	100·5
Specific gravity	—	2·46 (25°)	3·19 (25°)
Dielectric constant	—	8 (25°)	36·2 (35°)
Specific conductivity (ohm^{-1} cm^{-1})	—	$9\times10^{-8}(25°)$	$5\cdot4\times10^{-6}(25°)$
Heat of vapourization (kcal mole^{-1}) at b.p.	—	6·7	9·8
Entropy of vapourization (cal mole^{-1} deg^{-1})	—	23·3	26·5
Viscosity (millipoises)	—	6·2 (24°)	21·9 (25°)

Antimony(V) fluoride and potassium fluoride both combine with iodine pentafluoride to yield compounds of formulae ISbF$_{10}$ and KIF$_6$ respectively, both of which are readily soluble in hot, and sparingly soluble in cold, iodine pentafluoride. The potassium salt is a well-defined compound which is also obtained by the action of the pentafluoride on potassium nitrate (Aynsley, Nichols and Robinson, 1953) or iodide (Hargreaves and Peacock, 1960), and although the structure of the solid has not been determined by X-ray analysis there seems to be little doubt that the formulation K$^+$IF$_6^-$ is correct. The nature of the adduct with antimony pentafluoride is more doubtful, but from the conductivity in iodine pentafluoride and the formation of (impure) potassium hexafluorantimonate by the interaction of KIF$_6$ and ISbF$_{10}$ in iodine pentafluoride, the structure IF$_4^+$SbF$_6^-$ is suggested. The neutralization process may then be represented by the equation

$$K^+IF_6^- + IF_4^+SbF_6^- \rightleftharpoons KSbF_6 + 2IF_5. \tag{16}$$

Boron trifluoride also increases the conductivity of iodine pentafluoride, and passage of the gas into a solution of potassium fluoride in the interhalogen compound results in the formation of potassium fluoroborate. Sulphur trioxide is readily soluble and increases the conductivity; distillation of such solutions gives a constant-boiling mixture of composition $IF_5.1 \cdot 17SO_3$. It is possible that a fluorosulphonate is in fact formed; such compounds have been made by other methods (Roberts and Cady, 1960). Adducts are also formed with dinitrogen pentoxide, molybdenum and tungsten trioxides, and potassium periodate (Aynsley, Nichols and Robinson, 1953). The system HF—IF_5 has been studied in detail, but no compound formation has been detected.

A recent examination of the nature of the blue solutions formed when iodine dissolves in iodine pentafluoride shows these to contain the uncoordinated paramagnetic I^+ ion, formed by the reaction

$$IF_5 + 2I_2 \rightleftharpoons 5I^+ + 5IF_6^-. \tag{17}$$

Addition of potassium fluoride, which combines with the interhalogen, shifts the equilibrium towards the left hand side, and the solutions turn brown (Aynsley et al., 1963). Similar blue solutions have been obtained from the oxide I_2O_4 (Aynsley et al., 1953). Iodine(III) is also stable in cold iodine pentafluoride solution; when potassium iodide reacts with the pentafluoride, iodine is liberated and from the resulting solution the compound KIF_4 may be isolated (Hargreaves and Peacock, 1960).

D. COMPOUNDS OF FORMULA AB₇

The only representative of this class known at the present time is iodine heptafluoride, which has only a very narrow liquid range: it melts at 5–6° at 2 atm pressure; the vapour pressure of the solid reaches 760 mm at 4·5°, which is also the boiling point of the slightly supercooled liquid. As Greenwood (1951) has pointed out, the widely quoted value of 26·4 cal mole⁻¹ deg⁻¹ for the entropy of vapourization (which would suggest an associated liquid) is incorrect, having been calculated from the heat of sublimation of the solid instead of the heat of vapourization of the liquid; the true value must certainly be substantially lower.

Our knowledge of the chemical properties of iodine heptafluoride is very limited. There is no sign of interaction with sodium, potassium, and rubidium fluorides, which do not dissolve in the liquid (Schumb and Lynch, 1950). A brief report has, however, described addition compounds $IF_7.AsF_5$ and $IF_7.3SbF_5$; the structure $IF_6^+AsF_6^-$ was suggested for the former compound, largely on the basis of its decomposition to iodine heptafluoride and potassium hexafluoroarsenate on treatment with potassium fluoride (Seel and Detmar, 1958), but further details have not yet appeared. The present writer is of the opinion that interaction of caesium fluoride and iodine heptafluoride at high pressures and moderate temperatures might lead to the discovery of a compound containing the IF_8^- ion, and it may be that some future publication will describe fluoride transfer by the reaction

$$IF_6^+ + IF_8^- \rightleftharpoons 2IF_7 \tag{18}$$

in iodine heptafluoride solution.

REFERENCES

Andrews, L. J. and Keefer, R. M. (1961) *Adv. inorg. Chem. Radiochem.* **3**, 91.

Aoyama, S. and Kanda, E. (1937) *Bull. chem. Soc. Japan*, **12**, 455.

Arotsky, J. and Symons, M. C. R. (1962) *Quart. Rev.* **16**, 282.

Asprey, L. B., Margrave, J. L. and Silverthorn, M. E. (1961) *J. Amer. chem. Soc.* **83**, 2955.

Aynsley, E. E., Greenwood, N. N. and Wharmby, D. H. W. (1963) *J. chem. Soc.* 5369.

Aynsley, E. E., Nichols, R. and Robinson, P. L. (1953) *J. chem. Soc.* 623.

Banks, A. A., Davies, A. and Rudge, A. J. (1953) *J. chem. Soc.* 732.

Biltz, W. and Jeep, K. (1927) *Z. anorg. Chem.* **162**, 32.

Biltz, W. and Meinecke, E. (1923) *Z. anorg. Chem.* **131**, 4.

Boswijk, K. H. and Wiebenga, E. H. (1954) *Acta crystallogr.* **7**, 417.

Elma, R. J., de Boer, J. L. and Vos, A. (1963) *Acta crystallogr.* **16**, 243.

Eméleus, H. J. and Gutmann, V. (1949) *J. chem. Soc.* 2979.

Eméleus, H. J. and Sharpe, A. G. (1949) *J. chem. Soc.* 2206.

Finkelstein, W. (1926) *Z. phys. Chem.* **121**, 46.

Fischer, J., Liimatainen, R. and Bingle, J. (1955) *J. Amer. chem. Soc.* **77**, 5848.

Giauque, W. F. and Powell, T. M. (1939) *J. Amer. chem. Soc.* **61**, 1970.

Greenwood, N. N. (1951) *Rev. pure appl. Chem.* **1**, 84.

Greenwood, N. N. (1956). *In* Supplement to Mellor's "Comprehensive Treatise on Inorganic and Theoretical Chemistry," II, Part I.

Gutmann, V. (1950) *Angew. Chem.* **62**, 312.

Gutmann, V. (1951a) *Z. anorg. Chem.* **264**, 151.

Gutmann, V. (1951b) *Mh. Chem.* **82**, 156.

Hargreaves, G. B. and Peacock, R. D. (1960) *J. chem. Soc.* 2373.

Hepworth, M. A., Peacock, R. D. and Robinson, P. L. (1954) *J. chem. Soc.* 1197.

Hu, J.-H., White, D. and Johnston, H. L. (1953) *J. Amer. chem. Soc.* **75**, 5642.

Jander, G. (1949) "Die Chemie in Wasserähnlichen Lösungsmitteln Springer-Verlag, Berlin".

Leech, H. R. (1956) *In* Mellor's "Comprehensive Treatise on Inorganic and Theoretical Chemistry," Supplement II, Part I.

McIntosh, D. (1922) *Proc. roy. Soc. Can.* **16**, III, 302.

Moessen, G. W. and Kraus, C. A. (1953) *Proc. nat. Acad. Sci., Wash.* **38**, 1023.

Muetterties, E. L. and Phillips, W. D. (1957) *J. Amer. chem. Soc.* **79**, 322.

Oliver, G. D. and Grisard, J. W. (1952) *J. Amer. chem. Soc.* **74**, 2705.

Plotnikov, W. A. and Jakubson, S. (1928) *Z. phys. Chem.,* **138**, 235.

Plotnikov, W. A. and Mikhailowskaya, V. I. (1940) *Zap. Inst. Khim. U.S.S.R.* **7**, No. 1, 85.

Quarterman, L. A., Hyman, H. H. and Katz, J. J. (1957) *J. phys. Chem.* **61**, 912.

Rabinowitsch, M. (1926) *Z. phys. Chem.* **119**, 81.

Roberts, J. E. and Cady, G. H. (1960) *J. Amer. chem. Soc.,* **82**, 352, 353, 354.

Rogers, M. T. and Garver, E. E. (1958) *J. phys. Chem.* **62**, 952.

Rogers, M. T. and Katz, J. J. (1952) *J. Amer. chem. Soc.*, **74**, 1375.

Rogers, M. T., Pruett, R. D. and Speirs, J. L. (1955) *J. Amer. chem. Soc.* **77**, 5280.

Rogers, M. T., Speirs, J. L. and Panish, M. B. (1957) *J. phys. Chem.* **61**, 366.

Rogers, M. T., Thompson, H. B. and Speirs, J. L. (1954) *J. Amer. chem. Soc.*, **76**, 4841.

Rogers, M. T., Speirs, J. L., Thompson, H. B. and Panish, M. B. (1954) *J. Amer. chem. Soc.* **76**, 4843.

Rogers, M. T., Speirs, J. L., Thompson, H. B. and Panish, M. B. (1956) *J. Amer. chem. Soc.* **78**, 936.

Ryss, I. G. (1960). "The Chemistry of Fluorine and its Inorganic Compounds" (Translation), U.S. Atomic Energy Commission.

Schmeisser, M. and Scharf, E. (1960) *Angew. Chem.*, **72**, 324.

Schumb, W. C. and Lynch, M. A. (1950) *Industr. Engng. Chem. (Industr.)* **42**, 1383.

Seel, F. and Detmar, O. (1958) *Angew. Chem.* **70**, 163, 470.

Selig, H. and Shamir, J. (1964) *Inorg. Chem.* **3**, 294.

Sharpe, A. G. (1950) *J. chem. Soc.* 3444.

Sharpe, A. G. (1953) *J. chem. Soc.* 197.

Sharpe, A. G. and Woolf, A. A. (1951) *J. chem. Soc.* 798.

Siegel, S. (1956) *Acta crystallogr.* **9**, 493.

Siegel, S. (1957) *Acta crystallogr.* **10**, 380.

Sly, W. G. and Marsh, R. E. (1957) *Acta crystallogr.* **10**, 378.

Smith, D. F. (1963) *Science*, **141**, 1039.

Taylor, N. W. and Hildebrand, J. H. (1923) *J. Amer. chem. Soc.* **45**, 685.

Vonk, C. G. and Wiebenga, E. H. (1959) *Acta crystallogr.* **12**, 859.

Waentig, G. and McIntosh, D. (1915) *Proc. roy. Soc. Can.* **9**, 207.

Wheat, J. A. and Browne, A. W. (1936a) *J. Amer. chem. Soc.* **58**, 2410.

Wheat, J. A. and Browne, A. W. (1938) *J. Amer. chem. Soc.* **60**, 371.

Wheat, J. A. and Browne, A. W. (1936b) *J. Amer. chem. Soc.* **60**, 1575, 1577.

Woolf, A. A. (1950) *J. chem. Soc.* 1053.

Woolf, A. A. (1950) *J. chem. Soc.* 3678.

Woolf, A. A. and Emeléus, H. J. (1949) *J. chem. Soc.* 2865.

Zelezny, W. F. and Baenziger, N. C. (1952) *J. Amer. chem. Soc.* **74**, 6151.

CHAPTER 8

Halides and Oxyhalides of Group V Elements as Solvents

D. S. PAYNE

Chemistry Department, The University, Glasgow, Scotland

I. Introduction 301
II. Experimental Methods.. 306
    A. Qualitative Solubility Considerations................................... 306
    B. The Examination of Solid Phases..................................... 307
    C. The Products of Electron Transfer.................................... 307
    D. Conductivity Measurements.. 307
    E. Transport Number Measurements..................................... 308
    F. Potentiometric Measurements.. 308
    G. Titrations Using Indicators.. 309
    H. Spectrophotometric Measurements................................... 309
    I. Viscosity Measurements.. 310
    J. Thermodynamic Measurements....................................... 310
    K. Isotopic Exchange Reaction.. 310
    L. Ebullioscopic and Cryoscopic Measurements......................... 310
III. Halides as Solvents... 311
IV. Oxyhalides as Solvents.. 327
V. Phosphoryl Chloride... 332
VI. Uses of Group V Halides and Oxyhalides as Solvents........................ 348
References.. 349

I. INTRODUCTION

Immediately after the recognition by Cady (1897) of the resemblances between liquid ammonia and water in the dissolution of inorganic salts, attention was turned to a search for other liquids with similar solvent properties. Brühl (1898) suggested that certain halides of elements such as phosphorus or arsenic might be solvents; the first experimental work, however, concerned antimony trichloride as a cryoscopic solvent (Tolloczko, 1899). Walden's classical investigations into non-aqueous solvents covered the halides and oxyhalides of phosphorus and the halides of arsenic and antimony (Walden, 1900). Certain of these were "good" solvents for inorganic materials and the resulting solutions were usually electrical conductors. The process of dissolution was interpreted in terms of ionization processes involving both solvent and solute. Little interest was shown in these halide and oxyhalide solvents until recent work, notably that of V. Gutmann and his collaborators working in Vienna, re-awakened interest. A large number of investigators have now worked in the field and the experimental techniques for handling these readily hydrolysed solvents are well established and tested. As the following account will show, the scope of this group of compounds as solvents has now been thoroughly examined and the nature of the solution species established in a number of instances. Interest has now turned to a more detailed physico-chemical examination of these systems, indeed for certain aspects of electrochemistry these experimentally difficult solvents offer considerable attractions because of the comparative simplicity of the interactions between solvent and ionic species (Porter and Baughan, 1958).

The elements of Group V, with the exception of nitrogen, give rise to two main series of halides, the trihalides and the pentahalides. Other halides such as tetraiododiphosphine (P_2I_4) and bismuth monochloride (BiCl) are known but are not appropriate to a discussion of solvent properties, as they are not readily accessible in amounts required for solvent investigations. The oxyhalides of this group vary from simple molecular compounds such as the nitrosyl and phosphoryl halides to the solid bismuth oxyhalides with layer structures. The halide and oxyhalide chemistry of nitrogen, phosphorus, arsenic, antimony and bismuth is dominated by the ready attack of nucleophilic reagents; all the compounds are sensitive to hydrolysis and work must always be carried out under strictly anhydrous conditions, if the results are to be significant. These conditions are readily achieved by working in totally enclosed systems, particularly under vacuum. There is also a general tendency for these halides and oxyhalides to react with hydrocarbon greases, so that special arrangements have to be made in handling to avoid contamination of this kind.

The stereochemistries most preferred by the elements phosphorus, arsenic, antimony and bismuth are either the tetrahedral (four co-ordination) or the octahedral (six co-ordination). Indeed phosphorus chemistry, particularly pentahalide chemistry, is dominated by the tetrahedrally disposed phosphorus atom. Thus phosphorus pentachloride exists as a solid based on the PCl_4^+ ion. The octahedral configuration is perhaps of greater general importance, dominating the formation of complex anions, such as $SbCl_6^-$, and AsF_6^-. The stabilities of these species, particularly the six co-ordinate ones are very much a matter of the size, as well as of the electronegativity of the attached groups. Only the high electronegativities of fluorine, chlorine and possibly of bromine enable the adequate utilization of the d-orbitals essential to the formation of compounds based on co-ordination numbers above four (Craig et al., 1954). It is, of course, also true that only in the case of fluorine and chlorine are the size relationships favourable to high co-ordination numbers. The electronegativities of phosphorus, arsenic, antimony and bismuth are all very close (2·06–1·67); the corresponding electronegativities of the halogens (4·0–2·2) are significantly higher. The polar character of most of the bonds between the halogens and nitrogen, phosphorus, arsenic, antimony and bismuth leads to the expectation of interactions of these molecules with ions or with other polar molecules. It is this prospect which is of great significance in determining solvent behaviour. In the oxyhalides the oxygen bonds are similarly strongly polar, so that further interactions are possible.

TABLE I

Halides of Group V

	M.p.°	B.p.°	Dielectric constant ϵ	Viscosity (centipoise) η	Density ρ (gcm^{-3})
PF$_3$	−151	−101	—	—	—
PCl$_3$	−112	74	3·5(17°) 4·7(22°)	—	1·56(21°)
PBr$_3$	−40	173	3·9(20°)	—	2·85(15°)
PI$_3$	61	dec. > 200	4·1(c. 65°)	—	—
AsF$_3$	−6	63	5·7(< −6°)	—	2·67(0°)
*AsCl$_3$	−13	130	12·6(17°)	1·225(20°)	2·16(20°)
*AsBr$_3$	35	220	8·8(35°)	5·41(35°) 4·44(40°)	3·33(50°)
AsI$_3$	146	403	7·0(c. 150°)	—	4·69(25°)
SbF$_3$	292	subl. 319	—	—	4·38(21°)
*SbCl$_3$	73	221	33·0(75°)	3·3(95°)	2·44(178°)
*SbBr$_3$	97	280	20·9(c. 100°)	6·81(100°)	4·15(23°)
SbI$_3$	167	401	13·9(c. 175°)	—	4·85
BiF$_3$	725	—	—	—	5·32(20°)
*BiCl$_3$	232	447	—	32·0(260°)	4·75(25°)
BiBr$_3$	218	460	—	—	5·72(25°)
BiI$_3$	408	> 500	—	—	5·88(17·5°)
PF$_5$	−94	−84	—	—	—
PCl$_5$	—	subl. 167	2·7(165°) 2·85(liq. at 160°)	—	1·60(160°)
PBr$_5$	< 100	dec. > 106	—	—	—
AsF$_5$	−80	−53	—	—	3·40(−73°)
SbF$_5$	7	150	—	—	2·99(23°)
SbCl$_5$	5	∼ 140	3·2(21°)	2·16(25°)	2·35(20°)
BiF$_5$	< 160	230	—	—	5·40(25°)

* Compounds with significant solvent properties.

The characteristic feature of a solvent is its ability to bring into a single phase (the solution), usually liquid, one or more other compounds (the solutes), usually solids. The mechanism of this phenomena is not confined solely to the separation and solvation of ions already present in a crystal lattice, but rather involves the general interaction of solvent molecules and solute, often leading to quite new compounds. The occurrence of these interactions in amounts large enough to be practically significant, and to warrant the use of the term solution and solvent, is controlled by the algebraic sum of a number of free energies. The magnitude and multiplicity of these energy terms vary considerably from system to system. However, in certain classes of compound with certain types of solute the overall energy change is generally favourable, and "good" solvent properties are encountered. Such groups of compounds are the trihalides, particularly those of arsenic and antimony, and the oxyhalides, notably nitrosyl and phosphoryl chlorides.

TABLE II

Oxyhalides of Group V

	M.p.°	B.p.°	Dielectric constant ϵ	Viscosity centipoise η	Density ρ (gcm^{-3})
FNO	−132·5	−60	—	—	1·33(−60°)
*ClNO	−61·5	−6	22·5(−27·5°)	0·586(−27°)	1·59(−6°)
			19·7(−10·0°)	0·547(−20°)	
BrNO	−55·5	∼0	13·4(15·2°)	—	—
FNO$_2$	−166	−72	—	—	1·49(−73°)
ClNO$_2$	−141	−14	—	—	1·41(−15°)
FNO$_3$	−181	−46	—	—	1·51(−46°)
ClNO$_3$	−107 (in vacuum)	18	—	—	—
POF$_3$	−39	−40	—	—	—
*POCl$_3$	1	108	13·9(22°)	1·15(25°)	1·71(0°)
POBr$_3$	56	192	—	—	2·82(45°)

*Compounds with significant solvent properties.

Whilst certain solutes dissolve in the halides and oxyhalides to give non-conducting species, these are not numerically very large and they will not be considered here in detail. Attention will be given largely to solutes which lead to conducting solutions, that is to the role of the halides and oxyhalides as ionizing solvents. Because of the pre-occupation of so much of inorganic chemistry with aqueous solutions, undue emphasis has been given to the consideration of solvent behaviour in terms solely of the dielectric constant. Reference to the physical properties of some of the halides and oxyhalides of Group V elements shown in Tables I and II shows that the dielectric constants, whilst greater than many organic solvents, are not particularly high when compared with solvents such as water ($\epsilon = 81\cdot1$ at 18°), anhydrous hydrogen fluoride ($\epsilon = 83\cdot6$ at 0°) or iodine pentafluoride ($\epsilon = 36\cdot2$ at 25°).

In addition to lowering the forces of Coulombic attraction the solvent is often also involved with the solute as an acceptor or donor of electrons, or as in the case of halides and oxyhalides, of halide ions. In this process of dissolution new chemical species are formed, and it is these which have been of particular interest to many investigators in this field.

The search for a unified approach to ionizing solvents in general has resulted in the application of the terms "acid" and "base" in the discussion of the ionic species involved in widely differing solvents. The Brønsted-Lowry definition of acid and base is clearly not applicable to the halide–oxyhalide solvents. The Lewis acid concept, in which an acid is regarded purely as an electron acceptor, is more nearly applicable, however it is not without its ambiguities. The Solvent-System concept of acids and bases developed by Gutmann and Lindquist (1954) is well suited to the halide solvents, focusing attention as it does on the possibility of ionic transfer processes. The investigation of any solvosystem is primarily a matter of recognizing the nature of the ions present. The interpretation to be placed on these ions, in terms of the solvent-system concept, necessitates the separation of the overall ion forming process into the individual transfer steps, such that "acid"+halide ion = "base" (cf. acid = base+proton, in aqueous systems), or that "base"+ solvent = "acid"+halide ion (cf. acid+solvent = base+proton, in certain aqueous systems). Halide solvents are all aniontropic solvents favouring fluoride, chloride, or iodide ion transfer; the "acids" are anion acceptors and the "bases" anion donors. A halide solvent MX_n may involve the equilibrium:

$$X^-_{\text{transfer}}$$

$$MX_n \quad + \quad MX_n \quad \rightleftharpoons \quad MX^-_{n+1} + MX^+_{u+1}. \qquad (1)$$

$$\text{Acid I} \qquad\qquad \text{Base II} \qquad\qquad \text{Base I} \quad \text{Acid II}$$

Such a solvent is ampholytic, reacting as both acid and base. Acids in such a solvent result in a decrease in the solvent halide ion concentration, for example, addition of an acceptor species of the form AX_4 leads to the formation of AX_6^{2-} thus consuming the X^- ions otherwise associated with the solvent. Bases lead to a corresponding increase in halide by the release of halide directly, as with, for example, tetramethylammonium halide. The utility of this concept as a method for a unified treatment of so called "acid–base" reactions is limited by the inherent difficulties associated with identifying with certainty the ionic species present in the solutions and those associated with the solvent. For simple halides the concept is perhaps most easily applied, for example in the case of arsenic trifluoride fluoride ion, transfer may occur thus:

$$AsF_3 \; + \; AsF_3 \; = \; AsF_2^+ \; + \; AsF_4^- \; .$$

$$\text{Acid I} \quad \text{Base II} \quad \text{Acid II} \quad \text{Base I} \qquad\qquad\qquad (2)$$

Base II is regarded as a fluoride donor, acid I as the fluoride acceptor and similarly base I as the fluoride donor, acid II as the acceptor. Potassium fluoride functions as a base in arsenic trifluoride giving, by fluoride donation, the anion AsF_4^-, whereas antimony pentafluoride functions, as an acid, by fluoride acceptance, giving the cation AsF_2^+ and the anion SbF_6^-.

The application of the solvent-system concept to phosphoryl chloride as a solvent has led to particular uncertainties as regards the interpretation of the species present in the solution; this particular problem will be referred to in greater detail later, here it can be noted that a simpler treatment may well be in terms of a Lewis acid–base interaction (Meek and Drago, 1961). Probably the idea of using the terms "acid" and "base" outside of protonic solvents is unnecessary and should not be attempted except where there is a clear advantage. The view of a cation–anion reaction as a "neutralization" of "acid" and "base" is not necessarily of assistance to our understanding of the system, indeed on the contrary these terms often necessitate additional explanation without adding significantly to the argument.

II. Experimental Methods

Understanding the nature of conducting solutions has always been one of the prime objects in electrochemistry, however, the highly developed theories and experimental techniques which have been evolved deal mainly with aqueous solutions and are not obviously directly applicable to halide and oxyhalide systems. The extension of electrochemical techniques and theories to these halide and oxyhalide solvent systems has recently been started, with results to be described later. The methods which are outlined below for the study of the species in solution cover the foundation work in the field of halide and oxyhalide solvents and only in small part refer to recent precise measurements of a kind similar to the well established work in the water solvent system. Conclusions can only be safely drawn from the results obtained by more than one experimental technique. It is dangerous, although often inescapable, to base conclusions on the result of only one technique.

A. QUALITATIVE SOLUBILITY CONSIDERATIONS

Examination of the solubility characteristics, not necessarily quantitatively, of a wide range of solutes gives an indication of the type of process involved in dissolution, as well as the general features of the solvent. It is of interest to establish at the commencement of an investigation whether typical salts such as the alkali metal halides, the quaternary ammonium halides and selected compounds such as iron(III), tin(IV), titanium(IV), or antimony(V) chlorides are soluble. In certain instances, accompanying colour changes may indicate the formation of complexes. As well as providing an overall picture of the solvent behaviour, this aspect of the investigation usually gives a guide as to the most suitable solutes to employ in later investigations.

B. THE EXAMINATION OF SOLID PHASES

The natures of the solid phases obtained from solutions by changes in concentration, or by changes in temperature, are of particular importance to the study of a solvent. Often these solids are conveniently described as "solvates" where simple addition of molecules of solvent to the solute has apparently occurred, e.g. $SbCl_5.POCl_3$ from antimony(V) chloride in phosphoryl chloride solution. In other cases, the resulting solid can be recognized as a complex between solvent and solute, e.g. $Me_4N^+AsCl_4^-$ from tetramethylammonium chloride in arsenic trichloride solution. The investigation of these solids has in only a few isolated instances been carried to a full X-ray structure determination; in the majority of cases the establishment of the formulae (that is, the ratio of solvent to solute molecules) is all that has been undertaken. By comparing the ratios for a series of solutes, deductions as to the chemical nature of the solvate can sometimes be made. The relation between the species present in solution and the solids obtained from it is difficult to be certain about, since ions present only at very low concentrations may be in equilibrium with the solid phase. However, where a complex ion is recognized in the solid it is reasonable to postulate, until evidence to the contrary is obtained, that this ion is present at a significant concentration in the solution.

C. THE PRODUCTS OF ELECTRON TRANSFER

The effect of electron transfer to a solvent cation can be studied, in certain cases, by the addition of suitable metals. It is especially useful when the product can be readily separated and identified. For example, in the case of nitrosyl chloride, the formation of nitric oxide by addition of zinc has been taken as evidence for the presence of the nitrosonium ion (Addison and Lewis, 1955). However, this method has only a limited applicability because of the difficulty of examining non-volatile or soluble products. An alternative procedure is to electrolyse the solution and to examine the electrode products, but again this is successful only when these are readily separated. In the case of self-ionization of a pure solvent, direct electrolysis presents considerable difficulties because of the very low conductance values. In one case, namely phosphoryl chloride, it has, however, been successfully applied (Spandau et al., 1960).

D. CONDUCTIVITY MEASUREMENTS

In dealing with the halides and oxyhalides as ionizing solvents, conductivity measurements have been very important. The self-ionization of a solvent is a feature of particular interest and a direct experimental approach may be attempted by measurement of the conductivity of the pure liquid. Clearly such measurements can equally well serve as a criterion of purity, since it is usual to find the conductivities of pure liquids to be very low. It is usually assumed that impurities present in the solvent will lead to an increase in conductivity. Measurement of the conductivities of pure halide solvents indicates that there is a trend, which is in line with the expected stability of the anionic and cationic species, thus

$$PCl_3 < AsCl_3 < SbCl_3 < BiCl_3.$$

Whilst measurement of the absolute conductivities is of interest in the application of modern electrolyte theory to these non-aqueous solutions, so far only a limited amount of data, which can be adequately tested by application of the Debye-Hückel Theory, has been collected. Usually it has been found sufficient to examine the change of conductivity in the course of the addition of a solution of one solute to that of another. The resulting changes in conductance depend on the nature of the reaction. Kolthoff and Laitinen (1941) describe the shape of conductimetric titration curves for a number of aqueous acids and bases of varying strengths. There are two essential features, firstly when reaction occurs to give ions of different mobility, or a decrease or increase in the total number of ions, an inflexion in the plot of conductivity against mole ratio occurs at the equivalence point, and secondly, the change of conductivity before or after the equivalence point is regular, often linear, so that the equivalence point may be determined by the simple intersection of two curves. The details of the curves vary greatly depending on a number of factors, but it can be taken that the occurrence of an intersection of two sections at a particular mole-ratio is evidence for a separate chemical entity. This method is particularly well suited to the halide and oxyhalide solvents because of the very great tendency in these solvents for the formation of complex halide ion species from electrolyte and non-electrolyte species.

E. TRANSPORT NUMBER MEASUREMENTS

This is a fundamental method of investigating the ionic species present in solution. However, its application is difficult experimentally in the halide–oxyhalide solvents because of the difficulties associated with measurement of the small changes in anolyte and catholyte composition associated with the passage of practically realizable amounts of current (Gutmann and Himml, 1955).

F. POTENTIOMETRIC MEASUREMENTS

Halide and oxyhalide solvents should respond to electrodes indicating halide ion activity, in the same way as the hydrogen electrode responds to changes in hydrogen ion activity in aqueous solutions. Halide ion mobility is essential to the conduction process just as hydrogen ion mobility is in aqueous solutions. The ion activity is conveniently represented by an expression of the form

$$pX = \log_{10} [X^-],$$

assuming that the activity coefficient can be taken as unity. So far only chloride ion indicators have been employed and their use has been confined to potentiometric titrations. The silver-silver chloride indicator electrode (Andersson and Lindquist, 1955) can be employed in a concentration cell of the type

$$Ag, AgCl \mid Cl^-(c_1) \mid\mid Cl^-(c_2) \mid AgCl, Ag$$

in arsenic trichloride, the reference electrode consisting of a solution of tetramethylammonium chloride of known concentration separated from the titration cell by a ground glass stopper. The silver–silver chloride electrode is not, however, a suitable electrode for solutions in phosphoryl chloride. The metals copper, silver, gold, magnesium, zinc, mercury, aluminium, lead, molybdenum and platinum have been examined as alternatives (Gutmann and Mairinger, 1957): however, only molybdenum is suitable for the construction of a sensitive indicator electrode; the equilibrium $MoCl_2 \rightleftharpoons Mo^{2+} + 2Cl^-$ seems to be involved. For more precise e.m.f. measurements in solutions of high dilution, a calomel electrode and chlorine electrode have been successfully applied (Gutmann, 1959).

G. TITRATIONS USING INDICATORS

The sulphophthaleins, well known as indicators for hydrogen ion in aqueous systems, also function as chloride ion indicators in phosphoryl chloride solution (Gutmann and Hubacek, 1963). The colour changes, which are reversible, are usually different from those encountered in aqueous systems. With these indicators, titrations can be conducted in much the same fashion as in aqueous solutions, the main type of information obtained thereby is of the stoichiometry of the reactions, although it is possible to use these indicators to compare relative chloride donor strength.

H. SPECTROPHOTOMETRIC MEASUREMENTS

The problems of identifying and estimating the relative amounts of species present in solution are particularly suited to spectroscopic investigations. Unfortunately relatively few of the species encountered in halide and oxyhalide solution can be identified unambiguously spectroscopically. In certain instances, notably where the tetrachloroferrate(III) ion was present, the method has been most successful (Baaz et al., 1961a). Infrared methods can give valuable information as to the nature of the solvates, as for example in consideration of the P=O shift in a series of phosphoryl halide complexes as an indication of the existence of an oxygen donor bond (Sheldon and Tyree,

11

1959). The application of Raman spectroscopy has so far been limited, which is unfortunate because this powerful tool is particularly suited to the simple symmetries of the ionic species present in the halide and oxyhalide solvents. Whilst the presence of the NO^+ ion has been established by Raman spectra (Gerding and Houtgraaf, 1953), evidence of comparable reliabliity for other cations postulated as being present in the halides and oxyhalides of Group V has not been obtained.

I. VISCOSITY MEASUREMENTS

The understanding of aqueous solutions has been assisted by studies of the forces of viscous flow; however, outside of this field data is limited. The only measurements available amongst halides and oxyhalides are for melts of the compounds $GaCl_3.POCl_3$ (Greenwood and Wade, 1957) and $GaBr_3.POBr_3$ (Greenwood and Worrall, 1958). Here all that can be deduced is that the unit of flow is a complex unit. From the only other record of viscosity data, namely that of $SbBr_3$ and acetone, no evidence for complex formation is obtained.

J. THERMODYNAMIC MEASUREMENTS

Unfortunately no data has been collected on the energy changes involved in the dissolution process in solvents of the halide and oxyhalide type. Similarly, very little data is available on the thermochemical aspects of the numerous solvates. It is to be hoped that this obvious omission will soon be made good, so that these solvent systems can be properly discussed.

K. ISOTOPIC EXCHANGE REACTION

In discussions involving the species present in solution, evidence concerning rates of exchange, as obtained by the use of isotopic tracers, is particularly relevant, since the extent of halogen interchange between solute and solvent can be recognized and possibly interpreted kinetically. So far only a limited number of experiments has been undertaken, but the results have been very significant in promoting our understanding of the nature of these solutions (Lewis and Sowerby, 1957a; Herber, 1960).

L. EBULLIOSCOPIC AND CRYOSCOPIC MEASUREMENTS

The earliest investigations concerned this aspect of these solvents and recently these measurements have been revived in an investigation of certain complex halides (Gutmann and Mairinger, 1960) and of the nature of titanium(IV), iron(III) and aluminium(III) chlorides (Gutmann and Mairinger, 1961) all in phosphoryl chloride solution. The technique employed consisted of the Swietoslawski ebulliometer employing thermistors for the measurement of the temperature differential.

III. HALIDES AS SOLVENTS

To be of interest as a working solvent, a halide must be available in reasonable quantity, have a m.p. below or conveniently close to room temperature, possess a b.p. above room temperature, be reasonably stable with respect to its elements, and have a suitable dielectric constant, coefficient of viscosity, and latent heat of vapourization. Table I shows those halides which are well suited as solvents. The general chemistry of these halides can be found in two recent reviews (George, 1960; Payne, 1961); nitrogen halides will not be considered, nor will iodides since these compounds are inherently too unstable to serve as effective solvents. It will appear that arsenic(III) and antimony(III) chlorides have been much more thoroughly investigated than any of the other halides; this is in part due to their availability and in part to their very obvious solvent properties and ease of manipulation.

The chemical aspects of solvent behaviour are reflected in the relative donor properties of the compounds. When these donor properties are compared by consideration of, for example, the reaction of the halides of Group V with boron(III) and aluminium(III) chlorides, only phosphorus(III) chloride and bromide are found to display noticeable, albeit feeble, donor characteristics; the trichlorides and tribromides of arsenic and antimony are very feeble donors, if donors at all (Holmes, 1960b). Phosphorus(III) chloride and bromide also show weak acceptor properties in their reaction with trimethylamine (Troost, 1954); similar acceptor properties may be ascribable to arsenic(III) and antimony(III) chlorides in the formation of compounds with trimethylphosphine and triethylamine (Holmes and Bertaut, 1958; Holmes, 1960a). With these feeble acceptor and donor properties, coupled with a low dielectric constant, the solvent properties of phosphorus(III) chloride are very limited. Even substances like iron(III) chloride and tetramethylammonium iodide, readily soluble in most halides, are only sparingly soluble.

Arsenic(III) chloride is a strongly polar molecule, pyramidal in form (Daure, 1929), giving a liquid of appreciable dielectric constant (12·8 at room temperature), which with its wide liquid range ($-18°$ to $+130°$ at atmospheric pressure) coupled with its ability to act as a chloride ion acceptor and donor in complex ion formation leads directly to "good" solvent properties. The extent of chloride ion transfer in pure arsenic(III) chloride, as inferred from the low specific conductivity of $1\cdot4 \times 10^{-7}\ \Omega^{-1}\ cm^{-1}$ (Andersson and Linquist, 1955) is clearly very small. The suggested self-ionization,

$$2AsCl_3 \rightleftharpoons AsCl_2^+ + AsCl_4^-,$$

implies that the solvent is ampholytic and that, using the solvent-system concept of acids and bases, the $AsCl_3$ molecule is acting in the role of an acid in accepting a chloride ion to give $AsCl_4^-$, and as a base in losing a chloride ion to give $AsCl_2^+$.

Alkali metal chloride complexes of arsenic(III) chloride, such as $Rb_3As_2Cl_9$ and $Cs_3As_2Cl_9$ (Wheeler, 1893a,b) and amine complexes such as

$$(EtNH_3)_2AsCl_5; \ (MeNH_3)_3As_2Cl_9; \ Me_2NH_2AsCl_4, \ and \ (Me_3NH)_2As_3Cl_{11}$$

(Petzold, 1933), are obtainable from aqueous systems. Tetra-alkylammonium chlorides are readily soluble in arsenic(III) chloride and from the resulting solu-

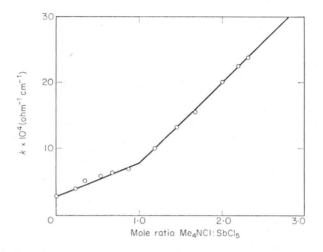

FIG. 1. Conductimetric titration of antimony(V) chloride with tetramethylammonium chloride in arsenic(III) chloride solution at 20°. Reproduced with permission from *Z. anorg. Chem.* (1951) **266**, 340.

tion the corresponding tetrachloroarsenate(III) salts are isolated as white, non-hygroscopic powders (Gutmann, 1951a). It is possible to dissolve a very small amount of potassium chloride in arsenic(III) chloride on heating, and on cooling a solid corresponding to $KAsCl_4$ is obtained (Gutmann, 1951a). By careful crystallization of the tetramethylammonium chloride from arsenic(III) chloride a solvate $Me_4NCl.3AsCl_3$ (possibly $Me_4NAsCl_4.2AsCl_3$ or $Me_4NAs_3Cl_{10}$) is obtained; two of the three arsenic(III) chloride molecules are loosely bound and are lost by heating to 100° at a pressure of 9 mm (Lindquist and Andersson, 1954). In the tetraethylammonium system, evidence for the compounds $Et_4NCl.2AsCl_3$ (possibly $Et_4NAsCl_4.AsCl_3$ or $Et_4NAs_2Cl_7$) and $3Et_4NCl.5AsCl_3$ (possibly $(Et_4N)_3(AsCl_4)_3.2AsCl_3$) is obtained from phase diagrams (Agerman *et al.*, 1958). Gutmann (1951a) lists the solubilities of a wide variety of halides, complex halides, oxides and complex oxides, some cyanides, metals and non-metals. The alkali and ammonium chlorides are only slightly soluble, likewise niobium(V) and tantalum(V) chlorides and the complex salt, $(Me_4N)_2SnCl_6$, whereas aluminium(III), tin(IV), vanadium(IV), iron(III) chlorides and Me_4NSbCl_6 and Me_4NCl, for example, are readily soluble. Walden (1900) drew attention, in his work on arsenic(III) chloride as solvent to the high solubility of a wide range of iodides and this has since been confirmed. Various non-metals such as sulphur, phosphorus and iodide are also readily soluble; the nature of these solutions is unknown. Metals, metal oxides and oxy-salts, such as sulphates or nitrates, are all very sparingly soluble.

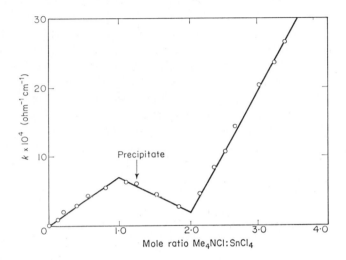

Fig. 2. Conductimetric titration of tin(IV) chloride with tetramethylammonium chloride in arsenic(III) chloride solution at 20°. Reproduced with permission from *Z. anorg. Chem.* (1951) **266**, 340.

Solutions of tetramethylammonium chloride and antimony(V) chloride in arsenic(III) chloride possess high conductivities. Conductimetric titration of these solutions gives the curve shown in Fig. 1, with a break at the 1 : 1 composition. A claim to have isolated a small amount of a white solid, with a composition close to $AsCl_3 . SbCl_5$, from the original antimony(V) chloride solution has not been substantiated; however its presence in solution has been assumed. The salt Me_4NSbCl_6 can be obtained from the solution after the titration. The change in conductance has been interpreted in terms of the reaction:

$$Me_4N^+AsCl_4^- + AsCl_2^+SbCl_6^- = Me_4N^+SbCl_6^- + 2AsCl_3 \qquad (3)$$

which is reasonable in so far as the only product appears to be the hexa-chloroantimonate(V) salt. Further, both solutions initially show high con-ductances and can give solids corresponding, apparently, to the cation and anion expected by chloride ion transfer in arsenic(III) chloride. A solution of tin(IV) chloride titrated with a solution of tetramethylammonium chloride gives a curve of the form shown in Fig. 2. Immediately the 1 : 1 ratio has been reached a precipitate of $(Me_4N)_2SnCl_6$ begins to develop. The break at the 1 : 1 ratio has been accounted for by postulating the equilibrium:

$$Me_4NAsCl_4 + SnCl_4 \rightleftharpoons Me_4NSnCl_5 + AsCl_3. \tag{4}$$

The Me_4NSnCl_5 species must then react with further $AsCl_4^-$ to give the hexachlorostannate(IV) ion. Examination of titanium(IV) and vanadium(IV) chlorides in a similar titration showed similar evidence for a 1 : 1 species. Solid materials corresponding approximately to these 1 : 1 compositions have been isolated, but not investigated further. Not all experimenters report the occurrence of definite interactions between arsenic(III) chloride and metal chlorides; for example, a report of the phase study of the system $AsCl_3 - TiCl_4$ states that there was complete miscibility. None of the solutions showed significant electrical conductivity (Eingorn, 1950).

Phosphorus(V) chloride dissolved in arsenic(III) chloride gives a conducting solution which, in distinction to antimony(V) chloride, does not give a break when titrated conductimetrically with a solution of tetramethylammonium chloride. On the basis of this evidence Gutmann (1952d) describes the solution as one containing $PCl_4^+AsCl_4^-$ rather than $AsCl_2^+PCl_6^-$. Cronander (1873a,b,c) observed the formation of a solid $AsCl_3.PCl_5$ from phosphorus(V) chloride dissolved in arsenic(III) chloride; repetition of this work by Kolditz (1957a) has, however, shown that a saturated solution in fact deposits large prism-like crystals of composition $2PCl_5.5AsCl_3$ (m.p. 40°). The solution of this compound in arsenic(III) chloride possesses an appreciable conductance (0·202 M solution, $\kappa = 6·9 \times 10^{-4}$ ohm^{-1} cm^{-1} at 25°), whilst cryoscopic evidence shows the solution contains 2·6 particles per formula weight. Two formulations of the compound are possible:

$$PCl_4^+PCl_6^-.5AsCl_3 \text{ and } PCl_4^+AsCl_4^-.1·5AsCl_3.$$

If the latter were to apply in the solution in arsenic(III) chloride, four particles per formula weight would be expected if dissociation was complete. Other evidence based on the conductance of the compound in acetonitrile supports the formulation as a hexachlorophosphate(V) rather than a tetrachloroarsenate(III), however in solution a proportion (about 30%) of the compound may be present in this latter form. A number of tetrachlorophosphonium(V) salts are conveniently prepared in arsenic(III) chloride solution. For example, $PCl_4^+PCl_5Br^-$ is the product of phosphorus(III) chloride and bromine (Kolditz and Feltz, 1957). Kolditz (1956) has used arsenic(III) chloride as solvent in the conversion of the ionic tetrachlorophosphonium(V) hexafluorophosphate(V) to a mixture of the molecular tetrachlorofluorophosphorane and the ionic tetrachlorophosphonium(V) fluoride.

Tellurium(IV) chloride dissolves in arsenic(III) chloride to give a conducting solution which when titrated conductimetrically with a solution of tetramethylammonium chloride gives breaks at the $1:1$ and $1:2$ ratio. At the $1:1$ ratio a solid of composition $Me_4NCl.TeCl_4.AsCl_3$ can be isolated, which is reasonably formulated as $Me_4N^+AsCl_2^+TeCl_6^{2-}$, and at the $1:2$ ratio $(Me_4N)_2TeCl_6$, is obtained. The $1:1$ compound can be regarded as an "acid" salt in the arsenic(III) chloride solvent system (Gutmann, 1952a). By using a solution of phosphorus(V) chloride (Gutmann, 1953) a more complex conductimetric titration curve is obtained with breaks at $2TeCl_4:1PCl_5$, $1TeCl_4:1PCl_5$ and $1TeCl_4:2PCl_5$ and with the separation of the corresponding solids in the form of solvates. Using the idea of the solvo-acid as a basis, Gutmann has suggested that the first of these breaks corresponds to the presence in the solution of $PCl_4^+(AsCl_2^+)_3(TeCl_6^{2-})_2$ formed by reaction of two moles of the solvoacid $(AsCl_2^+)_2TeCl_6^{2-}$ with one mole of the solvo-base $PCl_4^+AsCl_4^-$. The solid $PCl_5.2TeCl_4.3AsCl_3$ very readily loses solvent to give $2TeCl_4.PCl_5$, a known compound (Metzner, 1898). The $1:1$ compound is given the formulation $PCl_4^+AsCl_2^+TeCl_6^{2-}$ which loses solvent to give the compound $PCl_5.TeCl_4$ (Groeneveld, 1953). With tin(IV) chloride, yet another conductimetric titration curve is obtained with the precipitation of the solids of composition $TeCl_4.2SnCl_4$, $TeCl_4.SnCl_4$ and $2TeCl_4.SnCl_4$. In this case the evidence can be explained if the titrations involve the tellurium(IV) chloride as a solvo-base and the tin(IV) chloride as a solvo-acid thus:

$$(AsCl_2^+)_2SnCl_6^{2-} + TeCl_3^+AsCl_4^- \rightleftharpoons TeCl_3^+AsCl_2^+SnCl_6^{2-} + 2AsCl_3. \tag{5}$$

Titration of antimony(V) chloride with tellurium(IV) chloride gives a break at the $1:1$ and $1:2$ ratio with the precipitation of two solids. In this case also the tellurium(IV) chloride appears to function as solvo-base, giving rise to $TeCl_4.SbCl_5$ or $TeCl_3^+SbCl_6^-$ and $2TeCl_4.SbCl_5.AsCl_3$ or $(TeCl_3^+)_2AsCl_4^-SbCl_6^-$.

Yet another group of compounds, the alkoxychlorostibanes (Kolditz and Engels, 1959), $(RO)_nCl_{5-n}Sb$, dissolve in arsenic(III) chloride to give conducting solutions. With $SbCl_4OEt$ there is an initial equilibrium established involving the ions $SbCl_3(OEt)^+$ and $SbCl_5(OEt)^-$, however a slow reaction with the solvent then occurs to give antimony(V) chloride and $As(OEt)_3$ accompanied by corresponding changes in the conductance. The other members of this group of compounds behave likewise.

Since arsenic(III) chloride is a solvent favouring the formation of chloroanions and chlorocations, it suggests itself as a source of either arsenic(V) chloride, or tetrachloroarsonium(V) hexachloroarsenate(V). Attempts to prepare these compounds have been unsuccessful (George, 1960; Payne, 1961). However, reaction of solutions of phosphorus(V) chloride or antimony(V) chloride with chlorine in arsenic(III) chloride leads to the compounds $PCl_5.AsCl_5$ and $SbCl_5AsCl_2$, both of which appear to contain the $AsCl_4^+$ cation (Gutmann, 1951a,b). The investigation has been extended to an examination of the reaction of various metal halides with arsenic(III) chloride and chlorine, whereby a number of tetrachloroarsonium(V) complexes are produced, for example, $AsCl_4^+AlCl_4^-$ (Kolditz and Schmidt, 1958).

The behaviour of pyridine dissolved in arsenic(III) chloride has been the subject of several investigations since the original observation of Walden that the solution was a conductor (Walden, 1903). Two solvates of compositions Py_2AsCl_3 (Shirey, 1930; Montigie, 1935) and $PyAsCl_3$ (Dafert and Melinski, 1926; Gibson *et al.*, 1930) have been isolated. Pyridine is a medium strong electrolyte (Gutmann, 1954a) functioning thus:

$$C_5H_5N + 2AsCl_3 \rightleftharpoons C_5H_5NAsCl_2^+ + AsCl_4^-. \tag{6}$$

Removal of the solvent at room temperature leaves a solid of composition varying [from $C_5H_5N.1\cdot6AsCl_3$ to $C_5H_5N.1\cdot8AsCl_3$. By raising the temperature to 50° loss of arsenic(III) chloride occurs to leave $C_5H_5N.AsCl_3$.

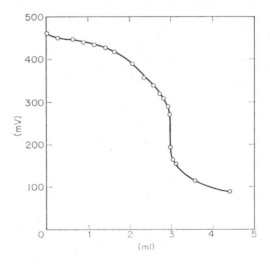

Fig. 3. Potentiometric titration curve for antimony(V) chloride against tetramethyl-ammonium chloride. End point 3·01 ml, calculated on 1 : 1 ratio, 2·96 ml. Reproduced with permission from *Acta chem. Scand.* (1955) **9,** 82.

Solutions of pyridine can be employed in titrations against tin(IV) and vanadium(IV) chlorides when breaks in the conductance at the 1 : 2 ratio are observed and solids containing the $C_5H_5NAsCl_2^+$ cation and the hexa-chlorostannate(IV) or hexachlorovanadate(IV) are obtained.

The physico-chemical study of arsenic(III) chloride as a solvent has, so far, been limited to a confirmation that the molar conductance of solutions of tetramethylammonium iodide, up to a concentration of $10^{-3}M$, follows the Debye-Hückel-Onsager equation. Potentiometric measurements in arsenic(III) chloride using a silver–silver chloride electrode (Andersson and Lindquist, 1955) have been confined to titrations. The titration of tetramethylammonium chloride with antimony(V) chloride shown in Fig. 3 shows that the electrode is behaving as a pCl electrode for the reaction $SbCl_5 + Cl^- \rightarrow SbCl_6^-$. By assuming that the liquid junction potential can be neglected and that both tetramethylammonium and antimony(V) chlorides are strong electrolytes in arsenic trichloride it can be shown that

$$\tfrac{1}{2}pk = \frac{460 - 215}{60} - \log_{10}[SbCl_5]$$

where k is the ionic product. Whence $pk > 15$ and the ionic product $[AsCl_2^+][AsCl_4^-]$ must be less than 10^{-15}. There are difficulties at present in the way of a more thorough examination of the potentiometric data because of the unknown liquid junction potentials and the uncertainties of activity coefficients in solvents of low dielectric constant. There is, further, a general lack of information on the degree of dissociation of electrolytes in arsenic(III) chloride.

The examination of solutions of arsenic(III) chloride has thus, so far, been confined largely to conductimetry and preparative studies. The evidence for the existence of the tetrachloroarsenate(III) ion in solution is wholly indirect. Such salts as have been isolated lose arsenic(III) chloride with varying ease. Even with the most stable, tetramethylammonium, this occurs at 160°. The $AsCl_4^-$ ion would be expected, on the basis of the distribution of the five electron pairs around a central arsenic atom, to consist of a trigonal bipyramid with one of the positions occupied by a non-bonded electron pair, with a corresponding distortion of the regularity of the structure. The high transport number (0·88–0·97) (Gutmann, 1956) for chloride ion in a solution of tetramethylammonium chloride in arsenic(III) chloride requires for its explanation, the ready transfer of chloride ion from $AsCl_4^-$ to $AsCl_3$, thereby showing the inherent instability of the tetrachloroarsenate(III) ion in these solutions (Lindquist, 1955). The evidence supporting the existence of the $AsCl_2^+$ ion in arsenic(III) chloride solutions is based solely on the interpretation of the changes in conductivity at certain mole ratios in the course of titrations. However, in the absence of alternative explanations, it appears essential to any description of these solutions.

In the case of arsenic(III) fluoride, its physical properties (m.p. $-6°$, b.p. 63°) and its reactivity make it less attractive than the chloride as a solvent. The specific conductivity of $2·4 \times 10^{-5}$ ohm^{-1} cm^{-1} at 25°, is of the same order as bromine trifluoride, iodine pentafluoride, and hydrogen fluoride (Woolf and Greenwood, 1950). Woolf and Greenwood point out that the ease of complex formation of a non-metal fluoride and an alkali-metal fluoride in a suitable solvent is related to the conductivity of the pure anion forming fluoride. Arsenic(III) fluoride has an appreciably higher conductivity than, for example antimony(V) fluoride ($\kappa = 1·2 \times 10^{-8}$ ohm^{-1} cm^{-1}), and it reacts readily with for example potassium fluoride to give $KAsF_4$, whereas antimony(V) fluoride does not (Woolf and Greenwood, 1950). The conductivity of arsenic(III) fluoride is increased markedly by dissolution of, for example, potassium fluoride or antimony(V) fluoride. From the latter solution a solid of composition $AsF_3.SbF_5$, can be isolated, whilst the titration of potassium fluoride and antimony(V) fluoride solutions gives rise to solid $KSbF_6$. It is also suggested, but not confirmed, that the compound $AsF_3.BF_3$ is formed when boron(III) fluoride is passed into a solution of potassium tetrachloroarsenate(III) in arsenic(III) fluoride (Woolf and Greenwood, 1950). Early experiments involving the reaction of arsenic(III) fluoride with halogen were inconclusive. However, Kolditz (1955) has shown that chlorine passed into this solvent at $0°$ gives a white crystalline substance, shown by conductivity and other studies to be $AsCl_4^+AsF_6^-$. It is somewhat soluble in arsenic(III) chloride and very soluble in arsenic(III) fluoride. Further examination of this reaction in arsenic(III) fluoride solution has shown that it does not proceed under strictly anhydrous conditions, traces of water being essential to ensure a smooth reaction (Dess et $al.$, 1956). Similar restrictions appear to apply to the reaction of bromine and iodine but no AsB_4^+ or AsI_4^+ compounds were isolated (Dess and Parry, 1956). Arsenic(III) fluoride, in part because of its solvent properties and its boiling point, is a good flourinating agent for non-metal chlorides, the reactions, however, rarely go to completion. For example, antimony(V) chloride is converted to tetrachlorostibonium(V) fluoride (Kolditz, 1957b) by the reaction

$$3SbCl_5 + AsF_3 \rightleftharpoons 3SbCl_4^+F^- + AsCl_3. \tag{7}$$

The existence of solid tetrafluoroarsenate(III) salts of K^+, Rb^+ and Cs^+ and the isolation of the compound $AsF_3.SbF_5$ has led to a suggested self-ionization for arsenic(III) fluoride akin to that for the chloride (Gutmann and Baaz, 1959b). The AsF_2^+ cation might be stabilized in solution by a bridged structure involving solvent molecules. The tetrafluoroarsenate(III) cation would be iso-electronic with selenium(IV) fluoride, which has a distorted trigonal bi-pyrimidal structure. Studies employing nuclear magnetic resonance (Muetterties and Phillips, 1957b) techniques have shown that although the tetrafluoroarsenate(III) ion is present in the solid, it does not appear to be a major component of arsenic(III) fluoride solutions of fluorides, since the fluoride undergoes very rapid exchange. Mixtures of boron(III) fluoride and arsenic(III) fluoride, whilst exhibiting a slightly enhanced conductivity did not show resonances other than those arising from the original compounds; the possibility of an unstable compound $AsF_2^+BF_4^-$ mentioned earlier, must on this evidence be suspect. The F^{19} spectrum of an arsenic(III), antimony(V) fluoride mixture showed only one concentration-dependent resonance peak, in a position between the resonances of the pure compounds. It would be expected that any compound between these fluorides would have non-equivalent fluorine atoms and would result in at least two, if not more, peaks in the fluorine spectrum. Probably very rapid exchange occurs through a bridge type structure of the form:

Similar bridged structures have been involved in consideration of the fluoride exchange in halogen fluorides (Muetterties and Phillips, 1957a).

The solvent properties of molten arsenic(III) bromide, first investigated by Walden (1902), have recently been re-investigated by Jander and his co-worker (Jander and Günther, 1958, 1959a,b). The alkali, alkaline earth and transition metal(II) bromides, the salts of oxyacids and the oxides, are not obviously soluble. Certain bromides such as mercury(II), indium(III), tellurium(IV), and bismuth(III) (Rettgers, 1893; Pusin and Makuc, 1938) are moderately soluble, as are arsenic(III) oxide and sulphide, merury(II) and iron(III) chlorides. The quaternary ammonium, boron(III), aluminium(III) (Isbekow and Plotnikow, 1911; Kendall $et\ al.$, 1923; Pusin and Makuc, 1938), gallium(III), tin(IV), titanium(IV), phosphorus(III) and (V), antimony(III) (Pusin and Löwy, 1926), and selenium(IV) bromides are all very readily soluble. A wide range of organic compounds including hydrocarbons, alcohols, jetones, esters and amines are also freely soluble.

In the case of the quaternary bromides and the organic bases, $\overline{\text{B}}$, solvates of the general form $R_4NBr.AsBr_3$ and $B.HBr.AsBr_3$ are common. Conductance measurements suggest that these solvates are more correctly regarded as salts of the tetrabromoarsenate(III) anion. Cryoscopic measurements have shown that in the case of the adducts between free base and arsenic(III) bromide the equilibrium

$$2R_3N + 2AsBr_3 \rightleftharpoons 2R_3N.AsBr_2^+ + 2Br^- \tag{8}$$

is present, although the results are not completely explicable unless associated species such as $(R_3N.AsBr_3)_2$ are also considered. Electrolytic dissociation increases with dilution as for weak electrolytes.

The addition of silver perchlorate to arsenic(III) bromide at 80° leads to decomposition and the evolution of bromine. At 50°, however, the reaction proceeds thus:

$$AsBr_3 + AgClO_4 \rightleftharpoons AsBr_2^+ClO_4^- + AgBr. \tag{9}$$

It is not possible to isolate the compound $AsBr_2^+ClO_4^-$ as such, but the solution is a good conductor and can be employed in conductimetric titrations. By analogy with the other halide solvo-systems a self-ionization process

$$2AsBr_3 \rightleftharpoons AsBr_2^+ + AsBr_4^- \tag{10}$$

is put forward to account for the specific conductivity of the pure solvent of $1 \cdot 6 \times 10^{-7}$ ohm^{-1} cm^{-1} at 35°. Most of solutes examined and the reactions studied can be interpreted in terms of the solvent-system of acids and bases

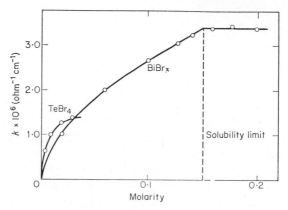

FIG. 4. Specific conductivity of tellurium(IV) and bismuth(III) bromide in arsenic(III) bromide solution at 93°. Reproduced with permission from *Z. anorg. Chem.* (1958) **297,** 100.

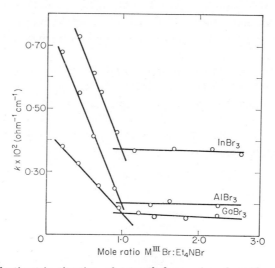

FIG. 5. Conductimetric titration of tetraethylammonium bromide with indium(III), aluminium(III) and gallium(III) bromide in arsenic(III) bromide solution at 93°. Reproduced with permission from *Z. anorg. Chem.* (1959) **298,** 243.

involving the AsBr$_2^+$ and AsBr$_4^-$ ions. The bromides of aluminium(III), gallium(III), indium(III), boron(III), tin(IV), mercury(II), bismuth(III) and tellurium(IV) appear as potential electrolytes with acid properties through their capacity to form complex bromo anions. This capacity is shown by the marked conductivity of their solutions, see, for example, the conductivity of bismuth(III) and tellurium(IV) bromide shown in Fig. 4. Conductimetric titrations between tetraethylammonium bromide and various anion-forming metal bromides are shown in Fig. 5. In the case of aluminium(III) bromide, the equation representing the reaction is

$$Et_4N^+ + Br^- + AsBr_2^+ + AlBr_4^- \rightleftharpoons Et_4N^+ + AlBr_4^- + AsBr_3. \tag{11}$$

This reaction can be followed potentiometrically using a gold indicator electrode, in which case a slow change in potential occurs until just after the 1 : 1 composition is reached and thereafter it remains constant. A variety of salts such as $KAlBr_4$, $CuAlBr_4$, $TlAlBr_4$ can be isolated as a result of "neutralization" reactions of this type. Similar results are obtainable with the other bromides listed above, however, in certain instances such as Pb(II) amphoteric properties emerge. This particular solvent offers a good method for the preparation of a wide range of complex bromides, which are otherwise difficult of access. Using simple metal oxides this solvent can conveniently be applied to the preparation of anhydrous bromides. Arsenic(III) oxide, sulphide and selenide dissolve to give oxy-, thio-, and selenobromides, thus:

$$AsBr_3 + As_2O_3 \rightleftharpoons 3AsOBr. \tag{12}$$

The arsenic(III) bromide system, like the corresponding chloride and fluoride systems, requires more detailed investigation before the correctness of the interpretation of the conductimetric titrations can be regarded as proved. No substantial evidence exists, apart from the conductimetric titration data, for the AsX_2^+ cation which has been postulated as being present in all these arsenic(III) halide solvents. Further investigations are clearly needed here.

Antimony(III) chloride (m.p. 73°, b.p. 219°–223°) was the first solvent of this group to be investigated. The pioneer work of Tolloczko on the cryoscopic properties (Tolloczko, 1901; Frycz and Tolloczko, 1912, 1913), was followed by the classical investigations of Walden (1900), Beckmann (1906) and Klemensiewicz (Klemensiewicz, 1908, 1924; Klemensiewicz and Balowna, 1930, 1931; Klemensiewicz and Zebrowska, 1934). Numerous investigators (Gmelin, 1949) have reported the general features of antimony(III) chloride as a solvent for inorganic and organic substances. In marked contrast to the other halide solvents already referred to, the potassium, rubidium, caesium, ammonium and thallium(I) chlorides, as well as the quaternary ammonium chlorides are easily soluble, at least after heating with the solvent for a short time. Mercury(II) chloride, bromide and iodide, as well as potassium fluoride and potassium bromide, are also readily soluble. Lithium, sodium, tin(II), bismuth(III) and iron(III) chlorides are only slightly soluble. The oxides and salts of a wide range of oxyacids examined were, with the exception of tetramethylammonium sulphate and perchlorate, either insoluble or dissolved with decomposition

(Jander and Swart, 1959a). A large number of addition compounds, mainly with the 1 : 1 ratio, has been reported to be formed with hydrocarbons, and with organic halogen, oxygen and sulphur-containing compounds (Gmelin, 1949). The solubility of proteins and components of nucleic acids in antimony(III) chloride is useful in studies of their NH and OH infra-red absorptions (Lacher *et al.*, 1949). With inorganic compounds the most numerous examples of addition compounds are the double and complex salts of formulae M^ISbCl_4, $M_2^ISbCl_5$, $M^ISb_2Cl_7$ and $M_3^ISb_2Cl_9$(M^I = Li, Na, K, NH_4, Rb or Cs), $M^{II}(SbCl_4)_2$ and $M^{II}SbCl_5$ (M^{II} = Be, Mg, Ca, Sr or Ba). A wide variety of other inorganic addition compounds has been reported, but their compositions do not appear to be readily rationalized in terms of particular ionic species so that no further mention will be made of them here. The conductivity of antimony(III) chloride (0.85×10^{-6} ohm^{-1} cm^{-1} at 95°) can be interpreted by postulating a self-ionization process, in which chloride is transferred to form a chloroanion:

$$2SbCl_3 \rightleftharpoons SbCl_2^+ + SbCl_4^-. \tag{13}$$

Additions of alkali-metal or quaternary ammonium chlorides lead to a considerable increase in conductivity. The physico-chemical study of these electrolyte solutions will be referred to later.

Application of the methods of conductimetric titration applied in the other halide systems has yielded similar results, incidentally thereby confirming in some measure the interpretations which have been made of the ionization processes, which appear to be generally applicable to the halides. For example, silver perchlorate reacts to give a precipitate of silver chloride and a solution thought to contain $SbCl_2^+ClO_4^-$. Similarly, aluminium(III), antimony(V) and tellurium(IV) chlorides lead to solutions of high conductance, presumed to contain the appropriate chloroanion, e.g.

$$AlCl_3 + SbCl_3 \rightleftharpoons SbCl_2^+ + AlCl_4^-. \tag{14}$$

Cryoscopic measurements support the formulation of triphenylmethylchloride as a strong electrolyte, giving rise to two ions in solution. Similarly, support is available, from the value of the van't Hoff factor, for accepting other alkali metal and quaternary ammonium chlorides as strong electrolytes, although in these cases there is a much greater concentration dependence of the results. In the case of tellurium(IV) and selenium(IV) chlorides, the van't Hoff factor lies between 0·5 and 1·0. In no case does it fit in with the simple chloride ion transfer, which would, if transfer and dissociation were complete, require a van't Hoff factor of 3; instead it would appear necessary to involve the idea of considerable association, or to admit the possibility of other complex reactions with the solvent antimony(III) chloride resulting in species containing more than one selenium or tellurium per ion or molecule. As well as the more obvious "neutralization" reactions involving tetramethylammonium chloride (presumed to be $Me_4N^+SbCl_4^-$ as the base analogue) titrated with $SbCl_2^+ClO_4^-$ (as the acid analogue), antimony(III) sulphate can be titrated (Jander and Swart, 1959b), the resulting conductimetric titration curve shows breaks at the 6 : 1 ratio, which appear to correspond to:

$$6Me_4N^+SbCl_4^- + Sb_2(SO_4)_3 \rightleftharpoons 3(Me_4N^+)_2SO_4^{2-} + 8SbCl_3 \tag{15}$$

and a break at 6 : 4 corresponding to the next stage:

$$3(Me_4N^+)_2SO_4^{2-} + 3Sb_2(SO_4)_3 \rightleftharpoons 6Me_4N^+Sb(SO_4)_2^- \tag{16}$$

giving an overall reaction:

$$4Sb_2(SO_4)_3 + 6Me_4N^+SbCl_4^- \rightleftharpoons 6Me_4N^+Sb(SO_4)_2^- + 8SbCl_3. \tag{17}$$

Compounds containing this $Sb(SO_4)_2^-$ anion have been recognized elsewhere (Metzl, 1906). Similar complex ions might be expected with the perchlorate ion, however, careful examination of the titration curve obtained in the titration with tetramethylammonium chloride shows only one break corresponding solely to the formal acid–base reaction. Conductimetric and potentiometric (using a gold reference electrode) titrations have established fully the similarities between this system and the arsenic(III) chloride system as far as compounds leading to chloroanions are concerned. A number of solvolytic reactions have been established (Jander and Swart, 1959c), for example potassium bromide and iodide are readily soluble in antimony(III) chloride, the product, in both cases, being $2KCl.SbCl_3$. Potassium fluoride however leads to $KF.2SbCl_3$. Oxides, sulphides, carbonates and acetates are all converted to the corresponding metal halide:

$$3M^{II}O + 2SbCl_3 \rightarrow 3M^{II}Cl_2 + Sb_2O_3. \tag{18}$$

Kolditz (1957a) has prepared from chloroform solution in the presence of excess antimony(III) chloride the adduct $2PCl_5.4SbCl_3$, closely similar to the arsenic(III) chloride adduct of phosphorus(V) chloride discussed earlier. Cryoscopic measurements in antimony(III) chloride and conductivity measurements in methyl cyanide show this compound to be

$$PCl_4^+PCl_6^-.4SbCl_3.$$

Recent work by Baughan has shown that an ionizing solvent such as antimony(III) halide is ideally suited for studying the interionic effects in solvents of lower dielectric constant than water (Porter and Baughan, 1958; Davies and Baughan, 1961; Baughan, et al., 1963). Cryoscopic measurements using a highly purified sample of the solvent, and fluorene, anthracene, benzophenone and dibenzyl as solutes, gave $k = 15.6 \pm 0.2$ (deg mole^{-1} kg.). The conductivity data measured at 99° of previous workers (Klemensiewicz, 1908, 1924; Klemensiewicz and Balowna, 1930, 1931; Klemensiewicz and Zebrowska, 1934) for thallium(I) chloride and bromide, potassium chloride and bromide, rubidium chloride and ammonium chloride and bromide gives linear Kohlrausch plots, which can be compared with the theoretical Debye-Hückel-Onsager slopes (Fig. 6). The interionic effects are

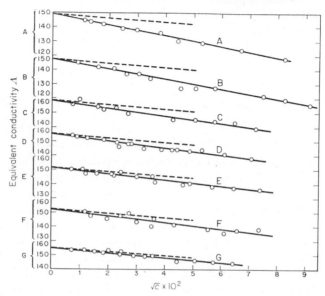

FIG. 6. Kohlrausch plots of the conductivity of halides in antimony(III) chloride measured at 99° (c is molarity). Reproduced with permission from *J. chem. Soc.* (1958) 745, Figure 1.

in keeping with a solvent of dielectric constant 30·4 (cf. methanol and ethanol). The fact that the limiting conductivities of the wide range of bromides and chlorides examined are so close (Λ_0TlCl = 149; TlBr = 148; KCl = 158; KBr = 156; NH_4Cl = 152; NH_4Br = 152; RbCl = 155) suggests that both chloride and bromide have abnormally high mobilities, which is confirmed by the experimentally determined value of about 0·9 obtained for chloride ion (Frycz and Tolloczko, 1912, 1913). This high transport number, also observed with arsenic(III) chloride, implies a favourable rate for the chloride transfer reaction:

$$SbCl_3 + SbCl_4^- \rightarrow SbCl_4^- + SbCl_3. \qquad (19)$$

Antimony(III) chloride is a much better solvent than arsenic(III) chloride for the alkali halides. Examination of the cryoscopic data in terms of the van't Hoff factors for a number of 1 : 1 electrolytes shows that the i-factors tend to the limiting value of 2 at infinite dilution. The non-ideality of the electrolyte solutions, derived from freezing point data and expressed as the molal osmotic coefficient ϕ, is given by $\phi = 1 - 1\cdot86m_2^{\frac{1}{2}}\sigma(0\cdot768\,\overset{\circ}{a}\,m_2^{\frac{1}{2}}) + bm_2$, where m_2 is the molality of the solute, $\overset{\circ}{a}$ is the distance of closest approach of anion and cation in Angstrom units and b is a constant added to correct for ion solvation. From experimental results with antimony(III) chloride as solvent, it is possible to obtain values for $\mathring{a}$ and to compare these with values calculated from interatomic distances assuming that the conducting anionic species in solution is $SbCl_4^-$, i.e.

	$\mathring{a}$ Theoretical	$\mathring{a}$ Experimental
KCl	5·5	2·1
CsCl	5·9	4·5
Me$_4$NCl	7·7	13·0

The experimental data for potassium and caesium chloride includes effects of association. Since the Bjerrum critical distance for a uni-univalent electrolyte at the melting point of antimony(III) chloride is 7·3 Å, ion pair formation would, in fact, be expected. For tetramethylammonium chloride, which is a strong electrolyte, the observed distances of closest approach exceeds both the critical distance and also the theoretical values, which suggests the presence of, at least, one complete solvation shell around the Me_4N^+ cation. The conductivities of various organic chlorides (Davies and Baughan, 1961) in antimony(III) chloride measured at 75° have shown that these compounds ionize principally by formation of the R_2Cl^+ ion, thus:

$$2RCl \rightleftharpoons R_2Cl^+ + Cl^-. \tag{20}$$

In more dilute solution the more normal process of ionization $RCl \rightleftharpoons R^+ + Cl^-$ occurs. Solutions of aromatic hydrocarbons in antimony(III) chloride are highly coloured and give well resolved electron spin resonance spectra (Baughan et al., 1963). Comparison with the corresponding spectra of solutions of perylene in 98% sulphuric acid, which have been shown to contain a carbonium ion, demonstrates the presence of a positive ion in these solutions. In the case of naphthalene the positive ion differs from that in sulphuric acid in that additional lines appear in the e.s.r. spectrum. The oxidation of hydrocarbons is thus conveniently carried out in antimony(III) chloride solution; the preliminary work which has so far appeared makes it seem likely that this will prove an exceptionally useful general method for the preparation of hydrocarbon cations.

As a result of the availability of precision measurements of the conductivity of triphenylmethyl chloride and tetramethylammonium chloride a more dependable description of this system is available than of any other. Baughan has pointed out that for a number of non-protonic solvents the Walden product $\lambda_0\eta$ of NMe_4^+ is around 0·3, which would correspond to a mobility for the NMe_4^+ ion of about 13 in antimony(III) chloride, giving a transport number for the chloride ion of 0.87. The conductimetric-titration for potassium chloride or triphenylmethyl chloride in antimony(III) chloride solution against antimony(V) chloride shows it to follow a curve typical of a strong acid-strong base in water. The reaction is

$$SbCl_4^- + SbCl_5 \rightleftharpoons SbCl_3 + SbCl_6^- \tag{21}$$

in which the $SbCl_4^-$ ion is abnormally mobile and the $SbCl_6^-$ ion is not (Jander and Swart, 1959a,b,c). If, in fact, hexachloroantimonate(V) and potassium or triphenylmethyl ions are about equal in mobility, the shape of this curve would imply a high transport number (0.86) for the chloride ion. The evidence for the high mobility of the chloride ion is thus very strong, the mechanism of this conduction is, however, not so well established, although it is convenient to assume that the essential, albeit, perhaps transient species is the tetrachloroantimonate(III) ion. Davies and Baughan (1961) in an attempt to correct the conductivity data for the effects of solvent conductivity have found that their observed specific conductivity for the pure solvent of 4–6×10^{-6} ohm^{-1} cm^{-1} at $75°$ was apparently too great. The self-ionization, which is strongly dependent on pretreatment, appears due principally to impurities (a volatile arsenic(III) chloride or an ammonium salt is suggested) which increase rapidly at $99°$, but more slowly at $75°$, and hence possibly arise from the glass. Nonetheless, results are at least partially in accord with the solvent ionization scheme:

$$2SbCl_3 \rightleftharpoons SbCl_2^+ + SbCl_4^-.$$

Antimony(III) chloride is thus a solvent in which simple carbonium ions can be obtained and studied in bulk, as well as being a convenient solvent for the physiochemical study of interionic attractions. However, little direct evidence as to exact species present in the solvent, in self ionization, or of complex chloroanions in solution has emerged. Specifically, antimony(III) chloride is a useful solvent for the observation of N—H, O—H and C—H fundamental vibrations in amino acids and proteins (Lacher et al., 1949, 1954).

Antimony(III) bromide has solvent properties for inorganic and organic compounds comparable with the chloride (Jander and Weiss, 1957). Bromides are appreciably more soluble, and from the solutions, compounds such as

$$M_3^I Sb_2 Br_9 \; (M^I = K, \; NH_4, \; Rb) \; \text{and} \; M^I SbBr_4 \; (M^I = Tl^I, \; Me_4 N)$$

are obtained. The specific conductivity of the pure solvent is 0.9–1.0×10^{-5} ohm^{-1} cm^{-1} at $100°$ (Jander and Weiss, 1959). As with antimony(III) chloride various conductivity measurements and conductimetric titrations have been employed in the study of the system. The viscosities, conductivities and densities of mixtures of antimony(III) bromide and aluminium bromide have shown the presence of a maximum in the conductivity curve at the

1 : 1 mole ratio, corresponding to a melt of the compound $SbBr_3.AlBr_3$, $SbBr_2^+AlBr_4^-$ (Gorenbein, 1945).

Antimony(III) iodide (m.p. $166.5 \pm 0.5°$) concentration cells employing antimony electrodes at $250°$ have been employed in a study of a lower iodide of antimony. The resulting oxidation–reduction system can be interpreted in terms of a two electron reduction of antimony(III) iodide. The current in the cell is carried by ions derived from the solvent, presumably SbI_2^+ and SbI_4^-. The conductivity of the molten iodide is considerably increased by the addition of potassium iodide corresponding to an increase in the number of tetraiodoantimonate(III) ions (Corbett and Albers, 1960).

Antimony(V) chloride has poor solvent properties for most inorganic halides. For example mercury(II) chloride dissolves only to the extent of 0.8% at $120°$. Antimony(III) chloride, exceptionally, dissolves to give a 20% solution at $40°$ (Ehrlich and Dietz, 1960). The dissolution of iodine(III) chloride in antimony(V) chloride leads to the formation of the compound $ISbCl_8$ (Vonk and Wiebenga, 1959).

Examination of molten bismuth(III) chloride shows that its most significant solvent property is its ability to dissolve metallic bismuth (Corbett, 1958a,b). The resulting subhalide species is the ion Bi_2^{2+} (Bredig, 1959; Keneshea and Cubicciotti, 1959; Bredig et al., 1960). Beer's Law is obeyed by solutions of bismuth metal in molten bismuth(III) chloride, only in dilute solutions (Boston and Smith, 1958). At high concentrations a change in the spectral profile accompanies the non-adherence to Beer's Law (Boston and Smith, 1962). The overall solvent behaviour is best represented by a family of solution equilibria of which the simplest is $4Bi^+ \rightleftharpoons Bi_4^{4+}$, but which involves others such as $4Bi^+ + 4Bi^{3+} \rightleftharpoons Bi_8^{16+}$ (Boston et al., 1963).

IV. OXYHALIDES AS SOLVENTS

In view of the bond polarities in the molecules, and the stability of the oxyanions, the oxyhalides suggest themselves as a group of compounds likely to possess useful solvent properties. The oxyhalides differ from the halides in that they can act as oxygen, as well as halogen, donors. They are, in fact, appreciably better halide ion donors than the halides. Although the number of oxyhalides of nitrogen, phosphorus, arsenic, antimony and bismuth is large, only a few have liquid ranges suitable for solvent work. The mixed halides such as $POFCl_2$ and POF_2Cl are not available in quantity and have not been studied. In any case in mixed halides of Group V, re-organization reactions (Schwarzmann and van Wazer, 1959) can occur so that studies in mixed oxyhalide might prove difficult. The general chemistry of the oxyhalides of nitrogen has been examined in detail (George, 1960). However, only nitrosyl chloride has so far been considered as a solvent, no doubt largely because of its ready availability, since there is no reason to think that similar properties will not be found in the other nitrosyl halides and the nitryl and other halides. The oxyhalides of arsenic, antimony and bismuth are more complex, and are solids possessing three dimensional structures, for example antimony oxychloride SbOCl has an infinite sheet of composition $(Sb_6O_6Cl_4)^{2+}$ held together by chloride ions.

Two oxyhalides, nitrosyl chloride (ClNO) and phosphoryl chloride ($POCl_3$), are particularly well suited for use as solvents because of their accessibility and physical properties (Table II). The chemical and physical properties of nitrosyl chloride are the outcome of a polar molecule with two strongly electronegative atoms (Beckham et al., 1951). The nitrogen to chlorine bond length of 1·95 Å is abnormally long (Gerding et al., 1960). Liquid nitrosyl chloride ($\epsilon = 19·7$ at $-10°$ and 22·5 at $-27°$) has notable solvent properties for nitrosonium salts, due to the solvation of the NO^+ ion (Burg and Campbell, 1948; Burg and McKenzie, 1952). The solvated ion arises from the possibility of a stable adduct involving a chlorine bridge, $(O—N—Cl—N—O)^+$, in which the stability is attributed to resonance between structures.

$$[:\ddot{O}{=}N{—}\ddot{Cl}{—}N{=}\ddot{O}:]^+, \quad [:\ddot{O}{=}N{—}\ddot{Cl}:]\!\cdot\!\overset{+}{N}{\equiv}O:, \quad \text{and} \quad :O{\equiv}\overset{+}{N}\!\cdot\![:\ddot{Cl}{—}N{=}\ddot{O}:].$$

As would be expected, simple cations, such as those of the alkali metals, are not solvated in this way and the solubility of alkali halides are hence much lower than salts of the nitrosonium cation. Compounds such as $NOAlCl_4$, $NOFeCl_4$ and $NOSbCl_6$ are readily soluble and are strong electrolytes. However certain salts, namely, $(NO)_2SnCl_6$, $(NO)_2TiCl_6$ and $NO^+HSO_4^-$ are not soluble.

A number of solids have been isolated in which nitrosyl chloride is combined with a metal or non-metal chloride, usually one known to form chloroanions readily; these compounds can be obtained by dissolving the chloride, or sometimes even the metal, in nitrosyl chloride. In other cases it is necessary to employ a solvent for the reaction, and a variety of solvents including the anhydrous hydrogen halides have been employed (Waddington and Klanberg, 1960a). These solids are either $1 : 1$ $MCl_n.NOCl$, as for example with:

$BiCl_3$	(Partington and Whynes, 1948, 1949)
	(Hewitt and Holliday, 1953)
	(Olah and Tolgyesi, 1961)
BF_3	(Waddington and Klanberg, 1960a)
	(Olah and Tolgyesi, 1961)
$AlCl_3$	(Gerding and Houtgraaf, 1953)
	(Burg and Campbell, 1948)
$GaCl_3$	(Partington and Whynes, 1948, 1949)
$InCl_3$	(Partington and Whynes, 1948, 1949)

$TlCl_3$	(Partington and Whynes, 1948, 1949)
$AsCl_3$	(Waddington and Klanberg, 1960a)
	(Lewis and Sowerby, 1957b)
$SbCl_3$	(Waddington and Klanberg, 1960a)
$SbCl_5$	(Burg and Campbell, 1948)
	(Seel, 1943)
	(Seel and Bauer, 1947)
	(Rheinbolt and Wasserfuhr, 1927)
SbF_5	(Waddington and Klanberg, 1960a)
$BiCl_3$	(Rheinbolt and Wasserfuhr, 1927)
	(Sudborough, 1891)
	(van Heteren, 1899)
UO_2Cl_2	(Addison and Hodge, 1961)
$MnCl_2$	(Partington and Whynes, 1948, 1949)
	(Asmussen, 1939)
$FeCl_3$	(Burg and McKenzie, 1952)
	(Rheinbolt and Wasserfuhr, 1927)
	(van Heteren, 1899)
$CuCl$	(Burg and McKenzie, 1952)
	(Sudborough, 1891)
	(Asmussen, 1939)
$AuCl_3$	(Partington and Whynes, 1948, 1949)
	(Sudborough, 1891)
$ZnCl_2$	(Partington and Whynes, 1948, 1949)
	(Sudborough, 1891)
	(Asmussen, 1939)
$HgCl_2$	(Partington and Whynes, 1948, 1949)
	(Rheinbolt and Wasserfuhr, 1927)

or they are 2 : 1, $MCl_n.2NOCl$, as for example with:

$AlCl_3$	(Burg and McKenzie, 1952)
$FeCl_3$	(Burg and McKenzie, 1952)
$ZrCl_4$	(Perrot and Devin, 1958)
	(Gutmann and Himml, 1956)
$ThCl_4$	(Perrot and Devin, 1958)
$PdCl_2$	(Partington and Whynes, 1948, 1949)
$PtCl_2$	(Partington and Whynes, 1948, 1949)
	(Asmussen, 1939)
$SnCl_4$	(Burg and Campbell, 1948)
	(Partington and Whynes, 1948, 1949)
	(Asmussen, 1939)
$PbCl_4$	(Rheinbolt and Wasserfuhr, 1927)
	(Asmussen, 1939).

These adducts can be regarded, in most instances, as chloro-anion salts of the nitrosonium ion, $NO^+MCl^-_{n+1}$ and $(NO^+)_2MCl^{2-}_{n+2}$. The nitrosonium ion, is well established in salts such as $NO^+ClO^-_4$ and $NO^+HSO^-_4$ and the formulation of the adducts of nitrosyl chloride with various chlorides as ionic compounds is in no doubt. The adduct $NOCl.AlCl_3$ shows Raman lines corresponding to the NO^+ and $AlCl^-_4$ ions. The force constant for the NO group, however, suggests that the bonding is not completely ionic in character (Gerding and Houtgraaf, 1953). Transfer of the chloride to the aluminium may not be complete so that the compound might be best regarded as $AlCl_3 \ldots Cl.NO$, rather than $NO^+AlCl^-_4$; however, it is also possible to formulate the solid in such a way that an oxygen bridge between Al and N could occur, e.g.

$$
\begin{array}{c}
Cl \\
| \\
Cl—Al—O—N—Cl \\
| \\
Cl
\end{array}
$$

The interpretation of the conductivity of nitrosonium hexachloroantimonate(V) in liquid sulphur dioxide similarly requires the acceptance of a form other than that involving the simple ions (Seel, 1943; Seel and Bauer, 1947). Further detailed structural work on this and other complexes is required before the state of the solids can be known with certainty. The 1 : 2 compounds of aluminium and iron(III) chlorides involve an additional loosely bound molecule of nitrosyl chloride; their dissociation pressures at 0° of 180 mm and 224 mm are in keeping with this interpretation (Burg and McKenzie, 1952).

Solutions of the nitrosonium salts in nitrosyl chloride are good conductors, and typical data at $-20°C$ is

$$NO^+AlCl^-_4, \kappa = 1{\cdot}17 \times 10^{-2} \text{ ohm}^{-1} \text{ cm}^{-1} \text{ at } 0{\cdot}098 \text{ M};$$
$$NO^+FeCl^-_4, \kappa = 1{\cdot}34 \times 10^{-3} \text{ ohm}^{-1} \text{ cm}^{-1} \text{ at } 0{\cdot}0099 \text{ M};$$
$$NO^+SbCl^-_6, \kappa = 2{\cdot}35 \times 10^{-2} \text{ ohm}^{-1} \text{ cm}^{-1} \text{ at } 0{\cdot}140 \text{ M}.$$

The molar conductance of $NO^+FeCl^-_4$ at $-10°$ in nitrosyl chloride can be fitted to the Shedlovsky equation and a value of Λ_0 of 401·2 obtained; the data also leads to values for the degree of dissociation of the tetrachloroferrate(III) compound:

concentration (mole/l)	0·328	0·481	0·704	1·53	2·19	4·65	6·13
degree of dissociation	0·937	0·916	0·885	0·820	0·792	0·717	0·693

This interpretation of the results involves the application of the Debye-Hückel-Onsager theory to the nitrosyl chloride solvo-system, which appears justified. The high value of Λ_0 arises from the high transport number (0·88) of the NO^+ in the system. The high mobility of the nitrosonium ion, which has yet to be confirmed, must involve a chain mechanism for the conductance analogous to the transport of the H^+ ion in the water system (Burg and McKenzie, 1952). High mobilities have been observed for the chloride ion in antimony and arsenic(III) chlorides (Seel *et al.*, 1959), where a chain mechanism must also apply.

The application of the acid–base concept of Gutmann and Lindquist leads to the postulate of a solvent self-ionization equilibrium of the form $ClNO \rightleftharpoons NO^+$ (solvated) $+ Cl^-$ (solvated). Nitrosonium salts thus function as acids and chlorides as bases. The results of conductivity titrations support this as is shown by Fig. 7, in which tetramethylammonium chloride was

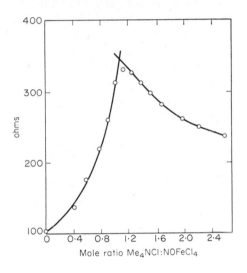

Fig. 7. Conductimetric titration of nitrosonium tetrachloroferrate(III) with tetramethylammonium chloride in nitrosyl chloride solution at $-10°$. Reproduced with permission from *J. Amer. chem. Soc.* (1952) **74**, 3147.

titrated with $NO^+FeCl_4^-$, the decrease in conductivity (increase in resistance) as the titration proceeded is due to the replacement of the highly mobile nitrosonium ion by the less mobile tetramethylammonium ion. Titrations of $NO^+BF_4^-$ and of $NO^+ClO_4^-$ with tetramethylammonium chloride showed a decrease of non-volatile chloride and a corresponding change in conductance, but the reactions were not complete due to solvolysis of the resulting salt. Nitrosonium salts of condensed phosphate anions can be conveniently prepared by dissolving silver salts in nitrosyl chloride:

$$4Ag_3PO_4 + 12ClNO \rightarrow (NO)_2P_4O_{11} + 5N_2O_3 + 12AgCl \qquad (23a)$$

$$3Ag_4P_2O_7 + 12ClNO \rightarrow (NO)_4P_6O_{17} + 4N_2O_3 + 12AgCl \qquad (23b)$$

$$Ag_3P_3O_9 + 3ClNO \rightarrow (NO)P_3O_8 + N_2O_3 + 3AgCl \qquad (23c)$$

$$Ag_4P_4O_{12} + 4ClNO \rightarrow (NO)_2P_4O_{11} + N_2O_3 + 4AgCl. \qquad (23d)$$

The reactions involve more than the replacement of the silver cation by the nitrosonium ion, the nitrosyl chloride bringing about additional P—O—P bond formation (Seel *et al.*, 1959).

The understanding of the chemistry of nitrosyl chloride solutions has been greatly helped by investigation of exchange using tracer studies. The rapid exchange of ^{36}Cl between nitrosyl chloride and aluminium, gallium, indium(III), thallium(III), iron(III) and antimony(V) chlorides confirms that these compounds exist in solution in the form of complexes, in which the chloride atoms are all equivalent and rapidly exchanged (Lewis and Sowerby, 1957a,b,c). The exchange between metal chlorides which are not significantly soluble, and nitrosyl chloride has also been followed using tracer methods (Lewis and Sowerby, 1956). Zinc, cadmium and mercury(II) chloride showed a rapid exchange between the chlorides and nitrosyl chloride presumed to involve the formation of 1 : 1 complexes. This was followed by a slower heterogenous exchange between the complexes and the solvent. No exchange was observed with chlorides, such as sodium or potassium, which do not form complexes nor with chlorides which form very stable complexes, for example $(NO^+)_2SnCl_6^{2-}$. Silver chloride was found to exchange with liquid nitrosyl chloride only in the presence of light; the exchange therefore probably proceeds through photochemical decomposition.

Nitrosyl fluoride (FNO), has been investigated only with respect to its reactions with metals, many of which it attacks with the formation of the corresponding nitrosonium fluoro-anion salts, for example tin gives $(NO^+)_2SnF_6^{2-}$ (Sokol'skii and Knunyants, 1960). Although no investigation of its solvent properties has yet been made, a large number of nitrosonium fluoro-anion salts have been prepared (Addison and Lewis, 1955).

Nitryl fluoride (NO_2F) and nitryl chloride both have boiling points too low for convenient investigation of their solvent properties. The number of complexes based on the nitronium ion, NO_2^+ is, however, very large (Hetherington and Robinson, 1957), especially with fluoro-anions. The physical properties (Table II) suggest that it is unlikely that an extensive solvo-system chemistry exists, as is found with nitrosyl chloride.

V. Phosphoryl Chloride

By far the most extensive investigation of the halides and oxyhalides of Group V elements as solvents has been undertaken with phosphoryl chloride, largely because of its ready availability, convenient liquid range, ease of purification and obvious solvent properties. The investigation of phosphoryl chloride has covered almost every approach to the problem of elucidating solute behaviour in a particular solvent system. However, whilst it is true to say that the general features of the system have thereby been elucidated, there is still need for a considerable amount of work to finally and convincingly demonstrate the exact nature of the ionic equilibria present in the solvent. Since it is clearly of importance in the evaluation of the work that follows, the question of the solvent purity will be considered first. The criterion of purity of the solvent used in the numerous investigations has been that of its specific conductivity. Early work by Walden (1903) employed a sample with a specific conductivity at 25° of $1 \cdot 7 \times 10^{-6}$ ohm^{-1} cm^{-1}, but the recent work by Gutmann (1952a) has employed a sample purified by repeated distillation in glass giving a highly purified product with a conductivity of $1 \cdot 55 \times 10^{-6}$ ohm^{-1} cm^{-1} at 20°. More recently the need for measurements of conductances of greater precision has led to the purification of the solvent still further, so that the conductivity was reduced to 2×10^{-8} ohm^{-1} cm^{-1} at 20° (Gutmann and Baaz, 1959c). The chief impurities in phosphoryl chloride are polyphosphoryl chlorides and hydrogen chloride, both formed by hydrolysis of phosphoryl chloride; they are removed by careful and repeated fractional distillation. The examination of solvent properties and the measurement of physical properties has to be conducted in special apparatus, usually all glass, designed to avoid, or to minimize, contact with moisture; such apparatus is somewhat restrictive in use and results and observations are never as easily obtainable as with aqueous systems. The conductivity of purified phosphoryl chloride requires in explanation the postulate of a self-ionization process. Walden's original proposal for this involved the formation of a series of cations by the loss of successive chloride ions, but no evidence was then available to substantiate the presence of any such species, and ions with charge beyond one unit are no longer considered to occur. In line with the self-ionization processes postulated, and to some degree substantiated for the halide solvents, phosphoryl chloride might behave thus:

$$POCl_3 + POCl_3 \rightarrow POCl_2^+ + POCl_4^-. \tag{24}$$

Gutmann (1959) has preferred to generalize this equation thus:

$$(POCl_3)_n + (POCl_3)_m \rightleftharpoons (POCl_3)_{n-1} POCl_2^+ + (POCl_3)_m Cl^- \tag{25}$$

in which the $POCl_2^+$ cation and chloride anion are both regarded as solvated. With a specific conductivity as low as 2×10^{-8} ohm^{-1} cm^{-1} the extent of this self-ionization is clearly very small, the ionic product is not greater than 9×10^{-14} (Gutmann and Baaz, 1959c). A potentiometric measurement has given the value 5×10^{-14} (20°) (Gutmann, 1959). Direct electrolysis of pure solvent is not feasible, but the electrolysis of a $0 \cdot 14$ M solution of triethylammonium chloride (Spandau et al., 1960) yields chlorine at the anode and a polymeric solid of composition PO at the cathode,

$$POCl_3 \rightleftharpoons POCl_2^+ + Cl^- \qquad (26a)$$

$$\text{Anode} \qquad Cl^- \rightarrow \tfrac{1}{2}Cl_2 + e \qquad (26b)$$

$$\text{Cathode} \qquad 3POCl_2^+ + 3e \rightarrow PO + 2POCl_3. \qquad (26c)$$

The ratio of chlorine to phosphorus monoxide was in the ratio $3:1$, as required by the electrode equations. It would appear from this that these ions were in fact the only ones involved in the discharge reactions at the electrode and thus provide strong evidence for a $POCl_2^+$ cation. However, an alternative explanation could be that the triethylammonium ion was discharged at the cathode and reacted with the solvent to give

$$Et_3NH^+ + e \rightarrow Et_3N + [H] \qquad (27a)$$

$$3[H] + POCl_3 \rightarrow PO + 3HCl. \qquad (27b)$$

Overall equation:

$$3Et_3NH^+ + 3e + POCl_3 \rightarrow PO + 3Et_3NH^+ + 3Cl^-. \qquad (27c)$$

Transport number measurements with a solution of tetramethyl-ammonium chloride give an average value of 0.8 for the chloride ion (Gutmann, 1959), closely similar to the values obtained with arsenic(III) and antimony(III) chlorides which are attributed to the occurrence of a chloride transference process. Such a transference in phosphoryl chloride would be in line with the self-ionization process discussed above.

The general features of phosphoryl chloride as a solvent (Gutmann, 1952b) are closely similar to the other halide and oxyhalide solvents already discussed. Thus solutes such as $SiCl_4$, $SiBr_4$, $SnBr_4$ (Oddo and Tealdi, 1903), dissolve readily without dissociation or association. $(CH_3)_4NCl$, $(C_2H_5)_4NCl$, PCl_5, PBr_5, $AsCl_3$, $BiCl_3$, $BiBr_3$, BiI_3, ICl_3, SCl_4 (Oddo and Tealdi, 1903), $PtCl_4$ (Oddo, 1905) are readily soluble but cryoscopic measurements show that they undergo dissociation. The compounds

$AlCl_3$	(Oddo and Tealdi, 1903)
BBr_3	(Oddo and Tealdi, 1903)
$SbCl_5$	(Köhler, 1880)
$SnCl_4$	(Casselmann, 1856)
$TeCl_4$	(Lenher, 1908)
$TiCl_4$	(Ruff and Ipsen, 1903)
BCl_3	(Gustavson, 1871)

all dissolve with evidence of compound formation, likewise $FeCl_3$, but the solubility here is lower. Numerous iodides and bromides are soluble but the colour change accompanying dissolution suggests that some reaction has occurred. Similarly salts of various oxyanions such as potassium dichromate and permanganate dissolve, but with an accompanying reaction. The alkali metal and ammonium chlorides are only slightly soluble. Data for the solubility and conductivities of some of these alkali metal salts is shown in Table

III. In general these salts are not sufficiently soluble to permit them to be used in work with phosphoryl chloride, and it is more convenient to use the quaternary ammonium chlorides instead. The chlorides of the alkaline earth metals, silver(I), mercury(I) and thallium(I) are also only very sparingly soluble.

TABLE III

Solubility and Specific Conductivity of Saturated Solutions of Alkali Metal Salts Measured at 20° and the Equivalent Conductance at a Dilution of $V = 1000$

Salt	Solubility (g/l)	Specific conductivity of saturated solution (ohm^{-1} cm^{-1})	Equivalent conductance at $V = 1000$ l/mole
LiCl	0·05	$6·6 \times 10^{-6}$	4·0
NaCl	0·31	$3·0 \times 10^{-5}$	6·4
KCl	~0·60	$3·4 \times 10^{-5}$	6·7
NH$_4$Cl	0·46	$3·6 \times 10^{-5}$	6·9
RbCl	0·87	$8·3 \times 10^{-5}$	14·6
CsCl	1·26	$1·1 \times 10^{-4}$	16·0
KF	~0·40	$2·6 \times 10^{-5}$	6·4
KBr	0·51	$4·3 \times 10^{-5}$	14·5
KI	~1·71	$1·2 \times 10^{-4}$	23·1
KCN	~0·73	$3·3 \times 10^{-5}$	7·2
KCNO	~0·80	$3·1 \times 10^{-5}$	9·0
KCNS	~0·76	$2·9 \times 10^{-5}$	6·6

The solubilities of quaternary ammonium salts are high (Baaz and Gutmann, 1959b) and the equivalent conductances follow closely values predicted by electrolyte theory. For example, data for the equivalent conductance of tetraethylammonium chloride measured from $1·4 \times 10^{-3}$ to $7·3 \times 10^{-5}$ M follows a linear relationship with $\sqrt{c}$ over much of the concentration range. The Debye-Hückel-Onsager equation can be successfully applied to this data (Gutmann and Baaz, 1959c) and similarly to that for other quaternary ammonium salts (Fig. 8 and Table IV). Walden's rule can be applied to give ionic mobilities for the Et$_4$N$^+$, Pr$_4$N$^+$, Cl$^-$, Br$^-$, I$^-$, and ClO$_4^-$ ions of 25·6, 18·9, 15·6, 27·4, 23·4, 22·7, and 27·8 respectively. These mobilities are confirmed by comparison with those in other solvents (particularly water). The calculated Stokes radii for the ions, derived from the ionic mobility data, supports the solvation of the chloride, bromide and iodide ions; the number of solvent molecules being from 0·5 to 2 per ion. The Stokes radii are confirmed by a consideration of the Bjerrum parameters, obtainable from the conductivity data.

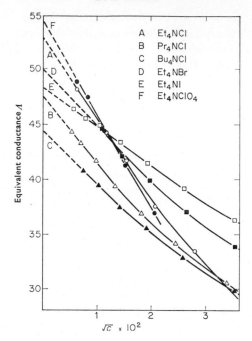

FIG. 8. The conductance of quaternary ammonium salts in phosphoryl chloride at 20°
(c in molarity). Reproduced with permission from *Mh. Chem.* (1959) **90**, 260.

TABLE IV

Values of Experimental and Calculated Λ_0 for a Series of Quaternary Ammonium
Salts in Phosphoryl Chloride Measured at 20°

Substance	Λ_0 from $\Lambda - \sqrt{c}$	Λ_0 calculated by method of Fuoss[a]
Et_4NCl	53·0	53·0
Pr_4NCl	47·6	46·3
Bu_4NCl	44·4	43·0
Et_4NBr	50·0	49·0
Et_4NI	48·5	48·3
Et_4NClO_4	54·4	53·4

[a] Fuoss, 1935.

Triethylamine is a "potential" electrolyte in phosphoryl chloride; it reacts
with the solvent to give a conducting solution (Baaz and Gutmann, 1959a),
which is well represented by equilibria:

$$Et_3N + POCl_3 \rightleftharpoons (Et_3N.POCl_2^+ \ Cl^-) \rightleftharpoons Et_3N.POCl_2^+ + Cl^- \qquad (28)$$

whence $\Lambda_0 = 48{\cdot}5 \pm 1$. From the ionic mobility of the chloride ion, the mobility of the cation can be obtained and hence the Stokes radius. This, on comparison with the estimated sizes of the ions $(Et_3N)_2POCl^{2+}$ and $(Et_3N)_3PO^{3+}$ as well as $(Et_3N)POCl_2^+$, confirms the presence in the solution of the latter. The $(Et_3N)POCl_2^+$ ion is presumably tetrahedral in shape, with the phosphorus surrounded by two chlorine atoms, one oxygen and a nitrogen. The equilibrium constant for the system is comparable with that observed for the corresponding aqueous system,

$$Et_3N + H_2O \rightleftharpoons (Et_3NH^+ \ OH^-) \rightleftharpoons Et_3NH^+ + OH^-. \tag{29}$$

The $POCl_2^+$ cation in phosphoryl chloride solution, however, possesses a greater affinity for triethylamine than does the proton in water so that the equilibrium lies well to the right. A solution of triethylamine hydrochloride in phosphoryl chloride gives rise to three equilibria:

$$Et_3NH^+ + POCl_3 \rightleftharpoons Et_3NPOCl_2^+ + HCl$$

$$-Cl^- \ \Big\Updownarrow \ +Cl^- \qquad -Cl^- \ \Big\Updownarrow \ +Cl^-$$

$$Et_3N\,.\,HCl \qquad\qquad Et_3N + POCl_3 \tag{30}$$

By examining the conductivity of this system the affinity of the proton for triethylamine in phosphoryl chloride can be shown to be at least not greater that of the $POCl_2^+$ cation. In dilute solution $Et_3N.HCl$ gives Et_3NH^+ and $(Et_3N)POCl_2^+$ in approximately equal proportions. Passage of nitrogen through the solution causes the conductivity to fall, ultimately reaching the value of triethylamine itself (Baaz and Gutmann, 1959c). Conductimetric titrations in phosphoryl chloride solutions of pyridine with vanadium(IV), phosphorus(V) and tantalum(V) chlorides show breaks at the 1 : 2 ratio (corresponding to $(Py.POCl_2^+)_2VCl_6^{2-})$ and 1 : 1 ratio (corresponding to $Py.POCl_2^+PCl_6^-$ and $Py.POCl_2^+TaCl_6^-$) (Gutmann, 1954b).

Solutions of a number of chloride acceptors such as antimony(V) and boron(III) chloride lead to solutions of high conductance. Antimony(V) chloride is of special interest because the structure of the solid phase obtainable from the solution is known (Fig. 9), and it contains an antimony bonded directly to oxygen (Lindquist and Bränden, 1959; Bränden and Lindquist, 1963). The conductance of solutions of antimony(V) chloride in phosphoryl chloride (Baaz and Gutmann, 1959d) is readily interpreted simply in terms of the equilibrium:

$$Cl_5SbOPCl_3 \rightleftharpoons SbCl_6^- + POCl_2^+ \tag{31}$$

for which an equilibrium constant of 4×10^{-6} has been evaluated. The equilibrium constant for the reaction;

$$SbCl_6^- + POCl_3 \rightleftharpoons Cl_5SbOPCl_3 + Cl^- \tag{32}$$

is not more than 10^{-9}. Mobilities obtainable from the conductance data fit with unsolvated $POCl_2^+$ and $SbCl_6^-$ ions. Although initial experiments gave a transport number for the $POCl_2^+$ ion of 0·95 (Gutmann and Himml, 1955) this has not been confirmed by later work (V. Gutmann, personal communication). Further examination of the solution shows that in concentrated solutions, colloidal aggregates of indefinite composition, presumably involving oxygen co-ordination, appear on standing (Baaz and Gutmann, 1959d). The resulting change is accompanied by a fall in the conductance. Lindquist (Bränden and Lindquist, 1963) has pointed out that the ionic formulation previously postulated (Gutmann, 1952f) for the solid adduct of antimony

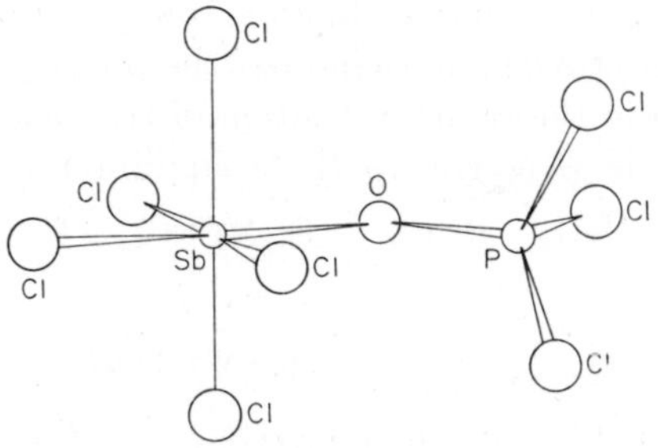

Fig. 9. The structure of $SbCl_5.OPCl_3$. Reproduced with permission from *Acta chem. Scand.* (1963) **17**, 358.

pentachloride and phosphoryl chloride does not have a favourable lattice energy and hence would not be expected to be stable. Other ionization processes are possible in this system, viz.

$$Cl_3POSbCl_5 \rightleftharpoons Cl_3POSbCl_4^+ + Cl^- \qquad (33a)$$

$$\rightleftharpoons Cl_2P^+OSbCl_5 + Cl^-. \qquad (33b)$$

However, the evidence from the conductance titrations of tetramethylammonium chloride and antimony(V) chloride giving $Et_4N^+SbCl_6^-$ would appear to support the presence of an antimony-containing anion. A solid of composition $POCl_3.2SbCl_5$ ($POCl_3.SbCl_4^+SbCl_6^-$) has been reported in phase studies of the system $POCl_3$–$SbCl_5$ (Leman and Tridot, 1959).

In the case of boron(III) chloride there is strong conductimetric and potentiometric evidence to show that the phosphoryl chloride solution of this compound involves the equilibrium (Baaz et al., 1960a):

$$BCl_3.POCl_3 \rightleftharpoons POCl_2^+ + BCl_4^-. \qquad (34)$$

The examination of the solid adduct $BCl_3.POCl_3$ by infra-red techniques has led, however, to conflicting views. On the one hand the structure $POCl_2^+BCl_4^-$ is put forward (Fraser et al., 1960; Gerrard et al., 1961), on the other, an oxygen donor complex (Waddington and Klanberg, 1960b; Peach and Waddington, 1962). As no other example of solids in which phosphoryl chloride acts as a chloride donor are known, the evidence favours the oxygen co-ordinated form. The rapid halogen exchange at 0° between phosphoryl chloride and boron(III) chloride which occurs in solutions which are rich in phosphoryl chloride has been found not to occur when boron(III) chloride is in excess (Gutmann, 1952e). The absence of exchange clearly indicates that the species $POCl_2^+$ and BCl_4^- are not present in solution in equilibrium with the component halides. It would thus appear that even in solution the phosphoryl chloride acts as an oxygen donor rather than a chloride donor. The exchange process observed at high concentrations of phosphoryl chloride may be the effect of the high dielectric constant of the solvent promoting an ionic exchange thus:

$$POCl_3 \rightleftharpoons POCl_2^+ + Cl^- \qquad (35a)$$

$$Cl^- + Cl_3^*B.OPCl_3 \rightleftharpoons (ClCl_3^*BOPCl_3^-) \rightleftharpoons Cl^{*-} + Cl_3B.OPCl_3. \qquad (35b)$$

It is difficult to see why, if at this stage a solvated tetrachloroborate(III) ion is formed, it would not also be formed, at least in an amount sufficient to promote a rapid exchange, in the boron(III) chloride rich system. The conductivity of boron(III) chloride solutions and the conductimetric and potentiometric titration data are difficult to explain without a boron-containing anion. One possible alternative is for the complex to ionize thus:

$$Cl_3B.OPCl_3 \rightleftharpoons Cl_3B.OPCl_2^+ + Cl^- \qquad (36)$$

but this would not appear compatible with a break in the conductimetric titration curve of boron trichloride with tetraethylammonium chloride. Spectrophotometric investigation of the iron(III) chloride–boron(III) chloride–phosphoryl chloride system likewise supports the presence of the tetrachloroborate(III) ion in the early stages of the reaction, on addition of further tetraethylammonium chloride the system changes over to one containing the tetrachloroferrate(III) ion. Further experiments on the conductivity of dilute solutions of boron(III) chloride in phosphoryl chloride and vice versa are promised (Herber, 1960). These and other results will be awaited with interest, meanwhile the role of boron(III) chloride as a chloride ion acceptor must be accepted tentatively, the evidence so far would place boron(III) chloride between iron(III) and titanium(IV) chloride in a series of decreasing chloride acceptance.

The aluminium halides have solubilities and conductivities as shown in Table V. The conductivity of aluminium chloride rises to a maximum at around 40° and then drops rapidly with increasing temperature. A solvate of formula $AlCl_3.POCl_3$ is obtained only on long standing. Similarly the bromide gives $AlBr_3.POCl_3$, whereas the iodide gives a compound $AlI_3.2POCl_3$ (Gutmann, 1952e). An examination of the phase diagram for aluminium chloride and phosphoryl chloride shows a further two compounds $AlCl_3.2POCl_3$ and $AlCl_3.6POCl_3$ (Groeneveld and Zuur, 1957, 1958). The first of these has been confirmed by a direct preparation (Raman and Murthy, 1960). Gallium(III) chloride behaves in a similar fashion giving solvates $GaCl_3.POCl_3$ and $GaCl_3.2POCl_3$ (Greenwood and Wade, 1957; Greenwood and Perkins, 1957; Greenwood, 1958). Similarly solvates $GaBr_3.POBr_3$ and $GaBr_3.POCl_3$ have been reported. The structures of these solvates have so far only been investigated spectroscopically. Evidence for the structure $POCl_2^+GaCl_4^-$ has come from the Raman spectrum of the molten compound. Ten lines were observed, four of which corresponded in position and polarization to the

TABLE V

Solubility and Conductivities of Aluminium Halides at 20°

	Solubility (g/1000 g) $POCl_3$	Specific conductivities (ohm^{-1} cm^{-1})			Colour
		0·05 M	0·1 M	0·2 M	
AlF_3	c. 0·5	$4·4 \times 10^{-6}$			Colourless
$AlCl_3$	60·0	$3·6 \times 10^{-4}$	$7·7 \times 10^{-4}$	$1·52 \times 10^{-3}$	Light yellow
$AlBr_3$	153	$4·5 \times 10^{-4}$	$9·1 \times 10^{-4}$	$1·82 \times 10^{-3}$	Yellow brown
AlI_3	170	$4·0 \times 10^{-4}$	$8·1 \times 10^{-4}$	$1·62 \times 10^{-3}$	Deep red

spectrum of the known $GaCl_4^-$ (tetrahedral, symmetry T_d) and the remaining six lines could be assigned to frequencies caused by $POCl_2^+$ (planar, symmetry C_{2v}) (Woodward et al., 1956; Greenwood, 1958). An examination of the Raman spectra and a detailed examination of the infra-red spectra of these aluminium and gallium halide adducts suggests a contrary view of the structure in which oxygen is held to be the bridging atom (Gerding et al., 1960). The energy change involved in the formation of the gallium(III) chloride complex is

$$GaCl_3(g) + POCl_3(g) \rightleftharpoons GaCl_3.POCl_3(g), \quad \Delta H = -22·6 \text{ kcal.} \qquad (37)$$

The evidence so far would appear to support the idea that these solids are in fact essentially oxygen donors, in which perhaps only relatively weak interactions are involved in the crystal lattice.

The nature of the solution of aluminium chloride in phosphoryl chloride is equally uncertain. Conductance titrations such as those between zinc(II), tin(IV) and antimony(V) chlorides with aluminium(III) chloride lead to breaks in the curve, 1 : 2 in the case of tin(IV), and 1 : 1 in the case of antimony(V) and zinc(II). At the same time precipitation of, for example, $2AlCl_3.SnCl_4.2POCl_3$ and $AlCl_3.SbCl_5.3POCl_3$ occurs (Gutmann, 1952f). Similarly, titration of aluminium chloride and tetraethylammonium chloride gives a break at $1:1$ and a curve characteristic of the formation of soluble ionic compound involving a feeble chloride acceptor. Closer examination of the titration of antimony(V) chloride shows that the curve is in fact more complex than the original experiments suggested. The breaks obtained depend on the direction of the titration, for example aluminium chloride with antimony(V) chloride gave no significant break at the $1:1$ composition, but a break at the $1:2$ ($AlCl_3.2SbCl_5$) (*vide supra*), whereas antimony(V) chloride with aluminium(III) chloride gave breaks at $1:1$, $1:2$ ($2AlCl_3.SbCl_5$) and possibly $1:3$ ($3AlCl_3.SbCl_5$). The formation of colloidal micelles during the titration of antimony(V) chloride with aluminium chloride may explain some of the features of the conductimetric curves. The results are made more difficult to interpret by the slow establishment of the equilibrium between solid and solution. The overall picture obtained from conductimetric, potentiometric and preparative studies is one involving several species in solution, which lead to the solvates mentioned earlier. The bonding of the phosphoryl chloride to the aluminium in these solvates is most probably through an oxygen bridge. The $AlCl_4^-$ ion appears to be the only anionic species present; there is no evidence for $AlCl_5^{2-}$ or $AlCl_6^{3-}$ species. The $AlCl^{2+}$ and Al^{3+} species occur solvated thus

$$AlCl(OPCl_3)_5^{2+} \text{ and } Al(OPCl_3)_6^{3+};$$

the corresponding $AlCl_2^+$ ion does not appear to be involved. The system is made complex by the possibility of polymeric species, for example:

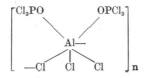

or even more complex two dimensional polymers (Baaz *et al.*, 1960d). Ebullioscopic measurements support the presence of polymeric species breaking down with time, true equilibrium being very slow to attain (Gutmann and Mairinger, 1961). In a 0.3 M solution the transport number of the tetrachloroaluminate ion has the very low value of 0.04. This may be explained by a switch mechanism (Gutmann and Himml, 1955). Similar studies of aluminium chloride in acyl halides have shown that the aluminium is transported to both anode and cathode simultaneously (Wertyporoch and Firla, 1932). The transport experiment does not assist greatly in supporting the postulate of a solvate $POCl_2^+$ and a $AlCl_4^-$ ion, since alternative more complex systems might similarly give a very low transport number.

Titanium(IV) chloride is appreciably soluble in phosphoryl chloride, giving a conducting yellow solution from which a solvate $TiCl_4.2POCl_3$ can be obtained (Gutmann, 1952e). The solvate $TiCl_4.POCl_3$ which can also

12

be obtained has a dimeric structure involving two octahedrally disposed titanium atoms linked through a bridge of two chlorine atoms. The phosphoryl chloride molecules are in the trans positions on a diagonal of the molecule (Bränden and Lindquist, 1960). Three crystal modifications of this compound exist. The oxygen bridge structure for the solid solvates is supported by the infra-red data (Sheldon and Tyree, 1959) and also by the crystal structure of a ternary compound $TiCl_3(OPCl_3)_3^+SbCl_6^-$ (Adolfsson et al., 1960). Conductimetric titrations of titanium(IV) chloride solutions with tetraethylammonium chloride show a maximum at the 1 : 1 ratio followed by a break at the 1 : 2 ratio (Adolfsson et al., 1960); however, another form of the curve has been reported, which although it shows similar breaks at 1 : 1 and 1 : 2 ratios, does not show the maximum (Gutmann, 1952f). Clearly the interpretation of the shape of the conductimetric curves must be treated with caution until reproducible results are available. During the titration tetraethylammonium hexachlorotitanate(IV) is precipitated: it has been observed previously that the presence of solids leads to difficulties in understanding the form of conductimetric curves. Potentiometric experiments in which solutions of titanium(IV) chloride were titrated with tetraethylammonium, antimony(V) and iron(III) chlorides show the existence of the species $TiCl_6^{2-}$, $TiCl_{5 \text{ solv.}}^-$ and $TiCl_{3 \text{ solv.}}^+$ in solution. The behaviour of the titanium(IV) chloride depends wholly on the relative donor or acceptor strength of the other chloride. Thus, with antimony(V) chloride, the species predominating can be shown to consist of $Cl_3Ti(OPCl_3)_3^+$ whereas with iron(III) chloride, a much weaker chloride acceptor, photometric measurements show an equilibrium to exist:

$$(TiCl_{3 \text{ solv.}})^+(FeCl_4)^- \rightleftharpoons (TiCl_4)_{\text{solv.}} + (FeCl_3)_{\text{solv.}}. \tag{38}$$

The ratio of chloride donation and acceptance appears largely dependent on concentration. In very dilute solution titanium(IV) chloride is almost exclusively a donor, in concentrated solution it is often an acceptor (Baaz et al., 1960c). Ebullioscopic results on mixtures of potassium chloride and titanium(IV) chloride in 1 : 1 mole ratio show the presence of a $TiCl_5.POCl_3^-$ species as well as $TiCl_6^{2-}$]. The potassium salt of this ion, $KTiCl_5.POCl_3$ has been isolated as a solid (Gutmann and Mairinger, 1961). The solutions, covering a range of concentrations, thus involve the equilibria:

$$Cl_5Ti.OPCl_3^- + Cl^- \rightleftharpoons TiCl_6^{2-} + POCl_3 \tag{39a}$$

$$Cl_5Ti.OPCl_3^- + POCl_3 \rightleftharpoons Cl_4Ti(OPCl_3)_2 + Cl^- \tag{39b}$$

$$Cl_4Ti(OPCl_3)_2 + POCl_3 \rightleftharpoons Cl_3Ti(OPCl_3)_3^+ + Cl^-. \tag{39c}$$

Tungsten(VI) chloride is readily soluble in phosphoryl chloride to give a red solution. On adding tetraethylammonium, potassium or caesium chlorides a yellow solvated WCl_7^- species is formed, which cannot, however, be isolated as a salt. Other metallic chlorides supply chloride ions for the formation of the WCl_7^- ion, the sequence of donor strengths to tungsten(VI) chloride, as determined by potentiometric and spectraphotometric methods, being

$$Et_4NCl{\sim}KCl{\sim}CsCl > ZnCl_2 > AlCl_3 > SnCl_4.$$

There is no evidence to show that tungsten(VI) chloride can behave as a chloride ion donor itself (Baaz et al., 1961g).

Iron(III) chloride dissolves in phosphoryl chloride to give a reddish brown solution at a concentration of 0·01 M, but on dilution the colour changes so that at 10^{-4} M the solution is yellow (Gutmann, 1959). From the solution solid solvates of composition $2FeCl_3.3POCl_3$ (Dadape and Rao, 1955), $FeCl_3.POCl_3$ (Dadape and Rao, 1955; Gutmann and Baaz, 1959e) and $2FeCl_3.POCl_3$ (Ruff, 1904) are obtained. The ultra-violet spectrum of these solutions shows clearly that in the concentrated solution there are no tetra-chloroferrate(III) ion species present, on dilution however the colour change corresponds to the appearance of this ion. The red solution on evaporation gives a brown amorphous solid, but by carefully cooling the solution, or by adding carbon tetrachloride, a red crystalline product of composition $2FeCl_3.3POCl_3$ is obtained (vide supra). It is also possible by pumping both the brown and red materials to obtain the yellow crystalline $FeCl_3.POCl_3$ (vide supra) (Baaz et al., 1960b). The brown coloured solid is a highly condensed species, rich in phosphoryl chloride. The addition of various chlorides to the red-brown solution produces the absorption characteristic of the tetrachloroferrate(III) ion and there is a corresponding change in the conductivity. The formation of the tetrachloroferrate(III) ion can be conveniently followed potentiometrically (Baaz et al., 1960c,d; Gutmann and Baaz, 1959e), spectrophotometrically (Baaz et al., 1960b, 1961a,b,c; Gutmann and Baaz, 1959d), conductimetrically (Baaz et al., 1960c,d; Gutmann and Baaz, 1959d), or ebullioscopically (Gutmann and Mairinger, 1960). The extent of chloride donation varies; thus $HgCl_2$, BCl_3, $TiCl_4$, $SnCl_4$ and PCl_5 all react to give a solvated unipositive cation whereas $ZnCl_2$ and $AlCl_3$ react to give up two chloride ions and possibly three in the case of $AlCl_3$. Donor strength in this reaction follows the series

$$Et_4NCl{\sim}KCl{\sim}ZnCl_2{\sim}AlCl_3 > TiCl_4 > PCl_5{\sim}AlCl_3 \gg SbCl_5{\sim}$$
$$HgCl_2 > BCl_3{\sim}SnCl_4$$

(Baaz et al., 1961d). Only in certain instances can the reaction be considered to have gone to completion. However, although spectrophotometric measurements suggest this is so in the case of tetraethylammonium, aluminium and zinc chlorides (Baaz et al., 1960c), in the case of titanium(IV), and phosphorus(V) chlorides the spectrum for the uncomplexed solvated iron(III) chloride is always present (Baaz et al., 1961d). Ebullioscopic measurements on the degree of dissociation of potassium tetrachloroferrate(III) (Gutmann and Mairinger, 1960) confirms results obtained by conductivity measurements (Gutmann and Baaz, 1959d). Only simple ion-pair association appears to be present, the dissociation constant of $KFeCl_4$ (Gutmann and Mairinger, 1961) is 3×10^{-4} compared with $KSbCl_6$, 9×10^{-4}; $K(Cl_5TiOPCl_3)$, 3×10^{-4}, and

$$[Al(OPCl_3)_6][FeCl_4]_3, \; 9 \times 10^{-5}.$$

Photometric studies of 0·01 M phosphoryl chloride solutions of iron(III) chloride when a suitable Lewis base, $\overline{B}$, is present show that chloride ion transfer occurs. For example, both pyridine and triethylamine react thus:

$$C_5H_5N + POCl_3 + FeCl_3 \rightleftharpoons C_5H_5N.POCl_2^+ + FeCl_4^-. \tag{40}$$

The Lewis base assists in the chloride ion transfer by the formation of the $\overline{B}.POCl_2^+$ cation by displacement of a chloride ion at the P—Cl bond. With tetraethylammonium permanganate and chlorate reaction occurs, e.g.

$$MnO_4^- + 4FeCl_3 \rightarrow Mn^{3+}{}_{(solv.)} + 4FeCl_4^- + 2Cl_2 \tag{41}$$

and with tetraethylammonium bromide, a bromotrichloroferrate(III) ion is formed (Baaz et al., 1961a).

The formation of conducting solutions of iron(III) chloride requires the formation of the tetrachloroferrate(III) ion. This can arise in a number of ways:

$$FeCl_3 + POCl_3 \rightleftharpoons POCl_2^+ + FeCl_4^- \tag{42a}$$

$$(x+1)FeCl_3 + yPOCl_3 \rightleftharpoons FeCl_{3-x}(OPCl_3)_y]^{x+} + xFeCl_4^- \tag{42b}$$

$$xFeCl_3 + MCl_n + yPOCl_3 \rightleftharpoons MCl_{n-x}(OPCl_3)_y]^{x+} + xFeCl_4^- \tag{42c}$$

$$FeCl_3 + \overline{B} + POCl_3 \rightleftharpoons \overline{B}.POCl_2^+ + FeCl_4^-. \tag{42d}$$

Reaction (a) has no evidence to substantiated it other than the fact that the tetrachloroferrate(III) ion appears on dilution of an iron(III) chloride solution. However, no compounds in which the $POCl_2^+$ has been recognized have yet been examined. Reaction (c) is well illustrated by the example given above, for example, aluminium chloride and iron(III) chloride react in this way. Likewise reaction(d) is simple and the reaction scheme is well substantiated. The interpretation of the behaviour of solutions of iron(III) chloride in terms of reaction(b) was first put forward by Meek and Drago (1961). Solutions of iron(III) chloride in triethylphosphate behave exactly as solutions in phosphoryl chloride. The solutions are red at 0·1 M and addition of further solvent causes a change in colour, whilst addition of lithium chloride does not appreciably change the absorption spectrum of the resulting yellow solution. It would thus appear that the solution contains the iron in the form of tetrachloroferrate(III) ion without the necessity of the chloride from the phosphoryl chloride. Similarly, it was possible to show breaks in the conductimetric titration curves similar to those reported earlier in this chapter for phosphoryl chloride solutions. The inference is that reaction(b) is one of the equilibria present in phosphoryl chloride solutions. The position of the equilibrium represented by this equation must depend upon a number of factors, notably the basicity, the dielectric constant and the solvating ability of the solvent. It would appear that the essential feature of phosphoryl chloride is not its ability to undergo self-ionization, which must be very slight indeed, but rather its capacity to act as an oxygen donor under certain conditions and a halide donor under others (Gutmann and Baaz, 1959a).

The effect on the solvent behaviour of the substitution of one of the chlorides in phosphoryl chloride by a phenyl group is not very great. A comparison of the properties is shown in Table VI:

TABLE VI

Comparison of Properties of Phenyl Phosphoryl Chloride and Phosphoryl Chloride

	$POCl_3$	$PhPOCl_2$
Density at 25°	1·648	1·197
M.p. (°C)	$+1$	$+3$
B.p.° (760 mm)	108	258
Viscosity at 25° (centipoise)	1·15	4·44
Dielectric constant at 25°	13·9	26·0
Molar volume	6·7	6·3
Specific conductivity at 25° (ohm^{-1} cm^{-1})	2×10^{-8}	9×10^{-8}
Λ_0 for Et_4NCl	53	14·5

Conductivity measurements of tetraethylammonium chloride in phenyl phosphoryl chloride ($PhPOCl_2$) are in accord with electrolyte theory. Iron(III) chloride gives conductivity values which do not vary regularly with concentration, behaviour similar to that found with this solute in phosphoryl chloride. Conductimetric titrations of tetraethylammonium chloride with a variety of chlorides, show breaks corresponding to the uptake of one chloride ion by boron(III), aluminium(III), iron(III), phosphorus(V) and antimony(V) chlorides. Zinc(II), titanium(IV) and tin(IV) take up either one or two chloride ions depending upon the conditions of the titration. Boron(III), titanium(IV) and phosphorus(V) chlorides donate one chloride ion to iron(III) and antimony(V) chlorides to form the corresponding tetrachloroferrate(III) and hexachloroantimonate(V) salts (Baaz et al., 1961h). Potentiometric methods have confirmed that mercury(II), boron(III), aluminium(III), iron(III), antimony(III), phosphorus(V) and antimony(V) and in addition mercury(II) chlorides each accept only one chloride ion from tetraethyl-ammonium chloride. As with the conductivity data, potentiometric data suggests that zinc(II), titanium(IV) and tin(IV) chlorides accept one or two chloride ions depending upon the stoichiometry of the ions in solution. Aluminium(III) chloride donates two chloride ions to iron(III) and anti-mony(V) chlorides giving rise to a doubly charged solvated chloroaluminate ion (Baaz *et al.*, 1961i). Spectrophotometric studies show that iron(III) chloride dissolves in phenyl phosphoryl chloride to give a red solvated complex which is transformed into the yellow tetrachloroferrate(III) ion on the addition of a chloride donor, particularly the alkali or tetraethylammon-ium chlorides. The evidence for chloride ion transference follows the results described above and obtained from conductimetric and potentiometric studies. The donor strength to iron(III) chloride of the chlorides decreases in the order

$$KCl \sim Et_4NCl > AlCl_3^* \geqslant TiCl_4 > PCl_5 > ZnCl_2^* > BCl_3 \sim SnCl_4 \sim$$
$$AlCl_3^{**} > HgCl_2 > SbCl_3$$

* as monochlorodonors, ** as a dichlorodonor.

There appears to be little difference between iron(III) and antimony(V) chlorides as acceptors with this series of donors as measured photometrically (Baaz *et al.*, 1961c). The potentiometric measurements suggested the series of acceptors as

$$FeCl_3 > SbCl_5 \geqslant SnCl_4 > BCl_3 \geqslant HgCl_2 \sim PCl_5 > TiCl_4 > AlCl_3 > ZnCl_2.$$

Similarly the potentiometric data suggested that chloride ion activity in the solution decreased in the order

$$Et_4NCl > AlCl_3 > TiCl_4, \ BCl_3 > ZnCl_2 > PCl_5 > SbCl_5 > FeCl_3.$$

Triphenylmethyl chloride reacts with acceptors such as zinc(II), alumin-ium(III), iron(III), boron(III), titanium(IV), tin(IV) and antimony(V) chlorides in phosphoryl and phenylphosphoryl chloride to give a series of tri-phenyl carbonium salts, $Ph_3C^+MCl_{n+1}^-$. The acceptor strength towards chloride ion in this case diminishes in the order

$$FeCl_3 > SbCl_5 > SnCl_4 > BCl_3 > ZnCl_2 \sim TiCl_4 > AlCl_3 \sim HgCl_2 > SbCl_3 > PCl_5$$

for phenyl phosphoryl chloride (Baaz *et al.*, 1961e), and in the order

$$FeCl_3 > SbCl_5 \sim BCl_3 \sim SnCl_4 \geqslant TiCl_4 > AlCl_3 > ZnCl_2 > HgCl_2 > SbCl_3 > PCl_5$$

for phosphoryl chloride (Baaz *et al.*, 1961f). The order is different in detail from that observed with other chloride ion donors in phenylphosphoryl and phosphoryl chloride, but the essential features are the same, namely that iron(III) chloride and antimony(V) chloride are amongst the best acceptors, antimony(III) and phosphorus(V) chloride amongst the worst. The formation constants for the reaction

$$Ph_3C^+ Cl^- + MCl_n \rightleftharpoons Ph_3C^+ + MCl_{n+1}^- \tag{43}$$

shown in Table VII have been obtained using spectrophotometric methods. Phosphoryl chloride thus promotes the transfer of chloride ion more than phenylphosphoryl chloride, despite the difference in dielectric constant. The difference is a function of the ability of the phosphoryl group to solvate the anion and perhaps also the cation. This behaviour of chlorides as chloride ion acceptors or donors is not confined to the halide and oxyhalide solvents; recent work by Gutmann and his collaborators (Baaz et al., 1962a,b,c; Gutmann et al., 1963; Gutmann and Hampel, 1963; Hubacek et al., 1963) in methyl cyanide, benzoyl chloride and other solvents has shown the occurrence of this type of solute behaviour in a widely differing range of solvents. The donor and acceptor strength series vary from solvent to solvent as might be expected.

TABLE VII

Formation Constants of the Complex $Ph_3C^+MCl_{n+1}^-$

Solute	Solvent	
	$POCl_3$	$PhPOCl_2$
$ZnCl_2$	12	5·3
BCl_3	100	10·8
$AlCl_3$	14	0·19
$FeCl_3$	290	130
$TiCl_4$	16	5·3
$SnCl_4$	85	15·5
$SbCl_5$	110	39·4

The ability of various sulphophthaleins to function as chloride ion indicators promises to be of value in studies of chloride transfer processes. The colour changes involved are close to those observed with aqueous solutions:

Chloride ion donors

A $\xrightarrow{\hspace{1cm}}$ B

(red)   Chloride ion acceptors   (yellow)

The changes involve ionization equilibria (Gutmann and Hubacek, 1963) analogous to those encountered with proton containing solvents. In certain cases, addition of $POCl_2$ groups has been shown to be involved in one of the coloured forms (Gutmann and Hubacek, 1963).

VI. Uses of Group V Halides and Oxyhalides as Solvents

So far little use has been made of the solvent properties of the halides and oxyhalides of Group V elements other than in the preparation of otherwise difficultly accessible chlorocomplexes. Arsenic(III) chloride is particularly suitable for reactions leading to complex chlorides and fluorides, similarly arsenic(III) bromide for complex bromides. Phosphoryl chloride is a convenient solvent for preparative use since it is always anhydrous, and is well suited to direct chlorination experiments. It is readily volatile so that any excess of solvent is removed easily. The application of the halide solvents for electrochemical studies has already been mentioned. Recently it has appeared that analytical applications of phenylphosphoryl chloride are possible particularly as solvents for electrochemical experiments, such as polarography (Gutmann and Schöber, 1962; Dehn et al., 1962, 1963; Dehn and Schöber, 1963).

Titanium(IV) and tin(IV) chlorides can be conveniently titrated in phosphoryl and arsenic(III) chloride solutions with various nitrogen bases using benzanthrone as indicator. The results show a considerable spread but may none the less find analytical application, as has been claimed (Paul et al., 1959a). A similar analytical result has been claimed using crystal violet as internal indicator (Paul et al., 1959b).

In conclusion it should be emphasized that the halides and oxyhalides do not appear to be particularly unusual in their solvent behaviour. The hydrogen bonding which largely determines the characteristics of water is, of course, absent in these solvents, but there is an ability to associate and to solvate other halides, which is similar in nature if different in magnitude. In particular, the acceptor character of phosphorus makes for the possibility of phosphoryl bridging $P=O \cdots \cdot P$ comparable with hydrogen bonding and the solvent characteristics of phosphoryl chloride can be seen in this light. The oxyhalides are good donors through the oxygen atom, giving rise to numerous complex solvated cations, and sometimes anions. The self-ionization of these solvents is not an essential feature of their behaviour, however, it is clear that by their very nature as chloride donors and acceptors, and by reason of their high dielectric constants, that a small amount of self-ionization is bound to occur. The importance of this self-ionization, and the associated ideas of acids and bases, would appear to have been greatly overstressed in many discussions in the past. It is now emerging that other solvents show similar behaviour although they do not necessarily contain chloride ions. The Group V halides and oxyhalides remain fruitful solvents for the ready study of chlorocomplex formation and undoubtedly there is a great deal still to be elucidated about the nature of the solutions.

The author would like to thank Professor V. Gutmann for discussion and useful criticism.

REFERENCES

Addison, C. C. and Hodge, N. (1961) *J. chem. Soc.* 240.
Addison, C. C. and Lewis, J. (1955) *Quart. Rev.* **9**, 115.
Adolfsson, G., Bryntse, R. and Lindquist, I. (1960) *Actachem. Scand.* **14**, 949.
Agerman, M., Andersson, L. H., Lindquist, I. and Zackrisson, M. (1958) *Acta chem. Scand.* **12**, 477.
Andersson, L. H. and Lindquist, I. (1955) *Acta chem. Scand.* **9**, 79.
Asmussen, R. W. (1939) *Z. anorg. Chem.* **243**, 127.
Baaz, M. and Gutmann, V. (1959a) *Mh. Chem.* **90**, 276.
Baaz, M. and Gutmann, V. (1959b) *Mh. Chem.* **90**, 256.
Baaz, M. and Gutmann, V. (1959c) *Mh. Chem.* **90**, 744.
Baaz, M. and Gutmann, V. (1959d) *Mh. Chem.* **90**, 426.
Baaz, M., Gutmann, V. and Hübner, L. (1960a) *Z. anorg. Chem.* **91**, 694.
Baaz, M., Gutmann, V. and Hübner, L. (1960b) *Mh. Chem.* **92**, 537.
Baaz, M., Gutmann, V. and Hübner, L. (1961a) *Mh. Chem.* **92**, 707.
Baaz, M., Gutmann, V. and Hübner, L. (1961b) *J. inorg. nucl. Chem.* **18**, 276.
Baaz, M., Gutmann, V. and Hübner, L. (1961c) *Mh. Chem.* **92**, 135.
Baaz, M., Gutmann, V. and Hübner, L. (1961d) *Mh. Chem.* **92**, 272.
Baaz, M., Gutmann, V. and Kunze, O. (1962a) *Mh. Chem.* **93**, 1142.
Baaz, M., Gutmann, V. and Kunze, O. (1962b) *Mh. Chem.* **93**, 1162.
Baaz, M., Gutmann, V. and Masaguer, J. R. (1961e) *Mh. Chem.* **92**, 582.
Baaz, M., Gutmann, V. and Masaguer, J. R. (1961f) *Mh. Chem.* **92**, 590.
Baaz, M., Gutmann, V. and Talaat, M. Y. A. (1960c) *Mh. Chem.* **91**, 548.
Baaz, M., Gutmann, V. and Talaat, M. Y. A. (1961g) *Mh. Chem.* **92**, 714.
Baaz, M., Gutmann, V. and West, T. S. (1961h) *Mh. Chem.* **92**, 164.
Baaz, M., Gutmann, V., Talaat, M. Y. A. and West, T. S. (1961i) *Mh. Chem.* **92**, 150.
Baaz, M., Gutmann, V., Hampel, G. and Masaguer, J. R. (1962c) *Mh. Chem.* **93**, 1416.
Baaz, M., Gutmann, V., Hübner, L., Mairinger, F. and West, T. S. (1960d) *Z. anorg. Chem.* **310**, 302.
Baughan, E. C., Jones, T. P. and Stoodley, L. G. (1963) *Proc. chem. Soc. Lond.* 274.
Beckham, L. J., Fessler, W. A. and Kise, M. A. (1951) *Chem. Rev.* **48**, 319.
Beckmann, E. (1906) *Z. anorg. Chem.* **51**, 111.
Boston, C. R. and Smith, G. P. (1958) *J. phys. Chem.* **62**, 409.
Boston, C. R. and Smith, G. P. (1962) *J. phys. Chem.* **66**, 1178.
Boston, C. R., Smith, G. P. and Howick, L. C. (1963) *J. phys. Chem.* **67**, 1849.
Bränden, C. I. and Lindquist, I. (1960) *Acta chem. Scand.* **14**, 726.
Bränden, C. I. and Lindquist, I. (1963) *Acta chem. Scand.* **17**, 353.
Bredig, M. A. (1959) *J. phys. Chem.* **63**, 978.
Bredig, M. A., Levy, H. A., Keneshea, F. J. and Cubicciotti, D. (1960) *J. phys. Chem.* **64**, 191.
Brühl, J. W. (1898) *Z. phys. Chem.* **27**, 319.
Burg, A. B. and Campbell, G. W. (1948) *J. Amer. chem. Soc.* **70**, 1964.
Burg, A. B. and McKenzie, D. E. (1952) *J. Amer. chem. Soc.* **74**, 3143.
Cady, H. P. (1897) *J. phys. Chem.* **1**, 707.
Casselmann, W. (1856) *Liebigs Ann.* **98**, 213.
Corbett, J. D. (1958a) *J. phys. Chem.* **62**, 1149.
Corbett, J. D. (1958b) *J. Amer. chem. Soc.* **80**, 4757.
Corbett, J. D. and Albers, F. C. (1960) *J. Amer. chem. Soc.* **82**, 533.
Craig, D. P., Maccoll, A., Nyholm, R. S., Orgel, L. E. and Sutton, L. E. (1954) *J. chem. Soc.* 332, 354.

Cronander, A. W. (1873a) *Bull. Soc. chim. Fr.* [2], **19**, 499.

Cronander, A. W. (1873b) *Ber. dtsch. chem. Ges.* **5**, 1466.

Cronander, A. W. (1873c) *Uppsala Univ. Årsskr.* 1.

Dadape, V. V. and Rao, M. R. A. (1955) *J. Amer. chem. Soc.* **77**, 6192.

Dafert, O. and Melinski, Z. A. (1926) *Ber. dtsch. chem. Ges.* **59**, 788.

Daure, P. (1929) *C.R. Acad. Sci., Paris* **188**, 1605.

Davies, A. G. and Baughan, E. C. (1961) *J. chem. Soc.* 1711.

Dehn, H., Gutmann, V. and Schöber, G. (1962) *Mh. Chem.* **93**, 1357.

Dehn, H., Gutmann, V. and Schöber, G. (1963) *Mh. Chem.* **94**, 312.

Dehn, H. and Schöber, G. (1963) *Mh. Chem.* **94**, 316.

Dess, H. M. and Parry, R. W. (1956) *J. Amer. chem. Soc.* **78**, 5735.

Dess, H. M., Parry, R. W. and Vidale, G. L. (1956) *J. Amer. chem. Soc.* **78**, 5730.

Ehrlich, P. and Dietz G. (1960) *Z. anorg. Chem.* **305**, 158.

Eïngorn, L. N. (1950) *Ukr. Khim. Zh.* **16**, No. 4, 404.

Fraser, M. J., Gerrard, W. and Patel, J. K. (1960) *J. chem. Soc.* 726.

Frycz, K. and Tolloczko, S. (1912) *Festschrift Univ. Lwow* 1912, **1**, 1.

Frycz, K. and Tolloczko, S. (1913) *Chem. Zbl.* **1**, 91.

Fuoss, R. M. (1935) *J. Amer. chem. Soc.* **57**, 488.

George, J. W. (1960) *Progr. inorg. Chem.* **2**, 33.

Gerding, H. and Houtgraaf, H. (1953) *Rec. Trav. chim. Pays-Bas* **72**, 21.

Gerding, H., Koningstein, J. A. and Van der Worm, E. R. (1960) *Spectrochim. Acta* **16**, 881.

Gerrard, W., Mooney, E. F. and Willis, H. A. (1961) *J. chem. Soc.* 4255.

Gibson, S., Johnson, J. B. A. and Vining, D. C. (1930) *J. chem. Soc.* 1710.

Gmelin (1949) "Handbuch der anorganischen Chemie", Part 18B.

Gorenbein, E. Y. (1945) *J. gen. Chem., Moscow* **15**, 729.

Greenwood, N. N. (1958) *J. inorg. nucl. Chem.* **8**, 234.

Greenwood, N. N. and Perkins, P. G. (1957) *J. inorg. nucl. Chem.* **4**, 291.

Greenwood, N. N. and Wade, K. (1957) *J. chem. Soc.* 1516.

Greenwood, N. N. and Worrall, I. J. (1958) *J. inorg. nucl. Chem.* **6**, 34.

Groeneveld, W. L. (1953) *Rec. Trav. chim. Pays-Bas* **72**, 617.

Groeneveld, W. L. and Zuur, A. P. (1957) *Rec. Trav. chim. Pays-Bas* **76**, 1005.

Groeneveld, W. L. and Zuur, A. P. (1958) *J. inorg. nucl. Chem.* **8**, 241.

Gustavson, G. (1871) *Z. Chem.* (2) **7**, 417.

Gutmann, V. (1951a) *Z. anorg. Chem.* **266**, 331.

Gutmann, V. (1951b) *Z. anorg. Chem.* **264**, 151.

Gutmann, V. (1951c) *Mh. Chem.* **82**, 473.

Gutmann, V. (1952a) *Mh. Chem.* **83**, 159.

Gutmann, V. (1952b) *Mh. Chem.* **83**, 279.

Gutmann, V. (1952c) *Mh. Chem.* **83**, 164.

Gutmann, V. (1952d) *Mh. Chem.* **83**, 583.

Gutmann, V. (1952e) *Z. anorg. Chem.* **269**, 279.

Gutmann, V. (1952f) *Z. anorg. Chem.* **270**, 179.

Gutmann, V. (1953) *Mh. Chem.* **54**, 1191.

Gutmann, V. (1954a) *Mh. Chem.* **85**, 491.

Gutmann, V. (1954b) *Mh. Chem.* **85**, 1077.

Gutmann, V. (1956) *Svensk kem. Tidskr.* **68**, 1.

Gutmann, V. (1959) *J. phys. Chem.* **63**, 378.

Gutmann, V. and Baaz, M. (1959a) *Z. anorg. Chem.* **298**, 121.

Gutmann, V. and Baaz, M. (1959b) *Angew. Chem.* **71**, 57.

Gutmann, V. and Baaz, M. (1959c) *Mh. Chem.* **90**, 239.

Gutmann, V. and Baaz, M. (1959d) *Mh. Chem.* **90**, 271.

Gutmann, V. and Baaz, M. (1959e) *Mh. Chem.* **90**, 729.

Gutmann, V. and Hampel, G. (1963) *Mh. Chem.* **94**, 830.
Gutmann, V. and Himml, R. (1955) *Z. phys. Chem., Frankfurt* **4**, 157–64.
Gutmann, V. and Himml, R. (1956) *Z. anorg. Chem.* **287**, 199.
Gutmann, V. and Hubacek, H. (1963) *Mh. Chem.* **94**, 1019, 1098.
Gutmann, V. and Lindquist, I. (1954) *Z. phys. Chem., Leipzig* **203**, 250.
Gutmann, V. and Mairinger, F. (1957) *Z. anorg. Chem.* **289**, 279.
Gutmann, V. and Mairinger, F. (1960) *Mh. Chem.* **92**, 529.
Gutmann, V. and Mairinger, F. (1961) *Mh. Chem.* **92**, 720.
Gutmann, V. and Schöber, G. (1962) *Mh. Chem.* **93**, 1353.
Gutmann, V., Hampel, G. and Masaguer, J. R. (1963) *Mh. Chem.* **94**, 822.
Herber, R. H. (1960) *J. Amer. chem. Soc.* **82**, 792.
Hetherington, G. and Robinson, P. L. (1957) *Chem. Soc. Special Publication* No. 11, p. 23.
Hewitt, F. and Holliday, A. K. (1953) *J. chem. Soc.* 530.
Holmes, R. R. (1960a) *J. Amer. chem. Soc.* **82**, 5285.
Holmes, R. R. (1960b) *J. inorg. nucl. Chem.* **12**, 266.
Holmes, R. R. and Bertaut, E. F. (1958) *J. Amer. chem. Soc.* **80**, 2980, 2983.
Hubacek, H., Stančie, B. and Gutmann, V. (1963) *Mh. Chem.* **94**, 1118.
Isbekow, W. and Plotnikow, W. (1911) *Z. anorg. Chem.* **71**, 332.
Jander, G. and Günther, K. (1958) *Z. anorg. Chem.* **297**, 81.
Jander, G. and Günther, K. (1959a) *Z. anorg. Chem.* **298**, 241.
Jander, G. and Günther, K. (1959b) *Z. anorg. Chem.* **302**, 155.
Jander, G. and Swart, K. H. (1959a) *Z. anorg. Chem.* **299**, 252.
Jander, G. and Swart, K. H. (1959b) *Z. anorg. Chem.* **301**, 54.
Jander, G. and Swart, K. H. (1959c) *Z. anorg. Chem.* **301**, 80.
Jander, G. and Weiss, J. (1957) *Z. Elektrochem.* **61**, 1275.
Jander, G. and Weiss, J. (1959) *Z. Elektrochem.* **63**, 1037.
Kendall, J., Crittenden, E. D. and Miller, H. K. (1923) *J. Amer. chem. Soc.* **45**, 963.
Keneshea, F. J. and Cubicciotti, D. (1959) *J. Phys. Chem.* **63**, 1472.
Klemensiewicz, Z. (1908) *Bull. int. Acad., Cracovie*, **6**, 418.
Klemensiewicz, Z. (1924) *Z. phys. Chem.* **113**, 28.
Klemensiewicz, Z. and Balowna, Z. (1930) *Roczn. Chem.* **10**, 481.
Klemensiewicz, Z. and Balowna, Z. (1931) *Roczn. Chem.* **11**, 683.
Klemensiewicz, Z. and Zebrowska, A. (1934) *Roczn. Chem.* **14**, 14.
Köhler, H. (1880) *Ber. dtsch. chem. Ges.* **13**, 875.
Kolditz, L. (1955) *Z. anorg. Chem.* **280**, 313.
Kolditz, L. (1956) *Z. anorg. Chem.* **286**, 307.
Kolditz, L. (1957a) *Z. anorg. Chem.* **289**, 118.
Kolditz, L. (1957b) *Z. anorg. Chem.* **289**, 128.
Kolditz, L. and Engels, S. (1959) *Z. anorg. Chem.* **302**, 88.
Kolditz, L. and Feltz, A. (1957) *Z. anorg. Chem.* **293**, 286.
Kolditz, L. and Schmidt, W. (1958) *Z. anorg. Chem.* **296**, 188.
Kolthoff, I. M. and Laitinen, H. A. "pH and Electro Titrations", 2nd edition, 1941, John Wiley and Sons, Inc., New York.
Lacher, J. R., Campion, D. E. and Park, J. D. (1949) *Science* **110**, 300.
Lacher, J. R., Croy, V. D., Kianpour, A. and Park, J. D. (1954) *J. phys. Chem.* **58**, 206.
Leman, G. Tridot, G. (1959) *C.R. Acad. Sci., Paris* **248**, 3439.
Lenher, V. (1908) *J. Amer. chem. Soc.* **30**, 740.
Lewis, J. and Sowerby, D. B. (1956) *J. chem. Soc.* 150.
Lewis, J. and Sowerby, D. B. (1957a) *J. chem. Soc.* 336.
Lewis, J. and Sowerby, D. B. (1957b) *J. chem. Soc.* 1617.
Lewis, J. and Sowerby, D. B. (1957c) *Chem. Soc. Special Publication*, No. 10, p. 123.
Lindquist, I. (1955) *Acta chem. Scand.* **9**, 73.

Lindquist, I. and Andersson, L. H. (1954) *Acta chem. Scand.* **8**, 128.

Lindquist, I. and Bränden, C. I. (1959) *Acta chem. Scand.* **12**, 642.

Meek, D. W. and Drago, R. S. (1961) *J. Amer. chem. Soc.* **83**, 4322.

Metzl, S. (1906) *Z. anorg. Chem.* **48**, 146.

Metzner, R. (1898) *Ann. Chim. (Phys.)* (7), **15**, 254.

Montignie, E. (1935) *Bull. Soc. chim. Fr.* [5], **2**, 1365.

Muetterties, E. L. and Phillips, W. D. (1957a) *J. Amer. chem. Soc.* **79**, 322.

Muetterties, E. L. and Phillips, W. D. (1957b) *J. Amer. chem. Soc.* **79**, 3686.

Oddo, G. (1905) *R.C. Accad. Lincei Sed. solen.* Classe Sci. fis. mat. nat., (5) **10**, 452.

Oddo, G. and Tealdi, M. (1903) *Gazz. chim. ital.* **33**, II, 427.

Olah, G. A. and Tolgyesi, W. S. (1961) *J. org. chem.* **26**, 2319.

Partington, J. R. and Whynes, A. L. (1948) *J. chem. Soc.* 1952.

Partington, J. R. and Whynes, A. L. (1949) *J. chem. Soc.* 3135.

Paul, R. C., Singh, J. and Sandhu, S. S. (1959a) *Analyt. Chem.* **31**, 1495.

Paul, R. C., Singh, J. and Sandhu, S. S. (1959b) *J. Indian chem. Soc.* **36**, 305.

Payne, D. S. (1961) *Quart. Rev.* **15**, 173.

Peach, M. E. and Waddington, T. C. (1962) *J. chem. Soc.* 3450.

Perrot, R. and Devin, C. (1958) *C.R. Acad. Sci., Paris* **246**, 772.

Petzold, W. (1933) *Z. anorg. Chem.* **214**, 355.

Porter, G. B. and Baughan, E. C. (1958) *J. chem. Soc.* 744.

Pusin, N. A. and Löwy, S. (1926) *Z. anorg. Chem.* **150**, 167.

Pusin, N. A. and Makuc, J. (1938) *Z. anorg. Chem.* **237**, 177.

Raman, K. N. V. and Murthy, A. R. V. (1960) *Proc. Indian Acad. Sci.* **51**A, 270–9.

Rettgers, J. W. (1893) *Z. phys. Chem.* **11**, 328.

Rheinbolt, H. and Wasserfuhr, R. (1927) *Ber. dtsch. chem. Ges.* **60**, 732.

Ruff, O. (1904) *Ber. dtsch. chem. Ges.* **37**, 4513.

Ruff, O. and Ipsen, R. (1903) *Ber. dtsch. chem. Ges.* **36**, 1783.

Schwarzmann, E. and van Wazer, J. R. (1959) *J. Amer. chem. Soc.* **81**, 6366.

Seel, F. (1943) *Z. anorg. Chem.* **252**, 24.

Seel, F. and Bauer, H. (1947) *Z. Natur.* **126**, 397.

Seel, F. Schmutzler, R. and Wasem, K. (1959) *Angew. Chem.* **71**, 340.

Sheldon, J. C. and Tyree, S. Y. (1959) *J. Amer. chem. Soc.* **81**, 2290.

Shirey, W. B. (1930) *J. Amer. chem. Soc.* **52**, 1720.

Sokol'skii, G. A., Knunyants, J. L. (1960) *Izv. Akad. Nauk S.S.S.R. otd. khim. Nauk*, 779–83.

Spandau, H., Beyer, A. and Preugschat, F. (1960) *Z. anorg. Chem.* **306**, 13.

Sudborough, J. J. (1891) *J. Chem. Soc.* **59**, 655.

Tolloczko, S. (1899) *Z. phys. Chem.* **30**, 705.

Tolloczko, S. (1901) *Bull. int. Acad. Cracovie* **1**, 1.

Troost, W. R. (1954) *Canad. J. Chem.* **32**, 356.

Van Heteren, W. J. (1899) *Z. anorg. Chem.* **22**, 277.

Vonk, C. G. and Wiebenga, E. H. (1959) *Rec. Trav. Chim. Pays-Bas* **78**, 913.

Waddington, T. C. and Klanberg, T. (1960a) *Z. anorg. Chem.* **304**, 185.

Waddington, T. C. and Klanberg, F. (1960b) *J. Chem. Soc.* 2339.

Walden, P. (1900) *Z. anorg. Chem.* **25**, 209.

Walden, P. (1902) *Z. anorg. Chem.* **29**, 371.

Walden P. (1903) *Z. phys. Chem.* **43**, 445.

Wertyporoch, E. and Firla, T. (1932) *Z. phys. Chem.* A**162**, 398.

Wheeler, H. L. (1893a) *Amer. J. Sci.* [3], **46**, 90.

Wheeler, H. L. (1893b) *Z. anorg. Chem.* [4] 452.

Woodward, R. A., Garton, G. and Roberts, H. L. (1956) *J. chem. Soc.* 3723.

Woolf, A. A. and Greenwood, N. N. (1950) *J. chem. Soc.* 2200.

CHAPTER 9

Molten Salts as Solvents

H. Bloom and J. W. Hastie

Chemistry Department, University of Tasmania, Hobart, Tasmania, Australia

I. Summary... 353
II. Introduction... 354
III. The Nature of Molten Salts... 354
    A. Type of Entities Present....................................... 355
    B. Holes and Free Volume in Ionic Melts........................... 356
    C. Distribution Functions.. 357
    D. Nature of the Interionic Forces (Bonding) in Simple Melts............ 357
IV. Solutions of Salt and Water.. 357
V. Solutions of Salt and Organic Compounds............................... 358
    A. Solutions in an Organic Solvent................................. 358
    B. Solutions of Organic Compounds in Molten Salts..................... 360
VI. Solutions of Non-metallic Elements in Molten Salts....................... 361
    A. Sulphur... 361
    B. Iodine.. 361
VII. Solutions of Gases in Molten Salts..................................... 361
    A. Simple Solutions of Gas and Salt................................. 362
    B. Complex Solutions of Gases in Molten Salts........................ 362
VIII. Solutions of Metals in Molten Salts................................... 364
    A. Introduction... 364
    B. Solutions Without Significant Interaction......................... 365
    C. Solutions With Strong Solute–Solvent Interaction (i.e. Non-metallic
       Solutions)... 369
    D. Solutions of Metals in Salts of Another Metal—Displacement Solubility.. 373
IX. Solutions of Salt in Molten Salt....................................... 374
    A. Molten Salt Systems with Incomplete Miscibility..................... 375
    B. Molten Salt Systems with Complete Miscibility....................... 377
    C. The Structure of Molten Salt Solutions............................ 377
    D. Solvation and Complex Ion Formation in Molten Salt Mixtures......... 382
    E. Complex Ions and Reaction Kinetics.............................. 382
X. Application of Molten Salts as Solvents................................. 383
    A. Reactions Involving Organic Substances or Volatile Inorganic Liquids in
       Molten Salt Solvents.. 383
    B. Other Reactions Involving Inorganic Substances in Molten Salt Solvents 385
    C. Future Developments... 387
References.. 387

I. Summary

The chemical and physical properties and constitution of molten salts are discussed and also the need for such solvents. The main classes of solutions involving molten salts are systems involving salt and water, salt and organic substance, salt and non-metal, salt and gas, salt and metal, and salt with another salt. The properties of such systems are discussed. Where possible, tables of solubility are included and in certain cases the structure of the molten salt solutions are discussed. Examples of the application of molten salt solvents to chemical and industrial problems are given and the potential uses of such solvents are mentioned.

II. Introduction

In view of the growing importance and versatility of molten salts as solvents, the lack of solubility data, in general, is surprising. In fact molten salts are good solvents for a variety of materials, ranging from inorganic and organic vapours to high melting metals (even Pt) and oxides.

The considerable variety of salts and salt mixtures available leads to a potential class of solvents operative over a temperature range of more than one thousand degrees. For example, cryolite (Na_3AlF_6) melts at 1003°C, whilst the eutectic mixture, $AlCl_3 + NaCl + KCl$, melts at only 89°C. Molten halides form the most widely used molten salt system owing to their stability over a large temperature range, their effectiveness as solvents for a wide variety of materials, and their ready availability. Accordingly, in the following chapter we will deal mainly with molten halide salt systems.

Molten alkali-metal and alkaline-earth metal halides would be expected to be potentially useful solvents for carrying out chemical reactions owing to the large range of oxidation-reduction potentials available in such systems. For example, the range of stability in the $LiCl + KCl$ eutectic is about 3·5 V and in a $CsCl + MgCl_2$ eutectic, about 2·6 V at 700°C (Delimarskii, 1955). In aqueous solutions at room temperature the range of stability of xidizing and reducing agents is only approximately 1·2 V (Latimer, 1952).

III. The Nature of Molten Salts

Bloom and Bockris (1959) showed that the following information is necessary in order to define the structure of a molten salt:

(a) the type of entities present, i.e. ions, molecules, complex ions, etc;
(b) the nature and effect of holes or vacancies present;
(c) distribution functions relating to the relative positions of structural entities and holes;
(d) the nature of the bonds or interionic forces between the various entities in the melt.

The availability of the above information would suffice to define the structures of both simple salts as well as salt mixtures and a discussion of the nature of molten salts may profitably be considered in such terms, e.g. the distribution of holes or other forms of free volume is of fundamental importance to transport properties since without any free space in the liquid, transport processes would be unlikely. Also, if distribution functions were available it would be possible to calculate thermodynamic properties of the melt.

A. TYPE OF ENTITIES PRESENT

A fundamental property of most salts is the sharp increase in conductivity on melting. This, together with the general applicability of Faraday's Laws of electrolysis, establishes the ionic nature of molten salts. The large range of stability of the liquids at ordinary pressure (e.g. 612°C for NaCl) further substantiates the presence of strongly interacting entities (ions) in molten salts. Although the melts are essentially ionic, there may be varying degrees of ionic association exhibited by different salts, depending largely on the position of the cation in the Periodic Table. For example, mercuric chloride has a liquidus range of only 26°C and also a relatively small equivalent conductance, suggesting that the melt consists predominantly of uncharged entities. Biltz and Klemm (1926), tabulated conductivities of various chlorides and the results clearly indicate an increase of covalency as the cationic position shifts from left to right, as well as from top to bottom, in the Periodic Table.

X-Ray and neutron diffraction investigations have established that in the melting of ionic solids, there occur only relatively small structural changes as far as the first and second co-ordination shells are concerned. The structural determinations by Harris *et al.* (1951), Danilov and Krasnitskii (1955), Zarzycki (1957a,b) and Levy *et al.* (1960b) show that during melting of the alkali-metal chlorides, the co-ordination number for nearest neighbours (unlike ions) usually decreases from 6 to about 4. The cation–anion average interionic distance also decreases slightly but in contrast, the cation–cation and anion–anion distances increase slightly. Hence the structure in ionic melts is a partly disordered version of that in the corresponding solid, the main difference between melt and solid being the complete loss of long range order on melting. Simultaneously, the molar volume increases by about 25% for alkali-metal chlorides (Landon and Ubbelohde, 1956).

It is necessary to account for the simultaneous loss of long range order on melting, decrease of average distance between unlike-ions, increase of average distance between like-ions and increase of molar volume on melting, while still basically preserving the short range order of the crystal lattice. To do so one can assume, that during melting, the "ionic atmospheres" due to unlike-ions become more random and that "holes" or vacant "lattice sites" are introduced into the structure.

Assuming the fundamentally ionic nature of molten salts, consideration may be given to the types of ions present. In alkali-metal halide melts, values of molar refractivity are comparable to those obtained for the salts in their aqueous solutions at infinite dilution (Bloom and Rhodes, 1956). This strongly suggests that the states of ionization in both cases are identical.

Hence such melts consist of simple cations and anions only. Cryoscopic determinations (Van Artsdalen, 1956) in molten $NaNO_3$ indicate that salts such as NaCl dissolve to form ideal solutions and it is therefore likely that the solute dissolves as simple ions only.

On the other hand, the lowering of the freezing points of such solvents as $NaNO_3$ by heavy metal, divalent halides, show deviations from ideality and such halides are therefore thought to exist partly as associated ionic species. The cryoscopic data can be explained by assuming the following relative order of association:

$$CdBr_2 > ZnCl_2 > CdCl_2 > CuCl_2 > PbCl_2.$$

Activity coefficients of some of these salts in molten halide mixtures also support the same relative order of association (H. Bloom and J. W. Hastie, unpublished results). It is possible that in these molten halides there exists, besides simple constituent ions, complex ions such as $CdCl^+$, $CdCl_3^-$, $CdCl_4^{2-}$ or even $CdCl_6^{4-}$.

Association constants for $CdCl^+$ and $PbCl^+$ in molten nitrate solvents have been determined (Braunstein *et al.*, 1962), and the values are larger in each solvent for $CdCl^+$, than for $PbCl^+$. Similar values have been determined for $CdBr^+$ and CdI^+ (Braunstein and Lindgren, 1962). It is significant that the association follows the sequence

$$I > Br > Cl$$

which is the order of polarizability of the anion.

Magnetic susceptibility measurements (Farquharson and Heymann, 1935) preclude the possibility of singly-charged ions such as Cd^+ in melts of the heavy-metal dihalides. In these melts the ionization potentials make it clear that ions such as $CdCl^+$ and $CdCl_3^-$ are more energetically possible than Cd^{2+} and Cl^- and that the $CdCl^+$ ion is stereochemically more favoured than the $CdCl_3^-$ ion. The larger ion $CdCl_6^{4-}$ is also stereochemically possible in pure $CdCl_2$ melts in the region just above the melting point. A relatively small latent heat of fusion for $CdCl_2$, as compared to NaCl say, suggests that the solid structure does not break down completely into constituent Cd^{2+} and Cl^- ions, but into associated ions. Raman frequencies similar to those in the solid were observed in the melt by Bues (1955) and this also suggests correspondence between the structural units of the solid and the melt.

For salts such as nitrates that have complex anions in the solid, electronic and vibrational spectra clearly prove the existence of the same complex anions in the melt (e.g. NO_3^- exists as an entity in nitrate melts). In molten GaX_2 (where X = Cl, Br) the existence of the species GaX_4^- has also been well established spectroscopically (Wait and Janz, 1963).

B. HOLES AND FREE VOLUME IN IONIC MELTS

The volume increase on melting of ionic crystals such as the alkali-halides is in some cases greater than 25% (Landon and Ubbeholde, 1965). Cmopressibility experiments, however, indicate that the free volume per mole available for ionic vibration is only about 2% of the molar volume (Bockris and Richards, 1957). This suggests that the larger part of the volume increase is due to the formation of holes in the melt. Such holes may also provide the means for ionic transport through the molten medium. The formation of holes is also supported by the X-ray diffraction experiments referred to above.

Certain conductivity experiments (Campbell *et al.*, 1962) also suggest the presence of holes in molten salts. For example, if molten $LiClO_3$ is used as a solvent for organic species, the addition of 0–0·4 weight % nitrobenzene causes a fairly rapid decrease of conductivity. Addition of methanol (0–1·25%), however, causes only a slow decrease of the conductivity. The addition of 0–6% of water increases the conductivity of the melt considerably and this may be attributed to an increase in the degree of ionization of $LiClO_3$ due to the strongly polar water molecule. The marked effect of nitrobenzene on the conductivity is most likely due to a reduction in the number of holes in the melt, thus making difficult the movement of ions necessary for conduction. The fact that the smaller molecules of methanol decrease the conductivity of $LiClO_3$ more slowly is in accordance with this view.

C. DISTRIBUTION FUNCTIONS

The determination of distribution functions, which are a description of order in molten salts, would enable the calculation of thermodynamic properties. It is possible to check postulated functions by comparing the calculated thermodynamic properties with experimental ones.

D. NATURE OF INTERIONIC FORCES (BONDING) IN SIMPLE MELTS

In the case of the molten alkali-halides, the forces between the ions will be largely coulombic and each ion will tend to attract an environment of oppositely charged ions. The latent heat of fusion of such salts is only a small fraction of the value of the lattice energy, hence the breakdown of the solid to form a melt does not involve a completely random distribution of cations and anions. On the contrary, each ion tends to attract an environment of oppositely charged ions. As indicated on p. 356, the heavy-metal dihalides form ionic melts in which there is a tendency towards covalent bonding, resulting in complex ions such as $CdCl^+$.

IV. SOLUTIONS OF SALT AND WATER

Usually water is considered to be the solvating species and this is physically more correct since the salts or the ionic components of the salts are usually solvated by a sphere of water molecules. However, one may formally consider the salt as the solvent species.

Much of the present day knowledge of salt and water solutions is connected with those solutions where water is present in excess. Discussion of such solutions is given in standard textbooks on electrolyte solutions. Investigations involving the solution of water vapour in molten salts are discussed in Section VII.

V. SOLUTIONS OF SALT AND ORGANIC COMPOUNDS

Such solutions are unique in that the pure components differ markedly in their chemical bonding. Nevertheless there are surprisingly many examples of solutions of this type. Two types of solution arise, namely those that are formed by the addition of salt to an organic compound and those formed by addition of organic compound to the salt. The former type is the one which has received the most investigation.

A. SOLUTIONS IN AN ORGANIC SOLVENT

The existence of congruently melting compounds between solute and solvent, as indicated by phase diagrams, is a reasonable indication of chemical

TABLE I

Solutions of Salt in Organic Media
(Examples Involving Chemical Interaction)

System	Congruently melting compounds salt : org. ratio	Solubility of salt g : g org.	Temperature (°C)
$AsCl_3$+aniline	1 : 3		[a]
$AsCl_3$+1,3,5-xylidine	1 : 3		[a]
$SnCl_4$+o-nitroanisole	1 : 1		[a]
CaI_2+acetone	1 : 3	1·129	50 [b1]
$Ca(NO_3)_2$+acetone	1 : 1	0·184	50 [b]
$CaBr_2$+acetone	1 : 2	0·0292	40 [b]
LiBr+acetone	1 : 2	0·346	50 [b]
$ZnBr_2$+acetone	2 : 1	3·81	50 [b]
$SrBr_2$+acetone	1 : 1/2 : 3	0·00274	50 [b]
$CoCl_2$+acetone	1 : 1	0·0725	50 [b]
$PbCl_2$+triazole	2	7·6	200 [c2]

[1] Represents compounds formed in the solid phase of the saturated solution.
[2] Forms a red melt of a much higher m.p. than pure triazole.
[a] Pushin (1948).
[b] Bell et al. (1930).
[c] J. W. Hastie (unpublished results).

interaction in solution. Table I summarizes the solubility properties of these systems. Those systems in which there is no compound formation on solidification, or in the saturated solid phase, may reasonably be considered to be "physical solutions" without any strong solute–solvent chemical interaction. The solubility properties of such systems are summarized in Table II.

TABLE II

Solutions of Salt in Organic Media
(Cases without Chemical Interaction)

System	Solubility	Temperature (°C)	Comments
Salt+acetone	g salt : g acetone		
$LiCl$+acetone	0·0061	50	Solubility Decreases with increasing temperature[a]
$NiBr_2$+acetone			
NaI+acetone	0·309	50	
$CaCl_2$+acetone	0·000213	50	
$BaBr_2$+acetone	0·000246	50	
Salt+benzene	Wt % halide		
Al_2Br_6+benzene	80·11	51·5	Solubility increases with increasing temperature[b]
Al_2Cl_6+benzene	4·88	108·6	
Al_2I_6+benzene	59·57	110·7	
$PbCl_2$+triazole	11·6	140	⎧ Usually colour-less or pale
$NaCl$+triazole	2·9	132	⎨ yellow melts, depending on
$CsCl$+triazole	>2·9		⎩ concentration[c]

[a] Bell *et al.* (1930).
[b] Eley and King (1951).
[c] J. W. Hastie (unpublished results).

1. *Solutions of Salt in Acetone* (Bell *et al.*, 1930)

The solubilities of salts in acetone form two fairly distinct classes. The class of relatively high solubility of salt in acetone is invariably associated with strong solute–solvent interaction and solid compounds can be prepared from such solutions.

2. *Solutions of Salt in Triazole and Other Organic Melts*

Molten triazole (m.p. 121°C) is a good solvent for a large number of salts (A. Easteal and G. Ruthven, unpublished results). In some cases, especially with transition metal salts, strong interaction between solute and solvent is apparent and solid complex co-ordination compounds separate out of solution on cooling. At temperatures not too far above the melting point of triazole (about 140°C), salts such as $PbCl_2$ and the alkali-metal chlorides form colourless or pale yellow melts. No compound formation is apparent on solidification of the melt. However, at higher temperatures the solutions of $PbCl_2$ in triazole assume a red colour and the solubility of salt increases more than one hundred-fold.

There are few other cases where solutions of salts in organic melts have been studied. Recently, solutions of $NiCl_2$ in molten pyridine hydrochloride have been used in a study of the Ni^{II} absorption spectrum (Smith, 1965). Similar studies have also been made on U^{IV} in molten pyridinium chloride (m.p. 144°C) (Gruen and McBeth, 1959).

3. *Solutions of Transition Metal Chlorides in Methanol* (De Maine and McAlonie, 1961)

Conductances at 20° and 45°C, for $CaCl_2$, $CaCl_2.2H_2O$, $CrCl_3.6H_2O$, $MnCl_2.4H_2O$, $FeCl_2.2H_2O$, $CuCl_2$, $CuCl_2.2H_2O$ and $ZnCl_2$ respectively, dissolved in methanol, have been determined.

B. SOLUTIONS OF ORGANIC COMPOUNDS IN MOLTEN SALTS

At the high temperatures normal to molten salt media, most organic molecules would be expected to decompose. It is not unnatural, therefore, that very little is known about solutions of organic compounds in molten salts. Methanol is known to dissolve in molten $LiClO_3$ without producing any significant change of the properties of the solvent, and it is probably stable in such a melt. Nitrobenzene also appears to be stable in this solvent (Campbell *et al.*, 1962). Sundermeyer and co-workers (1958, 1962, 1963) carried out a considerable number of organic and pseudo-organic reactions by passing the organic vapours through molten salt solvents. Solubilities are not known, but it is clear that the organic molecules must spend sufficient time in the melt to react, either amongst themselves or with the solvent species. The reasonably rapid flow rates and good reaction yields also suggest considerable solubility of the organic component in the melt. The solvents used by these workers are mainly chlorides and pseudo-halides of the alkali and alkaline-earth metals. Temperatures of operation range from 89°C to more than 600°C, depending on the choice of the solvent. Solutes include organosilicones, carbon tetrachloride, ethane, acetylene, ethyl halides, alcohols, n-butyl chloride, etc. A list of the reactions occurring between these solutes and solvents will be given at the end of the chapter in the discussion of the applications of molten salt solvents.

VI. Solutions of Non-Metallic Elements in Molten Salts

A. SULPHUR

The nature of sulphur dissolved in various solvents has been studied by only a few workers: Paterno and Muzzuchelli (1908), Gardner and Fraenkel (1956), Krebs (1957), Greenberg et al. (1958) have studied solutions of sulphur in molten salts by absorption spectra and paramagnetic susceptibility measurements.

In both LiCl+KCl and LiBr+KBr eutectics, addition of sulphur gives rise to blue solutions and the close similarity of the spectra of these solutions indicates that there is no specific interaction between sulphur and the halide ion. From the Gouy measurements of paramagnetic susceptibility it was concluded that the solution contains a paramagnetic species. It is possible that these species are diatomic sulphur molecules since higher polymers are reddish in colour (Gardner and Fraenkel, 1956).

B. IODINE

The absorption spectra of solid iodine in molten KI+LiI, at 400°C and in molten KCl+LiCl at 400°C have been determined (Greenberg and Sundheim, 1958) and the results interpreted as indicating the presence of I_3^- in the former molten salt mixture and I_2Cl^- in the latter. The considerable solubilities ($10^{-3} - 10^{-4}$ molar) at 400°C are probably due to the ions I_3^- or I_2Cl^-, being readily accommodated into the quasi-lattice of the salt mixture.

VII. Solutions of Gases in Molten Salts

Most of the work done on these solutions has been in connection with nuclear reactor technology. For the determination of small to moderate solubilities of non-reacting gases in molten salt systems, the melt is equilibrated with a known pressure of the gas. The solubility may be found by analysing the melt, or by measurement of the loss in weight or change of pressure in the gas reservoir. It is significant to note that dissolved gases are evolved on solidification of those systems where no solid compound exists between the components of the salt and the gas. Solutions of gases in molten salts may conveniently be grouped according to whether or not there is chemical interaction between solvent and solute.

A. SIMPLE SOLUTIONS OF GAS AND SALT

1. *Solubility of Carbon Dioxide in Molten Alkali-Metal Halides* (Grjotheim et al., 1962; Bratland et al., 1963)

The gas solubilities at different temperatures are approximately equal to the free volume of the melts and it is therefore likely that chemical reactions do not occur in the dissolution process. The solubility of gases in molten potassium chloride is greater than in molten sodium chloride at the same temperature. This is in accordance with the larger free volume in the former salt (Bockris and Richards, 1957). For example, the solubilities expressed as moles of CO_2 per ml of solvent (at 1 atm pressure) are 4.6×10^{-6} and 4.0×10^{-6} at 850° and 950°C respectively for NaCl, and 6.0×10^{-6} and 7.0×10^{-6} at 850° and 950°C respectively for KCl.

2. *Solutions of Noble Gases in Molten Halides* (Grimes et al., 1958)

The solubilities of He, Ne, Ar and Xe in the melts,

$$NaF \text{ (53 mole \%)} + ZrF_4 \text{ (47 mole \%)}$$

and

$$NaF \text{ (50 mole \%)} + ZrF_4 \text{ (46 mole \%)} + UF_4 \text{ (4 mole \%)}$$

increase linearly with gas pressure, decrease with increasing atomic weight of the solute and increase with increasing temperature. The solubilities and heats of solution of He and Xe in both melts are very similar. Molten salts act therefore as normal liquids in dissolving such gases. The eutectic melts LiF (46.5%) + NaF (11.5%) + KF (42%) has similar solvent powers to the other fluoride melts mentioned (Blander et al., 1959). A model developed by Blander et al. (1959), which equates the free energy of formation of holes and the size of the gas molecules in a continuous fluid having the same surface tension as the solvent, yields solubility values which are in good agreement with those observed.

B. COMPLEX SOLUTIONS OF GASES IN MOLTEN SALTS

In cases where the gas reacts chemically with the solvent melt, large solubilities may be observed. For example, the solvent melt

$$CuCl_2 \text{ (25 mole \%)} + KCl \text{ (75 mole \%)}$$

is capable of taking up 0.75 moles of fluorine per mole of melt (Klemm and Huss, 1949). This is due to the chemical reaction,

$$CuCl_2 + 3KCl + 3F_2 = K_3(CuF_6) + 2\tfrac{1}{2}Cl_2. \tag{1}$$

Another example of this type is indicated by solutions of titanium tetrachloride vapour in an equimolar NaCl+KCl melt. The solubility of $TiCl_4$ in such solutions has been determined by several workers (e.g. Kroll, 1955; Kreye and Kellogg, 1957), but the results of Flengas (1960) are probably the most reliable because his method involved direct observation of the increase of weight of the salt solution in contact with titanium tetrachloride vapour and was therefore free of the errors introduced by sampling and quenching techniques. The rate at which $TiCl_4$ was taken up in solution was determined both in the molten and finely powdered solid salt mixtures. Figure 1 summarizes the results. From these results, it is clear that the molten salt solvent

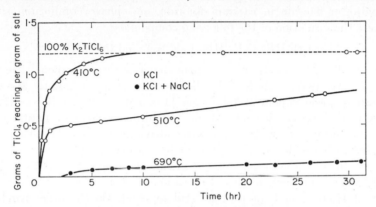

FIG. 1. Reaction rates between gaseous $TiCl_4$, and KCl or 1/1 mole KCl+NaCl at various temperatures (Flengas, 1960). (Reproduced by courtesy of the New York Academy of Sciences.)

mixture is capable of dissolving at least 14 mole % $TiCl_4$ while the solid salt mixture can dissolve 1 mole of $TiCl_4$ per 2 moles of KCl. X-Ray diffraction analysis of the solid indicates that a compound is formed, probably according to the reaction:

$$TiCl_4 + 2KCl = K_2TiCl_6. \qquad (2)$$

From the solubility results it is concluded that the optimum temperature range for the formation of this compound at a pressure of 1 atm of $TiCl_4$ is between 350° and 400°C. At temperatures above 800°C the solvation behaviour changes because of a reaction between $TiCl_4$ and NaCl probably forming Na_2TiCl_6.

Another example of chemical interaction between solvent and solute is given by solutions of hydrogen fluoride in molten NaF+ZrF$_4$ mixtures (Schaffer et al., 1959). In contrast with the behaviour of the noble gases in similar solvents, the solubility of hydrogen fluoride decreases as the temperature is increased. Also the dependence of its solubility on the nature of the solvent is far greater than that exhibited by noble gases in related solvents.

This is probably connected with the relatively high stability of compounds between NaF and HF. The solubility of hydrogen fluoride in molten alkali-metal fluorides increases with increase of atomic number of the metal. It is possible that this dependence of the solubility on the solvent may be related to the relative stabilities of some of the alkali-metal acid fluorides which have been noted at lower temperatures (Winsor and Cady, 1948).

The high solubility (Winsor and Cady, 1948) of hydrogen fluoride in caesium fluoride has a special use in that the solvent serves as an electrolyte for the electrolytic preparation of fluorine at room temperature (Mathers and Stroup, 1934). Considerable solvent–solute interaction is evident in solutions of hydrogen fluoride in caesium fluoride, and phase equilibrium studies indicate the formation of the following compounds:

$$CsF.HF, \quad CsF.2HF, \quad CsF.3HF \text{ and } CsF.6HF.$$

The $LiCl + KCl$ eutectic is capable of dissolving water vapour (Burkhard and Corbett, 1957) and the solubilities follow Henry's Law to 18 mm Hg pressure of water vapour at 480°C and 14 mm Hg at 390°C. Beyond 18 mm at 480°C there exists a sharp break due to hydrolysis of the LiCl at the higher water pressures but at 390°C no such behaviour is observed. The unusual tenacity with which water is retained by the melt is probably connected with the high charge density of the Li^+ ion. In fact if the $LiCl + KCl$ melt which was in equilibrium with H_2O vapour is evacuated for 1 h, up to 4 mm of H_2O per mole of LiCl are still retained. On the other hand, if a 62 mole % $NaCl + 38$ mole % KCl melt in equilibrium with water vapour at 700°C is evacuated for 15 min, no detectable amount of water is retained by the melt.

Water is also soluble in molten alkali-metal nitrates (Na, K, Cs), apparently accommodated in the interstices of the melt. Oxygen and nitrogen, on the other hand, are not appreciably soluble in these nitrate melts.

VIII. Solutions of Metals in Molten Salts

A. INTRODUCTION

Many molten salts act as solvents for metals; in particular molten halides often dissolve their parent metal. The ability of molten halides to dissolve their own parent metal was first suggested by the colouration produced in the melt by the electrolysis of molten rubidium and caesium chlorides (Bunsen and Kirchoff, 1861). Lorentz and Eitel (1915), from optical and X-ray studies on the solids, postulated that solutions of metals in molten salts were colloidal. However, Heymann and Friedlander (1930) showed this reasoning to be incorrect, since the solutions show none of the properties usually associated with colloids. It is now recognized that solutions of metals in molten salts fall into two categories.

(i) Those in which there is no appreciable chemical interaction between solvent (salt) and solute (metal). In these solutions the metal will impart some of its metallic character to the mixture.

(ii) Those in which considerable interaction between solute and solvent occurs.

There are also solutions that are not defined by either of these categories but are intermediate between the two. A discussion of the various theories of the nature of solutions of metals in molten salts is given by Delimarskii and Markov (1961) as well as by Bredig (1963).

B. SOLUTIONS WITHOUT SIGNIFICANT INTERACTION

Solutions of this type have also been referred to as "metallic". Metals of the first and second periods of the Periodic Table and the Lanthanides, mainly form this class of solutions, when dissolved in their own molten halides.

1. *Alkali-Metal Solutions in Molten Alkali-Metal Halides*

Bredig (1963) has summarized the physical properties of these systems. As shown in Table III for fluorides and chlorides, the consolute temperatures, i.e. temperatures at which there is complete miscibility between salt and metal in all proportions, decrease in the order:

$$Li > Na > K > Rb.$$

The temperatures range from about 1325° to 800°C for the fluorides.

The solubility of metals in their molten halides increases in the order:

$$Li < Na < K < Rb < Cs.$$

In each system involving caesium, there is complete miscibility and it is apparent that the size (or more specifically the charge density) of the alkali-metal cation is the most important feature involved in solubility relationships for these systems. The concentration of metal in the critical solution (namely that solution at the consolute temperature) increases from the fluoride to the iodide for the sodium, potassium and rubidium systems.

Supporting evidence for the non-existence of strong chemical interaction between solute and solvent in the above systems, is given by the activity coefficients (γ) of the salts (Bredig, 1963). These coefficients show increasing positive deviations from Raoult's Law with increasing metal concentration and these deviations are usually associated with systems having regions of immiscibility but with no strong chemical interaction. It is also probably significant that the plots of $RT\ln \gamma_{salt}$ versus ϕ^2_{metal} (where ϕ_{metal} is mole fraction of metal), for the KBr, RbBr and CsI systems, are only slightly curved. The approximate linearity of these curves is in accordance with the behaviour of regular solutions. Such solutions are characterized by an ideal entropy (in the

Raoult-Law sense) and only slight interaction between solute and solvent species.

Alternatively it has been suggested (Pitzer, 1962) that the excess free energy of mixing (i.e. $RT\ln\gamma_{salt}$) is due to the conversion of the metallic state of binding of the metal electrons to an ionic type of binding. This theory would predict a substantial positive excess entropy of mixing.

TABLE III

Alkali-Metal–Alkali-Metal Halide Systems

Metal-Salt System	Salt M.p. °K	Metal M.p. °K	Monotectic (for salt rich liquid only) Temp. °K	Mole % M	Eutectic (estimated by extrapolation) Mole % M	Consolute Temp. °K	Mole % M	Solubility in salt Temp. °K	Mole % M
Li+LiF	1121	452	1120	~1	—	1603	40		—[a]
Li+LiCl	883	452	882	~0·5	—	—			—[a]
Na+NaF	1268	370	1263	~3	10^{-9}	1453	28		—[ab]
								1273	7·6[c]
Na+NaCl	1073	370	1068	2·1	—	1353	50		—[b]
								1084	2·8[c]
								1273	33·0[c]
K+KF	1131	337	1122	4·9	3×10^{-4}	1177	20		—[ad]
								1221	23·3
K+KCl	1043	337	1024	10·5	10^{-9}	1063	39		—[b]
								1073	7·6[f]
Rb+RbF	1068	312	1046	~9	—	1063	21		—[ab]
Rb+RbCl	995	312	969	18	—	979	37		—[b]
Cs+CsF	976	302	No miscibility gap		10^{-3}	—		965	6·0[a]
Cs+CsCl	918	302	—		10^{-8}	—			—[e]
								899	9·0[b]

[a] Dworkin et al. (1962).
[b] Johnson and Bredig (1960).
[c] Bredig et al. (1955).
[d] Johnson and Bredig (1958).
[e] Bredig and Bronstein (1955).
[f] Belozerskii (1940).

For these systems, the specific conductivity increases markedly when metal is added to the molten salt and continues increasing with added amounts of metal. Hence Bronstein and Bredig (1958, 1961) concluded that a considerable part of the conduction is electronic. In the case of potassium iodide containing 42 mole % potassium, the electronic contribution to the conductivity is more than 99·5%. To explain the equivalent conductances of these systems, Bronstein and Bredig (1958, 1961) suggested that in these solutions:

(a) electron orbital overlap exists at relatively high metal concentrations;

(b) in sodium solutions of high metal content, electron pairs are trapped to form, for example, diatomic molecules of Na_2 (in lithium systems this electron pairing would be even more pronounced);

(c) the contribution to the specific conductivity by the metal solute increases greatly in going from the fluoride to the iodide systems, that is, with increase of atomic number or size of the halide ion.

(d) the metalic contribution to the specific conductivity decreases from sodium to potassium, i.e. with increasing size of metal ion.

2. Alkaline-Earth Metal Solutions in Molten Alkaline-Earth Halides

Only recently have accurate phase diagrams been determined for these systems. The phase diagram for the $Ba+BaCl_2$ system has been determined and is similar to those of the earlier alkali-metal+alkali-metal halide systems. Phase equilibria have also been reported for $Ca+CaF_2$ (Rogers et al., 1961), $Ca+CaCl_2$ (Peterson and Hinkebein, 1959), $Ca+CaBr_2$ and $Ca+CaI_2$ (Staffansson, 1959). Table IV gives the solubilities of the metal in

TABLE IV

Alkaline-Earth Metal + Alkaline-Earth Halide Systems

Metal-Salt System	Salt M.p. °K	Metal M.p. °K	Monotectic (for salt rich liquid only)		Eutectic		Consolute		Solubility in salt	
			Temp. °K	Mole % M	Temp. °K	Mole % M	Temp. °K	Mole % M	Temp. °K	Mole % M
$Mg+MgCl_2$	987	923	~987	0·2	~923	100·0	—	—	—	—[a]
									1073	1·08[b]
									1323	1·57[b]
$Ca+CaF_2$	1691	1110	1563	25·5	1094	98·6	1595±5	45	—	—[c]
$Ca+CaCl_2$	1045	1110	1093	2·7	1033	2·0	1610±5	62	—	—[a]
									1273	5·4[d]
$Ca+CaBr_2$	1015	1110	1100	2·3	1000	3·0	1610±5	64	—	—[a]
$Ca+CaI_2$	1053	1110	1104	3·8	1033	2·0	1650±5	74	—	—[a]
$Sr+SrF_2$									1273	9·66[d]
									1273	19·9[d]
$Sr+SrCl_2$	1145	1044	1112	5·5	?	?	?	?	—	—[a]
$Sr+SrBr_2$									1273	24·6[d]
$Sr+SrI_2$									1273	36·1[d]
$Ba+BaF_2$									1273	39·3[d]
									1323	21·9[d]
$Ba+BaCl_2$	1235	1002	1163	15·0	985	99·0	1290	50	—	—[a]
$Ba+BaCl_2$									1323	30·6[d]
$Ba+BaBr_2$									1323	36·7[d]
$Ba+BaI_2$									1323	39·4[d]

[a] Bredig (1963). [c] Rogers et al. (1961).
[b] Zhurin (1935). [d] Guntz and Benoit (1924).

these systems. In general these systems resemble the alkali-metal halide systems, and exhibit a rapid increase in solubility with increase of atomic number of the metal. For example, the maximum solubility in mole % for the following systems near the melting point of each salt is given by:

$$Mg+MgCl_2 : 0·5$$
$$Ca+CaCl_2 : 2·7$$
$$Sr+SrCl_2 : 5·5$$
$$Ba+BaCl_2 : 20.$$

Various equilibria have been suggested to explain the properties of the solutions, e.g. from activity measurements on the $Mg + MgCl_2$ system the proposed solution mechanism was $Mg + Mg^{2+} = (Mg_2)^{2+}$. The conductivity behaviour is also similar to that in the alkali-metal + alkali-metal halide systems except that the rate of change of specific conductivity with added metal is not as great for the alkaline-earth systems.

TABLE V

Lanthanide-metal + Lanthanide-Metal Halide Systems
Solubility Data

Metal-Salt system	Salt M.p. °K	Metal M.p. °K	Eutectic		Solubility in MX_3	
			Temp. °K	Mole % M	Temp. °K	Mole % M
$La + LaCl_3$	1131	1193	1099	9·0	1273	12·0[a]
$La + LaBr_3$	1061		1001	14·5	1173	15·5[ab]
$La + LaI_3$	1052		1007	8·2	1173	33[ac]
$Ce + CeCl_3$	1090	1068	1050	9·0	1171	9[a]
					1123	33[d]
$Ce + CeBr_3$	1005		960	12·0	1173	14[ab]
$Ce + CeI_3$	1034		988	8·8	1173	32[a]
$Pr + PrCl_3$	1059	1208	919	17·0	1073	19[ac]
$Pr + PrBr_3$	966		852	16·0	1023	18[ab]
$Pr + PrI_3$	1011		939	11·9	1073	29[a]
$Nd + NdCl_3$	1032	1297	913	14·0	1173	31[e]
$Nd + NdBr_3$	955		—	—	—	—[f]
$Nd + NdI_3$	1060		764	26·5	1073	37[e]
$Gd + GdI_3$	1204	1585	1098	14·0	1173	14[a]
$Y + YI_3$	1270	1782	1221	12·0	1423	15[f]

[a] Cubicciotti and Cleary (1952).
[b] Sallach and Corbett (1962).
[c] Druding and Corbett (1959).
[d] Cubicciotti (1949).
[e] Druding and Corbett (1959, 1961).
[f] Bredig (1963).

3. Lanthanide Metal Solutions in Molten Lanthanide Trihalides

These solutions are less "metallic" in character than those discussed in Section VIIIB, 1 and 2. Table V gives the solubilities of metal in the molten trihalide. A feature of these systems is that the phase diagrams indicate the existence of congruent and incongruently melting compounds. Stable solid compounds corresponding to the composition MX_2 were found in the $Nd + NdI_3$,

$Pr + PrI_3$, $Ce + CeI_3$ and $La + LaI_3$ systems. Also non-stoichiometric compounds such as $NdCl_{2.3}$, $NdCl_{2.2}$, $PrI_{2.5}$, $CeI_{2.4}$, $LaI_{2.4}$ appear to exist.

The specific conductivities of the metal + salt solutions increase in the order:

$$Nd < Pr < Ce < La \ll K.$$

C. SOLUTIONS WITH STRONG SOLUTE–SOLVENT INTERACTION (i.e. NON-METALLIC SOLUTIONS)

Non-metallic solutions of metals in their molten salts are defined as those which exhibit only a very slight change in conductivity of salt on addition of the metal. This indicates that the metallic electrons are in some way bound up in the melt and are not available for conduction. It is considered that this criterion outweighs, for example, the observable metallic lustre of solutions of bismuth in bismuth chloride (Cubicciotti, 1960).

A second criterion, distinguishing these systems from the "metallic" systems is the formation of stoichiometric solid halides of the metal in a lower valence state.

1. Transition Metal Systems

Little work has been done on metal solutions of this type. The $Ni + NiCl_2$ system has been studied by Johnson et al. (1958), the solubility of metal being 9 mole % Ni at the eutectic temperature of 980°C. The authors considered that Ni^+ ions were formed but alternative explanations are possible to explain the freezing point depression and heat fusion data. Solubility data are given in Table VI.

2. Post Transition Metal Systems

It has been suggested (Corbett et al., 1955, 1957, 1960) that the solubility of the metals in their molten halides depends on their ability to form a cationic species having a lower than normal oxidation state. Table VII indicates that this tendency increases with increasing atomic weight for each group. The solubility also increases in the order, $I < Br < Cl$, except that for cadmium and mercury the tendency is reversed.

(a) *Subgroup I.* The solubility of silver in molten silver chloride is 0·06 mole % at 700°C.

(b) *Subgroup II.* Mercury subhalides, Hg_2X_2 are well known and the chloride is stable to 525°C, where it decomposes into a salt-rich melt of almost the same composition and a small amount of liquid mercury phase containing 6·8 mole % $HgCl_2$ in solution (Yosim and Mayer, 1960). Hevesy and Löwenstein (1930) quote the solubility of Hg in $HgCl_2$ at 350°C as 50 mole % and in HgI_2 33·6 mole %.

The systems $Cd + CdX_2$ have been extensively studied (Aten, 1910; Lorentz and Eitel, 1926; Hevesy and Löwenstein, 1930; Farquharson and Heymann, 1935; Cubicciotti, 1953a,b).

TABLE VI

Transition Metal Systems—Solubility Data

System	Salt M.p. °C	Metal M.p. °C	Solubility	
			Temp. °C	Mole % M
Ni+NiCl$_2$			977	9·1[a]
Ag+AgCl	455	960·8	490	0·03[b]
			700	0·06[b]
Zn+ZnCl$_2$	262	419·47	500	0·18[c]
			500	$8·9 \times 10^{-5d}$
Zn+ZnI$_2$	446	419·47	500	0·28[c]
Cd+CdCl$_2$	568	40 (vac)	550	14·0[e]
			600	15·2[e]
			800	21·0[e]
			1000	30·0[e]
Cd+CdBr$_2$	567	40·0	550	14·0[d]
			600	13·9[f]
			700	20·0[f]
			900	28·0[f]
Cd+CdI$_2$	388	40·0	400	2·5[f]
			600	6·07[f]
			700	15·0[f]
			950	25·0[f]
Hg+HgCl$_2$	276	−38·87	280	7·0[d]
			350	50·0[g]
			400	18·0[g]
			500	40·0[g]
Hg+HgI$_2$	259	−38·87	230	25·0[d]
			280	35·0[d]
			350	33·6[d]

[a] Johnson et al. (1958).
[b] Corbett and Winbush (1955).
[c] Corbett et al. (1957).
[d] Hevesy and Löwenstein (1930).
[e] Aten (1910); Hevesy and Löwenstein (1930); Topol and Laudis (1960).
[f] Topol and Laudis (1960).
[g] Yosim and Mayer (1960).

The solubility of Cd in CdCl$_2$ at 600°C has been given as 15·2 mole %. The diamagnetic nature of the solution indicates that the mechanism of metal solubility is either through the formation of Cd_2^{2+} or a true solution of molecules or atoms. Freezing point depression measurements indicate that the subchloride Cd_2Cl_2 may be formed (Grjotheim et al., 1955). This compound disproportionates on solidification, as is seen by the presence of crystalline

TABLE VII

Post Transition-Metal Systems—Solubility Data

System	Salt M.p. °C	Metal M.p. °C	Solubility Temp. °C	Solubility Mole % M
$Al + AlI_3$	191·0	659·7	423	0·3[a]
$Ga + GaCl_2$	170·5	29·78	180	1·92[a]
$Ga + Ga_2Cl_4$		29·78	180	3·7[a]
$Ga + Ga_2Br_4$		29·78	180	14·0[bc]
$Tl + TlCl$	430·0	302·0	550	0·09[a]
			650	0·09[a]
$Sn + SnCl_2$	246·0	231·9	500	0·0032[a]
$Sn + SnBr_2$	215·5		500	0·068[a]
$Pb + PbCl_2$	501·0	327·4	600	0·02[a]
			700	0·052[a]
			700	0·055[d]
			800	0·123[a]
$Pb + PbI_2$	402·0	327·4	440	0·024[e]
			600	0·15[e]
			700	0·41[e]
$Sb + SbCl_3$	73·4	630·5	270	0·18[b]
$Sb + SbI_3$	167·0	630·5	200	1·69[bf]
			300	3·5[f]
			400	5·8[f]
$Bi + BiCl_3$	230·2	271·3	202	28·0[g]
			320	46·0[g]
			450	47·5[h]
			550	28·0[i]
			780	100·0[g]
$Bi + BiBr_3$	218·0	271·3	205	21·0[j]
			294	57·0[j]
			440	45·0[j]
			538	100·0[j]
$Bi + BiI_3$	439·0	271·3	336	48·0[j]
			458	100·0[j]

[a] Corbett and Winbush (1955).
[b] Corbett et al. (1957).
[c] Corbett and Hershaft (1958).
[d] Karpachev et al. (1944).
[e] Bredig (1963).
[f] Bruner and Corbett (1961).
[g] Yosim et al. (1959).
[h] Cubicciotti and Cleary (1952).
[i] Levy et al. (1960a).
[j] Yosim et al. (1962).

cadmium metal in the solid. Activity data may be interpreted in terms of the presence of $(Cd_2)^{2+}$ and also in terms of the formation of complex anions such as $(CdCl_4)^{2-}$ (Bredig, 1962).

The weight of evidence seems to suggest that Cd most likely dissolves in $CdCl_2$ to form $(Cd_2)^{2+}$. Thus the amount of cadmium passing into solution would be dependent on the concentration of Cd^{2+} already present in the solution; hence a semi-quantitative estimate of the free Cd^{2+} ions in the molten salt mixtures such as $CdCl_2 + NaCl$ and $CdCl_2 + KCl$, may be obtained from the solubility of cadmium metal in these solutions. In fact, the presence of potassium chloride strongly suppresses the solubility of Cd in molten $CdCl_2$ over a wide composition range, thus suggesting the removal of Cd^{2+} from $CdCl_2$ solutions in the form of complex ions, such as $CdCl_4^{2-}$.

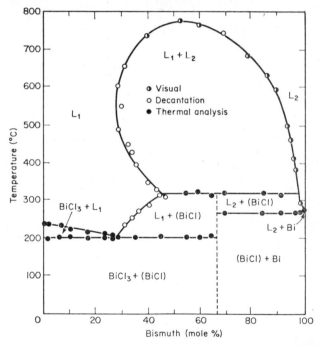

FIG. 2. Bismuth metal–bismuth trichloride system (Yosim *et al.*, 1959). (Reproduced by courtesy of the American Chemical Society.)

The metal solubility in the $Zn + ZnX_2$ systems (Corbett *et al.*, 1957) is only of the order of 1 mole %. By analogy with the cadmium systems we could attribute low solubility to the lack of free Zn^{2+} ions in molten $ZnCl_2$ which most probably exists in the form of complex ions. The smaller solubility of metal in this system relative to the Cd system is in accordance with the view that the smaller Zn^{2+} ion is more capable of forming stable complex ions than Cd^{2+}.

(c) *Subgroups III and IV.* In these subgroups the solubilities of metals in their molten halides are much smaller than under (a) and (b) above (Corbett and Winbush, 1955; Corbett et al., 1957).

(d) *Subgroup V* (Corbett and Albers, 1960). As, Sb, Bi all possess a stable trivalent oxidation state. The solubility of metals in their salts rises rapidly with increasing atomic number, the bismuth system forming sub-halides, BiX. The $Bi + BiCl_3$ phase diagram is shown in Fig. 2.

It should be noted that salts are themselves soluble in metals but usually to a much smaller extent than that of metal in salt, e.g. the solubility of $PbCl_2$ at 1000°C in Pb is approximately 1 mole % (Yosim and Luchsinger, 1960).

TABLE VIII

Equilibrium Constants for Displacement Solubility Reactions[1]

Equilibrium	Temperature °C	K
$Na + LiCl \rightleftharpoons NaCl + Li$	900	0·45
$K + NaCl \rightleftharpoons KCl + Na$	900	0·87
$K + NaI \rightleftharpoons KI + Na$	900	0·017
$3Na + AlCl_3 \rightleftharpoons 3NaCl + Al$	825	$\sim 5·0 \times 10^{-10}$
$Mg + ZnCl_2 \rightleftharpoons MgCl_2 + Zn$	—	$1·6 \times 10^{-5}$
$Cd + PbCl_2 \rightleftharpoons CdCl_2 + Pb$	600	$\sim 3·0 \times 10^{-2}$

[1] Abstracted from Delimarskii and Markov (1961).

D. SOLUTIONS OF METALS IN SALTS OF ANOTHER METAL—DISPLACEMENT SOLUBILITY

In these systems there is the equilibrium:

$$M_I + M_{II}X \overset{K}{\rightleftharpoons} M_IX + M_{II}. \tag{3}$$

It is possible to calculate the equilibrium constant K by determining the e.m.f. of the corresponding Jacobi-Daniell cell, assuming a negligible liquid junction potential between the two molten salts. For example, for the cell $Cd/CdCl_2/PbCl_2/Pb$ the reaction is,

$$Cd + PbCl_2 \rightleftharpoons CdCl_2 + Pb. \tag{4}$$

The equilibrium constant K may be considered to summarize the solubility behaviour of metals in unlike salts and some values are given in Table VIII.

Delimarskii and Markov (1961) list tables of K values for a large number of metals in molten halides. It should be noted that for many metals the

13

equilibrium $M + xPbCl_2 \rightleftharpoons MCl_{2x} + xPb$ is displaced almost completely to the right and as molten metallic lead can be separated easily from the rest of the system, this is a convenient method of preparing heavy metal chlorides in the anhydrous state. Inman *et al.* (1960) used such a reaction at 650°C to prepare UCl_3,

$$2U + 3PbCl_2 = 2UCl_3 + 3Pb. \tag{5}$$

In industrial electrolysis it is very important to know the electrochemical series of metals in any desired solvent and Delimarskii and Markov (1961) have tabulated electrode potentials of metals in various molten electrolytes as well as listing a qualitatively determined electrochemical series of metals in molten salts. It should be pointed out that such a series is not necessarily the same for different molten salt solvents. There is also a change of electrode potential with temperature so that in the cell reaction $Cd + PbCl_2 = CdCl_2 + Pb$, cadmium will displace lead below 650°C and lead will displace cadmium at higher temperatures.

TABLE IX

Electrochemical Series of Metals in Molten Salts[1]

Solvent	Temperature °C	Electrochemical Series
$NaCl + AlCl_3$	500	Na, Be, Al, Mn, Tl, Zn, Cd, Sn^{II}, Pb, Co, Ag, Cu^I, Hg^{II}, Sb^{III}, Bi, Ni.
$NaCl + AlCl_3$	700	Na, Al, Mn, Tl, Zn, Cd, Pb, Ag, Cu^I, Co, Hg^{II}, Sb^{III}, Ni, Bi.
$NaBr + AlBr_3$	700	Na, Al, Zn, Cd, Pb, Sn^{II}, Cu^I, Ag, Co, Hg^{II}, Ni, Sb^{III}, Bi.
$NaI + AlI_3$	700	Na, Al, Cd, Ag, Sn^{II}, Pb, Cu^I, Bi, Hg^{II}, Co, Ni, Sb.

[1] Abstracted from Delimarskii and Markov (1961).

IX. SOLUTIONS OF SALT IN MOLTEN SALT

In general, molten salts are better solvents for salts than any other solvent and the majority of molten salt systems are completely miscible. The few systems that exhibit immiscibility, i.e. the formation of two liquid phases, are of growing interest from the point of view of extraction of some inorganic solutes from multiphase systems.

The molten halides are generally miscible with one another, especially for true binary systems. Molten reciprocal systems of halides with metal salts of a different anion can however exhibit immiscibility, e.g. sodium borate+ sodium halide (Boleslaw and Scheidt, 1961).

The solubility of salts in molten salts as such has received very little attention in the past. Phase diagrams are the most useful indication of their solubility properties. For a discussion of the interpretation of phase diagrams and their relation to solubility the reader should refer to standard texts. Phase diagrams have been collected and presented in Landolt-Börnstein (1956).

A. MOLTEN SALT SYSTEMS WITH INCOMPLETE MISCIBILITY

Molten salt systems in which there is incomplete miscibility are listed in Table X.

Many other binary systems exhibit mutual immiscibility—they generally consist of an aluminium salt with an ionic salt, e.g. $AlBr_3$ with $NaBr$, KBr, NH_4Br, $CaBr_2$ and $TlBr$; and $AlCl_3$ with $NaCl$, KCl, NH_4Cl, $AgCl$, $SnCl_2$ and $SnCl_4$ (Kendall *et al.*, 1923).

The following molten reciprocal systems also have regions of immiscibility (Belyaev, 1960).

$AgCl$ or $AgBr$ with $LiNO_3$, $NaNO_3$, KNO_3, $TlNO_3$, $Ca(NO_3)_2$, Li_2WO_4, $LiVO_3$, $NaVO_3$, KVO_3, $NaCrO_4$, $NaMoO_4$, Na_2WO_4

AgI with $NaCl$, $LiCl$, $NaNO_3$, KNO_3, $TlNO_3$

$TlBr$ with nitrates

$TlCl$ with nitrates

$CdCl_2$ with some oxy-salts

$CdBr_2$ with some oxy-salts

LiF with $CsCl$, $CsBr$, PbO

PbO with NaF, KCl, $NaCl$, $RbCl$, $NaBr$, KF, KI

SiO_2 with MgF_2, CaF_2, SrF_2, BaF_2

Also, $Li_2SO_4 + PbCl_2$, $PbCl_2 + Ag_2S$, $B_2O_3 + NaCl$ and $B_2O_3 + KCl$.

On the basis of these observations of partial miscibility, various classes of systems are distinguishable. Various workers, Kendall *et al.* (1923) and Belyaev (1958, 1960), have attempted to relate factors such as position of ions in periodic classification, temperature of mixture, internal pressure differences, molar and atomic volumes, etc., with the observed partial miscibility of certain molten salt systems.

The following types of systems display partial immiscibility:

$$AX + BY; \quad AX + BX; \quad AX + AY,$$

the first being a reciprocal system and the latter two being binary systems.

1. *AX + BY Systems*

In such systems it is apparent that for incomplete miscibility, one of the component salts must be a compound of comparatively low polarity, (i.e.

13*

TABLE X

Molten Salt Systems with Incomplete Miscibility (Binary Systems)

System	Region of immiscibility mole % second component	Congruently melting compounds
$AlCl_3 + PCl_5$	74– > 78·9	1 : 1
$AlCl_3 + NaCl$	2 phases near $AlCl_3$	1 : 1
$AlCl_3 + KCl$	2 phases near $AlCl_3$	1 : 1
$Hg_2Br_2 + AlBr_3$	84·6–99·1	1 : 2
$SnCl_2 + SbCl_3$	8·8–98·6	$x : y$
$PbBr_2 + AlBr_3$	83·8–99·2	1 : 2
$AlCl_3 + NH_4Cl$	0·2–20·5	$x : y$
		1 : 1
$AlBr_3 + NaBr$	2·6–16·3	$x : y^a$
		7 : 2^a
		2 : 1^a
		1 : 1^a
$AlBr_3 + KBr$	0·4–22·1	$x : y^a$
		2 : 1^a
		1 : 1^a
$AlBr_3 + NH_4Br$	0·5–20·8	$x : y^a$
		3 : 1^a
		2 : 1^a
		1 : 1^a
$AlBr_3 + CaBr_2$	0·8–14·0	$x : y^a$
		2 : 1^a
$AgCl + AlCl_3$	82·4–99·3	$x : y^a$
		1 : 1^a
$AgBr + AlBr_3$	83·0–97·8	2 compounds^a
$TlCl + AlCl_3$	85·3–98·8	3 compounds^a
$TlBr + AlBr_3$	77·2–99·4	a
$SnBr_2 + AlBr_3$	85·8–98·2	a

^{a} Kendall et al. (1923). All other systems: Landolt-Börnstein (1956).

covalent) or a halide, oxide or sulphide of a transition or post-transition element, while the other component is a typical salt—usually of an alkali-metal. Exceptions to this rule are known, e.g. LiF + CsCl and LiF + CsBr systems have incomplete miscibility in the molten state.

2. AX + BX Systems

One of the component salts must be of low polarity, containing a multi-valent cation such as Al^{3+}, Bi^{3+}, Sb^{3+} etc., while the other is a typically polar salt. The formation of complex compounds is also favoured by these conditions although the compounds formed are usually not well characterized.

3. $AX + AY$ Systems

In such systems the anions are usually very different in size and charge density, e.g. salts such as silicates, titanates or borates together with simple alkali-metal halides.

B. MOLTEN SALT SYSTEMS WITH COMPLETE MISCIBILITY

Systems having complete miscibility are too numerous to list and the reader should refer to the phase diagrams for information on the equilibrium states of the systems.

The solubility of metal oxides in molten salts is of some interest in connection with the general problem of metal oxidation in these media. Thus Stern (1961) carried out a study of oxide solubility in molten NaCl at 900° for metals of the first transition series from Ti to Cu. The following regularities in the solubility data are noticed.

(a) Only oxides of metals having an odd atomic number, i.e. an odd number of $3d$ electrons, show any appreciable interaction with NaCl. Of the remainder, Cr_2O_3 is an exception only in the presence of oxygen.

(b) With the exception of V_2O_5 which oxidizes Cl^-, soluble oxides have possibly more than one oxide stable at 900°. All the insoluble oxides have only one stable oxide (NiO, Fe_2O_3 are included since their solubilities are very low).

(c) The metal to oxide ratio found in the melts for the soluble oxides is much greater than can be accounted for on the basis of a simple solubility, also the stoichiometry does not correspond to any known oxide stable in the solid state.

(d) In spite of the considerable scatter of solubilities, all the soluble oxides with the exception of copper dissolve to the extent 0·001–0·01 mole fraction of metal in the melt.

C. THE STRUCTURE OF MOLTEN SALT SOLUTIONS

There have been many reviews on the structure of molten salt mixtures (e.g. see Bloom, 1959; Blomgren and Van Artsdalen, 1960). As in the case for aqueous solutions, the physical and chemical nature of molten salt mixtures is better understood than for the individual molten salts. Most of the thermodynamic and structural methods of physical chemistry have been applied to molten salts for the elucidation of structure but, unfortunately, the number of systems that have received detailed attention by several methods are few. The heavy-metal dihalide + alkali-metal halide systems appear to have received the most attention and these will be discussed as examples of molten salt solutions.

The molten heavy-metal dihalide+alkali-metal halide systems have a wide range of thermodynamic properties from which the nature of solute–solvent interaction can be ascertained. Thermodynamic activity determinations have been particularly useful in this respect. It is thermodynamically possible to describe systems as "ideal", "regular" (for which there are varying degrees of entropy assumptions), or "complex". Ideal mixtures by definition do not involve any significant interaction between solute and

TABLE XI

Immiscibility in Reciprocal Molten Salt Systems

System	Region of immiscibility mole % second component
$FeO+NaF$	3·0–94·0
$AgCl+Li_2SO_4$	1·5–98·0
$AgCl+LiNO_3$	
$CdCl_2+Li_2SO_4$	6·0–80·0
$AgNO_3+NaCl$	29·0–76·0
$HgBr_2+AlCl_3$	50·0–99·0
$TlBr+KNO_3$	14·0–92·5
$TlI+KNO_3$	0·0–97·0
Tl_2SO_4+AgI	11·0–86·0
$TlNO_3+KBr$	
$TlNO_3+AgI$	1·5–93·0
$AlBr_3+NaI$	2·0–13·0
$AlBr_3+KI$	2·0–13·0
$Na_2B_4O_7+NaCl$	66·0–99·8
$BaCl_2+Na_2CO_3$	39·0–62·0
Ag_2SO_4+LiCl	41·0–87·0
$AgNO_3+KCl$	32·0–64·0
$CdSO_4+LiCl$	
$TlNO_3+KI$	24·0–72·0
$AgNO_3+LiCl$	
$TlI+AgNO_3$	45·0—53·0

solvent and the distribution of the species may be completely random (if Raoult Law ideality is assumed) or may involve a quasi-lattice arrangement with interlocking cation and anion semi-lattices, for Temkin ideality (Temkin, 1945). The ionic nature of the melts favours the latter ideality criterion. It should be noted that for binary systems of the type MX_2+AX, activity determinations make no distinction between the ideality models.

Systems containing LiCl appear to be very nearly ideal (e.g. $LiCl+CdCl_2$ and $LiCl+PbCl_2$). Systems containing NaX exhibit slightly negative activity deviations from the Temkin model. Other data, such as partial molar volumes, conductivities, surface tension and phase diagrams suggest that there is little or no tendency to produce ion-associated species and accordingly ideal entropy conditions should prevail (Bloom, 1959). The activity values found in these systems may then be explained in terms of a non-zero heat of mixing of solute and solvent, arising from coulombic interaction between the constituent ions. This is in fact the zeroth approximation of the familiar regular solution model. The high temperatures of molten salt systems would appear to favour the zeroth rather than the first or higher approximations.

On the other hand, molten systems of the type $MX_2 + KX$ show thermodynamic properties that are too different from those in an ideal or regular situation to be explainable by these models. The small activities of the component salts imply that they are partly bound up in solution in the form of complex ions. Other measurements such as conductivity, molar volume, cryoscopy and the more direct Raman spectra, are in agreement with this view. Systems such as $MX_2 + RbX$ and $MX_2 + CsX$ are even more pronounced in their non-ideal thermodynamic behaviour. This is interpreted in terms of an increasing stability of complex ions with decreasing charge density, or ionic potential, of the alkali-metal cation.

Bloom (1963) has discussed the factors influencing the formation of complex ions in molten salt mixtures. The tendency of certain ions such as Cd^{2+}, Zn^{2+} and Pb^{2+} to form complex ions leads to the formation of minima in the isotherms of equivalent conductance against composition as well as positive deviations in the molar volume isotherms. Gruen *et al.* (1958) and Wait and Janz (1963) have shown that in such molten salt solutions the applied properties such as ultra-violet, Raman and infra-red spectra show the formation of new species on mixing the component molten salts. These new species are termed complex ions and in the $KCl + CdCl_2$ system have been postulated as $CdCl_3^-$, $CdCl_4^{2-}$ or $CdCl_6^{4-}$ resulting from the reactions:

$$KCl + CdCl_2 = KCdCl_3 \qquad (6a)$$

$$2KCl + CdCl_2 = K_2CdCl_4 \qquad (6b)$$

$$4KCl + CdCl_2 = K_4CdCl_6. \qquad (6c)$$

The addition of chloride ions to the system in order to form complex ions, leads also to the addition of cations (in order to maintain electrical neutrality). The charge density and therefore polarizing power of the added alkali-metal cation is inversely related to its ionic radius, hence the addition of a highly polarizing ion such as Li^+ is sufficient to disrupt the tendency to form complexes. Alternatively it may be assumed that Li^+ competes strongly with Cd^{2+} for the available Cl^- ions. The tendency to destroy the efforts of ions such as Cd^{2+} to build up complex ions, will decrease with increase of ionic radius of the added alkali-metal cation, hence the addition of NaCl to molten $CdCl_2$ has less disrupting effect on the tendency of cadmium to build up complex ions. Similar considerations apply to the addition of LiCl and NaCl to molten $PbCl_2$. K^+, Rb^+ and Cs^+ will have increasingly less tendency to prevent the formation of the complex ions containing cadmium or lead; the progressively increasing conductance minima in these systems as the alkali-metal cation radius increases, support this view. The conductance isotherms for $PbCl_2 + MCl$ systems are shown in Fig. 3. Hence if complex

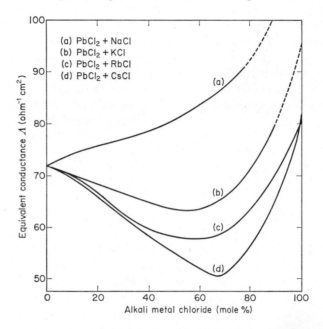

FIG. 3. Isotherms of equivalent conductance at 720°C (Bloom, 1963). (Reproduced by courtesy of the International Union of Pure and Applied Chemistry.)

ions tend to be produced, they will most likely be most stable in the presence of Cs^+ and least stable in the presence of Li^+.

On the basis of the foregoing considerations, the following classification of some salt mixtures may be made and are summarized in Table XII (Bloom, 1963).

From the systems so far studied it is possible to list the following factors which appear to determine the existence and stability of complex ions, resulting from strong solute–solvent interaction.

(a) Systems that form compounds in the solid state, as indicated by phase equilibrium studies, appear to favour the formation of complex species in the melt. This is not unreasonable since the melt may structurally be considered to be a disordered solid and it is likely that solid-like species exist on melting.

(b) Any factors that increase the covalent nature of the bonding in the complexes favour the stability of these species in the melt, e.g. the increased polarizability of the halide ligands in going from chloride to bromide favours covalent bonding.

(c) Since the complexes formed are of the type MX_n, any factors that enhance the central cation's ability to attract anions will promote complex formation. It is not surprising, therefore, that the tendency of M to form complex anions increases in the order,

$$Pb^{2+} < Cd^{2+} < Zn^{2+} < Mg^{2+}.$$

TABLE XII

Systems in which Complex Ions are Formed (Bloom, 1963)

System	Method of investigation	Complex ions postulated
$KCl + CdCl_2$	Conductivity, molar volume, Raman spectra, e.m.f., vapour pressure, cryoscopy	$CdCl_3^-$ $CdCl_4^{2-}$ $CdCl_6^{4-}$
$KCl + ZnCl_2$	Conductivity, Raman spectra, e.m.f.	$ZnCl_3^-$
$KCl + PbCl_2$	Conductivity, molar volume, transport number, surface tension, e.m.f., vapour pressure	$PbCl_3^-$ $PbCl_4^{2-}$ $PbCl_6^{4-}$
$KCl + MgCl_2$	Conductivity, molar volume	$MgCl_3^-$
$KCl + CuCl$	Conductivity	$CuCl_3^{2-}$
$KF + ZrF_4$	Vapour pressure	ZrF_5^-
$KI + CdI_2$	Conductivity, molar volume	CdI_4^{2-}
$RbCl + PbCl_2$	e.m.f. surface tension, conductivity, molar volume	$PbCl_3^-$ $PbCl_4^{2-}$ $PbCl_6^{4-}$
$CsCl + CoCl_2$	U.V. absorption spectra	$CoCl_4^{2-}$
$CsCl + NiCl_2$	U.V. absorption spectra	$NiCl_4^{2-}$
$CsCl + CuCl_2$	U.V. absorption spectra	$CuCl_4^{2-}$
$CsCl + NpCl_4$	U.V. absorption spectra	$NpCl_6^{2-}$
$CsCl + PbCl_2$	Conductivity, molar volume	$PbCl_3^-$ $PbCl_4^{2-}$ $PbCl_6^{4-}$
$NaF + AlF_3$	Conductivity, surface tension, cryoscopy	AlF_6^{3-} AlF_4^-

This is also the order of increasing charge density.

It should be pointed out that it is not always possible to deduce the existence of solid phase compounds from phase diagrams since many phase equilibria studies may not be sufficiently accurate. This is well borne out in the $FeCl_3 + NaCl$ system. In this system the phase diagram was originally interpreted (Cook and Dunn, 1961) to involve only a simple eutectic and it was expected that no complex ions would be formed in the melt. However, activity determinations seemed to indicate otherwise. Recent determinations of the phase diagram indicate the existence of the solid compound $NaFeCl_4$, the two eutectics being close to the melting point of the compound, hence complex ions are very likely in this molten system. The disrupting tendency of the Na^+ ion (which prevents complex formation in the similar Pb and Cd systems) appears to be outweighed by the opposing fact of a highly charged, relatively small, complexing cation (Fe^{3+}).

D. SOLVATION AND COMPLEX ION FORMATION IN MOLTEN SALT MIXTURES

Solvation effects, in ionic melts, may vary in intensity from slight tendency toward clustering, which may be observed as a non-ideal entropy of mixing, to the formation of covalent complex ions, resulting in non-ideal heats of solution. The formation of complex ions is therefore a special case of solvation. Complex ions such as $PbX_n^{(n-2)-}$ and $CdX_n^{(n-2)-}$ (where $n>2$) are partly ionic and the ligands will certainly undergo exchange reactions with other ligands of the same type in the solution.

Generally, mixtures that allow the formation of complex ions by solute-solvent interaction will be miscible in all proportions, although there are exceptions. The tendency for two components of a mixture to be immiscible, exhibits itself in the form of positive deviations in thermodynamic activities from the ideal values. This is clearly indicated in the Bi-Cd system. On the other hand, if there is any solvent–solute interaction, even with the retention of ideal entropy, the thermodynamic activities follow regular solution curves. These curves generally exhibit negative deviations from ideality as in the case with molten $AgBr + KBr$ mixtures (Hildebrand and Salstrom, 1932). If the solvent–solute interaction is strong enough for chemical bonding to occur, resulting for example in the formation of complex ions, then the activity deviations from ideality will necessarily be substantially negative as in the $CdCl_2 + CsCl$ system.

E. COMPLEX IONS AND REACTION KINETICS

The ability to complex a cation may be used to control the concentration of reactive species in oxidation–reduction equilibria (Van Artsdalen, 1959). This is important at high temperatures where molten salts are likely to corrode their metal containers; e.g. if corrosion occurs by the reaction:

$$2M^{3+} + A = 2M^{2+} + A^{2+}, \tag{7}$$

this may be reduced by the addition of X^- to the system provided complex ions such as MX_4^- are formed. The large complex ions produced will be of low mobility and will necessarily have lower rates of reaction than smaller and more mobile ions.

X. APPLICATION OF MOLTEN SALTS AS SOLVENTS

Molten salts have been used as reaction media for both inorganic and organic synthesis. The electrolytic uses of molten salts have received the most attention in the past, especially in connection with the deposition of metals. More recently, separation and extraction processes have been carried out in molten salt solvents.

For practical applications eutectic mixtures of salts have been preferred, mainly because of the advantage of lower operating temperatures. The KCl+LiCl eutectic especially has been widely used, as have the lower melting alkali-metal nitrate mixtures. Because of the importance of this mixture, its method of preparation will be briefly discussed here.

Preparation of an LiCl+KCl Eutectic

The hygroscopic nature of LiCl necessitates the use of special precautions in preparing the solvent. Inman *et al.* (1960) prepared the melt by mixing molten LiCl (pure grade) and molten KCl (Analytical Reagent) in a glass tube and filtering through glass wool into a Pyrex beaker. This eutectic was transferred to an electrolytic cell where it was remelted and pumped out until the pressure in the system fell to approximately 10^{-4} mm Hg. Anhydrous HCl was then bubbled through the molten eutectic in a stream of purified argon. The final traces of impurities, including dissolved HCl, were removed by pre-electrolysing the melt in vacuo with tungsten or molybdenum cathodes and carbon anodes, at a potential below the decomposition potential of the melt. The progress of the purification was followed either by the steadily falling residual current at constant potential or the steadily rising voltage at constant current.

A. REACTIONS INVOLVING ORGANIC SUBSTANCES OR VOLATILE INORGANIC LIQUIDS IN MOLTEN SALT SOLVENTS

Many organic compounds when bubbled through molten salt solvents undergo exchange reactions. For example, fluorination may take place when chlorine-containing compounds are allowed to come into contact with molten fluorides.

1. *Fluorination Reactions* (Sundermeyer, 1962b; Sundermeyer and Meise, 1962)

KF (45%)+NaF (45%)+LiF (10%) melt was found to be a suitable medium for fluorination of some organic compounds in the range 500°–600°C. Alternatively, if lower temperatures were necessary, the melts KF+ZnCl₂+ KCl or CaF₂+ZnCl₂+KCl were used. In the latter case a temperature as low as 250°C could be employed. The following reactions were found to occur readily in the molten salt solvents and the products were formed in good yield. It was often sufficient to bubble the compounds through the melt once only, using efficient stirring, e.g.

$$(CH_3)_3SiCl + NaF = (CH_3)_3SiF + NaCl \tag{8}$$
$$SOCl_2 + 2NaF = SOF_2 + 2NaCl. \tag{9}$$

2. *Pseudohalide Reactions* (Sundermeyer, 1962a)

Exchange reactions of pseudohalides such as cyanides, cyanates, and thiocyanates with halogens are possible because of the ready solubility of the pseudohalides of the alkali-metals in mixed alkali and alkaline-earth metal halide melts. For example using a LiCl + KCl melt as solvent the reaction,

$$SiCl_4 + cyanates \rightarrow Si(NCO)_4 \tag{10}$$

could be carried out with 55% yield.

3. *Organo-Azido Silane Reactions* (Sundermeyer, 1963)

Using a 54% $ZnCl_2$ + 46% KCl eutectic (m.p. 228°C) organo-azido silanes can be prepared at temperatures ranging from 230°–250°C. NaN_3 (10 to 20%) was suspended and partly dissolved in the eutectic solvent. The following reactions were carried out,

$$(CH_3)_3SiCl + NaN_3 = (CH_3)_3SiN_3 + NaCl \ (43\%) \tag{11a}$$
$$(CH_3)_2SiCl_2 + 2NaN_3 = (CH_3)_2Si(N_3)_2 + 2NaCl \ (69 \cdot 5\%) \tag{11b}$$
$$CH_3SiCl_3 + 3NaN_3 = CH_3Si(N_3)_3 + 3NaCl \tag{11c}$$

$(CH_3Si(N_3)Cl_2, CH_3Si(N_3)_2Cl$ and $(CH_3)_2Si(N_3)Cl$ are also produced).

4. *Dehydration of Alcohols* (Glemser and Kleine-Weischede, 1962)

Using a $58 \cdot 5\%$ $ZnCl_2$ + $41 \cdot 5\%$ NaCl melt at 340°C it was possible to carry out dehydration of alcohols by bubbling the alcohol vapour, with nitrogen as a carrier gas, through the melt. Olefins, together with some unaltered alcohol, were obtained.

5. *Hydrochlorination Reactions* (Glemser and Kleine-Weischede, 1962)

Using a $ZnCl_2$ (85%) + CuCl (15%) melt, dehydrochlorination of alkyl halides may be carried out, e.g. n-butyl chloride gave butene (95%) at 400°C, the optimum temperature, and $77 \cdot 5\%$ of the starting material reacted, whereas at 240°C only 24% reacted. The advantage of the high temperatures involved in molten salt media is indicated clearly by this example. However, if the temperature was too high, some of the product decomposed on the glass walls. It should be noted that an equimolar melt of $AlCl_3$ + NaCl was found to be unsatisfactory because of the partial polymerization of the butene.

Using an $AlCl_3$ melt the reverse reaction is also possible, e.g. in $AlCl_3$ + NaCl + $CuCl_2$ at 400°C, ethane and chlorine react to form 45% ethyl chloride. If a eutectic melt of $AlCl_3 + NaCl + KCl$ (89°C) is used, ethylene and hydrogen chloride give ethyl chloride in 82% yield.

The remaining 18% of ethylene polymerizes or cracks in the melt and this undesirable reaction increases with increasing temperature. Thus there is need, in some cases, for molten salt mixtures of low melting points. Ternary eutectic mixtures would appear to be the most suitable low temperature solvents.

6. Other Preparations Involving Reactions in Molten Salt Solvents

Sundermeyer *et al.* (1962) have prepared vinyl chloride in 97% yield by passing 1,1-dichloroethane vapour into molten $ZnCl_2 + KCl$ or $ZnCl_2 + CuCl$ respectively at 330°C. Alternatively, an equimolar mixture of acetylene and chlorine can be used with a melt containing a mercury salt. A melt containing $NaCl + AlCl_3$ at 175°C was found excellent for Friedel–Crafts reactions (Glemser and Kleine-Weischede, 1962).

7. The Preparation of Silane (Sundermeyer and Glemser, 1958)

A commercially important application of reactions involving molten salt solvents is in the preparation of silane. $SiCl_4$ vapour was passed into LiH dissolved in a $LiCl + KCl$ eutectic melt at 400°C and mono-silane was obtained in almost 100% yield. The LiH was regenerated by electrolysis, followed by the passage of hydrogen through the melt.

B. OTHER REACTIONS INVOLVING INORGANIC SUBSTANCES IN MOLTEN SALT SOLVENTS

Molten salt solvents are generally better solvents for certain substances than the conventional solvents, hence greater concentrations of reacting species can be used. Whilst the nature of a molten salt solvent differs from that of the usual room temperature solvents, concepts such as acid–base dissociation and "pH" are still valid in considering reactions in molten salts.

Molten alkali-metal nitrates may be considered to be analogous to the solvent water in that they both exhibit the property of acid–base dissociation, e.g.

$$NO_3^- \rightleftharpoons NO_2^+ + O^{2-} \tag{12}$$

which is analogous to the dissociation,

$$H_2O \rightleftharpoons H^+ + OH^-. \tag{13}$$

The dissociation constant of the first reaction is much smaller than that of the second. By bubbling NO_2 over platinum an electrode reaction,

$$NO_2 \rightleftharpoons NO_2^+ + e \tag{14}$$

may take place and this is analogous to the hydrogen electrode reaction,

$$\tfrac{1}{2}H_2 \rightleftharpoons H^+ + e. \tag{15}$$

The familiar acid–base, dichromate–chromate reaction, also occurs in molten salts (Blomgren and Van Artsdalen, 1960). Potassium dichromate dissolves in molten $NaNO_3$ to give the characteristic colour of the dichromate ion. The addition to this solution of a little solid sodium carbonate causes an acid–base reaction in which CO_2 is given off from the solution and its colour changes to that of the chromate ion:

$$Cr_2O_7^{2-} + CO_3^{2-} = 2CrO_4^{2-} + CO_2. \tag{16}$$

Oxidation reactions also frequently take place,

$$\text{e.g. } BrO_3^- + 5Br^- = 3Br_2 + 3O^{2-}. \tag{17}$$

If bromide ion is dissolved in molten sodium nitrate and a trace of sodium bromate added, bromine is then formed according to the above equation.

1. Metal Production in Molten Salt Solvents

(a) Commercial extraction of aluminium. In the extraction of aluminium from its bauxite ore, purified alumina is electrolysed in molten cryolite (Na_3AlF_6) as solvent. The nature of the solvent is considered to be completely ionic, the dissociation process of melting being,

$$Na_3AlF_6 = 3Na^+ + AlF_6^{3-}. \tag{18}$$

The AlF_6^{3-} is thought partly to dissociate as follows:

$$AlF_6^{3-} \rightleftharpoons AlF_4^- + 2F^- \text{ (Foster, 1960).} \tag{19}$$

(b) Extraction of actinides. Gruen et al. (1958) listed laboratory experiments for the preparation of Zr, Tl, U and Np from solutions of the tetravalent chlorides in a molten LiCl + KCl eutectic by reaction with Mg metal. Uranium metal has also been prepared by reaction of the double salt Cs_2UCl_6 with Mg metal in an equimolar $CsCl + MgCl_2$ melt at 550°C,

$$Cs_2UCl_6 + 2Mg = U + 2MgCl_2 + 2CsCl. \tag{20}$$

The uranium precipitate was separated from the molten salt by filtration and subsequent washing. Spectroscopic analysis showed the metal to be free of caesium and magnesium. Uranium metal may also be electrolytically deposited in a molten LiCl + KCl solvent with metallic uranium anodes.

(c) Separation of similar metals. Mixtures of similar metals dissolved as salts in molten salt-solvents may be separated readily by electrolysis. Molybdenum and tungsten have been extracted directly from the ore, scheelite in a molten salt-solvent (Zadra and Gomes, 1963). Different current densities were used to extract the metals separately.

(d) Extraction of magnesium from silicate minerals. Magnesium also can be extracted from its silicate minerals such as alinine and serpentine, by electrolysis (Labounski, 1963).

(e) Extraction of lead from galena. Lead may be extracted from the mineral galena in an equimolar mixture of sodium and potassium chlorides at 700°C. On passing a current through the mixture, lead is deposited at the cathode and chlorine and elementary sulphur are liberated on the anode (Gul'din and Buzhinskaya, 1961).

The refining of pig lead may be carried out by electrolysis in a molten KCl+LiCl solvent. $PbCl_2$ is dissolved in the solvent such that the relative proportions give a eutectic mixture (Delimarskii et al., 1961). Counter-current multi-stage molten salt-molten metal extraction has also recently been investigated for various metals (Josephson Jr., 1962).

2. Chromatographic Separations of Molten Salts (Gruen et al., 1958)

Approximately 0·01 M (with respect to the transition metal ions) solutions of the chlorides of Fe^{III}, Co^{II}, Ni^{II}, Cu^{II}, and UO_2^{II} in a molten $LiNO_3+KNO_3$ eutectic give well-defined coloured bands of the transition metal ions on a chromatographic column of γ–Al_2O_3. The absorbed ions may then be selectively eluted from the oxide column using a molten nitrate eutectic containing ammonium chloride (approx. 3 M). The success of the elution process depends markedly on the chloride concentration in the eluent.

3. Solvent Extraction of Molten Salts (Gruen et al., 1958)

Nitrates are particularly effective as salting out agents in aqueous systems. It is not surprising, therefore, that molten nitrates are also very effective. Transition metal ions such as Fe^{III}, Co^{II}, Ni^{II}, U^{VI}, Pr^{III}, and Nd^{III} dissolved in a $LiNO_3+KNO_3$ eutectic have been quantitatively extracted by tributyl phosphate at 150°C.

It is also possible to use inorganic extractants. Molten B_2O_3, which forms an immiscible phase with molten LiCl+KCl eutectic is capable of extracting transition metal ions from the chloride solvent.

C. FUTURE DEVELOPMENTS

The uses of molten salts as solvents will increase as the research continues to show added applications. The most important future developments appear to be in the field of fuel cells, extraction and purification of metals, chemical reactions involving organic and inorganic substances, and nuclear reactors.

REFERENCES

Aten, A. H. W. (1910) Z. phys. Chem. **73**, 578.
Bell, W. R. G., Rowlands, C. B., Bamford, I. J., Thomas, W. G. and Jones, W. J. (1930) J. chem. Soc. 1927, 31.
Belozerskii, N. A. (1940) "Collected Works on the Electrochemistry of Fused Salts" (Russian), St. Inst. appl. Chem., issue 35, 50.

Belyaev, I. N. (1958) *Zh. neorg. Khim.* **3**, 2805.

Belyaev, I. N. (1960) *Russian chem. Rev.* **29**, 899.

Blander, M., Grimes, W. R., Smith, N. V. and Watson, G. M. (1959) *J. phys. Chem.* **63**, 1164.

Biltz, W. and Klemm, W. (1926) *Z. anorg. Chem.* **152**, 267.

Blomgren, G. E. and Van Artsdalen, E. R. (1960) *Annu. Rev. phys. Chem.* **11**, 273.

Bloom, H. (1959) *Rev. pure appl. Chem.* **9**, 139.

Bloom, H. (1963) *Pure appl. Chem.* **7**, 389.

Bloom, H. and Bockris, J. O'M. (1959) "Modern Aspects of Electrochemistry Vol. II", pp. 160–261. Butterworths Scientific Publications, London.

Bloom, H. and Rhodes, D. C. (1956) *J. phys. Chem.* **60**, 791.

Bockris, J. O'M. and Richards, N. E. (1957) *Proc. roy. Soc.* **A241**, 44.

Boleslaw, L. D. and Scheidt, R. C. (1961) *XVIII Con. Pure Appl. Chem.* 170.

Bratland, D., Grjotheim, K. and Krohn, C. (1963) *XIX Con. Pure and Appl. Chem.* (Proceedings not yet published).

Braunstein, J., Blander, M. and Lindgren, R. M. (1962) *J. Amer. chem. Soc.* **84**, 1529.

Braunstein, J. and Lindgren, R. M. (1962) *J. Amer. chem. Soc.* **84**, 1534.

Bredig, M. A. (1962) *J. chem. Phys.* **37**, 451.

Bredig, M. A. (1963) "Mixtures of Metals with Molten Salts", ORNL–3391 UC–4–Chem.

Bredig, M. A. and Bronstein, H. R. (1955) *J. Amer. chem. Soc.* **77**, 1454.

Bredig, M. A. and Johnson, J. W. (1960) *J. phys. Chem.* **64**, 1899.

Bredig, M. A., Johnson, G. and Smith, W. (1955) *J. Amer. chem. Soc.* **77**, 307.

Bronstein, H. R. and Bredig, M. A. (1958) *J. Amer. chem. Soc.* **80**, 2077.

Bronstein, H. R. and Bredig, M. A. (1961) *J. phys. Chem.* **65**, 1220.

Bruner, B. L. and Corbett, J. D. (1961) *J. inorg. nucl. Chem.* **20**, 62.

Bues, W. (1955) *Z. anorg. Chem.* **279**, 104.

Bunsen, N. and Kirchoff, R. (1861) *Pogg. Ann.* **113**, p. 345 (now *Ann. Phys., Lpz.*).

Burkhard, W. J. and Corbett, J. D. (1957) *J. Amer. chem. Soc.* **79**, 6361.

Campbell, A. N., Kartzmark, E. M. and Williams, D. F. (1962) *Canad. J. Chem.* **40**, 890.

Cook, C. M. Jr. and Dunn, W. E. Jr. (1961) *XVIII Con. Pure Appl. Chem.* 110.

Corbett, J. D. and Albers, F. C. (1960) *J. Amer. chem. Soc.* **82**, 533.

Corbett, J. D. and Hershaft, A. (1958) *J. Amer. chem. Soc.* **80**, 1530.

Corbett, J. D. and Winbush, S. V. (1955) *J. Amer. chem. Soc.* **77**, 3964.

Corbett, J. D., Winbush, S. V. and Albers, F. C. (1957) *J. Amer. chem. Soc.* **79**, 3020.

Cubicciotti, D. (1949) *J. Amer. chem. Soc.* **71**, 4119.

Cubicciotti, D. and Cleary, G. (1952) *J. Amer. chem. Soc.* **74**, 557.

Cubicciotti, D. (1953a) *J. Metals. N.Y.* **5**.

Cubicciotti, D. (1953b) *Trans. Amer. Inst. mech. Engrs* **197**, 1106.

Cubicciotti, D. (1960) *J. chem. Educ.* **37**, 540.

Danilov, V. I. and Krasnitskii, S. Ya. (1955) *Dokl. Akad. Nauk S.S.S.R.* **101**, 661.

Delimarskii, Yu. K. (1955) *Zh. fiz. khim.* **29**, 28.

Delimarskii, Yu. K. and Markov, B. F. (1961) "Electrochemistry of Fused Salts", pp. 336. Sigma Press.

Delimarskii, Yu. K., Markov, B. F., Panchenko, I. D., Gutmann, E. B. and Kolotii, A. A. (1961) "Soviet Electrochemistry", Vol. III, p. 96. Consultants Bureau, New York.

De Maine, P. A. D. and McAlonie, G. E. (1961) *J. inorg. nucl. Chem.* **18**, 286.

Druding, L. F. and Corbett, J. D. (1959) *J. Amer. chem. Soc.* **81**, 5512.

Druding, L. F. and Corbett, J. D. (1961) *J. Amer. chem. Soc.* **83**, 2462.

Dworkin, A. S., Bronstein, H. R. and Bredig, M. A. (1962) *J. phys. Chem.* **66**, 572.

Eley, D. D. and King, P. J. (1951) *Trans. Faraday Soc.* **47**, 1287.

Farquharson, J. and Heymann, E. (1935) *Trans. Faraday Soc.* **31**, 1004.

Flengas, S. N. (1960) *Ann. N.Y. Acad. Sci.* **79**, 853.

Foster, L. M. (1960) *Ann. N.Y. Acad. Sci.* **79**, 919.

Gardner, D. M. and Fraenkel, G. K. (1956) *J. Amer. chem. Soc.* **78**, 3279.

Glemser, O. and Kleine-Weischede, K. (1962) *Liebigs Ann.* **659**, 17.

Greenberg, J. and Sundheim, B. R. (1958) *J. chem. Phys.* **29**, 1029.

Greenberg, J., Sundheim, B. R. and Gruen, D. M. (1958) *J. chem. Phys.* **29**, 461.

Grimes, W. R., Smith, N. V. and Watson, G. M. (1958) *J. phys. Chem.* **62**, 862.

Grjotheim, K., Gronvold, F. and Krogh-Moe, J. (1955) *J. Amer. chem. Soc.* **77**, 5824.

Grjotheim, K., Heggelund, P., Krohn, C. and Motzfeldt, K. (1962) *Acta chem. Scand.* **16**, 689.

Gruen, D. M., Fried, S., Graf, P. and McBeth, R. L. (1958) "Chemistry of Fused Salts", pp. 26. A/CONF. 15/P/940 U.S.A.

Gruen, D. M. and McBeth, R. L. (1959) *J. inorg. nucl. chem.* **9**, 290.

Gul'din, I. T. and Buzhinskaya, A. V. (1961) "Soviet Electrochemistry", vol. III, pp. 100–109. Consultants Bureau, New York.

Guntz, A. and Benoit, F. (1924) *Bull. Soc. chim. Fr.* **35**, 709.

Harris, R. L., Wood, R. E. and Ritter, H. L. (1951) *J. Amer. chem. Soc.* **73**, 3151.

Hevesy, G. and Löwenstein, E. (1930) *Z. anorg. Chem.* **187**, 266.

Heymann, E. and Friedlander, E. (1930) *Z. phys. Chem.* **148**, 177.

Hildebrand, J. H. and Salstrom, E. J. (1932) *J. Amer. chem. Soc.* **54**, 4257.

Inman, D., Hills, G. J., Young, L. and Bockris, J. O'M. (1960) *Ann. N.Y. Acad. Sci.* **79**, 803.

Johnson, J. W. and Bredig, M. A. (1958) *J. phys. Chem.* **62**, 604.

Johnson, J. W. and Bredig, M. A. (1960) *J. phys. Chem.* **64**, 64.

Johnson, J. W., Cubicciotti, D. and Kelley, C. M. (1958) *J. phys. Chem.* **62**, 1107.

Josephson, P. R. Jr. (1962) *Dissertation Abstr.* **22**, 2322.

Karpachev, S. V., Stromberg, A. G. and Iordan, E. (1944) *Zh. fiz. khim.* **18**, 43.

Kendall, J., Crittenden, E. D. and Miller, H. K. (1923) *J. Amer. chem. Soc.* **45**, 963.

Klemm, W. and Huss, E. (1949) *Z. anorg. Chem.* **258**, 221.

Krebs, H. (1957) *Z. Naturf.* **12**b, 795.

Kreye, W. C. and Kellogg, H. H. (1957) *Trans. electrochem. Soc.* **104**, 504.

Kroll, W. J. (1955) *Metallurgy* **9**, 366.

Labounski (1963) U.S. Patent 3,093,558.

"Landolt-Börnstein Zahlenwerte und Funktionen," Vol. II, Part 3 (1956). Springer-Verlag, Berlin.

Landon, G. J. and Ubbelohde, A. R. (1956) *Trans. Faraday Soc.* **52**, 647.

Latimer, W. M. (1952) "Oxidation Potentials", 2nd edition, 392 pp. Prentice Hall, Inc., New York.

Levy, H. A., Bredig, M. A., Danford, M. D. and Agron, P. A. (1960a) *J. phys. Chem.* **64**, 1959.

Levy, H. A., Agron, P. A., Bredig, M. A. and Danford, M. D. (1960b) *Ann. N.Y. Acad. Sci.* **79**, Art. 11, 762.

Lorentz, R. and Eitel, E. (1915) *Z. anorg. Chem.* **91**, 46.

Lorentz, R. and Eitel, W. (1926) "Pyrosole" Akademische Verlagsgesellschafte, M.B.H., Leipzig.

Mathers, F. C. and Stroup, P. T. (1934) *J. electrochem. Soc.* **66**, 245.

Paterno, E. and Muzzuchelli, A. (1908) *Gazz. chim. ital.* **38**, 137.

Peterson, D. and Hinkebein, J. A. (1959) *J. phys. Chem.* **63**, 1360.

Pitzer, K. (1962) *J. Amer. chem. Soc.* **84**, 2025.

Pushin, N. (1958) *J. gen. Chem., Moscow* **18**, 1599.

Rogers, P. S., Tomlinson, J. W. and Richardson, F. D. (1961) *Met. Soc. Conf.* **8**, 909.

Sallach, R. A. and Corbett, J. D. (1962) *Inorg. Chem.* **2**, 457.

Schaffer, J. H., Grimes, W. R. and Watson, G. M. (1959) *J. phys. Chem.* **63**, 1999.

Smith, G. P. (1965) "Electronic Absorption Spectra of Molten Salts", *in* "Molten Salt Chemistry" (M. Blander, ed.). Interscience, New York (in the press).

Staffansson, L. I. (1959) "The Physical Chemistry of Metals in their Molten Halides." Ph.D. Thesis, London.

Stern, K. H. (1961) *XVIII Con. Pure Appl. Chem. 177.*

Sundermeyer, Von W. (1962a) *Z. anorg. Chem.* **313**, 290.

Sundermeyer, Von. W. (1962b) *Z. anorg. Chem.* **314**, 100.

Sundermeyer, Von W. (1963) *Chem. Ber.* **96**, 1293.

Sundermeyer, Von. W. and Glemser, O. (1958) *Angew Chem.* **70**, Nr. **20**, 625.

Sundermeyer, Von W., Glemser, O. and Kleine-Weischede, K. (1962) *Chem. Ber.* **95**, 1829.

Sundermeyer, Von W. and Meise, W. (1962) *Z. anorg. Chem.* **317**, 334.

Temkin, M. (1945) *Acta phys.-chim. U.R.S.S.* **20**, 411.

Topol, L. E. and Laudis, A. L. (1960) *J. Amer. chem. Soc.* **82**, 6291.

Van Artsdalen, E. R. (1956) *J. phys. Chem.* **60**, 172.

Van Artsdalen, E. R. (1959) "The Structure of Electrolytic Solutions", (W. J. Hamer, ed.) p. 411–421. Wiley, New York.

Wait, S. C. and Janz, G. J. (1963) *Quart. Rev.* **17**, 225.

Winsor, V. R. and Cady, G. H. (1948) *J. Amer. chem. Soc.* **70**, 1500.

Yosim, S. J. and Luchsinger, E. B. (1960) *Ann. N.Y. Acad. Sci.* **79**, 1079.

Yosim, S. J. and Mayer, S. W. (1960) *J. phys. Chem.* **64**, 909.

Yosim, S. J., Darnell, A. J., Gehman, W. G. and Mayer, S. W. (1959) *J. phys. Chem.* **63**, 230.

Yosim, S. J., Ransom, L. D., Sallach, R. A. and Topol, L. E. (1962) *J. phys. Chem.* **66**, 28.

Zadra and Gomes (1963) U.S. Patent 3,075,900, 204.

Zarzycki, G. (1957a) *C.R. Acad. Sci., Paris* **224**, 758.

Zarzycki, G. (1957b) *J. Phys. Radium* **18**, 65A.

Zhurin, A. I. (1935) *Metallurgy* **10** Nr. 4, 87.

Author Index

A

Accascina, F., 9, 10, *43*
Acrivos, J. V., 17, *41*
Adams, R. M., 51, 57, 57, 67, 72, *79*
Addison, C. C., 307, 332, *349*
Adie, R. H., 176, *205*
Adler, J. H., 142, *208*
Adolfsson, G., 342, *349*
Aellig, C., 257, 258, *283*
Agerman, M., 312, *349*
Agron, P. A., 355, 371, *389*
Albers, F. C., 327, *349*, 369, 370, 371, 372, 373, *388*
Alder, B. J., 18, *42*
Anderson, H. H., 187, *205*
Andersson, L. H., 309, 311, 312, 316, *349*, *352*
Andre, S., 259, *282*
Andrews, L. J., 215, *249*, 259, *282*, 286, *298*
Aoyama, S., 286, *298*
Archibald, E. H., 83, 85, 88, 89, 90, 96, 97, 100, *115*
Argument, C., 182, *209*
Armstrong, G. T., 2, 3, *41*
Arnold, E., 18, *42*
Arotsky, J., 180, 182, *205*, 289, *298*
Asher, D. R., 274, *284*
Asmussen, R. W., 329, *349*
Asprey, L. B., 294, *298*
Atoji, M., 60, *79*
Aten, A. H. W., 369, 370, *387*
Audrieth, L. F., 2, 20, 25, 34, *42*, 242, *249*, 253, 260, *282*
Aynsley, E. E., 257, *282*, 289, 296, 297, *298*

B

Baaz, M., 212, 213, *249*, *250*, 309, 318, 333, 335, 336, 337, 338, 341, 342, 343, 344, 345, 346, 347, *349*, *350*, *351*
Baenziger, N. C., 291, *299*
Bagster, L. S., 264, *282*
Baker, W., 186, *205*

Balog, G., 50, 53, 59, *80*, 85, *115*
Balowna, Z., 321, 323, *351*
Bamford, I. J., 358, 359, 360, *387*
Banks, A. A., 292, *298*
Barabonova, A. S., 219, *251*
Bar-Eli, K., 33, *42*
Barnes, J. C., 244, *249*
Barr, J., 180, 205, *205*
Barraclough, C. G., 187, *205*
Bass, S. J., 125, 126, 127, 132, 133, 136, 137, 138, 139, 142, 162, *205*
Bateman, L. C., 259, *282*
Baude, E., 257, *282*
Bauer, H., 272, 273, *284*, 329, 330, *352*
Baughan, E. C., 190, *210*, 302, 323, 325, 326, *349*, *350*, *352*
Beach, H. T., 255, *282*
Beachell, H. C., 72, *79*
Beattie, I. R., 244, *249*
Becker, E., 18, *42*
Beckham, L. J., 328, *349*
Beckman, T. A., 18, *42*
Beckmann, E., 96, *114*, 321, *349*
Beilstein, 226, *249*
Bekier, E., 264, *282*
Belcher, R. L., 238, *249*
Bell, W. R. G., 358, 359, 360, *387*
Belozerskii, N. A., 366, *387*
Belton, W. E., 255, 257, *282*
Belyaev, I. N., 375, *388*
Benesi, H. A., 215, *249*
Benoit, F., 367, *389*
Bent, H. A., 217, *249*
Berger, A., 191, *205*
Bergin, M. J., 30, *43*
Bergius, F., 142, *205*
Bergstrom, F. W., 2, 23, 31, *42*, *44*
Berns, D. S., 244, *249*
Bernstein, H. J., 156, *210*
Bernstein, R. B., 276, *283*
Bertaut, E. F., 311, *351*
Berthoud, A., 5, *42*
Betz, H. F., 162, *207*
Beyer, A., 307, 333, *352*
Bickerton, J. H., 257, *282*

Biltz, W., 61, *80*, 287, 288, *298*, 355, *388*
Bingle, J., 295, *298*
Birch, A. J., 2, 13, 34, 36, 41, *42*
Birchall, T., 156, 190, 191, 192, 198, *205*, 207
Bjerrum, N., 261, *282*
Blander, M., 356, 362, *388*
Blennemann, D., 34, *43*
Blois, M. S., 180, 199, *208*
Blomgren, G. E., 377, 386, *388*
Bloom, H., 354, 355, 356, 377, 379, 380, 381, *388*
Bockris, J. O'M., 354, 357, 362, 374, 383, *388, 389*
Boez, A. K., 271, *284*
Boleslaw, L. D., 375, *388*
Bolton, J. R., 198, *205*
Bond, P. A., 255, 257, *282*
Booth, H. S., 257, *282*
Boston, C. R., 327, *349*
Boswijk, K. H., 292, *298*
Bouknight, J. W., 53, *81*
Bourke, P. J., 34, *42*
Bowman, G. B., 2, *43*
Bradley, A., 192, *205*
Brand, J. C. D., 128, 131, 139, 157, 159, 188, 204, *205, 206*
Bränden, C. I., 212, *249*, 337, 338, 342, *349*, *352*
Bratland, D., 362, *388*
Brauner, B., 172, 180, *206*
Braunstein, J., 356, *388*
Brayford, J. R., 122, 134, 139, 161, *206*
Bredig, M. A., 327, *349*, 355, 365, 366, 367, 368, 371, 372, *388, 389*
Briegleb, G., 60, *79, 81*
Bright, J. R., 259, *282*
Brivati, J. A., 198, *206*
Brockmann, R., 34, *43*
Bronstein, H. R., 366, *388*
Brost, G. A., 169, *210*
Brown, J., 34, *42*
Brown, T. H., 76, *79*
Browne, A. W., 95, *115*, 287, 288, *299*
Brubaker, C. H., 170, *206*
Brühl, J. W., 301, *349*
Bruner, B. L., 371, *388*
Bruner, L., 264, *282*
Bryntse, R., 342, *349*
Buckley, H., 178, *207*
Bues, W., 356, *388*
Buffagni, S., 229, 231, 232, 234, 236, *249*

Bull, W. E., 217, *249, 251*
Bunsen, N., 364, *388*
Bunton, C. A., 191, *206*
Burg, A. B., 257, 259, *282*, 328, 329, 330, 331, *349*
Burge, D. E., 273, 274, 277, 278, *282*
Burkhard, W. J., 364, *388*
Burwell, R. L., 246, 247, *249*
Busby, R. E., 240, *249*
Buzhinskaya, A. V., 387, *389*
Byrd, W. E., 259, *283*

C

Cadenbach, G., 53, 58, 74, 77, *79*
Cady, G. H., 65, *80*, 297, *298*, 364, *390*
Cady, H. P., 10, *43*, 264, 280, *283*, 301, *349*
Campbell, A. N., 357, 360, *388*
Campbell, G. W., 328, 329, *349*
Campion, D. E., 322, 326, *351*
Cannizzaro, S., von, 200, *206*
Carlson, R. L., 216, 224, 226, 228, 230, 231, 232, 234, 239, 243, 244, 246, *249, 250*
Carpenter, G. B., 95, *115*
Carrington, A., 198, *205, 206*
Carson, T., 179, *209*
Carter, R. P. Jr., 241, *250*
Casalino, A., 193, 196, 197, *209*
Casselmann, W., 334, *349*
Centnerszwer, M., 253, 255, 264, 273, *283*, 284
Chalandon, P., 223, 239, *251*
Chang, S., 87, *114*
Chatt, J., 41, *42*
Chedin, J., 173, *206*
Chittum, J. F., 5, *43*
Chou, D. Y. P., 37, *42*
Chretien, P., 181, *206*
Clark, H. C., 171, *206*
Clark, H. O., 18, *42*
Cleary, G., 368, 371, *388*
Clifford, A. F., 65, 72, 75, *79*
Clusius, K., 276, *283*
Coates, G. E., 170, 171, *206*
Cole, A. G., 30, *42*
Cole, R. H., 128, *207*
Conley, R. F., 10, *45*
Connick, R. E., 218, *249*
Conradi, J. J., 198, *210*
Cook, C. M. Jr., 382, *388*
Cook, D., 96, *114*
Cooling, G., 264, *282*

Corbett, J. D., 327, *349*, 364, 368, 369, 370, 371, 372, 373, *388*, *390*
Cornides, I., 6, *42*
Corwin, A. H., 192, *208*
Cotton, F. A., 217, 237, *249*
Coulter, L. V., 15, 30, *42*, *45*
Couture, A. M., 8, *42*, 140, *206*
Crage, C., 4, *42*
Craig, D. P., 302, *349*
Craig, R. A., 132, 167, 203, *206*, *209*
Cram, D. J., 24, 31, 41, *42*
Crittenden, E. D., 319, *351*, 375, 376, *389*
Cronander, A. W., 314, *350*
Crone, E. B., 255, *282*
Croy, V. D., 326, *351*
Cruse, K., 245, *250*, 265, *283*
Cseko, G., 6, *42*
Cubicciotti, D., 327, *349*, *351*, 368, 369, 370, 371, *388*, *389*
Curran, C., 259, *284*
Cuthrell, R. E., 30, *42*
Cutler, D., 17, *42*
Czapski, G., 35, *42*

D

Dacre, B., 125, 154, *206*
Dadape, V. V., 343, *350*
Dafert, O., 316, *350*
Daggett, H. M., 261, *283*
Dahmlos, J., 53, *79*
Dallinga, G., 198, *206*
Danford, M. D., 355, 371, *389*
Danilov, V. I., 355, *388*
Danyluk, S. S., 96, 101, *115*
d'Arcy, R. H., 164, *206*
Darnell, A. J., 371, 372, *390*
Dasent, W. E., 181, *206*
Daure, P., 311, *350*
Davidson, A. W., 142, *208*
Davies, A., 292, *298*
Davies, A. G., 323, 325, 326, *350*
Davis, S., 87, *114*
Davis, W. Jr., 76, *80*
Davis, W. J., 52, 53, 54, 60, *80*
Davison, A., 184, 185, *206*
Dawson, K. R., 238, *249*
Dawson, L. R., 230, 231, 232, 237, 240, 242, *249*, *251*
Dayton, J. C., 33, *45*

Deans, F. B., 169, *206*
de Boer, E., 198, 204, *206*, *210*
de Boer, J. L., 293, *298*
De Grotthuss, C. J. T., 29, *42*
Dehn, H., 348, *350*
Del Fresno, C., 86, *114*
Del Greco, F. P., 75, *79*
Delimarskii, Yu. K., 354, 365, 373, 374, 387, *388*
de Maine, P. A. D., 219, 235, *250*, 259, *283*, 360, *388*
Denison, W. A., 6, *45*
Deno, N. C., 160, 190, 196, 198, 199, 200, 201, 202, 203, 204, *206*, *209*
de Right, R. E., 197, *206*
Dess, H. M., 318, *350*
Detmar, O., 294, 297, *299*
Devin, C., 329, *352*
Devlin, O. M., 169, *210*
Dewald, J. F., 37, *42*
Deyrup, A. J., 63, *79*, 132, 133, 157, 159, 190, *208*
Dickerson, R. T., 86, *114*
Dietz, G., 327, *350*
Dingwall, A., 190, *206*
Dirian, G., 34, *42*
Dittmar, H. R., 197, *206*
Dodd, D. M., 130, 131, 162, *210*
Dodgen, H. W., 28, *43*
Dodger, H. W., 27, *44*
Dole, M., 141, *208*
Dolezalek, F., 172, *206*
Donoghue, J. T., 235, *249*
Dorfman, L. M., 35, 38, *42*
Down, J. L., 41, *42*
Drago, R. S., 213, 214, *216*, 217, 218, 222, 223, 224, 226, 228, 230, 231, 232, 234, 235, 236, 239, 241, 242, 243, 244, 246, *249*, *250*, *251*, 306, 344, *352*
Dravieko, F., 198, *206*
Dresdner, R. D., 53, *81*
Druce, J. G. F., 170, *206*
Drucker, J., 264, *283*
Druding, L. F., 368, *388*
Dullenkopf, W., 31, *45*
Dunn, T. M., 216, 229, 231, 233, 234, 236, *249*, *250*
Dunn, W. E. Jr., 382, *388*
Dutoit, P., 262, *283*
Dworkin, A. S., 366, *388*
Dye, J. L., 16, *42*
Dykhno, N., 6, *42*

E

Eaborn, C., 169, *206*
Easteal, A., 360
Eastham, J. F., 39, 40, *44*
Edwards, J. O., 166, *206*
Ehrlich, P., 327, *350*
Eigen, M., 136, *210*
Einarsson, P., 272, *284*
Eingorn, L. N., 314, *350*
Eitel, E., 364, *389*
Eitel, W., 369, *389*
Elbs, K., 172, *206*
Eley, D. D., 359, *388*
Ellendt, G., 245, *250*
Elliott, W. W., 197, *206*
Elma, R. J., 293, *298*
Elsey, H. M., 4, *42*, 280, *283*
Elving, P. J., 253, 260, *283*
Eméleus, H. J., 294, 295, *298*, *299*
Engels, S., 315, *351*
Ephraim, F., 257, 258, *283*
Esch, W., 172, *206*
Evans, R. V. G., 187, *206*

F

Fackler, J. P. Jr., 216, 242, *250*
Farquharson, J., 356, 369, *388*
Feder, H. M., 52, *79*
Fedorova, G. K., 99, *115*
Fellinger, L. L., 34, *42*
Feltz, A., 314, *351*
Fenske, M. R., 6, *42*, *43*
Fernelius, W. C., 2, 23, *42*, *43*, *44*, 259, *282*
Ferraro, J. R., 238, *250*
Fessler, W. A., 328, *349*
Fiat, D. N., 218, *249*
Fichter, F., 180, *206*
Field, F. B., 186, *205*
Figgis, B. N., 191, *206*
Fine, D. A., 216, 231, 237, *250*
Finkelstein, W., 288, *298*
Finkh, K., 172, *206*
Firla, T., 341, *352*
Fischer, F., 172, *206*
Fischer, J., 295, *298*
Fischer, W., 61, *80*
Fish, R. W., 101, *114*, 202, *208*
Fitzgerald, T. B., 259, *283*
Fleischer, J., 257, 258, 259, *283*

Flengas, S. N., 363, *389*
Fletcher, H. G., Jr., 77, *80*
Flexser, L. A., 190, *206*
Flowers, R. H., 125, 127, 129, 132, 133, 137, 138, 139, 142, 145, 146, 152, 162, 163, 164, 165, 167, 168, 169, 179, 180, 188, 193, 194, 205, *205*, *207*
Fluck, E., 99, *114*
Fohn, E. C., 30, *42*
Foote, H. W., 257, 258, 259, *283*
Foster, L. M., 386, *389*
Fowles, G. W. A., 2, 34, *43*
Fraenkel, G. K., 361, *389*
Francis, R., 217, *249*
Franck, E. U., 53, 54, 60, *79*, *81*
Franklin, E. C., 2, 5, 10, 25, 30, *43*, 254, *283*
Fraser, M. J., 102, *114*, 338, *350*
Fredenhagen, H., 74, *79*
Fredenhagen, K., 53, 58, 74, 77, *79*
Freed, S., 17, 18, *43*
French, C. M., 231, *250*
Fresco, J. M., 173, *209*
Freund, H., 273, *282*
Fried, S., 379, 386, 387, *389*
Friedlander, E., 364, *389*
Friedman, N. J., 238, *250*
Frost, A. A., 39, *43*
Frycz, K., 321, 324, *350*
Fujita, J., 187, *209*
Fuoss, R. M., 9, 10, *43*, 90, *114*, *115*, 234, 240, 244, *249*, *251*, 260, 261, *283*, 336, *350*

G

Gable, C. M., 162, *207*
Gagnaux, P., 236, 239, *250*
Gallagher, W. P., 110, *115*, 241, *250*
Gardner, D. M., 361, *389*
Garnet, C. S., 28, *45*
Garrett, A. B., 132, 167, 196, 203, *206*, *209*
Garton, G., 340, *352*
Garver, E. E., 292, 295, *299*
Gauldie, J., 192
Gebert, E., 216, 238, *250*
Gehman, W. G., 371, 372, *390*
Geier, R. G., 6, *42*, *43*
Geisel, E., 13, *45*
George, J. W., 311, 315, 327, *350*
Gerding, H., 212, *250*, 310, 328, 330, 340, *350*

Gerrard, W., 102, *114*, 338, *350*

Gerson, F., 102, *114*

Gianque, W. F., 3, *44*, 126, 129, 130, 154, 162, *207*, *208*, 254, *283*, 286, *298*

Gibson, C. S., 187, *206*

Gibson, S., 316, *350*

Giguère, P. A., 58, *79*, 130, 131, 155, 162, 163, *207*

Gilbert, L. F., 178, *207*

Gill, N. S., 235, *250*

Gillespie, R. J., 76, *79*, 88, 99, 112, *114*, 118, 122, 123, 125, 126, 127, 128, 129, 130, 131, 132, 133, 134, 135, 136, 137, 138, 139, 142, 145, 146, 148, 150, 152, 153, 154, 156, 157, 159, 161, 162, 163, 164, 165, 166, 167, 168, 169, 170, 171, 172, 173, 174, 177, 179, 180, 182, 187, 188, 189, 190, 191, 192, 193, 194, 196, 197, 198, 202, 203, 205, *205*, *207*, *208*

Glasstone, S., 85, *114*

Glazer, H., 254, *283*

Glebocka, M., 259, *283*

Glemser, O., 360, 384, 385, *389*, *390*

Glockler, G., 85, *114*

Glover, K. H., 231, *250*

Gluekauf, E., 137, 138, *208*

Gmelin, 255, 256, 276, *283*, 321, 322, *350*

Goddard, D. R., 173, *208*

Golben, M., 240, *249*

Gold, M., 13, 17, 18, 19, *43*, *44*

Gold, V., 100, *114*, 155, 179, 198, 199, 200, *208*

Gomes, 386, *390*

Goodgame, D. M. L., 237, *249*

Goodgame, M., 237, *249*

Gordon, S., 56, *80*

Gore, G., 83, 97, *114*

Gorenbein, E. Y., 327, *350*

Goubeau, J., 31, *45*

Gover, T. A., 226, 227, *250*

Grace, J. A., 201, *208*

Graf, P., 379, 386, 387, *389*

Graff, W., 95, 107, *114*

Graham, J., 122, 132, 135, 173, 174, 192, *207*, *208*

Grandcollot, P., 34, *42*

Grange, P., 85, *114*

Green, L. R., 6, 7, 8, 14, 15, *43*

Greenberg, J., 361, *389*

Greenwood, N. N., 127, 129, 145, 166, *208*, *210*, 289, 290, 292, 297, *298*, 310, 317, 318, 340, *350*, *352*

Griffiths, U. S., 240, *249*

Grigg, E. C. M., 274, *283*

Grimes, W. R., 362, 363, *388*, *389*, *390*

Grisard, J. W., 292, *298*

Grjotheim, K., 362, 370, *388*, *389*

Groeneveld, W. L., 315, 339, *350*

Gronvold, F., 370, *389*

Grossweiner, L. I., 38, *45*

Groves, P. T., 198, 201, 204, *206*

Grubb, H. M., 5, *43*

Gruen, D. M., 360, 361, 379, 386, 387, *389*

Gryder, J. W., 75, *79*

Gul'din, I. T., 387, *389*

Gunn, S. R., 6, 7, 8, 14, 15, *43*

Günther, K., 319, *351*

Guntz, A., 367, *389*

Gurney, R. W., 141, 142, *208*

Gur'yanova, E. N., 24, *43*

Gustavson, G., 334, *350*

Gutmann, E. B., 387, *388*

Gutmann, V., 88, *114*, 212, 213, *249*, *250*, 290, 294, *298*, 305, 308, 309, 310, 312, 314, 315, 316, 317, 318, 329, 333, 334, 335, 336, 337, 338, 339, 340, 341, 342, 343, 344, 345, 346, 347, 348, *349*, *350*, *351*

Gyr, E., 262, *283*

H

Hall, S. K., 122, 143, 150, 188, 205, *208*

Hallada, C. J., 13, 17, *43*, *44*

Hammett, L. P., 63, 71, *79*, 132, 133, 135, 157, 159, 190, 193, 196, 198, *206*, *208*, *210*

Hammick, D. L., 197, *206*

Hampel, G., 347, *349*, *351*

Hanby, W. E., 181, *209*

"Handbook of Chemistry and Physics" 39th Edition, 1957–8, 85, *114*

Hansley, V. L., 41, *45*

Hantzsch, A., 86, *114*, 142, 164, 192, 193, 195, 196, 199, 203, *208*

Hardy, M. L., 189, *210*

Hardy, W. B., 259, *283*

Hargreaves, G. B., 295, 296, 297, *298*

Harmon, K. M., 87, *114*

Harned, H. S., 7, *43*

Harper, D., 4, *42*

Harris, R. L., 355, *389*

Harrter, D. R., 158, 160, *208*

Hart, D., 216, 226, 228, 230, 231, 239, 241, 246, *249*
Hart, H., 101, *114*, 201, 202, *208*
Hasing, J., 15, *43*
Hastie, J. W., 356, 358, 359
Hathaway, B. J., 171, *208*, *209*
Haul, R., 34, *43*
Hawes, B. M. W., 199, *208*
Hawes, W. W., 9, 28, *43*
Hecht, H., 268, 270, *283*
Heggelund, P., 362, *389*
Heilbronner, E., 102, *114*
Hepler, L. G., 8, *43*
Hepworth, M. A., 294, *298*
Herber, R. H., 274, 276, *283*, 310, 339, *351*
Herbrandson, H. F., 86, *114*
Hermodsson, Y., 272, *283*
Hershaft, A., 371, *388*
Herzberg, G., 55, *79*, 85, *114*
Herzenstein, A., 264, *284*
Hess, G. P., 78, *80*
Hetherington, G., 332, *351*
Heubal, J., *115*
Hevesy, G., 369, 370, *389*
Hewitt, F., 328, *351*
Heymann, E., 356, 364, 369, *388*, *389*
Heyn, A. H. A., 30, *43*
Heyns, K., 34, *43*
Higler, W. S., 73, *80*
Hildebrand, J. H., 19, 21, *43*, 59, 60, *80*, *81*, 215, *249*, 287, *299*, 382, *389*
Hill, A. E., 259, *283*
Hill, M. E., 192, *205*
Hillesund, S., 5, *45*
Hills, G. J., 374, 383, *389*
Himml, R., 308, 329, 338, 341, *351*
Hindman, J. C., 76, *79*
Hinkebein, J. A., 367, *389*
Hitchcock, C. S., 85, 102, *115*
Hnizda, V. F., 5, 9, *43*
Hodge, J. D., 202, 203, *206*
Hodge, N., *349*
Hodgins, J. W., 13, *43*
Hofstra, A., 69, *80*, 198, *209*
Holliday, A. K., 96, 107, *115*, 328, *351*
Holm, C. H., 17, *44*
Holmes, L. H., *251*
Holmes, R. R., 110, *115*, 230, 231, 240, 241, *249*, *250*, *251*, 311, *351*
Holstead, C., 191, *208*
Hood, G. C., 157, *208*

Hornig, D. F., 58, 60, *80*
Horning, E. E., 162, *207*
Horning, W. C., 139, 157, 159, 188, 204, *206*
Horsfield, A., 18, *42*
Houser, J. J., 202, 203, *206*
Houtgraaf, H., 310, 328, 330, *350*
Howick, L. C., 327, *349*
Hu, J. H., 53, 54, *79*, 286, *298*
Hubacek, H., 309, 347, *351*
Hubbard, W. N., 52, *79*
Hübner, L., 212, *249*, 309, 338, 341, 343, 344, 346, *349*
Huggins, C. M., 218, *251*
Hughes, E. D., 122, 132, 135, 173, 174, *207*, *208*, 259, *282*
Hulme, R., 198, *206*
Hume, D. N., 216, 244, *249*, *250*
Hunt, H., 4, 5, *43*, *45*
Hunt, J. P., 28, *43*
Huss, E., 362, *389*
Huster, E., 18, *43*
Huston, J. L., 274, 275, 276, *283*
Hutchison, C. A. Jr., 14, 17, *43*
Hyman, H. H., 50, 51, 53, 56, 59, 64, 71, 72, 76, *79*, *80*, 86, 94, *115*, 292, *298*

I

Ihle, H., 34, *43*
Imhof, V., 239
Immig, H., 259, 268, 269, 270, 271, 272, *283*
Ingold, C. K., 122, 132, 135, 155, 173, 174, 176, 204, *207*, *208*, 259, *282*
Inman, D., 374, 383, *389*
Iordan, E., 371, *389*
Ipat'ev, V. V., 6, *43*
Ipsen, R., 334, *352*
Isbekow, W., 319, *351*
Ishida, K., 6, 21, *43*
Izrailevich, E. A., 4, *45*

J

Jache, A. W., 65, *80*
Jack, W. M., 72, *79*
Jackman, D. C., 37, *42*
Jackson, J. H., 218, *250*
Jaffe, H., 14, *43*
Jaffée, H. H., 102, *115*

Jakubson, S., 288, *298*
James, J. C., 128, *206*
Jander, G., 2, 20, *43*, 253, 255, 256, 257, 258, 259, 260, 263, 266, 267, 268, 269, 270, 271, 272, 273, 275, 280, *283*, *284*, 286, 288, *298*, 319, 322, 323, 326, *351*
Janjic, D., 236, 239, *250*
Janz, G. J., 96, 101, *115*, 356, 379, *390*
Jaques, C., 194, 195, *208*
Jarry, R. L., 52, 53, 54, 60, 76, *80*
Jarvie, A. W. P., 204, *206*
Jarvzelski, J. J., 201, *206*
Jasper, J. J., 259, *282*
Jeep, K., 288, *298*
Job, P., 216, *250*
Joesten, M. D., 217, 223, 224, 226, 230, 234, 236, 241, 243, *250*
Johnson, G., 366, *388*
Johnson, J. B. A., 316, *350*
Johnson, J. W., 366, 369, 370, *388*, *389*
Johnson, L. F., Jnr., 274, *283*
Johnson, R. E., 274, *283*
Johnson, W. C., 7, 13, 14, *43*, *44*
Johnston, H. L., 53, 54, *79*, 286, *298*
Jolly, W. L., 2, 8, 12, 13, 14, 15, 16, 17, 18, 19, 22, 25, 26, 27, *43*, *44*
Jones, G., 141, *208*
Jones, T. P., 323, 325, *349*
Jones, W. H., 28, *45*
Jones, W. J., 358, 359, 360, *387*
Jørgensen, C. K., 237, *250*
Jorgenson, M. J., 158, 160, *208*
Jortner, J., 15, *44*
Josephson, P. R. Jr., 387, *389*
Josien, M. L., 85, *114*
Jouber, J. M., 203, *209*

K

Kahovec, L., 95, *115*
Kanda, E., 286, *298*
Kaplan, J., 17, *44*
Karpachev, S. V., 371, *389*
Kartzmark, E. M., 357, 360, *388*
Kashtanov, L. I., 259, *283*
Katriskey, A. R., 158, *210*
Katz, J. J., 50, 51, 56, 57, 64, 67, 72, 77, 78, *79*, *80*, *81*, 86, 94, *115*, 292, 295, *298*, *299*
Katzin, L. I., 216, 238, 240, 242, *250*
Kay, R. L., 9, 10, *44*
Keefer, R. M., 215, *249*, 259, *282*, 286, *298*

Keenan, C. W., 37, 39, 40, *42*, *44*
Kelley, C. M., 369, 370, *389*
Kellogg, H. H., 363, *389*
Kelly, E. J., 39, 40, *44*
Kendall, J., 142, *208*, 319, *351*, 375, 376, *389*
Keneshea, F. J., 327, *349*, *351*
Kerr, G. T., 168, *210*
Kershaw, D. N., 193, *208*
Kianpour, A., 326, *351*
Kibbel, H. U., 166, *210*
Kikuchi, S., 7, *44*
Kilpatrick, M., 50, 51, 53, 56, 59, 64, 67, 69, 71, 72, 73, *79*, *80*, 85, 86, 94, *115*
King, P. J., 359, *388*
Kirchoff, R., 364, *388*
Kirkbride, B. J., 125, 130, 139, 154, *208*
Kirsanov, O. V., 99, *115*
Kise, M. A., 328, *349*
Kittel, C., 17, *44*
Kivelson, H. D., 254, *283*
Klanberg, F., 28, *43*, 84, 89, 92, 95, 96, 98, 99, 100, 104, 106, 107, 108, 109, 110, 111, 112, *115*, 281, *284*, 338, *352*
Klanberg, T., 328, 329, *352*
Klein, F. S., 33, *42*
Kleinberg, J., 2, 20, 25, 34, *42*, 242, *249*, 253, 260, *282*
Kleine-Weischede, K., 360, 384, 385, *389*, *390*
Klemenc, A., 86, *115*
Klemensiewicz, Z., 321, 323, *351*
Klemm, W., 355, 362, *388*, *389*
Kliman, H., 260, *284*
Knight, W. D., 17, *44*
Knöll, H., 259, *283*
Knollmüller, K., 95, *115*
Knunyants, J. L., 332, *352*
Kobayashi, M., 187, *209*
Koch, A. L., 77, *80*
Koch, F. K. V., 238, *250*
Kohl, O., 86, *115*
Köhler, H., 334, *351*
Kohlschütter, H. W., 84, 89, 98, 99, 112, *115*
Kolditz, L., 314, 315, 316, 318, 323, *351*
Kolotii, A. A., 387, *388*
Kolthoff, I. M., 308, *351*
Kon, H., 180, 199, *208*
Kongpricha, S., 75, *79*
Königstein, J. A., 212, *250*, 328, 340, *350*
Kopple, K. D., 77, 78, *80*

Korezynski, A., 259, *283*
Korinek, G. J., 218, *250*
Kornblum, J., 257, 258, *283*
Kosanovic, Dj., 188, 195, 196, *209*
Kosower, E. M., 225, 232, 236, 239, 241, 243, *250*
Kothner, von P., 192, *208*
Koubek, E., 219, 235, *250*
Krasnitskii, S. Ya., 355, *388*
Krauss, C. A., 2, 5, 9, 13, 15, 16, 30, *43*, *44*, 90, *114*, *115*, 260, *283*, 288, *298*
Krebs, H., 361, *389*
Kreye, W. C., 363, *389*
Krogh-Moe, J., 370, *389*
Krohn, C., 362, *388*, *389*
Kroll, W. J., 363, *389*
Kudo, S., 7, *44*
Kuhl, H., 170, *210*
Kuhn, L. P., 192, 204, *208*
Kuipers, G. A., 55, *80*
Kuivila, H., 196, *209*
Kunze, O., 347, *349*
Kunzler, J. E., 126, 129, 130, 131, 154, 162, *207*, *208*

L

Labounski, 386, *389*
Lacher, J. R., 322, 326, *351*
Ladyshnikova, N. I., 4, *45*
Lagowski, J. J., 30, *42*
Laidler, K. J., 8, *42*, 140, *206*
Laitinen, H. A., 10, 11, 28, *44*, 308, *351*
Lamberton, A. H., 191, *208*
Lamont, W. A., 77, *80*
Landesman, H., 218, *250*, *251*
Landolt-Börnstein, 375, 376, *389*
Landon, G. J., 355, 356, *389*
Lane, T. I., 53, 59, 64, 72, *79*
Lang, R., 239, 241, *251*
Langer, M., 179, *209*
Langford, C. H., 246, 247, *249*, *250*
Langford, P. O., 246, *250*
Lappert, M. F., 102, *114*
LaRoche, L., 217, 223, 224, 226, 230, 236, *250*
Lascombe, J., 85, *114*
Latimer, W. M., 25, *44*, 354, *389*
Laubicht, I., 274, 275, *284*
Lauder, I., 274, *283*
Laudis, A. L., 370, *390*
Lawroski, H., 6, *42*, *43*

Le Boucher, L., 61, *80*
Lecher, H. Z., 259, *283*
Lee, J. C., 34, *42*
Leech, H. R., 294, *298*
Le Fevre, R. J. W., 254, *283*
Lefrancois, B., 6, *44*
Leftin, H. P., 254, 260, 261, *284*
Lehmann, H. A., 162, *208*
Leighton, P. A., 31, *44*
Leisten, J. A., 88, 99, 112, *114*, 118, 134, 187, 188, 191, 192, 193, 194, 195, 196, 197, 198, 203, 204, *207*, *208*, *209*
Leman, G., 338, *351*
Lemons, J. F., 218, *250*
Lenard, J. I., 78, *80*
Lenher, V., 334, *351*
Lepoutre, G., 2, 16, 37, *42*, *44*
Lester, G. R., 226, 227, 228, 237, 242, *250*, *251*
Levine, R., 2, *44*
Levy, H. A., 327, *349*, 355, 371, *389*
Levy, R. A., 17, *44*
Lewis, J., 41, *42*, 307, 310, 329, 332, *349*, *351*
Lewis, J. I., 59, 67, *80*
Lia, J. S., 202, 203, *206*
Lichtin, N. N., 253, 254, 259, 260, 261, 266, 274, 275, 277, 281, 282, *283*, *284*
Lichty, D. M., 197, *209*
Lien, A. P., 73, *80*
Lier, A. P., 198, *209*
Liimatainen, R., 295, *298*
Liler, M., 150, 188, 195, 196, 197, *209*
Lindgren, R. M., 356, *388*
Lindquist, I., 212, 213, *249*, *250*, 272, *284*, 305, 309, 311, 312, 316, 317, 337, 338, 342, *349*, *351*, *352*
Lindquist, R. H., 18, *42*
Lippincott, E. R., 257, 281, 282, *284*
Lipscomb, W. N., 60, *79*
Loewenstein, A., 29, *44*
Long, F. A., 64, *80*, 157, *209*
Long, R. W., 60, *80*
Lorentz, R., 364, 369, *389*
Lowenstein, A., 191, *205*
Löwenstein, E., 369, 370, *389*
Löwy, S., 319, *352*
Luborsky, F., 69, 73, *80*
Lucasse, W. W., 13, 15, 16, *44*
Luchsinger, E. B., 373, *390*
Luchinskii, G. P., 254, *284*
Lugash, M. N., 201, *206*

Lupien, Y., 96, *114*
Lynch, M. A., 297, *299*

M

Maas, O., 95, 100, *115*
McAlonie, G. E., 360, *388*
McBeth, R. L., 360, 379, 386, 387, *389*
McBride, W. R., 31, *45*
McCaulay, D. A., 73, *80*, 198, *209*
MacClean, C., 198, *209*
Maccoll, A., 302, *349*
McConnell, H. M., 17, *44*
McCormick, R. H., 6, *42, 43*
McDaniel, D. H., 86, 87, *115*
MacDonald, D. K. C., 13, *42*
McElroy, A. D., 11, *44*
McFarlane, W., 184, 185, *206*
MacInnes, D. A., 28, *44*
McIntosh, D., 83, 85, 88, 89, 90, 95, 96, 97, 100, *115*, 286, 287, *298, 299*
McIntosh, R., 254, *284*
McKenzie, D. E., 328, 329, 330, 331, *349*
Mackor, E. L., 69, *80*, 198, *206, 209*, 240, *250*
MacLean, C., 69, *80*
McNeer, R. L., 240, *251*
Madan, S. K., 217, *249*
Mahler, J. E., 198, *210*
Mairinger, F., 309, 310, 341, 342, 343, 344, *349, 351*
Maki, A. G., 86, *115*
Makuc, J., 319, *352*
Marcinkowski, A. E., 244, *250*
Marcus, R. A., 173, *209*
Margrave, J. L., 52, *79*, 294, *298*
Markov, B. F., 365, 373, 374, 387, *388*
Markowitz, J. M., 253, 260, *283*
Marron, S. H., 162, *207*
Marsh, R. E., 295, *299*
Martens, R. D., 14, *44*
Martens, R. I., 7, *43*
Martin, D. R., 257, *282, 284*
Masaguer, J. R., 346, 347, *349, 351*
Masson, I., 178, 181, 182, *207, 209*
Masters, B. J., 274, 276, 277, *284*
Mathers, F. C., 364, *389*
Maybury, R. H., 56, *80*
Mayer, S. W., 369, 370, 371, 372, *390*
Meek, D. W., 213, 214, 217, 223, 224, 226, 230, 232, 233, 236, *249, 250*, 306, 344, *352*

Meinecke, E., 287, *298*
Meirboum, S., 191, *205*
Meise, W., 360, 383, *390*
Melinski, Z. A., 316, *350*
Mellor, J. W., 85, *115*, 176, 177, 180, *209*
Mellor's Comprehensive Treatise on In-
   organic and Theoretical Chemistry
   (1956), 50, 54, 63, 69, *80*
Mesech, H., 257, 258, 259, 263, *283, 284*
Metzl, S., 323, *352*
Metzner, R., 315, *352*
Meyer, A. W., 13, 14, *43, 44*
Meyer, F., 60, *79*
Meyer, J., 179, *209*
Michaelis, A., 259, *284*
Middaugh, R. L., 222, 223, *250*
Mikhailowskaya, V. I., 288, *298*
Miles, F. D., 179, *209*
Millen, D. J., 155, 163, 172, 173, 174, 176, *207, 208, 209*
Miller, H. K., 319, *351*, 375, 376, *389*
Minc, S., 244, *250*
Mishra, H. C., 177, 178, 180, 182, *205, 209*
Moede, J. A., 259, *284*
Moessen, G. W., 288, *298*
Monchick, L., 15, *42*
Monoszon, A. M., 9, 29, *44, 45*
Montignie, E., 316, *352*
Mooney, F. F., 338, *350*
Moore, B., 41, *42*
Morell, W. E., 60, *80*
Morris, A. G., 75, *79*
Morrison, G. C., 166, *206*
Motzfeldt, K., 362, *389*
Mountford, G. A., 154, *209*
Muetterties, E. L., 76, *80*, 294, 295, 296, *298*, 318, 319, *352*
Mulder, H. D., 30, *44*
Murray, F. E., 96, *115*
Murthy, A. R. V., 340, *352*
Muxart, R., 274, *284*
Muzzuchelli, A., 361, *389*

N

Nakata, S., 274, 275, *284*
Nakomoto, K., 187, *209*
Nayak, B., 191, *206*
Neilson, A. H., 55, *80*
Neumayr, S., 30, *45*
Newman, L., 216, *250*

Newman, M. S., 132, 167, 190, 193, 196, 199, 200, 203, *206*, *209*
Nicholls, D., 2, 34, *43*
Nichols, R., 296, 297, *298*
Nickerson, J. D., 254, *284*
Niedzielski, R. J., 222, 223, *250*
Nogradi, J., 271, 273, *284*
Norris, J. F., 203, *209*
Norris, T. H., 273, 274, 276, 277, 278, *282*, *283*, *284*
Nyholm, R. S., 235, *250*, 302, *349*
Nyman, C. J., 11, 27, *44*

O

O'Brien, R. J., 171, *206*
Oddo, G., 142, 190, 192, 193, 194, 196, 197, 199, 203, *209*, 334, *352*
O'Donnell, T. A., 53, 59, 64, 72, *79*
Ogg, R. A., 173, *209*
Ogg, R. A. Jr., 27, 31, *44*
Okawara, R., 171, *209*
Olah, G. A., 328, *352*
Oliver, G. D., 292, *298*
Onak, T. P., 218, *251*
O'Reilly, D. E., 14, 17, *43*
Orgel, L. E., 217, *251*, 302, *349*
Oubridge, J. V., 122, 125, 126, 127, 129, 132, 133, 137, 138, 139, 142, 162, 164, 165, 194, 205, *205*, *207*
Overstreet, R., 3, *44*
Owen, B. B., 7, *43*

P

Paddock, N., 174, *209*
Palm, V. A., 161, *209*
Panchenko, I. D., 387, *388*
Panish, M. B., 67, *80*, 292, 295, *299*
Pappas, P., 260, 261, *284*
Park, J. D., 322, 326, *351*
Parry, R. W., 318, *350*
Partington, J. R., 328, 329, *352*
Pascard, R., 123, *209*
Pastor, R. C., 17, *43*
Patel, J. K., 338, *350*
Paterno, E., 361, *389*
Patterson, A. Jr., 16, 18, *42*, *44*
Paul, M. A., 64, *80*, 157, *209*
Paul, R. C., 348, *352*
Pauling, L., 24, *44*, 62, *80*
Payne, D. S., 311, 315, *352*

Peach, M. E., 89, 90, 92, 93, 94, 96, 97, 98, 99, 100, 101, 102, 103, 104, 105, 106, 107, 109, 110, 111, 112, *115*, 338, *352*
Peacock, R. D., 257, *282*, 294, 295, 296, 297, *298*
Pearson, R. G., 39, *43*
Peck, R. E., 85, *114*
Pedersen, C., 77, *80*
Peeling, E. R. A., 122, 132, 135, 173, 174, *208*
Perkins, A. J., 53, *80*
Perkins, P. G., 340, *350*
Perrot, R., 329, *352*
Peterson, D., 367, *389*
Petruska, E. W., 168, *210*
Pettit, R., 198, *210*
Petzold, W., 312, *352*
Phillips, W. D., 76, *80*, 294, 295, 296, *298* 318, 319, *352*
Pimentel, G. C., 218, *251*
Pincher, S., 274, 275, *284*
Pinevich, G., 4, *45*
Piper, T. S., 223, 232, *250*
Piskur, M. M., 13, *44*
Pitzer, K., 366, *389*
Pitzer, K. S., 17, 18, 19, *41*, *42*, *43*
Plane, R. A., 238, *250*
Plank, C. J., 4, *45*
Pleskov, V. A., 9, 24, 29, *43*, *44*, *45*
Plotnikov, W. A., 288, *298*
Plotnikow, W., 319, *351*
Pollak, V. L., 17, *45*
Poole, H. G., 155, 173, 176, *208*
Pople, J. A., 156, *210*
Popov, A. I., 244, *251*
Porter, G. B., 302, 323, *352*
Potter, N. D., 274, 277, 278, *284*
Powell, T. M., 286, *298*
Powles, J. G., 17, *42*
Pratt, L., 184, 185, *206*
Preugschat, F., 307, 333, *352*
Pribble, M. J., 37, *42*
Price, F. P., 167, 168, 169, *210*
Proskauer, E. S., 234, 236, 239, 241, 243, *251*
Pruett, R. D., 295, *299*
Purcell, K. F., 216, 228, 230, 231, 239, *249*
Pushin, N., 358, *389*
Pusin, N. A., 319, *352*

Q

Quarterman, L. A., 50, 51, 72, 76, 78, *79*, *80*, 86, 94, *115*, 292, *298*

R

Rabinowitsch, M., 286, *298*
Rafos, R. R., 201, *208*
Raman, K. N. V., 340, *352*
Ransom, L. D., 371, *390*
Rao, K. N., 260, 261, *284*
Rao, M. R. A., 343, *350*
Ray, J. D., 173, *209*
Reavill, R. E., 168, *210*
Rebora, P. L., 34, *45*
Reeves, L. W., 218, *251*
Reid, C., 198, *210*
Reilly, C. A., 157, *208*
Rettgers, J. W., 319, *352*
Rheinbolt, H., 329, *352*
Rhodes, D. C., 355, *388*
Rice, 167
Richards, N. E., 357, 362, *388*
Richardson, F. D., 367, *389*
Richey, H. G., 202, 203, *206*
Riddich, J. A., 234, 236, 239, 241, 243, 251
Riehl, L., 258, *284*
Ritter, H. L., 355, *389*
Roberts, H. L., 340, *352*
Roberts, J. E., 297, *298*
Roberts, N. W., 34, *42*
Robinson, E. A., 88, *114*, 118, 122, 123, 125, 126, 127, 130, 131, 132, 133, 134, 137, 138, 139, 142, 143, 145, 146, 148, 150, 152, 153, 154, 159, 161, 162, 163, 164, 165, 166, 167, 168, 169, 170, 171, 172, 174, 177, 179, 180, 188, 196, 202, 205, *205, 207, 208, 210*
Robinson, P. L., 257, *282*, 294, 296, 297, *298*, 332, *351*
Rogers, M. T., 67, *80*, 292, 295, *299*
Rogers, P. S., 367, *389*
Roggenbuck, A., 34, *43*
Roper, G. C., 30, *42*
Rose, N. J., 226, *250*
Rosenbaum, J., 204, *210*
Rosenthal, M., 241, 242, *251*
Ross, V. F., 166, *206*
Rosse, R., 273, *284*
Rossini, F. D., 4, 8, *45*
Roth, W. A., 63, *80*
Rothschild, W. G., 55, *80*
Rowlands, C. B., 358, 359, 360, *387*
Royer, J. L., 178, *210*
Rubin, T. R., 162, *207*

Rudge, A. J., 292, *298*
Ruff, O., 13, *45*, 334, 343, *352*
Runner, M. E., 50, 53, 59, *80*, 85, *115*
Rupert, E. F., 95, *115*
Russell, H. Jr., 2, *45*
Rutherford, A., 128, *206*
Ruthven, G., 360
Rutledge, G. P., 76, *80*
Ryss, I. G., 294, *299*

S

Saires, G., 198, 201, 204, *206*
Sakakibara, S., 78, *80*
Sallach, R. A., 368, 371, *390*
Salstrom, E. J., 382, *389*
Salthouse, J. A., 87, 93, *115*
Sanderson, R. T., 25, *45*
Sandhu, S. S., 348, *352*
Sankuer, R. F., 16, *42*
Sargent, J., 65, *79*
Sastri, M. L. N., 58, 60, *80*
Satenstejn, A. I., 257, *284*
Savoie, R., 130, 131, 155, 162, 163, *207*
Scandola, E., 142, 190, 192, 194, 199, 203, 209
Schaffer, J. H., 363, *390*
Schaap, W. B., 10, *45*
Schally, A. V., 78, *80*
Scharf, E., 292, *299*
Scheidt, R. C., 375, *388*
Schierholz, H., 34, *43*
Schilt, A. A., 185, *210*
Schleich, K., 276, *283*
Schlenk, W., 264, *284*
Schmeisser, M., 292, *299*
Schmidt, F. C., 6, 10, 15, 30, *44, 45*
Schmidt, W., 316, *351*
Schmulbach, C. D., 217, *251*
Schmutzler, R., 331, 332, *352*
Schneider, W., 78, *80*
Schneider, W. G., 96, *114, 115*, 156, *210*, 218, *250, 251*
Schöber, G., 348, *350, 351*
Schott, G., 166, *210*
Schultz, J. W., 166, *206*
Schumb, W. C., 297, *299*
Schwarz, H. A., 35, *42*
Schwarzmann, E., 327, *352*
Scmid, M., 180, *206*
Scott, N. D., 41, *45*
Scott, R. L., 21, *43*

Sears, P. G., 226, 227, 228, 230, 231, 232, 237, 240, 242, *249*, *250*, *251*
Secor, H. Y., 39, 40, *44*
Seel, F., 258, 271, 272, 273, *284*, 294, 297, *299*, 329, 330, 331, 332, *352*
Selbin, J., *251*
Selig, H., 294, *299*
Senior, J. B., 180, 182, *207*
Shamir, J., 294, *299*
Shapiro, I., 218, *251*
Sharp, D. W. A., 86, 87, *115*
Sharpe, A. G., 294, 295, *298*, *299*
Shatenshtein, A., 6, *42*
Shatenshtein, A. I., 4, 30, 31, 32, 33, *45*
Shedlovsky, T., 261, *283*
Sheldon, J. C., 213, *251*, 310, 342, *352*
Shier, G. D., 218, *251*
Shin, K. H., 78, *80*
Shirey, W. B., 316, *352*
Shoemaker, C. E., 10, 11, 28, *44*
Shoolery, J. N., 218, *251*
Si Chang Fung, 27, *44*
Siegel, S., 295, *299*
Sienko, M. J., 2, 5, 12, *44*, *45*
Silberrad, O., 257, *284*
Silverthorn, M. E., 294, *298*
Simons, J. H., 50, 53, 59, 62, 66, 68, *80*, *81*
Sinclair, J. R., 30, *42*
Singer, S. J., 78, *81*
Singh, J., 348, *352*
Sisler, H. H., 2, *45*
Skelly, N. E., 244, *251*
Sly, W. G., 295, *299*
Smith, D. F., 55, 59, 76, *80*, *81*, 295, *299*
Smith, G. E., 16, *42*
Smith, G. P., 327, *349*, 360, *390*
Smith, H., 2, 34, 36, 41, *42*
Smith, H. A., 197, 200, *210*
Smith, N. V., 362, *388*, *389*
Smith, W., 366, *388*
Smyth, C. P., 85, 102, *115*
Sodek, H., 234, 240, *251*
Sokolova, L. N., 259, *283*
Sokol'skii, G. A., 332, *352*
Solomons, C., 122, 126, 129, 139, 145, 146, 150, 162, 163, 188, *207*
Solomons, S., 125, 127, 132, 133, 137, 138, 139, 142, 162, 205, *205*, *207*
Somiya, T., 131, *210*
Sommer, L. H., 168, *210*
Sottysiak, J., 6, 15, *45*

Sowards, D. M., 31, *45*
Sowerby, D. B., 310, 329, 332, *351*
Spalthoff, W., 53, 54, 60, *79*, *81*
Spandau, H., 307, 333, *352*
Speirs, J. L., 67, *80*, 292, 295, *299*
Staffansson, L. I., 367, *390*
Stairs, R. A., 5, *45*
Stančie, B., 347, *351*
Stavenhagen, A., 176, *210*
Steele, B. D., 83, 85, 88, 89, 90, 96, 97, *115*
Steele, B. O., 264, *282*, *284*
Stephens, W. R., 255, 257, *282*
Stephenson, C. C., 254, *283*
Stern, K. H., 377, *390*
Stevens, J. B., 158, *210*
Stewart, R., 190, *210*
Stokes, R. H., 138, *210*
Stoodley, L. G., 323, 325, *349*
Straub, D. K., 217, *250*
Strohmeier, W., 60, *79*, *81*
Stromberg, A. G., 371, *389*
Stroup, P. T., 364, *389*
Studer, F. J., 15, *45*
Sudborough, J. J., 329, *352*
Sugarman, N., 17, 18, *43*
Sulzberg, J., 201, *208*
Sundheim, B. R., 361, *389*
Susz, B. P., 223, 236, 239, *250*, *251*
Sutton, L. E., 302, *349*
Svirmickas, A., 76, *79*
Swart, K. H., 322, 323, 326, *351*
Swenson, G. W., 38, *45*
Swinehart, J. H., 219, *251*
Symons, M. C. R., 2, 18, *42*, *45*, 177, 178, 180, 182, 183, 198, 201, 204, *205*, *206*, *208*, *209*, *210*, 289, *298*
Szmant, H. H., 169, *210*
Szöke, A., 29, *44*

T

Taft, R. W., 160, *206*
Tajkowski, E., 6, *45*
Talaat, M. Y. A., 342, 343, 346, *349*
Tanaka, S., 187, *209*
Taub, I. A., 38, *42*
Taube, H., 218, 219, *250*, *251*
Taylor, N. W., 287, *299*
Taylor, R. C., 95, *115*
Tealdi, M., 334, *352*
Temkin, M., 378, *390*

Teodorovich, V. P., 6, *43*

Thomas, W. G., 358, 359, 360, *387*

Thompson, A., 127, 129, 145, 166, *208, 210*

Thompson, H. B., 67, *80*, 292, 295, *299*

Thompson, R. C., 205, *205*

Thornley, M. B., 139, 157, 159, 188, *206*

Tobe, M. L., 187, *205*

Toft, R., 264, *283*

Tolgyesi, W. S., 328, *352*

Tolloczko, S., 301, 321, 324, *350, 352*

Tomlinson, J. W., 367, *389*

Toops, E. E. Jr., 234, 236, 239, 241, 243, 251

Topol, L. E., 370, 371, *390*

Treffers, H. P., 135, 193, 196, *210*

Tremearne, T. H., 6, *45*

Tridot, G., 338, *351*

Troost, W. R., 311, *352*

Trotter, J., 171, *206*

Tsubomura, H., 239, 241, *251*

Tye, F. L., 100, *114*, 155, 179, 198, 200, *208*

Tyree, S. Y., 213, *251*, 310, 342, *352*

U

Ubbelohde, A. R., 355, 356, *389*

Ullman, D., 267, *283*

Ullstern, R. E. Jnr., 259, *284*

V

Valleé, R. E., 86, 87, *115*

Van Artsdalen, E. R., 356, 377, 382, 386, *388, 390*

van der Meij, P. H., 204, *206*

Van Der Voorn, P., 231

van der Worm, E. R., 212, *250*, 328, 340, *350*

Van der Waals, J. H., 69, *80*, 198, *209*

Van Heteren, W. J., 329, *352*

Vaniscotte, C., 6, *44*

van Wazer, J. R., 327, *352*

Vaughan, J. W., 228, *250*

Vegard, L., 5, *45*

Veis, A., 77, *81*

Verdier, P. H., 76, *79*

Verrigin Stuart, A. A., 198, *206*

Vidale, G. L., 95, *115*, 318, *350*

Vierk, A. L., 254, *284*

Viktorov, M. M., 257, *284*

Vining, D. C., 316, *350*

Voitovich, B. A., 219, *251*

Vonk, C. G., 293, *299*, 327, *352*

von Rosenberg, J. L., 198, *210*

Von Sundermeyer, W., 360, 383, 384, 385, 390

Vos, A., 293, *298*

W

Waddington, T. C., 84, 85, 86, 87, 89, 90, 92, 93, 94, 95, 96, 97, 98, 99, 100, 101, 102, 103, 104, 105, 106, 107, 108, 109, 110, 111, 112, *115*, 181, *206*, 281, *284*, 328, 329, 338, *352*

Wade, K., 310, 340, *350*

Waentig, G., 287, *299*

Waentig, P., 96, *114*

Wait, S. C., 356, 379, *390*

Walden, P., 253, 255, 263, 273, *284*, 301, 312, 316, 319, 321, 333, *352*

Walker, J. F., 41, *45*

Walker, J. W., 100, *115*

Walrafen, G. E., 130, 131, 162, 163, *210*

Walton, P. R., 204, *209*

Warshawsky, I., 37, *45*

Wasem, K., 331, 332, *352*

Wasif, S., 139, 142, 146, 173, 189, 193, 196, 203, *207*

Wasserfuhr, R., 329, *352*

Watson, G. M., 362, 363, *388, 389, 390*

Watson, H. R., 41, *42*

Watt, G. W., 2, 31, 34, *45*

Wayland, B., 224, 232, 234, 243, 246, *249*

Webster, D. E., 171, *208, 209*

Webster, M., 244, *249*

Weickel, T., 264, *284*

Weinland, R. F., 170, *240*

Weinstein, J., 86, *114*

Weiss, J., 326, *351*

Weissman, S. I., 198, *210*

Welch, C. M., 197, 200, *210*

Welch, F. E., 257, 281, 282, *284*

Wendt, H., 268, *283*

Wenz, D. A., 226, *250*

Werblan, L., 244, *250*

Wertyporoch, E., 341, *352*

West, R., 86, *115*

West, T. S., 341, 343, 345, 346, *349*

Westrum, E. F. Jr., 87, *114*

Weyl, W., 10, *45*

Weissberger, A., 234, 236, 239, 241, 243, 251

Wharmby, D. H. W., 289, 297, *298*
Wheat, J. A., 95, *115*, 287, 288, *299*
Wheeler, H. L., 312, *352*
Whipple, E. B., 76, *79*
White, D., 53, 54, *79*, 286, *298*
White, J. A., 84, 85, 87, 89, 90, 96, 98, 99, 106, 107, 108, 109, 112, *115*
White, J. D., 259, *284*
White, R. F. M., 128, 156, 157, *207*
Whitford, E. L., 197, *210*
Whitmore, F. C., 168, *210*
Whynes, A. L., 328, 329, *352*
Wicke, Von E., 136, *210*
Wickert, K., 256, 259, 265, 266, 267, 269, 280, *283*, *284*
Wiebe, R., 6, *45*
Wiebenga, E. H., 292, 293, *298*, *299*, 327, *352*
Wiesendanger, H. U. D., 28, *45*
Williams, D. F., 357, 360, *388*
Willis, H. A., 338, *350*
Winbush, S. V., 369, 370, 371, 372, 373, *388*
Winsor, V. R., 364, *390*
Wood, R. E., 355, *389*
Woodward, R. A., 340, *352*
Woolf, A. A., 294, 295, *299*, 317, 318, *352*
Worrall, I. J., 310, *350*
Wiig, E. O., 197, *210*
Wiles, L. A., 190, 197, *210*
Wilhoit, E. D., 230, 231, 232, 237, *249*, *251*
Wilkinson, G., 41, *42*, 184, 185, *206*
Williams, G., 189, *210*
Williams, J. F. A., 201, *210*
Williams, R. E., 218, *250*, *251*

Willis, J. E., 217, *249*
Wilmarth, W. K., 33, *45*
Winterstein, A., 204, *208*
Wise, S. S., 52, *79*
Wisotsky, M. J., 202, 203, *206*
Woldbye, F., 216, *251*
Wolsky, S. P., 15, *45*
Wyatt, P. A. H., 122, 125, 130, 131, 134, 139, 147, 154, 161, 162, 191, *206*, *208*, *209*, *210*

Y

Yates, K., 158, 190, *210*
Yeh, S. J., 102, *115*
Yoon, Y. K., 95, *115*
Yosim, S. J., 369, 370, 371, 372, 373, *390*
Yost, D. M., 2, *45*
Young, J., 374, 383, *389*
Young, T. F., 157, 163, *210*

Z

Zackrisson, M., 312, *349*
Zadra, 386, *390*
Zarzycki, G., 355, *390*
Zdanuk, E. J., 15, *45*
Zebrowska, A., 321, 323, *351*
Zelezny, W. F., 291, *299*
Zengin, N., 58, *79*
Zhurin, A. I., 367, *390*
Zintl, E., 30, 31, *45*
Zuur, A. P., 339, *350*
Zwicker, E. F., 38, *45*

Subject Index

(Numbers in bold type indicate the page on which a subject is treated most fully.)

A

Acetone, **237**, 247
Acetonitrile, **243**, 247
Acid–base reactions
  in hydrogen fluoride, 62, 75
  in liquid ammonia, 28
  in sulphuric acid, 152
  halides and oxyhalides, 331
Acidity
  ammonia, liquid, 23
  halide–oxyhalide solvents, 305
  hydrogen fluoride, 62
  hydrogen fluoride, liquid, solutes in, 72
  hydrogen halides, solutions in, 97
  iodine monohalides, 289
  sulphuric acid and its solutions, 121, 124, 157
  nitrosonium salts, 331
Alkaline-earth halides, 354, 367
Aluminium halides, 339
Amines, solutions of metals in, 41
Ammonia, liquid, physical properties of, 1
  crystal structure, 5
  density, 4
  dielectric constant, **5**, 19
  derived constants, 5
  electrical conductivity, 5
  heat capacity, 3
  heat of fusion, 3
  heat of vapourization, **3**, 25
  refractive index, 5
  surface tension, 5
  thermodynamic functions for gas at 25°, 4
  vapour pressure, 2, 3
  viscosity, **4**, 25
Ammonia, liquid, physical properties of solutions, 6
  electrolytes, 6
  metals, 10, 34
  non-electrolytes, 6
Ammonia, liquid, reactions in
  acid–base reactions, 28
  comparison with other solvents, 19
  ionic solvation, 26
  oxidation potential range, 22
  reactions of metal solutions, 34
Antimony
  bromide, 326
  chloride, 311, **321**
Arsenic
  bromide, 319
  chloride, **311**, 348
  fluoride, 317

B

Barium nitrate, 7
Basicity
  alkali metal iodides, 289
  ammonia, 20, 23
  halide–oxyhalide solvents, 305
  metal hydrogen sulphates, 118
  nitrosonium chlorides, 331
  solutions in hydrogen fluoride, 68, 69
  solutions in hydrogen halides, 97, 99–104
  solutions in sulphuric acid, 119, 174, 187–196
  sulphuric acid, 124
Bismuth chloride, 327
Bromine, 287
  pentafluoride, 295
  trifluoride, 292, 294

C

Caesium fluoride, 364, 365
Carbohydrates, 76
Cellulose, 77
Chlorine, 287
  pentafluoride, 295
  trifluoride, 292, 293
Co-ordinating solvents, 211
Co-ordinating solvents, criteria for establishing, 215
  conductivity, 219
  cryoscopy, 219
  infra-red spectroscopy, 216

Co-ordinating solvents (*contd.*)—
　nuclear-magnetic resonance, 217
　ultra-violet and visible spectroscopy,
　　215
Co-ordinating solvents, energetics, 200
Co-ordinating solvents, solute behaviour,
　226
　acetone, **237**, 247
　acetonitrile, **243**, 247
　dimethylsulphoxide, **230**, 248
　methanol and ethanol, **239**, 248
　nitromethane and nitrobenzene, **234**,
　　247
　NN-dimethylacetamide (DMA), **228**,
　　247, 248
　N-methylacetamide (NMA), **230**, 247
　pyridine, **241**, 248
　tetramethylene sulphone, **245**, 247

D

NN-Dimethylacetamide (DMA), **228**, 247,
　248
Dimethylsulphoxide, **230**, 248

E

Electrochemistry
　ammonia, liquid, 5, 9, 15
　co-ordinating solvents, 220
　halides and oxyhalides, 302, 321, 322,
　　327, 348
　halogens and interhalogens, 285, 296
　higher hydrogen halides, 88, 100 *et seq.*
　hydrogen fluoride, liquid, 49, 66–73
　molten salts, 353 *et seq.*
　sulphur dioxide, liquid, 253, 264
　sulphuric acid, 128, 135, 142, 179
Enzymes, 77
Ethanol, 239
Ethanol–sodium reaction, 39

F

Fluorides, 47, 65, 290, 292, 295, 296, 297,
　317, 364
Fluorine, liquid, 286

H

Halides
　alkaline-earth, 354, 367
　ammonium, 7

hydrogen, 7, 83
　metal, **7**, **354**, 364, 369, 373
　molten salts, 354
　of Group V elements, 301
　potassium, 10
　silver, 20
Halides and oxyhalides of Group V
　Elements, 301
　acidity and basicity, 305, 311
　alkaline-earth halides, 354, 367
　aluminium halides, 339
　experimental methods, 306
　halides, **311**, 348
　oxyhalides, **327**, 348
　phosphoryl chloride, 306, 328, **332**, 348
　solutes, 312–332, 334–348
　conductivity measurements, 307
　cryoscopic measurements, 310
　ebullioscopic measurements, 310
　examination of solid phases, 307
　isotopic exchange reaction, 310
　physical properties, 303, 304
　potentiometric measurements, 308
　products of electron transfer, 307
　qualitative solubility considerations, 306
　spectrophotometric measurements, 309
　thermodynamic measurements, 310
　titrations using indicators, 309
　transport number measurements, **308**
　viscosity measurements, 810
Halogens, 286, *see also* Interhalogens
　bromine, 287
　chlorine, 287
　fluorine, liquid, 286
　iodine, 288
　physical properties, 286
　reactions of, 286
　solutes, 287–289
Henry's Law, 6
Hydrogen chloride, liquid, 83, *see also*
　Hydrogen halides
Hydrogen fluoride, liquid, 47
　equipment for studying, 47
　physical properties of, 52
　solutes in, 64
　solutions of compounds of biological
　　importance, 76
Hydrogen fluoride, liquid, properties of
　acidity, 62
　physical properties, 52
　polymerization, 59
　self-ionization, 57

Diane Allen was born in Leeds, but raised at the family's farm deep in the Yorkshire Dales. After working as a glass engraver, raising a family, and looking after an ill father, she found her true niche in life, joining the Magna Large Print publishing firm in 1990. Rising through the firm, she is now the general manager and has recently been made Honorary Vice President of the Romantic Novelists' Association. Diane and her husband Ronnie live in Long Preston in the Yorkshire Dales, and have two children and four beautiful grandchildren.

FOR THE SAKE OF HER FAMILY

It is 1912 in the Yorkshire Dales. Alice Bentham and her brother Will have lost their mother to cancer. Money is scarce and pride doesn't pay the doctor, or put food on the table. Alice gets work at Whernside Manor, looking after Lord Frankland's fragile sister Miss Nancy. Will and his best friend Jack begin working for the Lord of the Manor at the marble mill. But their purpose there is not an honest one. For a while everything runs smoothly. But corruption, attempted murder and misplaced love are just waiting in the wings. Nothing is as it seems and before they know it, Alice and Will's lives are entwined with those of the Franklands — and nothing will ever be the same again.

DIANE ALLEN

FOR THE SAKE OF HER FAMILY

Complete and Unabridged

CHARNWOOD
Leicester

First published in Great Britain in 2012 by
Macmillan
an imprint of
Pan Macmillan
London

First Charnwood Edition
published 2013
by arrangement with
Pan Macmillan
a division of
Macmillan Publishers Limited
London

A catalogue record for this book is available
from the British Library

ISBN 978–1–4448–1584–9

Published by
F. A. Thorpe (Publishing)
Anstey, Leicestershire

Set by Words & Graphics Ltd.
Anstey, Leicestershire
Printed and bound in Great Britain by
T. J. International Ltd., Padstow, Cornwall

This book is printed on acid-free paper

This book is dedicated to my family, especially my husband Ronnie, who is always there, no matter what life throws at us. My daughter Lucy, her husband Steven, Amy our little princess, Ben the newest member of our family, also my son Scott and his wife Zoe and their children, the beautiful Amelia and Ollie, our little soldier.

I'd like to thank good friends Helen Bibby and Hilda Stronach for their encouragement and help. Also Judith Murdoch and Wayne Brookes, to whom along with my readers I owe everything.

1

The screams carried up into the high pasture — agonizing, soul-stripping screams. Alice sat, hands covering her ears; she just couldn't bear it any longer. When was it going to end? Surely the doctor could make it stop? In defiance of the screams she kicked her boot into the hard, frost-filled ground, not bothering that the solid earth hurt her foot.

Bess Bentham's husband and children had watched helplessly as her condition deteriorated, turning her from a beautiful buxom woman to a frail, skeletal form. For months she had struggled to perform chores around the farm or look after her family. The aged country doctor's fees were something they could ill afford, so Bob Bentham had delayed as long as possible before sending for him. With hindsight, the family wished he had acted sooner.

Alice, the younger of the two Bentham children, sat behind the tall pasture wall that backed onto the great high-reaching peak of Whernside. She was a stubborn child, a true Bentham, Dales bred, proud and too feisty for her own good — just like her father, or so her mother had often told her. When she was in one of her moods, she'd a face on her that could turn milk sour. Now, as her mother lay dying, she was angry at the whole world and knew no other way than to take it out on the frozen earth that her mother would soon be buried under.

Shivering, Alice got to her feet, pulling her jerkin around her; the bottom of her skirt was stiff where she had got it wet going through the farmyard. It was November and bitterly cold; already the highest points of Whernside were capped with a covering of snow. Shoving her fingerless-mittened hands into her pockets, she looked towards the farm and thought about her mother lying on her deathbed. Much as she wanted to be by her mother's side, Alice couldn't have endured another minute in the low-beamed house. For days, the smell of death had filled every nook and cranny, making it unbearable. When the doctor had finally been summoned to concoct potions to ease the pain, Alice had taken her chance to flee. She sighed and shook her head, remembering the look on her father's face as he told her to come back indoors. Instead she had slammed the kitchen door and run as fast as her legs would carry her. Didn't he realize she had to get away, if only for a minute or two? All she wanted was to escape the sorrow and to breathe the clear, fresh air on the fellside.

The screaming stopped suddenly and was replaced with a deathly silence. Alice could hear her heart beating; the pounding was so strong, it felt as if it was escaping through her chest wall. The breath from her mouth came out in pure white clouds as she waited for further sounds from home. But the farm was silent now, so terribly silent. A snowflake fluttered to earth and

Alice was listening so intently she could have sworn she heard it land. Gathering her skirts around her, she got up and ran, slipping and almost tumbling as she raced along the cobbled droving road. By the time she reached the farmyard she was fighting for breath, her face flushed from the cold air biting at her cheeks and her haste to reach her dying mother.

'Miss Alice . . . ' Dr Bailey bowed his head. It pained him, having to break the news to this young lass, knowing how the words he was about to say would change her life. 'I'm afraid your mother died a few minutes ago. You have my condolences. Now, go and join your father and brother. I'm sure you will find comfort in one another's grief.'

His face was grey and sombre as he mounted the gig, pulling a wool blanket over his knees to guard against the bitter wind before lifting the whip to stir the two patient bays into motion. He paused for a moment, as if uncertain whether to offer guidance, then said, 'Your mother loved you. She'd have wanted you to show the same love to your father and brother, so you must be strong now for her sake. I'll stop by and tell Mrs Batty of your loss — you'll need her help to lay your mother out.' And with that he tipped his hat and whipped the team into motion, the gig swaying from side to side as it descended the rocky path towards the village of Dent.

Alice watched the gig until it turned out of the yard. Tears filled her eyes, and no matter how she tried she couldn't keep them from rolling down her cheeks. She hadn't meant to leave her mum;

all she'd wanted was a moment's peace — surely Mum would have known that? Her hand trembled as she lowered the catch on the oak door into the kitchen. If she could have turned and run away, she would have, but she had to be brave. Wiping her nose with the back of her mitten, she stuck out her chin, swiped away the tears that would not stop falling, and entered the kitchen of Dale End Farm.

★　★　★

'So, you've decided to show your face, then? Your mother asked for you with her dying breath, and where were you? I'll tell you where you were — up that bloody fell, like a raggle-taggle gypsy child.' Bob Bentham was angry with his daughter, but secretly he was even angrier with himself for not getting the doctor to his wife sooner. He turned away from Alice and spat a mouthful of saliva mixed with black chewing tobacco into the fire, making it hiss. Then he reached for his pipe and tobacco tin from above the mantel. 'You'd better go and say your goodbyes now, before old Ma Batty gets here.'

Alice stayed where she was, trembling and snivelling, head bowed, not wanting to go up the darkening stairs.

'Now then, our Alice, come on. I'll go up with you.' Will, her big brother, put his arm around her in sympathy. Hard as it was for him, he knew that for a sixteen-year-old it must be even worse. Bowing his head, his lanky body too tall for the low roof of the homely kitchen, he led her towards the stairs.

'I'm frightened, our Will. I've never seen a dead person before.' Alice's body shook as Will squeezed her tight.

'It's not the dead 'uns that hurt you, lass, it's the buggers that are wick that does that,' Bob said sharply, his eyes never leaving the fire.

Will held Alice's hand as they climbed the creaking wood stairs to their parents' room. Downstairs, she could hear her father muttering to himself and riddling the fire embers; he was cross with her and it'd take him time to come round.

The oil lamp next to the bed was burning and, with the coming of the night and the dark snowy skies closing in, shadows from the flames were leaping on the dim walls, creating sprites that danced on the whitewashed stone. Alice turned her remorseful gaze to her mother's corpse. Bess seemed at peace, her long hair loose around her alabaster skin.

'Do you think our mum's in heaven now?' Alice asked, wondering if her mother could still see her and hear her.

'I'm sure she is. She's probably looking down on us and blowing kisses.' Will gave her arm a reassuring squeeze. 'Time to say your goodbyes, our Ali. Give her a kiss — she'd like that.'

'If Mum is in heaven, she knows I should have been with her instead of sitting up the fell. She won't love me any more.' Tears began to fall from Alice's eyes and she started sobbing, grief taking over her small, crumpled body.

'Yes, she'll know you were up the fell, but she wouldn't have wanted it any other way. You always were headstrong, Mum knew that. That's why it's our job to look after Father. She asked that of us with her dying breath. So, don't you worry, she loved you for the spirited person that you are — she told me so.'

Alice controlled her sobbing for a brief moment and bent to kiss her mother's brow. Already the skin was cold and bluish white. The brief contact made her feel sick and her legs turned to jelly. What was she going to do without her mother? She almost dissolved into sobs again, but by holding her breath and blowing her nose she managed to bring her emotions under control.

'There, our lass, she knows you loved her. Go and brush your hair, then come downstairs and make some supper before Mrs Batty gets here. She'll want to lay Mum out in the parlour while her husband brings the coffin. Reckon it'll be down to us to get everything ready — Father doesn't seem up to it. I'll see to the parlour while you do us all some bacon and eggs. We've not eaten all day, and you know Mother — she wouldn't have wanted that, now, would she?'

'I did love her, our Will.' Resolving to pull herself together and stop sniffling, Alice placed her hands on her hips and announced: 'Don't worry, I will look after everybody as Mother would have wanted. I'll not let Father down again.' With that, she went off to her bedroom to tidy herself.

Will ran his hand along the banister, ducking his head to avoid the low ceiling above the stairs.

'Is she all right — our lass?' Bob asked his son. 'I was a bit hard on her when she came waltzing in. I was angry, what with her mother having asked for her, and Alice not there.' Bob knew his own faults, one of which was a tendency to be too hasty with his words. A fault that he could also see in Alice; it even made him smile sometimes, the fact that she was so like him.

'She's all right, Father. Alice was with Mum in her own way; she was just upset. You know how she always goes and hides up behind that top wall in the high pasture when things get too much for her.' Seeing the pain on his father's face, Will briskly changed the subject: 'Now then, I'm going to make the parlour ready while Alice fixes some supper for us all. Why don't you have a rest; it's been a difficult day for you. I know you're going to miss Mother, but we'll always be here to see to things.'

'Aye, I don't know what I'll do without her, our lad. My Bess was everything to me, and I let her down. I should have got the doctor. Brass isn't worth anything compared to them you love.' Bob sighed and put his head in his hands.

'We'll be all right, Father,' said Will, patting his father on the shoulder. 'Our Alice is nearly a woman and a good hand about the place, and with my job at the big house, we'll get by. The last thing Mother would have wanted is for you to be upset.' Hearing Alice come down the stairs,

Will turned. 'Are you all right, our Ali?'

'I'm fine. I'll go and make us something to eat.' Alice felt shaky and she knew she was white as a sheet, but she had to be grown-up and handle the situation like a woman. The family needed her.

'That'll be grand, Alice.' Her father tried to force a smile. 'You're not a bad lass. I'm sorry I shouted at you — it was the shock of losing your mother. Do you want me to cut you some bacon off the flitch in the dairy? I'll do that while you go out and see if the hens have laid us some fresh eggs. If you can feed them at the same time, that would be a grand help.'

'I'll do that, Father, you don't have to ask. I'll feed Jip, too — poor old dog will be wondering what's happened. He got overlooked this morning.'

Taking her shawl from behind the door, Alice wrapped it around her. Then, determined to show her dad that she was not going to let him down, she drew herself to her full height, opened the back door and stepped out into the bitter evening air.

Outside, it was still trying to snow and the sky was heavy and threatening. Having made sure the dog was fed, Alice moved on to the hen hut to check for eggs and to feed the clucking brown birds. The smell of poultry and the warmth of the tarred hut made her remember how, as a child, she used to collect eggs with her mother. The memory conjured an image of Mum laughing as Alice hid behind her skirts because she was frightened of the one hen that always

8

was too curious for its own good. Forcing herself to focus on the present, Alice checked the nesting boxes for eggs: only half a dozen, but that would do for supper. She'd heard Dad say that they hadn't been laying so well because of the cold weather. Making a pocket in her shawl to put them in, she closed the hut door behind her.

She was turning to make her way back to the house when Mr and Mrs Battys' cart arrived, with her mother's cheap, rough-made coffin strapped on the back. Alice looked at it, hoped it was strong enough to protect her mother from the cold, dark earth. It was a pauper's coffin, probably not even the right size for her mother's frail body. Tears came to her eyes and a feeling of bitterness filled her stomach. One day, she vowed, she would have money. No one she loved would ever again be given a pauper's funeral. And no one she loved would die for want of cash to pay a doctor. She would make certain of that.

The light from the kitchen spilled out onto the dour couple as they carried the shabby coffin into the house. Alice lingered in the yard, watching as Will pulled the curtains in the parlour — when she caught herself referring to the shabby living room as a parlour, Alice smiled; her mother had always called it 'her parlour', furnishing it as posh as money would allow. It might not have chandeliers and sparkling crystal ornaments like the manor, but Mum had kept it spotless and loved. It was only right that she would be laid to rest in there for folk to pay their respects.

Alice delayed a while longer, sheltering inside the barn, giving old Mrs Batty time to make her mother respectable and for the coffin to be carried into the parlour. She'd have stayed there until the sickeningly pious Battys had gone, but eventually the cold drove her into the kitchen to face them.

'Ah, Alice — we were wondering where you'd got to.' Bob looked at her with concern.

'I was just making sure all was fed, Father. And I closed the barn doors before the snow comes.' Having placed the eggs in a dish and hung her shawl up, she turned to look at the couple who dealt in death. 'Mr and Mrs Batty, thank you for seeing to our needs and being so quick bringing the coffin.' It cost her an effort to be polite; she felt more like spitting the words at them. In her mind's eye she pictured the Battys' yard with its ugly pile of coffins, hastily thrown together and left out there in all weathers, until some poor soul like her mother needed burying. These coffins were meant for the poor. The lovingly polished oak coffins intended for the posh folk of the dale could only be seen if you peered through the door leading to the workshop.

'Aye, you've got a grand lass here, Bob.' Ernie Batty smacked his hands together, his ample body slumping into a kitchen chair. 'A right polite bit of a lass.'

'We were sorry to hear of your mother's death, Alice.' Hilda Batty put her arm around Alice. 'She's at peace now, my dear. I've made her look so pretty, at rest in her coffin.'

Cringing at the old woman's hand of death resting on her skin, Alice moved away on the pretext of getting supper ready.

'Right then, Bob, we'll be on our way.' Ernie Batty heaved himself to his feet. 'Now, you know I don't want to ask this,' he said, his face turning sombre, 'but I need paying for the coffin, and my old lass here will expect a bit of something for laying your good lady out.'

'Tha'll get the money. You can take this for your bother now and I'll give you the rest at the end of the month when our Will gets paid.' Scowling, Bob reached up to the tin cashbox kept above the fireplace. Opening it up, he threw what coins he had onto the table. 'I've always been a man of my word, tha knows that.' The cheek of the man! Asking for his money before his wife was even cold, let alone buried. 'Alice, open that door and see Mr and Mrs Batty out.' The sooner they were gone, the faster he and his family could grieve in peace.

'With pleasure, Father.' Alice darted to the door, eager to get rid of the predatory couple.

'Our condolences once again.' Ernie bowed his head as he left the building, his wife shoving him out of the door as he tried to count the handful of coins.

The snow was falling steadily now. There was a good covering on the ground already, the wind whipping it up into white blankets over the walls. As their horse and cart set off down the lane, the sound of Mrs Batty chastising her husband for having no tact could be heard above the howling of the wind.

11

Alice put her arm around her father. 'Never mind, Father. We'll manage. We will get the money some end up.'

'I know, lass. Grovelling old devil — fancy asking for his brass straight away. Now, I'm going to have five minutes with your mother. I need to talk to her.'

Patting Alice on the shoulder, Bob turned and wearily made his way into the parlour and his beloved Bess.

Alice went to join Will, who had been sitting quietly next to the fire since letting in the Battys. 'One day I'm going to have so much money that people like the Battys will have to grovel to me, same way they expected our father to grovel to them tonight. You'll see, Will: my parlour will be a proper parlour with maids and servants, and I'll be a lady.'

Will looked up. 'Alice, does that really matter? We've just lost our mother, Father's in mourning, and at the moment we haven't a penny — so stop thinking of your bloody self for once.'

Alice flicked her long blonde hair from out of her face and got up to start supper. Why did people always get her wrong? She wasn't thinking only of herself; she was thinking of all of them and the parlour they were going to share.

★　★　★

It was five long days before they could bury poor Bess. The snow had fallen for forty-eight hours, covering the dale with a white blanket so thick that it made travel impossible, and digging a grave was out of the question. When the mourning family did finally manage the journey down the rough stony track into the little churchyard of Dent village, it was raining. The rain added to the greyness of the day, bringing with it encircling mists.

Walking behind the coffin in the shadow of the four bearers, Alice shed tears for her dead mother. In church, she silently took her seat in the pew, smiling bravely as her big brother squeezed her hand in sympathy. As she gazed through brimming eyes at the rough wooden coffin, a steady stream of raindrops splashed down on it from a hole in the church roof. The light from the candles fragmented and shone like a miniature rainbow in the drips. Anger swelled up into her throat as the congregation sang 'Abide with Me'. She cursed the world as she looked out of the church window, the trees outside waving their branches wildly in the wind, raging with the same anger as Alice.

Some day, she told herself, things would be right; they'd have money and a fine house. She didn't know how, but as long as she had breath in her small body she would fight for her family and never would they have to beg for help again.

2

There, that was the parlour dusted; another job done for the day. The sun shone through the small-paned windows only weakly yet, but it gave hope that spring was on its way. During the four months since her mother's death Alice had been keeping house, cleaning, cooking and helping out around the farm. She didn't want to admit it, but having more responsibility had turned her from a girl into a young woman.

Alerted by a random sunbeam to a streak of coal dust that had managed to survive the attention of the duster, she turned to give the edge of the dresser one last going over. It was then that the gap caught her eye . . .

Not the clock, please not the clock! Alice gazed unbelieving at the space where the little brass carriage clock had stood. Crestfallen and exhausted, she slumped into the one comfy chair that the Bentham family owned. In the absence of the clock, the green chenille mantelpiece cover looked bare, its tassels hanging limp over the unlit fire, held in place only by the two grinning Staffordshire pot spaniels. Her mother had been so proud of that clock, which had been presented to her when she left service at Ingelborough Hall to get married.

It wasn't the fact that the clock was missing that made her put her head in her hands and sob; it was the fact that she knew all too well

14

what had happened to it. How could he!

Anger spurring her on, she surveyed the room for other missing items. What else had he pilfered? At least the paintings were still hanging, the highland cattle serene as ever in the face of her distress. The mock-silver teapot was still on the table, but then it would be — mock silver wasn't worth much. Hands on hips, mind racing, she forced herself to take a deep breath. If only her worries could be expelled as easily as a lungful of air. Never mind, it was done now. Too late to get the clock back, even though she had a good idea where it was. Besides, the loss of the clock paled into insignificance alongside the real problem: how the hell was she going to cope if things carried on like this? She might be only sixteen, but the seriousness of their situation was not lost on her.

'Ali, get the pot on — we'll not go hungry tonight!' Will's voice rang out, followed by the sound of the kitchen door closing. 'Would you look at these two!' He appeared in the parlour doorway, stooping because of the lack of headroom, his gun resting on one shoulder and two very dead rabbits in his other hand, dripping blood onto the clean floor. 'What's up, our lass? What's to do — you've not been worrying over supper, have you?'

Alice turned from the window and smiled. 'Why should I worry about supper when we have the finest shot this side of Leeds living under our roof? Now get yourself out of this parlour, Will Bentham, before you get blood everywhere.' She pushed him lovingly out of the doorway. 'Them

15

rabbits are a grand size, all right. Just you be careful that Lord Frankland doesn't catch you — he'd have you up in front of the magistrates before you had time to blink.'

'They're from our high pasture, Ali, honest. Besides, even if they were that bastard Frankland's, he wouldn't miss 'em — too busy carrying on with his floozies, from what I hear.' Will lumbered out into the farmyard, tugging his knife out of his pocket ready to skin and gut his kill.

'You listen to too much gossip, our Will. His lordship's a gentleman, and he's always polite to me.'

'That's 'cos he has an eye for the ladies — I'd watch him, if I was you. And I don't need to listen to gossip. I know exactly what he's like because I see him every day, working his charms at the big house. When it comes to what goes on at the manor, what I don't know isn't worth knowing, our lass.'

'You talk rubbish, our Will, but I'm glad you caught those rabbits. I don't know what we'd have had for supper otherwise. Get a move on and skin 'em, then I can stick them in the pot and have everything ready by the time Father returns.'

Alice busied herself filling the big stockpot and placed it to boil on the Yorkshire range. She'd decided not to tell Will about the missing clock; no need to worry his head when he had enough on already, looking after the farm and working three days a week for the Franklands.

Besides, she knew who had taken it, and why

16

— and there was nothing she or Will could do about it.

* * *

Uriah Woodhead wiped the pint tankards with a cloth that had seen better days, spitting on the stubborn marks and rubbing them vigorously, before hanging them back on the hooks around the bar of the Moon Inn. At this time of day, the pub was quiet; in fact, he had only one customer. Over the last few months, the man had become his best customer, but it was high time he went home. Soon the place would start to fill with evening drinkers and the last thing Uriah wanted was a non-paying guest sleeping in his snug. Stepping out from behind the bar, he gave the wretched body of Bob Bentham a rousing shake.

'Aye, I'll have another pint with you,' Bob slurred, dribble running down the front of his already filthy jerkin as he stumbled to his feet.

'Nay, I don't think you will. Come on, Bob, you know you've had enough. Besides, your credit's run out — that little clock's not worth what you've already drunk. Only reason I took it off you was because I knew you had no brass; it's not as if it's much use to me.' Seeing that his words were having no effect and the man was about to settle back into his seat in the snug, Uriah grabbed him by the arm and began steering him towards the door. 'Time you got yourself home, Bob. Your lass will be wondering where you're at. She's having it hard, from what I hear.'

'You bastard!' protested Bob, swinging his fists in an effort to resist the strong arms hauling him over the threshold. 'You've robbed me, you thieving bugger!'

Dodging the drunken punches with ease, the landlord ejected Bentham from the premises with a final push that sent him sprawling onto the narrow cobbled street.

'Get yourself home and square yourself up, Bob. You've a family that needs you.' With a shake of his head, Uriah closed the door on him. It was sad to see a man go downhill so fast. Sometimes his trade was not the best to be in.

Bob lifted himself up and, head swimming, stumbled along using the walls of the cottages lining the street to steady himself. His erratic gait and frequent falls soon began to draw taunts from the local children, who abandoned their games to enjoy the spectacle of him sprawling on the cobbles. Their laughter ringing in his ears, he dragged himself out of the village and along the road home. At least it was a mild spring evening; during the winter there had been times when Bob had felt like giving up and crawling into a hedge, drifting off to sleep while the warmth of the alcohol still filled him with a fake sense of well-being, hoping that the bitter cold would do its work and end his suffering, and he would wake up in the arms of his Bess . . . How he missed his Bess. Without her, he was lost.

He paused to rest his weary body on a seat at the side of the road. From this vantage point he had a wonderful view over the dale. Looking around him, he noticed the first flowers of spring in the roadside bank: delicate wood sorrel and the pale yellow hues of the first primroses. His Bess would have been picking them and bringing them into the house. Bending to take in the sweet smell of the flowers, he lost his balance and toppled into the road, landing on his back. Not knowing whether to laugh or cry, he lay there for a while, until he became aware of the sound of hooves tripping along the road. A few minutes later, a horse and trap came to a halt inches from his head.

'What are you doing, man? I could have killed you, rolling about in the road in this bad light!' Dismounting, Gerald Frankland leaned over the dishevelled pile of rags, only to recoil immediately. 'Good God, you stink! How much have you had to drink? You're a disgrace, man!'

Raising himself up and squatting on his heels, cap in hand, Bob dared not look Lord Frankland in the eye. Of all the people to come down the lane, why did it have to be him! He felt a hand pulling him to his feet. Dizzy with drink and stomach churning, he tried to draw himself to his full height. 'Beg pardon, sir. Didn't mean to be in the way,' Bob mumbled, doing his best not to slur his words.

'For goodness' sake, Bentham, pull yourself together. I can't have my tenants carrying on like this.' Gerald Frankland studied the swaying figure with a look of disgust. He had heard that Bentham had taken the death of his wife badly, but he hadn't realized things had come to this. 'Well, I suppose I can't leave you here in that state. God knows how you'd get home. Climb in the gig and let's get you back where you belong.'

Shoving the malodorous body into the trap, Frankland turned towards Dale End Farm, whipping the horse into a trot. He was going to have stern words with Bentham's son once he got his drunken father home. Young Will was a fine lad — couldn't do without him. He'd shown an uncanny knack with horses and was a bloody good shot with that two-bore rifle of his. After last autumn's pheasant shoot, a number of his friends who'd travelled up from London for the event had told him how impressed they were with the lanky lad who'd made such a good job of running the show. Damn shame about the father, though. If this sort of behaviour continued, he'd have to strip them of the tenancy. Bloody locals, you gave them a roof over their heads and this was how they repaid you!

*　*　*

Alice stood in the doorway, peering down the lane for any sign of her father. She was both anxious and yet at the same time dreading his return. These days there was no way of knowing what state he would be in, or what his mood would be. It could be anything from sentimental and loving, cheerfully serenading her with music-hall songs, or argumentative and lashing out at Will with his fists. What her poor mother would have made of it, she didn't know. As dusk descended on the farmyard and the missel thrush trilled its last song of the evening, Alice wished she could be like that little bird: free to

20

sing and to spread her wings and fly away as far as possible.

'Come in, our lass. It might be spring, but it soon gets chilly. He'll be home in his own time.' Will had started lighting the oil lamps for evening. The flame flickered as he beckoned for her to come away from the door. 'The devil looks after his own, you know — and the way Father's been acting lately, it wouldn't surprise me if he's possessed.'

'Don't say stuff like that, our Will, it'll bring us bad luck.' Alice closed the door behind her. 'I can't help feeling he's been getting worse lately.'

'I wish I knew where he's been getting his brass from. Can't see old Woodhead letting him sup for nothing. Happen he's doing odd jobs for his beer money. Doesn't seem likely, though — there's plenty jobs around here wanting doing, and he can't be bothered to lift a finger.'

Alice kept silent. Much as she wanted to tell Will about Mother's treasured possessions disappearing, she didn't want to cause trouble between father and son, especially as her father might return in a fighting mood.

They both stood frozen in place for a moment at a sound from outside: hoofbeats, coming into the yard. Racing to open the door, they were aghast to find Gerald Frankland struggling to get their father down from his trap.

'Don't just stand there — help me with him, lad!' Lord Frankland bellowed at Will. 'I can't stand smelling him for another minute. Get him washed and tidied up — the man's a disgrace.'

Will rushed quickly to the aid of his employer,

21

propping his father up and carrying him into the warm kitchen. His lordship followed, removing his gloves and hat before seating himself next to the fire. Alice busied herself putting the kettle on the range to boil, not knowing what to say and do in the presence of the landlord. Will seemed equally at a loss; having deposited his father in a kitchen chair, he stood over him looking as if he wished the ground would swallow him up.

Scowling, Frankland leaned back in the Windsor chair and crossed his long legs. With his dark hair and sharp cheekbones, he looked every inch the refined country gent. 'You're lucky he's alive, the drunken fool. I nearly ran him over, lying there in the middle of the road. How long has he been like this? If he wants to stop in one of my farms, he's going to have to straighten himself up.'

Will, tongue-tied, offered no reply. Seemingly unperturbed by this, Lord Frankland surveyed the kitchen; it was tidy and spotless, but a little sparse. His gaze came to rest on the stockpot, its bubbling contents filling the room with a herby aroma. 'I suppose whatever's cooking in there has been poached from me.'

Inwardly, this amused him. He'd known for a while that the rabbit population was being held in place by Will, but had not said anything; after all, in feeding his family Will was reducing the estate's vermin population.

'Now see here,' Frankland continued, 'either your father straightens himself up or I'll have to consider renting this farm to another tenant. Take this as a warning.' He rose from his seat

22

and gathered up his gloves and hat as if to leave, but on reaching the door he turned and faced Alice. 'How old are you, girl? And what's your name?'

Alice blushed. 'I'm Alice, sir. I'll be seventeen in June.' She could feel her pulse and heart pounding as she dared to look at the dark-haired lord.

'So, old enough to come and work at the manor. My sister wants someone to attend to her needs. You look presentable enough, and I think you might be suitable. Come and see Mrs Dowbiggin next week. I'll arrange for her to show you what will be expected of you.'

'But I don't want a job,' Alice protested. 'I've enough to do here.'

'She'll be with you, sir — I'll bring her myself.' Will stepped forward, desperate to rectify his sister's mistake. 'Our Alice doesn't think what she says sometimes, sir. We are most grateful, thank you; that'll be a grand help to us. Say thank you, our Alice.'

Alice glared at her forelock-tugging brother. She didn't want to work at the manor and there was no way that she was going to kowtow to the likes of the Franklands. Nevertheless she curtsied, knowing that was expected of her, and then thanked him in a cool tone of voice.

'A girl with spirit, eh! That's what I like. Right, I'll see you both next week.' He waved a glove at the snoring body of Bob. 'And get him sober. I bid you goodnight.'

Nothing was said until the sound of the horse

and trap faded down the lane. Then Will turned on his sister: 'How many times have I told you, our Ali — always be right with them at the manor, especially himself. We need this farm.' Will kicked his father's foot as he snored, oblivious in his drunken sleep. 'I was right: the old fool fetched the devil into this house tonight. I never wanted you to work at the manor, but we've no option now. You'll have to watch yourself, lass, and as for Father, he can just bloody well straighten himself up.'

'Don't be hard on him, Will — he's missing Mother. And I'll be fine; I can look after myself. But you want to decide which tune you're dancing to: either Lord Frankland's the devil or he's a saint in our hour of need.'

Will fell silent. He hated Gerald Frankland. He hated the way he looked down his nose at those who worked for him. The way he leered at the young women from the village — and the fact that, for all his breeding, he was no gentleman.

'Just you remember this, Ali: no matter what happens, keep your thoughts to yourself and never let them know you're scared,' Will retorted.

'What do you mean, our Will? I don't understand.'

'You'll find out soon enough. I've heard some tales about him — and his sister. Take it as a warning.'

Alice had never seen this side of Will, and it worried her. Why did he hate Lord Frankland so much? Could things really be that bad at the manor?

Alice stood gazing up at the austere grey façade. Whernside Manor was a huge square Georgian building with ramparts running around the bottom of the roof, giving it the appearance of a Gothic castle. The notorious Sill family had built it, using their ill-gotten gains from slave trading in Jamaica. Local legend had it that the house was haunted by a young slave boy who had been beaten to death by the only son of the Sill family. With his dying breath he had cursed his master and the master's family, proclaiming that none of them would bear offspring and they would all die in poverty. Sure enough, his curse came true: one by one the Sill men died in suspicious circumstances and both daughters died old maids with not a penny to their names.

It was also rumoured that an underground passage ran between the manor and one of the houses that the Sill family used to own. It had been used for secretive transfer of their serving slaves. Alice shuddered at the thought. Dark days, indeed; she was not proud of the slaving history that tainted her beloved Dales.

The gravel crunched under her feet as she nervously made her way to the front door of the manor. She hesitated before plucking up the courage to climb the spotless granite steps and rap the polished brass door knocker. Adjusting her hat and smoothing her skirts, her heart beating wildly, Alice waited for someone to answer.

'Yes, what do you want? We don't encourage

beggars here!' The tall, sombre-faced butler peered down at her, his hand resting on the huge oak door's handle as if preparing to close it in her face.

Alice had never been so insulted. 'I'm not a beggar,' she retorted. She'd have liked to tell him exactly what she thought of his arrogant tone, but instead she bit her tongue, paused for a moment to consider how to phrase her response, and then announced: 'I'm here to see Miss Frankland. My name's Alice Bentham, and I'm to help her with her needs.'

'Well, Alice Bentham, your first lesson at the manor is that servants always use the back door. You are never to climb these steps and knock on this door again. Typical farm girl — no manners,' he sneered. 'Now, go around the back and ask for Mrs Dowbiggin. She'll take you to Miss Frankland, who I'm sure awaits you.' And with that he closed the door, leaving Alice feeling worthless on the steps.

She stood for a minute in shock, humiliated and at the same time furious with the pompous butler. How dare he take her for a beggar! And how dare he say she had no manners. It was him who had no manners, snooty old sod. She didn't want this bloody job anyway.

Defiantly she turned on her heel, marched back down the steps and set off up the drive. Blow it, she wasn't going to work for this hoity-toity lot; she was a Bentham and they were nothing but off-comed-uns. No doubt Will would have something to say when she got home, but she didn't care.

26

'Leaving us so early, Miss Bentham?' a voice shouted after her. Alice stopped in her tracks and slowly turned round to see Lord Frankland walking round the side of the manor, riding crop in hand. 'Are we not to your liking, Alice? Have you fallen out with my dear sister Nancy so soon? Surely she's not that wearing?'

Alice could detect a hint of mockery in his voice and noticed a slight smile on his face. She was doing her best not to stare, but his elegant dress and good looks had her enthralled.

'No, sir, not at all. Indeed, I did not get to see your sister, sir — as a matter of fact I've not even been invited across the threshold.' She couldn't stop herself; she had always been brought up to tell it as it was, so why should she stop now?

'I bet it was Faulks, my butler. Better than any guard dog, but a bit too much bite sometimes. Come, Alice, let me invite you into my home.'

He waited for her to retrace her steps to the main entrance and opened the front door for her. Hesitantly, Alice stepped into the great hall with her new employer behind her. At his bidding, she followed his example and took off her hat and coat, which he then thrust into the arms of Faulks, who had appeared like lightning at the sound of his master's voice.

'Faulks, this is Miss Alice Bentham. She is to assist my sister — whatever she needs, you will see that she gets it.'

'Yes, sir.' The butler bowed, giving Alice a questioning sideways glance before scurrying away with the clothing.

'Well, that's told him,' said Lord Frankland,

casually leading the way across the marble-tiled hallway. 'Come, Alice, let me introduce you to my sister. I'm sure she'll find you a tonic — it will be good for her to have someone her own age to talk to: she's always complaining about the staff all being too old. That's why I've taken you on, along with the fact that you seem to have a few more skills than some of the local girls.'

Transfixed by the grandeur of the hallway, Alice was still standing just inside the front door, taking it all in. How her mother would have loved the huge chandelier, the delicate ornaments, the smell of fresh polish and the huge sweeping staircase. The beauty of it all took her breath away; it was like a dream.

Lord Frankland, who had started up the stairs only to realize that Alice wasn't at his side, gestured impatiently for her to follow. 'Come, Alice, I haven't all day, and Nancy is waiting. If there's one thing she doesn't possess, it's patience, as I am sure you will shortly find out.'

With bygone generations of the Frankland family gazing down at her from the portraits lining the walls, the awestruck young girl gathered her skirts and hurriedly followed him up the luxuriously carpeted stairs.

★ ★ ★

The room was dark, the curtains still drawn, preventing the sharp spring light from entering.

'Nancy, I bring you a companion, someone to entertain you, to help you with your toilet and hopefully temper your moods, dear sister. This is

Alice Bentham; her father is a tenant of mine and her brother Will is one of my best men.' He strode across to the window and tugged the curtains open, flooding the room with light. 'How can you live in such darkness, girl? It's a beautiful day — come on, get out of bed and say hello to your latest companion and help.'

Once Alice's eyes were accustomed to the light, she was able to make out the shape of a body on the lavish four-poster bed. It stirred and moaned and then, much to Alice's surprise, an arm snaked from under the covers, seized a candlestick from the bedside table and hurled it at Lord Frankland.

Ducking out of the missile's range, he remonstrated with his sister. 'Now, Nancy, be reasonable — you'll frighten poor Alice. She's not used to your ways. Heaven knows who is.' Clearly exasperated, he shook his head and made for the door. 'Enough! Get out of bed and show a few manners. I'm going to leave you to get acquainted, so stir yourself.' And then he was gone.

Bemused, Alice stood wondering what to do next. Should she speak, should she go, should she tidy the curtains that had been flung back and left any old how? The words of her brother echoed through her mind — was there a monster lurking under those covers? She caught sight of her reflection in the wardrobe mirror: a shabby little farm girl, out of place in these grand surroundings. What on earth was she doing here?

'Do you not speak?' Alice was shocked to hear a voice from deep under the bedcovers. 'Has my brother brought me a mute? That would be useful. At least you wouldn't be able to talk about me.'

'I can speak, miss,' Alice retorted sharply. Then, remembering where she was, she fell silent again, awaiting instructions.

'Well, Alice, contrary to what my brother may have led you to believe, I do not require a companion. In fact, I like to keep my own company. I'm tired of his mealy-mouthed 'companions'. I don't know why he's brought me another one. Now get out of my room and go home.' This speech ended in a huge sigh, as if the effort had left the speaker completely drained.

No one had ever accused Alice of being mealy-mouthed, and she wasn't accustomed to being spoken to as if she were worthless. It was all she could do to stop herself from giving the little madam a piece of her mind. Instead, having carefully edited her thoughts, she said in a quiet, even tone: 'Miss Frankland, your brother asked me to help you and that's what I'm here to do. Let me assure you, I am not mealy-mouthed. In fact, I was always told to speak my mind, as long as it didn't cause offence.'

Suddenly the bedcovers moved, thrown dramatically from the bed to reveal the slight body of Nancy Frankland. At the sight of her, Alice let out an involuntary gasp. Framed by a shock of jet-black hair, dark eyes blazed at her from a face that had once been beautiful but was now a grotesque mask, the skin on the left side so scarred and twisted that the eye was almost obscured by angry red flesh.

'I see my brother didn't tell you about me. But then again, why would he? After all, he is quite desperate to find someone to amuse me. See, Alice, how could you befriend such a monster as I? Am I not truly ugly? A poor little rich girl who can never be seen in public. Now, perhaps you'd like to tell me what you think, without offending me?'

Regaining her composure, Alice plucked up the courage to reply: 'My mother always told me beauty was skin-deep, it's the person inside that matters.' She hesitated, not knowing if she had overstepped the mark, unsure whether to carry on. 'I've always been known as a plain Jane. My chin's too long and my hair's lank, but my family still love me — as I'm sure your family love you.'

'I must give you your due, Alice. You've not screamed, you've not given me a sugar-sweet reply and curtsied or smiled at me before fleeing the room in revulsion; perhaps you are made of sterner stuff.'

Moving to the edge of the bed, Nancy picked up a robe and put it on over her high-necked nightdress. Then she went to her dressing table, sat stiffly in the chair and looked into the mirror. 'How can anyone love this face, Alice? Look at me — how am I ever to live a life? I'm so ugly, I never want to be seen outside these four walls.'

Alice was overcome by a wave of pity; plain she might be, but at least she could always pretty herself up with a new hat and a bit of rouge. Putting on a brisk air, she approached the dressing table. 'Now, Miss Nancy, feeling sorry for yourself never did any good for anyone. Here, let me brush your hair, that'll make you feel better. I've never seen such a beautiful comb as that one.' She gestured to a dragonfly-shaped comb that glittered and glistened in the sharp morning light.

'What good are beautiful things on such an ugly face?' Nancy picked up the filigree dragonfly and toyed with it. 'A useless reminder of the past.'

Alice reached for a mirror-backed brush and went to work on the thick, dark hair; it was silky and smooth and smelled of perfume. Smiling at Nancy's reflection in the mirror, she started to pile the hair on top of her head.

'Stop it! Stop it at once! You can see even more of my face when you do that. You stupid bitch, are you doing it on purpose? Have you come to mock me?'

Spinning round, Nancy grabbed Alice's hand, making her drop the brush. As it hit the floor, the glass shattered into pieces. 'Get out! Get out of my room now!'

Without a word, Alice stooped to pick up the shards of glass, cutting her fingers in the process. Then she stood and looked at her accuser, blood dripping down her fingers.

'What I see before me is not an ugly rich girl but a spoilt, self-pitying rich girl. I was only looking at the shape of your face so that I could decide what to do with your hair, miss. But I can see I'm not wanted here. As for being a bitch — why, even our old dog has more manners than you do. Good day, Miss Nancy. I'll see myself out.'

She could feel her legs and her hands shaking as she descended the grand staircase. Faulks and a woman who she supposed must be Mrs Dowbiggin were standing in the hallway, heads together, obviously discussing what they had overheard of the goings-on upstairs.

'Will you be leaving us so soon, Miss Bentham?' The sneer that Alice had seen from Faulks on the doorstop was even more prominent.

'I am, and what's more I'll not stop another minute where I'm not wanted.' Alice set the remains of the brush on the hall table and wiped her bleeding fingers on the edge of her skirt.

'I'll get your things.' Faulks disappeared through a door and returned a moment later with Alice's well-worn coat and hat. 'I presume you'll be leaving by the back door,' he said, and immediately began ushering her through the hallway, until they were both stopped in their tracks by a voice from the top of the stairs.

'Stop! I will not let you go! Come here this minute. How dare you talk back to me! I am Miss Nancy Frankland.' Nancy was hanging over the banister, her long, dark hair cascading down and her robe floating around her, lending her the appearance of a ghostly apparition.

'I will return once you have calmed down — if your brother wants me to.' Alice turned from the screaming banshee to face the butler. 'And no, Faulks — I will leave by the front door. I may not know my place, but I do know one thing: I have more manners than the lot of you put together.'

33

Turning on her heel, head held high, Alice marched across the hallway, opened the huge front door and descended the steps. Her anger and indignation carried her homeward with such speed, before she knew it she was back in the farmyard.

★ ★ ★

'Flippin 'eck, our lass, you slammed that door hard. What's up with you?' Turning in his chair, Bob Bentham registered the red cheeks, firm chin and hands on hips, and knew immediately that something was amiss.

'Never have I been treated so badly, Father,' Alice huffed, hanging her coat on the hook. Rolling up her sleeves, she made straight for the stove, took the boiling kettle from the hob and poured scalding water over the dirty pots that filled the sink. 'And I'll not be going back. No one speaks to me like that.' She added an equal measure of cold water from the pitcher by the kitchen door and set about doing the washing-up.

'Calm down, lass, things can't be that bad. Our Will says they're a strange lot, but that's the higher classes for you: inbred and flighty. You'll have to get used to them.' He knocked his pipe, emptying its contents into the embers of the fire before refilling and lighting it. 'Mind you, they say that sister of his is strange. Nobody ever sees her. He brought her to the house in the middle of the night and she's not been seen since.'

'Now you tell me! I bet our Will knows more

than he's letting on. Why won't he tell me?' Alice could feel her face going redder than ever.

'Some folk reckon she's a witch — eyes that burn into your soul.' Bob gazed into the fire, brow furrowed in concentration as he tried to recall the gossip. 'Others say she's mad. 'Course, nobody really knows, because only her brother and that miserable couple of house servants ever see her.' He looked up from the fire. 'Did you see her? What does she look like? Is it right, is she a witch?' Bob was on the very edge of his chair, eager to hear his daughter's account.

'Well, I'm sorry to disappoint you, but all I saw was a spoilt brat with a temper — she called me a bitch! As for that butler — who does he think he is!' The pots and dishes in the sink were getting rough treatment as Alice vented her anger. But then she paused and turned to her father. 'I can understand her feeling sorry for herself, though. Her face is all marked and twisted. What happened to her? Must have been something terrible — and she doesn't look much older than me.'

'Nay, lass, I don't know. 'Appen our Will'll tell you; him and that Jack earwig all sorts. Ask him when he comes home. Only thing I know is that her brother has some strange-looking friends that come and go at all hours. Nevertheless, he's always done right by us. We could have a worse landlord, a lot worse. And Will reckons he's not a bad boss either; him and Jack have done well for themselves, working at the manor. It's just the company he keeps — rum lot.'

'If you ask me, Father, his lordship's all right.

But his sister definitely needs a lesson in manners. I'll not be rushing back, no matter what you and our Will might think.'

'You'll do what Lord Frankland wants you to do, our lass. We need to keep a roof over our head, remember. So don't go getting on your high horse. Right then . . . ' He got to his feet and stretched himself. 'I'm off for a stroll into Dent. I'll be back for my supper, so don't start pulling that long face. I'm only going to have a bit of banter with some of my cronies, stretch my legs on this grand spring evening.'

Bob put his top coat on and fingered the few pence that he had in his pocket. Might just be enough for a pint or two. He looked up and caught Alice watching him as she wiped the pots and put them away. She knew him all too well, and she'd a sullen face on her if you didn't do what she wanted. He'd get round to that stonewalling in the bottom meadow tomorrow; that should keep her off his back for a bit.

'Fire needs stoking, our Alice. And the dog could do with something to eat — it's been moping about all day.' With a parting wave, he was off down the track, heading for the Moon Inn in search of a cold pint and a bit of gossip from anyone who would talk to him.

Alice followed him out into the yard. By the time she'd finished pumping water from the well, his cheery whistle had faded into the distance. She knew damn well that would be the last she'd see of him until throwing-out time at the Moon. Drying her hands on her apron, she went over to the old dog. It was lying with its head resting on its paws, soulful eyes looking up at her. 'I know, old lad, you're hungry. He doesn't care about you any more, does he? He doesn't care about anyone any more.' She gave a sigh and went into the house in search of some food for the poor animal, emerging with a bowl of stale bread soaked in milk. The old dog gulped it down, thankful that its stomach at last felt a little fuller.

She stayed with the dog until it had finished eating its meal, then urged it to join her on a walk. Wrapping her shawl around her, Alice wandered up the rough lane to the top pasture, the dog trotting in front of her, occasionally stopping when it caught the scent of a rabbit, sniffing the air and looking around in the hope that the meal of bread would soon be followed by some fresh meat. A distant sheep bleated, reminding Alice that it would soon be lambing time, the busiest part of the year on the farm. How would they manage this spring? If only her father would come to his senses . . .

As she walked on, inevitably her thoughts returned to Whernside Manor. She wondered what had happened to Nancy Frankland to make her behave so. Alice was conscious that her parting words had been a bit harsh, but she had her pride and it wouldn't stand for anyone calling her names or sneering at her the way that butler had done.

On reaching the wall at the bottom of Whernside, Alice sat herself down and gazed out upon the dale where she had been born. The sun was about to set and its dying rays were turning the sky to a gorgeous pink that slowly filtered into hues of gold before changing again to a deep blue. The whole dale seemed to shine, bathed in a clear frosty veil, which took Alice's breath away with its tranquil beauty. She leaned against the wall and listened to the cry of a curlew. The return of the curlews from their winter holiday on the coast had always been one of the harbingers of spring in the Dales, but this year all the months since her mother's death had somehow blended into one another. Alice couldn't even remember Christmas; it was as if it had never happened.

Only when the sun finally gave up the battle and disappeared behind the great rocky outcrop of Combe Scar did she stir herself, suddenly feeling the cold, the temperature having fallen with the sun. Shivering, she wrapped her shawl around her, whistled the faithful Jip to her side and set off for Dale End. Will would be home soon and no doubt he would have heard about her visit to the manor. She knew he wouldn't be best pleased with her. Only that morning he had cautioned her to 'keep 'em sweet'. Sweet! She had been anything but sweet. Why did she have to have such an attitude? She only hoped her outburst wouldn't make things difficult for Will.

As soon as she arrived home, Alice busied herself getting the fire going and preparing supper for Will. She was busy laying the table when he opened the door. Knowing that a lecture was imminent, she didn't dare look round, not wanting to see his scowling face.

'Well, bugger me, our lass, what you been up to today? You're the talk of the manor, woman!'

'I couldn't help myself, our Will. She provoked me.'

'What do you mean, she provoked you? Whatever it is you think you've done, it can't be that bad — Miss Nancy wants you there tomorrow. First time she's ever asked someone back.' Will sat down to take his boots off, undoing the laces slowly and not looking up to see his sister's face. 'Jack's to pick you up in the trap, first thing in the morning; I had to tell him before I left tonight. Cost me a penny, you did — I had a bet on with Jack that you'd not last more than a day.'

'She asked for me? I don't believe you. Why would she want me back, after what I said?'

'Have you been telling it how it is, then, our lass? Old Frankland said you were like a breath of fresh air, just what his sister needed.'

'But . . . I don't know if I want to go back. They . . . She doesn't have any manners, and she swears, and them servants treated me like a lump of dirt.'

'She's spoilt, our lass. Treat her straight and you'll be fine. I've never set eyes on her, but I've heard her often enough. Her tantrums are that loud, you can hear them from the stables. Everyone's frightened of her, so she gets her own way. As for that stuffed-shirt Faulks and old Mrs Dowbiggin, they're both used to having their own way too. I wouldn't let 'em bother you.'

Alice was stunned. For a moment she stood there, watching Will kick his boots off, trying to fathom it out. Then she came to her senses: 'You can put those boots back on, our Will. Father's gone to Dent; no doubt he's in the Moon, spending what money we have left. He'll not be home in time to milk the cow, and the sheep could do with being looked at in case we have an early lambing. So don't get the idea you've finished for the day.'

'See? Keep saying it as it is and you'll be all right, our lass — you boss us around enough!' With a heavy sigh, Will reached for his boots and wearily began lacing them up again. 'I know he's my father and I should respect him, but I'm getting a bit fed up of doing his jobs as well as my own. I tell you what, our lass, Jack and I have been talking about leaving and finding something else. Now's the time to make our fortune, while we're still young.' He got to his feet and grabbed his coat and hat. 'I don't want to stay here and end up like Father, that's for sure. Anything's better than working for nothing, still forelock-tugging when you're nearly in your grave.'

'You can't leave me, Will. I couldn't manage on my own, not with Father in this state!'

'I know, but we can't carry on as we are. If he doesn't straighten up soon . . . ' With a despairing shake of the head, he walked out, slamming the kitchen door shut behind him.

Alice was left feeling utterly wretched. As if it wasn't bad enough that she had to return to the manor in the morning, now she had the worry of Will and his itchy feet. She prayed that he would not leave — not yet, anyway. Please God, not yet. She couldn't face life on her own with a drunk of a father.

3

'It's no use you tutting, Jack Alderson — you'll just have to wait! I can't do things any faster . . . It isn't as if I want to go, mind . . . I don't know why you were sent for me in the first place.'

Both Jack and the horse found their patience stretched to the limit as they waited for their unwilling passenger to finish running around the farmyard in an effort to get all the jobs done before departing for the manor. Having finally climbed aboard, she sat panting for breath and fidgeting, making constant adjustments to her shawl and hat, obviously nervous about her imminent re-entry into the unfamiliar world of the manor.

'Are we right now?' Jack cast a quick glance in her direction, not daring to look into the ice-blue eyes of his best friend's sister. He was afraid that, if their eyes met, Alice would read his thoughts. Thoughts that he had harboured for the past year but didn't dare do anything about. How come that scraggy bit of a girl had turned into such a beautiful woman? And what would Will make of him fancying his sister? Jack made a conscious effort to put aside all such thoughts for the moment and go back to treating her as the lass he had grown up with.

'Well, what are you waiting for? Let's get going!' Clearly Alice was in one of her assertive moods. 'You'll probably be bringing me back again as soon as we get there.'

The morning had not started well at Dale End Farm. Alice had woken to discover that her father had not returned — no doubt he was in a hedge somewhere, sleeping off his hangover. In addition to making herself presentable for the sneering folk at the manor, she'd had to milk the cow, feed Will and send him on his way, as well as attending to all the other jobs that needed doing — and everything had had to be done at twice the speed that it should have been. She was going to have stern words with her father tonight, even if it wasn't her place to do so.

With a rueful shake of his head, Jack whipped the horse into motion. God, she was a feisty one, but she looked so pretty when she was angry that he couldn't help smiling.

'What are you smiling at, Jack Alderson? I can't see anything to grin about. My father's gone missing, I'm entering into a job that I don't want, stuck all day with a spoilt brat when there's chores waiting to be done at the farm, and all the while you're leading my brother on, trying to get him to leave the dale. I don't see how things could get much worse.'

'Don't you blame me for Will's wandering feet — that's down to your father's antics and Lord Frankland putting ideas in Will's head, telling him what a good worker he is.' He turned to face her, his voice softening. 'It'll be good to see you working at the manor, Alice. You can tell me what Miss Nancy looks like — I've never seen her. Nobody has. And I'll show you around the place, when you have some spare time . . . if you want me to.' Will blushed and stumbled over this last sentence, his confidence ebbing away under Alice's scrutiny. His eyes returned to the road ahead, focusing intently, as if the bumpy old farm lane required his undivided attention.

Alice had never known Jack to blush, and she thought she knew the reason why: 'So you fancy your chances with Miss Nancy, do you, Jack? Look at you, all tongue-tied and blushing. Wait until I tell our Will!' she joked at the bashful Jack's expense. She could see his face glowing even redder with embarrassment, his dark hair complementing his rosy cheeks. 'I wouldn't be setting my sights on her, Jack. She's too posh for you, and a right madam, besides.'

'It's not like that, Ali, honestly it isn't. I know my place. So you needn't tell Will anything.'

Both fell silent as they entered the driveway of Whernside Manor. To Alice, the building looked even more daunting than it had the previous day, especially now she knew what the occupants were like. Jack slowed the carriage, but continued past the grand front entrance and pulled up at the back door.

'Good luck, Alice,' he said, as he helped her alight from the gig. 'I'll be in the stables if you need me.' Then he gave her a parting smile and turned away, leading the horse across the yard.

Alice sighed. There was a sick feeling in the pit of her stomach, and she really didn't want to enter that cold, unwelcoming building. She was hesitating on the doorstep when Mrs Dowbiggin came bustling out. In her long black dress with its pristine starched white collar and cuffs, she looked every inch the perfect housekeeper.

'Oh, hello, dear. So you've come back. I said to Reggie — Mr Faulks to you — that it took some courage to stand up to Miss Nancy. We've never dared, you know. She's got a temper, has that one; likes her own way. Anyway, she must have taken quite a fancy to you or you wouldn't be back. Either that or the master has. Wouldn't be the first time that some slip of a lass has taken his fancy.'

Before Alice could get a word in, Mrs Dowbiggin took her by the arm and began steering her across the yard.

'Seeing as you're here, you can come and help me bring the washing in from the orchard — I could do with another pair of hands to help me fold the sheets. It's Alice, isn't it, dear? Well, since you are going to be part of the team, Alice, let me inform you of the rules of the house, the main one being that the house servants do not consort with the outside staff. It's just not done.'

This remark was accompanied by a disapproving glance in Jack's direction. Still reciting rules, she bustled onward in the direction of the orchard, where white sheets were billowing in the wind. Alice fell in beside her, nodding and occasionally managing to fit in a word of assent. Mrs Dowbiggin certainly could talk. She'd not given Alice a second glance yesterday, but she was making up for lost time now. Though her sole topic of conversation thus far had been the many rules and regulations of the manor, at least she was talking to Alice as if she counted for something and not like some worthless beggar.

Together they retrieved the sheets from the washing line and folded them ready for ironing, then loaded them into a wicker linen basket and carried it between them back to the manor. When they entered the kitchen, the fresh smell of spring air clung to the sheets, its perfume filling the room.

'Well, here we are, dear. Would you like a drink of tea before you go up and see Miss Nancy? She'll be waiting for you. Master Gerald made her get up this morning and put on a dress in readiness for your arrival. She even ate some breakfast, which is highly unusual.' Mrs Dowbiggin shook her head and sighed as she bustled to the huge kitchen range and put the kettle on the glowing fire.

'Thank you,' said Alice, 'but I think I'd better go straight up and see Miss Nancy. After all, it is her I'm answerable to — her and Lord Frankland. I need to apologize to her for being a bit sharp yesterday. I know I shouldn't have, but I'm not used to being talked to in such a manner.'

'My advice, Alice, is to start as you mean to go on — and you certainly did that, my girl. It'll have done her no harm. Why, I even got a thank you this morning! I could have dropped down dead on the spot — I haven't had a thank you from her in months. Now, do you know the way to her room or will you need Reggie to show you?'

'I'll be fine, thank you, Mrs Dowbiggin. It's best if I find my own way around.' In truth, Alice

45

wanted to be by herself for a moment, to walk through the beautiful hallway and to sweep up that magnificent staircase at her own pace, taking in the glorious scene.

Leaving the warm kitchen with its copper pans, jelly moulds and drying herbs mounted on the walls, she climbed the few steps up to the level of the hallway. Almost on tiptoe, keenly aware of the echo of her footsteps in the great hall, she crossed to the stairs and gingerly mounted them. When she came to Miss Nancy's door, she hesitated for a moment to compose herself before knocking.

'Enter.' The voice that she'd last heard screaming abuse at her came from the other side.

Alice turned the doorknob, not knowing what to expect. All she knew was that she had to keep calm; these people owned her family home and no matter what she thought of them or how they behaved, she had to show them respect.

Nancy was sitting in the chair next to the dressing table, wearing a dark blue satin dress with a sash. She was facing away from Alice, her dark hair cascading down her back and reaching almost to her waist.

'Miss Nancy.' Alice curtsied. 'May I apologize for my abrupt behaviour yesterday. I had no right to talk to you in such a manner.' It galled her to have to beg her ladyship's pardon, but the more she'd thought about the way she had acted, the more Alice regretted having been so forthright. What with worrying about her father and mulling over the previous day's events, she felt as though she hadn't had a moment's sleep.

46

Nancy turned. Though the girl appeared demure and contrite, Nancy could detect no fear in her eyes and she did not drop her gaze when confronted with that scarred face.

'I, too, should apologize. I was no lady — as my brother was quick to point out. I have bad days, I'm afraid, when my temper and memories get the better of me. Let us both start afresh today, Alice. I need someone to help me and become my companion, for I never go outside of these four walls. Though I should add that is my own choice.' She patted the seat next to her, summoning Alice to join her. 'Now, tell me a little about yourself. My brother informs me that you have recently lost your mother. You must miss her; I know I miss my parents deeply. If it wasn't for my brother, I fear I would go out of my mind with despair . . . ' Her voice trailed and faltered, as if she was reliving the deaths of her parents. Pulling herself together, Nancy continued: 'He also tells me that your brother — Will, is that his name? — is his best shot and the star of his beloved shooting parties. How grown men can take pleasure in shooting innocent birds, I do not know.'

Alice sat in stunned silence, her hands clasped tight on her lap. She could hardly believe this was the same person she'd encountered yesterday. At the mention of her brother's name, she couldn't resist a little show of pride:

'Our Will is getting big-headed with the praise that he keeps getting — it'll be the undoing of him.' She gave a smile to show that she was joking. Looking into the face of her new employer, she continued: 'I do miss my mother, and I'm so sorry to hear that you have no parents. I didn't realize . . . ' She would have liked to know what had happened to them, but didn't dare pry, especially when the conversation was going well.

Perhaps sensing her interest, Nancy immediately steered her companion away from the painful subject of her family: 'Tell me, Alice, what goes on in the world outside these four walls? All my brother talks about are his boring friends, who spend all their time drinking, shooting and playing cards. I know nothing of the locals, and I'm sure there must be plenty of tales to tell. But first, let us have some tea.'

She got up and rang a small bell by the side of her bed. Within minutes, Faulks arrived. Barely acknowledging his presence, Nancy commanded: 'Tell Mrs Dowbiggin we would like tea and some of her excellent biscuits. I'm sure Alice would like to sample them.' Then, dismissing him like an unwelcome intruder, she proceeded to interrogate Alice.

While enjoying the tea and biscuits that Faulks laid out before them, Alice tried to portray the inhabitants of the dale. She told Nancy about the shopkeepers in Dent, the comings and goings of merchants, the various characters who frequented the market, and how most of the farmers did their deals in the bar of the Moon Inn rather than through the local fairs. She mimicked some of the locals and passed on the latest gossip of the dale, the general chit-chat that made up everyday life. So engrossed was she in trying to convey the smells and sights of the dale, she quite forgot where she was. In fact, the time went so quickly she could hardly believe it when she realized it was lunchtime already.

'I'm sorry, I didn't mean to keep talking this long. You must be weary of my voice,' Alice apologized.

'Indeed I am not — I have enjoyed your company immensely,' protested Nancy. 'My brother was right: in you he has found someone to entertain me. However, you must forgive me, Alice, but I am getting a little tired. I usually have a midday nap. Would you mind leaving now, and I will see you in the morning. I shall look forward to carrying on our conversation tomorrow.'

★ ★ ★

Though things had gone better than she could have imagined, Alice nevertheless breathed a sigh of relief as she closed the bedroom door behind her.

'Would you like a bite of lunch, Miss Bentham?' Mrs Dowbiggin asked as Alice joined her and Faulks in the kitchen.

The butler, no doubt remembering how she had spoken to him the previous day, maintained a deadpan expression as he studied Alice in silence.

'There's just enough for a little one.' Mrs Dowbiggin's smile seemed genuine as she motioned to the near-empty stew pan.

'That's very kind, thank you,' said Alice. 'I am

a little hungry. I missed breakfast this morning.' In truth, 'a little hungry' was an understatement. She was ravenous, having been too much on her best behaviour to do more than politely nibble at the biscuits served with tea earlier. The stew smelled so good, her mouth started salivating at the thought of it.

'You can sit there.' Mrs Dowbiggin ushered her to the chair at the end of the immaculately scrubbed pine table. 'Here you go — you will all the better be for having that in you. My, you're a little 'un. Isn't she a dot, Reggie? So slim.'

'It's not my place to say. If you'll excuse me, I'd better take Miss Nancy her lunch before she has her nap.' Faulks rose from his chair, donned his jacket and picked up the tray, which was all laid out in readiness, then strutted from the kitchen like a prize cock.

'Stuffy old devil,' muttered Mrs Dowbiggin. 'Thinks hisself God's gift! Still, his heart's in the right place, once you get to know him.' She ladled stew into a dish and added a huge chunk of freshly baked bread, then placed it in front of Alice. 'Here, you set to and eat that — it'll fill you for the day.' Looking on approvingly as Alice ate, she sank into the chair opposite and sipped her cup of tea. Obviously delighted to have someone to talk to, she leaned across the table, her ample bosom heaving as she quizzed the newcomer on the morning's events: 'She's behaved herself, then, Miss Nancy? She has good days and bad days, you know. I reckon it's the pain from her scars.'

'Forgive me if I'm talking out of turn, Mrs

Dowbiggin,' said Alice, 'but do you know how Nancy got the scars? She must have been a great beauty; it's a pity her face is marked so.'

'Well, dear, it is a cruel story. It happened before Master Gerald and Miss Nancy came to Whernside, back in the days when the family lived in Russia. You know where I mean?'

'Yes, I've heard of Russia.'

'From what I hear, Nancy was very young at the time and Master Gerald was in his late teens. Their parents owned a mine near Moscow — in fact, Master Gerald still has involvement in it, but that's another matter.' Mrs Dowbiggin paused to draw breath. 'Anyway, the workers in Russia decided they'd had enough of toiling long hours for a pittance of pay and so they went on strike. Very soon the trouble spread all over the country and things began to turn nasty, with workers out to get their revenge on employers. Unfortunately, the Franklands being English, they came in for a lot of resentment and the troublemakers accused them of raking in a profit at the expense of poor Russians. One night a mob of them set the Franklands' mansion alight, burning it to the ground. Master Gerald was spared, being at school here in England at the time, but Miss Nancy was found the next day, wandering in the garden in a terrible state. Poor girl must have seen some frightful things. Both her parents died in the fire, nothing left of them but ashes. And Nancy's face and shoulders were so badly burned it took ages for the skin to heal.'

51

She paused and took a long, deep drink of her tea. 'Terrible, terrible times. So it's understandable why she's the way she is.'

'Gossiping again, Hilda?' Faulks had sneaked in through the kitchen doorway unnoticed. 'Don't let Master Gerald hear you — he'll have you out of the house as fast as you can say 'Eggs is eggs'.' Giving both women a haughty glare, he resumed his seat.

'Oh, what's it to you, you old misery? The lass has to know how the land lies if she's to work here. It's only fair she knows what she's up against. Aye, and while I'm on the subject, you'd best steer clear of Master's gambling mates, Alice. Some of them are not to be trusted.'

'Hilda, that's enough! I will not have gossip in my kitchen.'

'Since when did the kitchen become yours? I'll have you know this is *my* kitchen and I will gossip all I like in it. In any case, it's not gossip; it's giving good advice to a young, vulnerable lass. Now go and get me the brasses from out of the parlour so I can give 'em a polish.'

With a baleful look, Faulks grudgingly left the room.

'Sometimes he gets ideas above his station, that one. Have you finished your dinner, dear? And is there anything else I can tell you?'

Giving Alice no time to answer, Mrs Dowbiggin whisked away the empty plate and began getting the brass cleaner out and spreading newspaper on the kitchen table, ready for the afternoon's polishing session.

'Would you like to give me a hand, dear? I hate

52

this job and there are so many brasses to clean. If you've time, I'd appreciate the door knocker, bell and letter box being polished. That'd give me ten minutes' peace before I have to start preparing this evening's meal.'

'I'll do all the outside bits for you, Mrs Dowbiggin, but then I have to go home. I've to make dinner for our Will and my dad. Thank you for telling me about the family history.' Alice picked up the tin of Brasso and two orange cloths: 'Are these to be used for polishing?'

'That's it, lass. Much obliged, that'll help a lot.' Mrs Dowbiggin turned away and began taking the copper pans down from the shelf in readiness for their clean.

Resolving to do the front door first, Alice set off in that direction. The huge lion door knocker had caught her eye yesterday as she had nervously stood on the huge steps. Now here she was, part of the manor. How curious that twenty-four hours could alter things so quickly.

She had just finished smearing Brasso liquid on the features of the lion and was about to start polishing when she heard Will calling her name. He sounded agitated.

'Alice, Alice — for God's sake, leave that alone! It's Father — they've found Father!'

*　★　*

The yard of the Moon Inn was crammed with curious onlookers, all trying to peer into the dark orifice of the beer cellar.

'Back now, get yourselves back!' Arms out

wide, Uriah Woodhead was frantically trying to steer the crowd away. 'Give the doctor some room now.'

Moments later, the doctor emerged into the light, his wiry old body struggling to climb the cellar steps. He was shaking his head.

'Well, Dr Bailey, is he . . . is he dead?' Uriah Woodhead pulled his handkerchief out of his pocket and wiped his brow. The sweat was pouring off him. Ever since he'd made the gruesome discovery, he'd felt as if he was having a heart attack.

'Aye, he's dead, all right. Looks like he tumbled down your cellar steps and dislodged one of the barrels. When it fell on top of him, it broke his neck clean in two.'

The crowd gave a gasp of horror. Poor old Bob Bentham: what an awful end to his life. What would become of his family?

His voice rising above the murmurs of sympathy and concern, Uriah was anxious to absolve himself of any blame: 'I told him to get hissel' home. Silly old bugger, I thought he'd gone. How was I to know he'd go creeping around in my yard?' For all his protests, Uriah was feeling guilty. He'd meant to close the cellar doors before the evening rush got underway, but in the event he never got round to it. By then it was too dark to see Bob lying at the foot of the steps. It had given Uriah a terrible shock when he went down at lunchtime and stumbled over his body.

'Don't you fret, man.' Dr Bailey patted him on the shoulder. 'You had no way of knowing that this was going to happen. He'd not been coping well since losing his wife last year. It's a shame for his family, but at least Bob's at peace with hisself now. I'll class it as death by misadventure, but I'll have to tell the local constable what's happened, to make it official. All right with you if I go into the Moon to make out the death certificate? I could do with a tot of brandy . . . '

Seeing that his heavy hint had fallen on deaf ears, Dr Bailey added: 'Medicinal purposes only, of course.' Still no response from Uriah. Reluctantly admitting defeat, the doctor left Uriah and went into the bar.

No sooner had the doctor gone than the sound of running feet reached them from the cobbled street. The villagers fell silent when they recognized Will and, a hundred yards behind him, his sister Alice. Both were breathing heavily, their faces taut with anxiety, as the crowd parted to let them through. Uriah Woodhead immediately stepped forward to intercept Alice, drawing her away from the cellar entrance.

'You want nothing of looking down there, Alice. Come inside, lass. My Annie will take care of you.'

Will glanced sharply at Uriah, then descended the steps. A lantern illuminated his father's lifeless body, lying among the beer barrels. Falling to his knees, Will took his father's limp hand and clasped it to his chest. He wanted to rant and rave at the old fool for letting it come to this, but then grief overcame him and his shoulders heaved with dry sobs. He was still bending over the body when Ernie Batty arrived.

'Leave him to me now, lad.' The portly undertaker patted him gently on the back. 'Let's have him out of this dark place, eh? Mrs Batty and I will see to him, don't you worry.'

Wiping his nose on the sleeve of his corduroy jacket, his eyes full of tears and his nose running like a tap, Will climbed the cellar steps. He emerged to find the crowd had gone — dispersed by the local bobby, they'd all hurried off to their homes, the gossips among them eager to spread the word and discuss the Benthams' misfortune over a cup of tea.

A lone figure was waiting in the yard: Uriah. 'Now, lad, come into the pub. My missus is looking after Alice. I can't tell you how sorry we are for the both of you.' The landlord wasn't good with words at the best of times; knowing what to say under these circumstances was beyond him. Putting an arm around the boy, he led him into the snug. Alice was already there, hands shaking, eyes red with tears. Annie Woodhead sat by her side, doing her best to console her.

'Well, is it him? Tell me, our Will, is it him?' she pleaded. 'Happen this lot have got it wrong; happen it's some passing tramp that fell in, not knowing the hole was there.' Alice didn't want to believe that in the space of four months they had lost both parents.

'No, Ali, it's Father . . . ' Will wished he could say something to ease his sister's grief, but in his state of shock, words failed him.

Numb with pain and looking for someone to blame, Alice jumped up from the bench, eyes

56

blazing, and turned on Uriah. 'You killed him! It was you who killed him! You've even pinched my mother's clock — it's right there on the mantelpiece.' She motioned to the carriage clock that had been her late mother's most cherished possession, occupying pride of place in her parlour.

Uriah, his face flushed in a mixture of embarrassment and anger, felt compelled to defend himself against the accusation. 'Now wait a minute, Alice. I'm as shocked as you are about this. I thought your father had gone home. The only way I'm responsible is that I left the cellar door open overnight. As for the clock, well, he traded it for beer. I only took it because I felt sorry for him — that's my biggest sin; happen I did encourage him to drink. God knows, I wish I hadn't now, but a man's got to make a living.'

Alice, spent after her angry outburst, had collapsed in a sobbing heap. Wrapping his arms around her and stroking her hair, Will said in a low voice, 'Shh, our Ali, you're upset. Uriah's not to blame and you know it.'

'I've spoken to Ernie Batty. He'll put your father in the chapel of rest until you've arranged a date for the funeral. I've told him I'll pay.' Uriah considered himself an honourable man, at least in business, and the last thing he wanted was the death of one of his regulars on his conscience. Drawing up a stool, he sat down opposite the grieving youngsters. 'If there's anything that me and the missus can do for the pair of you, let us know. Your father was a good man; he just couldn't cope with life without your mother.' He reached out a hand and patted Alice's arm as she sobbed into the jacket of her brother.

'Thank you, Mr Woodhead, that's good of you. I don't know how me and my sister would have managed to pay for a funeral.' Will got to his feet, gently drawing his sister with him. 'We'd best be off home now. It's a lot to cope with, today's happenings. We need a bit of time to ourselves.'

With quiet dignity, Will helped Alice through the door and into the evening air. Jack was waiting in the lane with his horse and trap. The moment he saw them, he dropped the reins and reached out to Alice. Thankful for the presence of a friend, she ran to him, burying her head in the warmth of his tweed jacket, clutching him tightly as if she were clinging to a rock, afraid of being swept away if she released her hold.

'Shh, I'm here. Don't cry, Alice,' he soothed, wrapping his arms around her. He wanted to squeeze her and tell her everything was all right, that he would always be there for her and that she would never need anyone else, but he was mindful of Will's presence and didn't want him to think he was taking advantage of the situation. While Will settled things with Ernie Batty and thanked Uriah Woodhead once more for agreeing to pay for the funeral, Jack held on to Alice, lovingly stroking her long blonde hair, which smelled like the wild thyme that grew on the fellside. Her blue eyes brimming with tears, she looked up at him.

'Take us home, Jack . . . although I no longer

58

know where home is. What are we going to do? No parents and no money — whatever are we going to do?'

He helped her up into the trap, whipping the horse into action the moment Will climbed aboard. They rode in silence, broken only by the alarm call of a nesting blackbird, disturbed from her nest by the sound of the horse and trap. The piebald, familiar with the trail to Dale End, needed no words of guidance from Jack as it carried its grieving load homewards.

4

Kneeling by her father's grave, Alice removed the previous week's flowers and set a freshly picked posy of white dog daisies in their place. Rising from her knees, she looked around her. The graveyard was set on a gently sloping hillside, with views all the way up to the head of the dale. The scurrying clouds cast shadows on the flanks of Combe Scar, which was covered with the white balls of fluff of grazing sheep and their lambs. She took in a deep breath of the clear air with its smell of peat and sphagnum moss — how she loved that smell. Up here, surrounded by the graves of her kin, with the warm spring breeze on her face and the sounds of birdsong and the lamenting bleat of a distant lost lamb in her ears, she was reminded at every turn of her deep and abiding attachment to Dent and the surrounding dales. She wanted to carry on living here, until it was time for her to be laid to rest in this churchyard in the company of her parents and grandparents and generations of her kind; she only hoped that someone would love her enough to mourn over her.

'Paying your respects, Miss Bentham?'

Startled from her reverie, she turned to find Lord Frankland staring at her. He doffed his hat in acknowledgement.

'I'm sorry, I didn't hear you behind me. I was lost in my thoughts . . . ' Alice hesitated, uneasy in his company as usual. She was never sure how to address him or whether she was supposed to curtsy. After the death of her father, Gerald Frankland had been nothing but caring and considerate, insisting that she need only attend the manor one day a week. That was bound to change, though, now that all the sheep had been lambed and normality had returned to Dale End.

'Nancy is missing you, Alice. Indeed, Nancy's not the only one who is missing you. I swear Mrs Dowbiggin is just about begging me to ask you to become a member of our live-in staff, and even Faulks asked after you the other day — now that surely is a miracle!' He smiled at her, then continued. 'What's more, it's time that a decision was made with regard to that farmstead of mine. The place isn't big enough to support the pair of you, and Will is too good a worker for me to let go. So, I shall come by this evening and speak to you both, if that's convenient?' Without waiting for Alice to reply, he turned and set off along the churchyard path towards the kissing-gate entrance.

Alice almost took to her heels in pursuit, but thought better of it; she had her pride, and she wasn't going to be seen begging the right to live in the farm. Will would sort it tonight. He'd tell Lord Frankland that, with her help, he could manage to do his job and still keep the farm on. Besides, now that she was finished at the graveyard she was off to see Uriah Woodhead, who'd promised her some work at the Moon Inn. In all their discussions on the subject of what was to be done, both Alice and Will were in agreement on one point: it was not good for the two of them to be dependent on the manor. Better not to have all your eggs in one basket, as her mother used to say. A day at the manor and a few days' work at the Moon would keep the wolf from the door. As for the tenancy, she was sure Will would sort something out.

★ ★ ★

True to his word, Lord Frankland arrived in the early evening. Things got off to a civil enough start, but for the last half-hour the sound of heated debate had filled the kitchen of Dale End as Gerald Frankland's voice was raised in disagreement with young Will Bentham.

'I tell you, Will, that's simply not possible. These are difficult times, and I must address my assets. This cottage will be sold and the land amalgamated into the manor's estate, and that's final. I've got to generate income from somewhere — the import of Italian marble is affecting my profits; the stuff we produce at the marble works is practically worthless nowadays. I think you'll find my terms are more than generous. I'm offering accommodation and full-time employment for both you and your sister . . . '

Will, red in the face and befuddled by talk of addressing assets and amalgamating land, stared dumbly at Lord Frankland. The last thing he wanted was for his sister and him to be beholden to the manor, twenty-four hours a day. 'Never be a bought man': the words of Uncle Will — his namesake who returned a hero from fighting in the Crimean War — kept running through Will's mind.

' . . . what's more, I'll guarantee you a good price for your stock. So there you have it: we can either do this the gentlemanly way, or I can evict you. Let's face it, what would the pair of you both do without a job or home? And how much do you think you'll get for your stock with the market the way it is? See sense, man!' Gerald Frankland hadn't come to Dale End with the intention of making threats, but he was fast running out of patience with the stubborn young whipper-snapper.

Will rubbed his head. He knew that he was in no position to haggle a bargain for himself, but at least he could make life easier for Alice.

'All right, you can have our farm back and we'll sell you the stock. I will even come and live at the manor, in the room above the stables. But not our Alice — she's not moving into the manor. Uriah Woodhead has offered her work and accommodation at the Moon. She can still come and befriend Miss Nancy one day a week, but she'll spend the rest of her time working for Uriah.' As he spoke, Will studied his employer's reaction: was it the farm he wanted, or was it his little sister? So far as Will was concerned, the look on Frankland's face told the real tale.

Having been warned by Will to keep out of the way while he and Lord Frankland conducted their business, Alice was sitting on the stairs, eavesdropping on the conversation. Tears filled her eyes as Will finally submitted to Lord Frankland's demands. Her beloved home! She loved living halfway up Whernside, away from everyone, with a view from her bedroom window that extended right down the dale. Her new home would be the attic bedroom of the Moon; all she would be able to see from there would be the rooftops of the village houses. Perhaps a room at the manor would have been better, but Will had been adamant that she should not live under the Franklands' roof and be forever at their beck and call.

'Good! I'll get someone to value the stock, and let's say a month's notice on the house.' Lord Frankland's voice took on a less satisfied tone as he continued: 'I don't think you are being fair to your sister. She's worthy of something better than being a serving girl in a hostelry. I could offer her comfort and security in my employment.' Lord Frankland tapped his walking stick sharply on the ground and stared intently into young Will's face.

'I'm sorry, sir, but I reckon she will be best suited to living in the village. She can come and visit Miss Nancy anytime she pleases, in addition to the day we have agreed to. You have my word on that. But she'll be staying at the Moon Inn.' Will may not have been able to save the farm, but he would continue to look after his little sister's best interests; he owed her that.

'Very well. We'll leave it that way for now. Perhaps you'll change your mind in time.' Setting his hat hard upon his head, he turned towards the door. 'As for your own future — I have great plans for you. Once this business with the farm is sorted out, I'll be taking you up to Stone House. I have a little job for you at the marble works.' Without so much as a backward glance at the worried look on Will's face, he was gone.

* * *

Hearing the door close, followed by the clatter of hooves, Alice hurried downstairs to find Will. He was sitting in what used to be their father's chair, head in hands. At the sound of the bottom stair creaking with Alice's weight, he looked up.

'I'm sorry, Ali. I'm so sorry. I tried, but you can't argue with the man who holds all the cards. And now the bastard is going to make me work at Stone House. I don't want to go up there. The men there are a bunch of foul-mouthed old navvies, left over from building the railway, and the foreman is the worst of the lot — drunk nine times out of ten and doesn't give a damn about anyone's safety. There's an accident at the marble works nearly every week. What am I to do?'

Alice sat on the edge of the chair and put an arm around her brother. She'd never seen him in such a state; no matter what they'd had to face, he'd always remained strong and cheerful.

'It isn't your fault, Will. You did your best for us. We may not have the farm, but as long as we've got work and one another, we'll survive. Just promise me you'll not leave me. I've no one else in the world but you. Promise me, Will

65

— promise me!' Her face was set; she wanted her brother to know that she was in deadly earnest and this was not a promise to take lightly.

Will lifted his head, eyes red with tears. For all that he was a grown man of nineteen, it was hard fighting battles that he could not win, leading a life that he had no control of. Meeting his sister's gaze, he felt his resolve strengthen. 'I promise, Ali. I'll always be here for you.' He gave her a shaky smile. 'Besides, who ever gets the better of Jack and me? As long as you are safe at the Moon with old Uriah and his wife, we will be all right.'

'That's better, Will. We Benthams never give in. Why, before you know it you'll be running that marble works. And I'll meet a rich gentleman who'll keep me in a manner befitting my breeding.' She smiled and dropped a mock curtsy. 'And then we can both tell old Frankland where to shove his job!'

In her heart of hearts, Alice was deeply troubled. It had been hard enough losing their parents, but now they had lost their home, the one thing that had kept them together. From now on it was going to be a battle to survive. But she had no doubt whatsoever that she would survive, come hell or high water, because she was a Bentham and a Bentham never gave in — not as long as she had breath in her body, anyway.

* * *

Will Bentham wiped the sweat from his brow. It was almost time to go; just one more job

66

remained to be done, and then he would have to turn his back on his family home. His heart was heavy: the last job was the one he was going to hate the most.

He looked down into the trusting eyes of old Jip; he'd been a good dog, long in the tooth but faithful to the end. He threaded the string that was to hold Jip to the wood stock tight, so that he couldn't move his head. Then he patted him and whispered, 'I'm sorry, old mate.' Tears filled Will's eyes as he raised his gun and fired at the farm's most-loved animal. The dog slumped to the ground and Will untied him, making sure he was dead, and then lovingly carried him up the path to a place where he had seen him sitting in the past, surveying his kingdom. There he had dug a hole just big enough to hold Jip's body. Laying the dog tenderly down, he slowly filled in the hole, fresh earth and salty tears falling upon the black and white fur until the body was covered.

'I'm sorry, old lad, but you'd not have worked for anyone else — you were too old for anyone to want.' He stood tall and looked out over the valley. 'I hate that bastard Frankland. I've lost everything, even my bloody dog.' He wiped his nose and spat, then lifted the spade onto his shoulder and set off down the hill, the dusk closing in around him.

5

The attic bedroom of the Moon Inn was squat, to say the least; the only source of light was the skylight and that was overshadowed by the pub's tall chimneys, which spent nine months of the year belching smoke. The few possessions that Alice had brought with her from Dale End looked strangely out of place in her new home. And was it her imagination or had the Staffordshire pot dogs' smiles developed a downward tilt? Now ensconced on the small chest of drawers in the corner, they certainly looked much sadder than they had on the mantelpiece in her mother's parlour. Still, the woollen blanket that her mother had knitted brought a splash of colour, as did the posy of meadow flowers she had picked that morning before leaving home. They brightened up the black iron fireplace where she had placed them, nestled in a vase that had belonged to her grandmother.

'There, Alice, I've brought you a jug of water for your morning's ablutions. I thought you might like this too.' Mrs Woodhead handed Alice her mother's carriage clock. 'It'll only get broken down in the bar, so let's have it back where it belongs. Your mother would have wanted that.'

'Thank you, Mrs Woodhead, that is very thoughtful of you.' Alice was too choked at this act of kindness to say more. Her hands held the clock lovingly, fingers tracing the outline of its face. Seeing it brought back sweet memories, but also reminded her of everything that had been lost.

'Nay, lass — it's got a double purpose. You'll need to know the time if you're working for us. I want you up bright and early, lighting fires and making breakfasts for Mr Woodhead and any guests that's staying with us. No use having a dog and barking yourself, is there?' This was accompanied by a laugh that sounded to Alice very much like a bark. 'So let's have you down in the kitchen at five in the morning. Oh, and one other thing: when we are alone, you may call me Annie, but in front of residents and Mr Woodhead, I think we had better be more formal.' Briskly adjusting her mob cap, which was struggling as usual to confine the abundance of auburn curls, a legacy of her Scottish ancestors, Mrs Woodhead bustled from the room.

Five o'clock! The only time Alice was ever up that early was when the sun beamed through her window in midsummer, and the combination of clear blue skies and the twitter of swifts compelled her to venture out of doors and up the fellside before anyone else was awake. Now she was going to have to do that every morning — not in order to breathe in pure mountain air, but to lay coal fires and prepare other people's meals, without so much as a glimpse of the outside world.

As she placed the clock in its new place next to her bed, Alice realized that she would never again see it as a reminder of her old life at the farm. From here on the clock would be her master. She'd be counting off the hours to Sunday lunchtime, her one afternoon of rest; maybe even counting to the day she went to the manor.

Oh, why had she sat listening on the stairs that terrible evening instead of marching in there and fighting for her birthplace, for her right to remain at Dale End? Alice tightened her fists in frustration, fingers going white and numb with anger. Perhaps working at the Moon hadn't been the right decision, but for the time being she had no alternative but to put her head down and make the best of it. It would do for now, but she had no intention of remaining in this attic bedroom a moment longer than she had to. When and if an opportunity arose to better herself, she would be ready to grab it with both hands — and damn the consequences.

★ ★ ★

'Put your back into it, you lazy bugger! No wonder they fecking well call you Glassback Murphy.' Sean O'Hara wiped his brow with his sleeve; sweat was dripping off him as he oversaw the loading of the marble slab. That Murphy was going to have to go: he was bloody useless. The rest of them weren't much better. 'Come on, men — what are you waiting for? Open the sluice gate, damn you. Let's get this wheel turning. Bloody stuff won't cut itself!'

As the crew rushed to obey his commands, the

great waterwheel powered the saw into action. About fecking time, thought O'Hara. Sure, hadn't he been up since the crack o' dawn getting that chunk o' stone in place — and what the feck for? All so some rich man in London could have a new fireplace in his dining room, and lean against it hobnobbing with his well-to-do friends. Those types had more money than sense. Sure, what was wrong with an open fire, so long as you'd a tot of whisky in hand?

There, that was the trickiest part of the job done. He could leave the buggers to it for a while. Boss wouldn't show up for a few hours yet, so he might as well nip home for a quick nap.

He was almost at the cottage door when he heard horses' hooves striking the cobbles of the works yard. Hurrying in the direction of the sound, he found Lord Frankland dismounting from his trap, accompanied by two young men who seemed vaguely familiar, though the Irishman couldn't remember where he knew them from.

'Ah, O'Hara — just the man.' He turned to indicate his companions: 'The tall fellow is Will Bentham; the other is Jack Alderson. I want you to show them around the quarry and mill, and explain to them what it is we do here. Think you can manage that, O'Hara?'

'To be sure, sir.' Sean eyed the two young men, trying to fathom why they would be wanting a tour around the quarry and works. They didn't look like management; judging by their clothes, they were a couple of farm lads.

71

Their faces gave nothing away. If anything, they appeared every bit as bemused as he was. 'Are they to be working for me, sir? Only, I've all the men I need, and I — '

'For the time being, I just want them to observe and report back to me. Since taking the place over after the death of my parents, I've been too busy with other commitments to give the marble works much attention. It strikes me that a couple of pairs of fresh eyes are needed to judge how efficiently the place operates. I myself will be out of the country for the next few weeks — my business in Russia requires my attention. In the meantime, I expect you to take care of them, O'Hara, and show them everything. And I do mean everything.' Gerald Frankland tapped the Irishman lightly on the shoulder with the tip of his stick, as if pressing home the message.

'I will, sir. Don't you worry, sir, I'll show them how well run Stone House is. I'm sure they'll be impressed, indeed they will, sir.' Despite his jovial tone, O'Hara was inwardly seething. The last thing he needed was two wet-behind-the-ears farm boys sticking their noses in and running back to his lordship telling tales. Pair of spies, that's what they were. So far as O'Hara was concerned, the marble works was running very nicely, thank you; he'd spent the last few years arranging things to his satisfaction. And if these two thought they were going to interfere . . . His thoughts were interrupted by another tap of Frankland's stick on his shoulder.

'One more thing — these fellows are locals, but they'll need transport to get to and from their living quarters. See to it that the horse and buggy is at their disposal for the duration of their stay.'

'But, sir, I might need it myself.' So far as O'Hara was concerned, this was the final insult. His face betrayed his indignation, and the mutinous look in his eye prompted a steely response from Lord Frankland.

'I've seen you with that gelding I got you, O'Hara. Good horse, but it doesn't appear to enjoy being mastered by you. Now, Jack here is my top man when it comes to horses — he might just bring it under control for you.' He laid a hand on Jack's shoulder and nudged him slightly to the fore of the group.

Jack was at a loss what to say. Smiling nervously, his blush getting the better of him, he reached out to shake O'Hara's hand.

'If you can make anything of that beast, you might as well have him, the flighty bastard!' O'Hara ignored the outstretched hand. 'Only thing he understands is the touch of the whip. Ah! You're welcome to him — go on, take him, fecking useless brute.' As if to emphasize his contempt for Lord Frankland, his horse and the two cuckoos about to occupy the marble works nest, O'Hara spat on the path, then stormed off in the direction of his cottage.

'Well, boys, you heard what I said.' Gerald Frankland, unfazed by the Irishman's wrath, slapped them both on the back. 'Your silence on the way up here and the look on your faces told me everything I needed to know — the gossip I've been hearing about Stone House is true.

When I return in a fortnight, I shall expect you to report to me and tell me exactly what is going on here. Don't let O'Hara bully you — he's a brute of a man, but he'll not dare hurt you while he knows you've got my support.'

'I'm not happy with this, sir.' Will looked Gerald Frankland in the eye. Why had he picked him and Jack? They knew nothing of marble works.

'Nonsense, lad, it'll be the making of you. Right, I'll be off. I suggest you spend the first couple of days watching and listening, and then start asking questions. Get to know the workers, see what they have to say. By the end of the fortnight, I expect you to be able to tell me everything there is to know about Stone House.' He mounted the trap and turned his horses in the direction of home. 'And, Jack, take a good look at that gelding — it was in a bad way last time I saw it.' With that he whipped the horses into action, and the trap was soon lost in a cloud of dust as it sped off towards the manor.

Will and Jack watched him depart, feeling like a pair of foundlings abandoned in a hard, dangerous world. Ever since Frankland had first mentioned his intention of sending them to Stone House, they'd been dreading this day. Both lads had assumed they were going to be joining the marble works crew; though neither of them had relished the prospect, it would have been preferable to this. Telling tales on the burly Irishman was risky enough — O'Hara was notorious for his violent temper — but Frankland had forewarned the man. He was

74

going to be watching them like a hawk.

Will turned to his friend. 'What do you make of that, Jack? Talk about a carry on! I don't know if I'm right happy with what he expects us to do. I'm not one for snooping on folk.'

'Before we do anything else, let's go take a look at that gelding. I don't like to hear of any animal being bad done to.' Jack's soft nature was taking over. 'As for the rest, I reckon we'll be all right if we stay together and steer clear of O'Hara. At least we can go back to the manor of a night.'

'OK, we'll give it a go. But I still think he should do his own dirty work.' Will had never cared for Gerald Frankland — toffs weren't to be trusted, as far as he was concerned — and his recent eviction from Dale End Farm had only served to reinforce that view.

Together they set off up the rough, weed-filled yard in search of the stable. Guided by the reek of rotting manure, they followed their noses until they reached a tall wooden door. When they opened it, vile-smelling remains of what had once been bedding tumbled out onto the yard floor. Peering into the gloom of the stable, they saw what looked to be a decrepit old nag, its back and flanks covered with festering sores and its ribs showing through as if it had been starved for some time. It flinched in fear as Jack entered the stable. Speaking gently all the while, Jack gradually calmed the beast so that he could run his knowing hands over its body and judge its age by checking its teeth. His face was grim and his jaw taut with fury by the time he'd finished.

Will couldn't remember the last time he'd seen his mild-natured friend so angry.

'We're stopping, Will, 'cos of this poor fellow. He looks at least twenty, but he's only a young 'un. If O'Hara can treat a horse like this, God knows what we're going to find at the works and quarry. By God, I'd like to do to him what he's done to this animal, the bastard.'

Will simply nodded. There was no point arguing: they were stuck with their new job as spies for the manor. Life was not going to be comfortable for the next fortnight. Then again, it was only fourteen days. What could happen in fourteen days?

6

'Now, sir, would we like another dish of porridge?' Alice smiled sweetly at the toothless leer of Old Todd, a travelling salesman who stopped at the Moon at least once a month, making him the inn's most regular guest. She swore if he slapped her bottom one more time, she would accidently spill his porridge right down the front of his throbbing breeches. That would cool his ardour for a while, dirty old man!

She'd only been at the Moon a week when Old Todd, whose lecherous eyes never missed a single move she made, caught her putting some bits of bacon in her apron pocket. Just a few offcuts she was planning to give to Will so he wouldn't go hungry; they had more food in that place than she'd ever seen in her life, and when she found out they were in the habit of throwing the offcuts away, she didn't think anyone would mind if she helped herself. But Old Todd had accused her of stealing, and then he'd threatened her, saying if she didn't come to a 'little understanding' with him, he'd tell Annie Woodhead and then she'd be kicked out on the street and everyone in the dale would know she was a thief. Left with no choice, Alice had agreed to his 'little understanding' and gone to meet him in the churchyard, where she'd had to endure his fumbling hands on her and his stinking breath. It had been such a relief when he'd packed his bags and departed on his travels, but now he was back, leering at her every time she passed his table. How she hated the sight of him.

Working at the Moon had opened her eyes to a whole new world. But no matter what went on in the bar or under the Moon's roof, it stayed there; tittle-tattle was frowned upon. 'No matter what, keep your mouth closed and get on with your job,' Mrs Woodhead had told her. Alice had never worked so hard in her life, but still she was thankful for a roof over her head and a full stomach. Annie Woodhead was proving to be a good cook and a fair boss; she always made sure that Alice got her meals and had her privacy in the evening, when all the jobs were done.

Her only break was on a Sunday afternoon, when she could do as she pleased. Usually that meant spending time with Will, catching up on the week's events. Wednesdays were spent at the manor; though she'd never have believed it in the light of their stormy first meeting, Nancy Frankland had turned out to be Alice's saviour. Although she had a temper and sometimes did not get out of her bed, now that Alice understood the pain, both physical and mental, that tormented that petite body, she was prepared to make allowances. She was convinced that if she could only persuade Nancy to leave the manor occasionally and join her in visiting some of her favourite haunts it would do the poor girl the world of good. As it was, she would settle for enticing her out of her bedroom and down the stairs . . .

Her thoughts were interrupted by a hand grabbing at her skirts as she collected the empty dishes from Old Todd's table. Alice flinched, but much as she hated him, she knew she daren't upset him. She'd been naïve enough to believe that if she submitted to his 'little understanding' it would only be the once. Now she knew better: he had a hold on her and he wasn't going to let her forget it.

'What about it, lass — fancy doing an old man a favour for an extra bob or two?' Drooling at the thought of sex with a young virgin, he wiped his toothless mouth on his sleeve, smearing saliva over his chin.

Feeling sick at the thought of the old lecher's hands on her, Alice retreated to the safety of the main bar.

'Is Mr Todd giving you bother, Alice? He's always been an old devil where the lasses are concerned. I wouldn't mind, but his daughters are about your age. If only his wife knew. I bet he's up to his tricks in every pub in the district.' Annie Woodhead gave the culprit a discreet glance, watching him check his pocket watch while he finished his breakfast tea. 'I'll have words, if you want?' she whispered.

'You'll do no such thing, Annie Woodhead!' snapped Uriah, whose hearing was sharp enough when it suited him. 'That's what keeps the randy old devil coming back to us — he still thinks he's a young stallion. Besides, Alice can handle him, can't you, girl?' He winked at her and smiled.

'I can handle Mr Todd. I just wish he'd realize how daft he makes himself look. Has he no

79

respect for his wife and family?'

'While the cat's away, the mice will play — surely you should know that?' Uriah winked at her again and nodded at Mr Todd's empty teapot.

Annie gasped. 'Uriah Woodhead! Is that what you think? Well, let me tell you, there will be no playing around when I'm here — or away — so you can think on.' Annie slammed her tea towel on the counter. 'You go and fill his teapot, Uriah — I bet he won't feel your bottom, dirty old devil!'

Still fuming, she watched as her husband went to ask the offending customer if he needed more tea. 'That'll teach him to make light of men's advances. You can't trust any man, lass, no matter how honourable they might seem. I feel I owe you that advice, seeing your mother's not alive, bless her soul.'

'Don't worry, Mrs Woodhead. Old Todd's 'armless enough. I reckon he just fancies his chances, but he's playing the wrong game with me — I'm waiting for Mr Right. He must be tall, good-looking and, above all, wealthy, because I never want to be poor again.'

'Aye, lass, we have all wanted one of them in our time. Trouble is, you get what you're given or what your heart determines. Take me and Uriah — his mother and mine fixed us two up. They knew that I could cook and that he'd inherit the Moon one day, so we were lined up for one another as soon as we left school. Never mind love and looks; they didn't enter into it. But after a while you come to feel a bit of something about one another.' Seeing her young helper gazing out into the yard as she wiped the pots, obviously lost in daydreams about Mr Right, Annie laughed. 'Have you been out with a lad yet, Alice?'

Alice shook her head.

'That young Jack Alderson always looks so sweet on you — I'm surprised he hasn't asked you out.'

'Jack? Jack Alderson? Oh! The thought of it!' Alice turned her nose up in disgust. 'Him and our Will are best friends — they'd talk about me. Besides, he hasn't any money.'

'Money isn't everything, miss, just remember that. And don't you be so haughty about Jack. He's a grand lad, and his father has a good farm at the top of the dale. It's their own, too, so they'll not be short of a bob or two. Aye, think on, young lady. All too often them that flash the cash are the ones with nothing in their bank balance — take it from one who knows.'

Hands on hips, Annie Woodhead glared at her young employee. She hadn't realized that the girl was so shallow. Who did she think she was? With no family to speak of and no real roof over her head, Alice Bentham could do a lot worse than young Jack. It was high time she realized that beggars can't be choosers. The more Annie thought about it, the more riled she got. She was even beginning to wonder whether taking the young orphan in had been such a good idea.

Sensing Annie's outrage, Alice kept her head down and focused on cleaning the pumps and wiping the bar down. She hadn't meant to cause

81

offence, but when the woman started trying to pair her off with Jack . . . well, it just didn't bear thinking about. No, her sights were set on something better than a common farm lad. Mind you, she hadn't realized that Jack's dad owned his own farm; she'd always thought it was rented, like theirs had been. Perhaps it wouldn't hurt to be nicer to Jack — after all, he did blush every time he talked to her, and it was true that he never seemed short of a bob or two. She'd ask after him on Sunday when she met Will. Right now, though, she needed to come up with a quick excuse to leave the bar for a few minutes — and it would only be a few minutes, she thought grimly, rubbing the brass foot rest with vigour.

'Just going to pick up the bread from Mason's, Mrs Woodhead. Shan't be long.' Without waiting for a reply, she grabbed her shawl and basket and darted out of the bar. Sooner she got there, the sooner it would be over.

★　★　★

As she hurried to the secret rendezvous place, Alice's stomach heaved with revulsion at what was to come. Still, if that was the price of his silence, what choice did she have? The prospect of being branded a thief and the whole village getting to hear about it was far more terrifying than the thought of the old man pawing at her.

Her footsteps echoing on the cobbles, she turned into the deserted churchyard. What kind of man chose a church for such a disgusting purpose as these 'little understandings'?

'So, you've made it, bonny lass,' came a voice from the side entrance of the church. 'I knew tha would.'

Alice looked at the disgusting old man, the bulge in his trousers fighting to be released. He must have been fumbling with himself while he waited for her. When he reached out to stroke the side of her face, she couldn't help but cringe.

'Now, lass, remember our arrangement: if you keep quiet, I'll keep quiet. And don't forget, there's a florin in it for you . . . '

He pushed her back against the granite church wall, fumbling with the buttons on his breeches, his breathing heavy with excitement. Thoughts rushed through Alice's head, cutting out reality as he pulled her skirts up and tugged her bloomers down. His fingers caressed her intimate parts, making her quiver and causing him to lose control. He tried to thrust his tired manhood into her, but in a repeat of last month's performance, he was too late. Anticipation had got the better of him. His moment had come and gone, leaving him weak and embarrassed.

To Alice's relief, he hurriedly buttoned his breeches, hiding the offending organ, and then reached into his waistcoat pocket. His face was ruddy and his breath was short as he pressed the florin into Alice's palm.

'Remember, lass — you say nothing, I say nothing. I'm back next month, so you can earn yourself another bob or two.'

With that he slipped away, leaving Alice feeling

sick and disgusted with herself. She pulled up her bloomers and adjusted her skirts, then leaned against the church wall, her body shaking, the florin clutched in her hand. No matter how she tried to justify her actions, a niggling voice kept telling her that she was no better than a common whore, taking the old man's money. She knew her parents would be ashamed of her, firstly for stealing, but more so for letting a dirty old man touch her. A tear trickled down her cheek and she rubbed it away with the back of her hand.

Sticking her head out of the doorway to make sure he was gone, she did her best to compose herself before heading to the baker's to pick up the bread. The shiny florin was still clutched in her hand. She'd been certain that everything would go the same as it had the previous month: all over in no time and him incapable of anything more than a bit of fumbling. But even so, was it really worth a florin and his silence? If she told the Woodheads about the bacon, and explained that she hadn't meant to steal from them, that she'd only been trying to look after Will, perhaps they would understand. The way she saw it, it was Old Todd who was in the wrong, taking advantage of a young girl who was down on her luck.

If he tried to blackmail her again, she promised herself that she would tell Annie. Surely she would understand?

★　★　★

It was a beautiful summer's day. The sun shone, dragonflies skimmed and darted over the glittering river — and best of all it was a Sunday, so Alice could lie back in the long meadow grass amid the smell of new-mown hay instead of being cooped up in the Moon.

'Yes! Yes! Our Ali, did you see that?' Will's voice rang out from the direction of the river, where he was playing 'ducks and drakes'. 'Seven leaps with one stone, right across to the other side of the Dee. Bet you can't do that!'

'When are you going to grow up, Will? Skimming stones is for kids.' Alice was in no mood for her brother. She was having a hard time driving horrible thoughts of Old Todd from her head, and here was Will, so full of himself after his week with Jack at Stone House marble works that he hadn't even noticed how unhappy she was.

'Pardon me for breathing! What's up with you, my lady? You used to enjoy playing in the river. Besides, it's Sunday — we've got the whole afternoon to ourselves, nobody breathing down our bloody necks.' He picked a buttercup and tickled his growling sister under the chin with it. Furious, she snatched the flower out of his hand.

'I'm fed up with having no home, no money and no say in where my life is going. I don't want to be a serving girl in a pub with part-time work at the manor. I want to be looked after, have fine clothes, maids and servants and a gentleman husband.' Alice crossed her legs and pulled her skirt over them, then lay on her back, the sun's rays filtering through her eyelashes, dreaming of the things she could do if she only had money.

'Well, hard luck, our lass — you're stuck here with me.' Alice was forever harping on about wanting fine this and fancy that. Sometimes it seemed to Will that all his little sister thought about was brass. 'If I'd known my company was going to be such a disappointment, I'd not have bothered coming. I should have gone shooting with Jack instead.'

Alice sat up quickly, brushing the buttercup debris from her bodice. 'How is Jack? He wasn't at the manor when I called on Miss Nancy.'

'He's all right. Why the sudden interest? Usually you don't look the side he's on.'

'I've missed his friendly face, that's all. And I was thinking, since he has such a kind disposition, perhaps I could entice Nancy downstairs next week so that she could meet him — I'm sure she gets fed up of my face. Of course, I'd have to get Lord Frankland's permission first.'

'Hark at you: 'a kind disposition'! You mean he's soft.' Will was taken aback as much by his sister's change in attitude as her newly acquired vocabulary. Alice never had a good word for his best mate. It was the opposite with Jack; he was always asking for news of Alice. 'Any road, you'll not be seeing Jack or his lordship next week. Jack'll be at the marble works with me, and his lordship's away in Russia until the end of the week. And when he does return, first thing he'll want to do is see us.' Seeing the effect his words were having on Alice, Will decided to antagonize her further by playing up his newfound importance: 'Me and Jack are his lordship's right-hand men at the moment. We have a lot to report. He'll not have time for you.'

'You two — his lordship's right-hand men? Since when!' Alice sat up.

'As I've been telling you for the last hour, since he's had us up at Stone House watching what goes on there. And by God, is he going to be altering things when we tell him what's happening up there. Do you ever listen to a word I tell you?'

'Not if I don't have to. It's always 'Me and Jack this . . . Me and Jack that . . . ' I just shut it all out.'

Alice primly smoothed down her hair and then put her hat on as if she were preparing to depart. Ever since she was a baby, Will had been able to gauge her mood by the set of her chin; when it was set firm — as it was now — there was no reasoning with her. He took out his pocket watch and glanced at the time.

'I can see I'm wasting my breath here.' Slipping the watch back into his waistcoat, he picked up his cap and set it on his head. 'The trouble with you, our Alice, is you think of nothing but yourself. If you'd bothered to listen, you'd know the work I've been doing at Stone House could very well lead to something better. By the end of the week, when his lordship comes back, I know for certain there'll be one out of work up there. And he's in a cottage that might just do us two — that is, if you can be bothered to live in a two-up two-down.'

Alice said nothing, just sat and watched him as

he turned away from her, thumbs in waistcoat pockets and his cap at a jaunty angle, and set off along the riverbank. When he got to the bridge, he raised his hand in a wave. She didn't bother to wave back. Let him stew. Always going on about his life, couldn't be bothered to ask about her. She tore off tufts of grass and threw them in the river, watching as they were carried by the current, veering round stones and whirling in giddy circles. All the while, Will's words echoed in her ears, bringing back memories of another occasion when she'd been told that she thought only of herself: the day her mother died, the day her father had shouted at her for hiding up the fell while her mother lay dying. Was she so selfish? She didn't think so. She was trying to make the best of her life, that's all.

Tears welling in her eyes, Alice pulled her feet together and wrapped her arms around her knees, slowly rocking her body back and forth. She felt so lonely: nobody in the world to look after her, and now she'd upset Will on their afternoon off. Her and her big mouth and sulky moods!

★ ★ ★

There had been times when the only thing that kept Will and Jack at Stone House was the knowledge that on Lord Frankland's return O'Hara would be brought to account for his brutal, tyrannical behaviour. Finally the two weeks had come to an end and they could stop counting the days: this morning they would make their report.

They had decided to talk to his lordship at the manor rather than risk being overheard at the marble works. As they sat on the kitchen-garden wall awaiting his summons, Will could see that Jack was nervous. He was nervous himself; from the moment Lord Frankland had given them their orders, they'd known that a difficult choice lay ahead. Spying for their employer didn't sit easy with them; it went against the grain to run to the boss telling tales. What's more, though he hadn't dared lay a hand on them over the past fortnight, O'Hara had watched them like a hawk, his menacing presence and reputation for violence sufficient to remind them that they would suffer if they didn't keep quiet.

'I say we tell him exactly how it is, every last detail.' Jack couldn't hide how he felt about the foul-mouthed foreman. After devoting much of the fortnight to tending the horse and trying to nurse it back to health, he hated its abuser with a vengeance.

'If you don't, I'm certainly going to. Once his lordship hears about all those illegal money-making schemes, I bet you anything he'll have O'Hara gone by the end of the day. It's small wonder that Stone House isn't making any profit.'

'Aye, he'll lose his job, all right. And then the bastard will come after us. He'll break our necks for telling on him.'

Knowing the truth of this, they both fell silent. They remained that way for some time, until Will decided to break the gloom by introducing a lighter topic of conversation.

'I don't know what got into our Ali last Sunday. One minute she was in the mood from hell, and the next — you'll not believe this, Jack — she actually asked after you! She can be a funny bugger sometimes, our lass.' Will kicked his heels against the kitchen-garden wall.

'What did she say? Is she missing seeing me at the manor?' Will blushed from head to toe.

'Aye, she did say she missed you. She was thinking of introducing you to Miss Nancy — rather you than me! Two crazy women together? Good luck with that, mate.' Will grinned and slapped him on the back.

'Will, I've been thinking about this for a while now . . . Would you mind if I asked your sister to take a walk with me one evening, or perhaps on Sunday when she has more time?' Jack stared at his feet and shuffled the gravel underneath them, not daring to look his best friend in the face.

'You what? Our lass? Get away! God, you must be a glutton for punishment, either that or you're light in the head, man! Do you honestly mean it? Because if you do, I suppose I'd better say you can. Not that it's up to me — she's her own woman, our Ali. I daren't tell her anything. You'll soon find that out yourself.'

'Cheers, Will. I've kept looking at her and thinking how bonny she is.' Jack beamed.

'Man, I don't want to know! She's my sister — just you remember that.' Will grinned.

He was still smirking at the thought of Jack walking out with Alice when the kitchen door opened and Lord Frankland appeared.

'Gentlemen, would you care to join me?'

Jack and Will followed him in, stopping just inside the door. They felt awkward in the unfamiliar surroundings, and both were aware of Mrs Dowbiggin casting sideways glances at them as she scuttled around the kitchen.

'Sit down.' Lord Frankland nodded at the kitchen chairs around the large pine table in the centre of the room. He turned to the housekeeper: 'That'll be all, Mrs Dowbiggin. Can you make yourself scarce for an hour — I need to talk to these two young men.'

'Yes, sir.' She curtsied. 'But I hope you don't mind when lunch is late.'

It was unheard of for the master to bring outside staff into the manor. And what was so important that he wanted to deprive her of her beloved kitchen for a whole hour? Unable to contain her curiosity, Mrs Dowbiggin loitered at the kitchen door after closing it, hoping to eavesdrop on their conversation.

Gerald Frankland smiled at both young men and raised his finger to his mouth, warning them not to say a word. Then he swung open the door that Mrs Dowbiggin had just departed through.

'Hello, Hilda — was there something you'd forgotten?' He'd learned from experience that in the manor, walls had ears in the shape of Mrs Dowbiggin. This was something he did not want her to know about. Red-faced and stuttering, the housekeeper took off along the corridor.

Lord Frankland closed the door behind her. Pulling up a chair, he sat opposite them and leaned across the table.

'Right, men — tell me how it is. I want the truth, mind. No half-cocked stories or unfounded gossip, and no keeping things back out of loyalty to any of the men up there. The whole truth and nothing but the truth — and if I get it, you shall both reap the benefits of my gratitude.' He fixed them with his gaze, reading their faces as if trying to judge whether his instincts about them had been correct. 'I know I left you in an awkward situation, but since you've both survived to tell the tale, I obviously made the right decision.'

Will and Jack looked at one another. It was time to tell him all, but where to start?

'Most of the men at Stone House are good workers — rough around the edges, but they work.' Will was the first to speak. 'Your main trouble is O'Hara. Jack here will back me up when I say you can't trust him as far as you can throw him.' Jack nodded in agreement. 'He never pulls his weight; he's always drunk; he has numerous little deals on the side, where he gets a part payment from a customer in return for not telling you what he's supplying them with.'

Frankland's face darkened and Will paused, expecting to be interrupted, but his lordship merely nodded for him to carry on.

'O'Hara lends money to the workers up there and charges them a high rate of interest, threatening them with losing their jobs if he doesn't get his money. We haven't seen the books that his wife keeps, but one of the workers told me that there's one lot with the true figures and then the one that she gives you.'

Will stopped. Beside him, Jack had remained quiet, watching anxiously as their employer's expression went from stern to thunderous. By the time Will had finished, Lord Frankland looked as if he was going to explode.

The chair legs scraped across the polished floor tiles as he sprang to his feet and began pacing back and forth between the window and the table, pounding his fist into his hand.

'Damn the man! I knew he was up to something. Damn him to hell, he's taken advantage long enough. And you say his wife keeps two sets of records? My God, I'll make him pay. I'll have him off my property before this day's out.' Suddenly he paused in his rant, a look of concern on his face. 'Has he done anything to disrupt your activities while you were there, or made threats? I dare say he'll want to get even with the pair of you when he realizes his days of easy money have come to an end.'

'Mostly he's kept his distance from us,' said Jack. 'Apart from a couple of times when he cursed me for looking after the horse and not letting him take it out. Bloody criminal, the way he treated the poor creature.' Jack wanted the abuse O'Hara had inflicted on the horse to be taken into account.

Their conversation was halted when the kitchen door was abruptly flung open and one of the workers from Stone House rushed in. He pulled up when he saw them, and for a moment just stood there, struggling to breathe after his long run, while they looked on dumbstruck.

Then he drew in a great lungful of air and, twisting his cap in his hand, turned to Lord Frankland.

'Begging your pardon, sir, but come quick, sir, please, come quick. It's O'Hara — he's threatening to kill some of the men and he's set his cottage on fire. He's gone mad, sir — he's gone mad!'

★ ★ ★

With Jack and Will at his heels, Gerald ran to the stables. The three of them rode as fast as they could, but by the time they reached the top of the dale it was clear the fire had taken hold. Smoke from the burning cottage could be seen billowing and clinging to the treetops all the way down the valley. The heat and smell of the fire striking fear into their souls, they tethered their horses a safe distance away and made for the cottage. Before them was a scene of absolute chaos. Men were dashing backwards and forwards from the nearby stream with buckets of water in an effort to put out the blaze, but it looked as if their efforts would be in vain. The flames were leaping into the air, licking at the upper bedroom windows. Choking thick black smoke made it difficult to see, but they could hear the horse in the stable across the yard frantically trying to kick down the door in an effort to escape.

Dodging the bucket-laden workers, Jack ran to the stable. Shrugging off his jacket, he opened the door. The horse's eyes were wild, its nostrils flaring in fright. Jack used his jacket to cover the horse's head so that he could lead it away to safety.

In the meantime Gerald Frankland had swiftly taken command, ordering his workers to form a human chain passing buckets of water to combat the fire. Suddenly a shout went up: one of the men thought he caught a glimpse of Mrs O'Hara at an upstairs window. Flames were climbing the curtains and the windowpane exploded with the intensity of the heat. This was immediately followed by a series of booms and an almighty rumble as the timber rafters collapsed and the roof came crashing down with a great cloud of smoke. If O'Hara's wife had been in there, it was too late to save her.

'Stand back, men, stand back!' Stripped to his shirt, sweat pouring off his brow, Gerald Frankland ordered his men clear. When the smoke subsided, all that remained of the cottage was a smouldering shell. 'Don't bother with the cottage, men — it's gone. Keep the outbuildings wet; at least we can save them!'

As he set about reorganizing the human chain, a voice rang out, making itself heard above the raging fire and the frenzied efforts to put it out. 'You, ya bastard! I'm going to kill you!'

All eyes turned to the stocky figure of O'Hara, standing with a shotgun aimed at Frankland's head.

Gerald stood, frozen with fear. Trying hard to control the tremor in his voice, he attempted to reason with the man. 'Don't do it, man. There's nothing to be gained by shooting me. You're in enough trouble already — you've killed your wife and burned my cottage down. If you put the gun down — '

'I've nothing to lose, then, have I? No home, no wife — I'm left with bloody nothing all because you had to send your spies in and get 'em to tell tales about me — snivelling bastards!'

Raising the shotgun level with his eye, he took aim at Gerald Frankland's forehead and pressed his finger on the trigger.

Helpless, Frankland closed his eyes, waiting for the bullet that would end his life. A shot rang out, breaking the silence, and the whole scene stopped still. It was a few seconds before Frankland dared to open his eyes. Only then did he realize that the shot had not been fired by O'Hara and the bullet had not been for him.

His shotgun half cocked and still smoking, Will was standing over the writhing body of O'Hara. 'Thought I'd better fetch my gun, sir. I knew that there'd be trouble.'

Will looked on in disgust as O'Hara, now screaming abuse and yelling in pain from the shot to his leg, was bundled into the works buggy by the men he'd tormented for so long. Frankland gave orders that he be taken to Dent police station; the doctor could attend to him there.

'I hope I'll not be charged, sir. It was either his leg or your head.'

'You'll not be charged, Will, I'll see to that. I owe you my life, and I'll not forget it. I owe you dearly.' Gerald Frankland grasped Will's hand and shook it. He was indeed grateful to the lad whom he had so recently made homeless.

Turning from Will, he surveyed the smouldering buildings and the blackened faces of the workers looking to him for orders. What to do now? Would the place ever be the same again? He couldn't help wondering whether he had brought all this on himself by not doing his own dirty work. Perhaps if he hadn't gone to Russia, things would have gone differently. But when the lovely Tatiana sent for him, he was powerless to resist. Even in the midst of all this devastation, the memory of her smile, the feeling of her hand touching his skin and those dark eyes gazing into his as she implored him to stay had the power to drive all else from his mind.

The crash of an outbuilding collapsing jolted him back to reality. Seeing his property reduced to charred piles of rubble brought back other, less pleasant memories of Russia. He had been on his way back from England when his parents' house was burned down, but the embers were still smouldering next day when he arrived, and he was present when their remains were found in the ashes. That fire, too, had been started as an act of revenge by Frankland employees. Was history repeating itself?

He feared what would happen were Nancy to hear of today's events. She would surely lose her mind completely if she learned of the fire, let alone how close her brother had come to being killed. The poor girl had been making such good progress since becoming friends with young Alice Bentham. He smiled at the thought of the feisty young farm girl. From the very first time he'd spoken to her in the small kitchen of Dale End, he'd felt drawn to her. Not that she was particularly pretty — if anything, she was rather plain, and she had none of the allure or refinement of his Tatiana — yet something about her brought a smile to his lips.

Again it took a sudden noise in the yard to break his reverie. His mind seemed to be all over the place — perhaps it was an after-effect of the shock. Those moments he'd spent staring into the barrel of O'Hara's gun had been the most unnerving of his life.

Summoning Will and Jack to his side, he told them: 'Go home, the pair of you — you've been through enough today. I'll see you both in the morning.'

'But what about the police?' said Will. 'Shouldn't I wait for them to get here?'

'I'll speak to them. No doubt they will need to talk to you, but it doesn't have to be right away. When you do speak to them, I want you to say exactly what happened — we have nothing to hide. Go on, now — get yourselves home.'

Frankland waited until Will and Jack were out of sight before gathering his remaining workers together. Those two lads had seen enough already; he didn't want them to be on hand for the unpleasant task that lay ahead.

'Right, men, I'm afraid we have a grim job in store. We need to go through what's left of the cottage until we find the remains of Mrs O'Hara.' He gazed around him at the smoke rising from the rubble, and the weary, ashen faces of his workers. Under his breath, he added:

98

'Poor woman — she might have been crooked, but she didn't deserve this.'

* * *

Will and Jack were only too relieved to leave the smoke and misery behind. Never in their wildest dreams had they imagined that their activities of the last two weeks would end in such destruction and heartbreak. O'Hara had obviously cracked at the prospect of his world falling apart, but for him to set the cottage alight with his wife in it was unthinkable.

Having ridden to the manor in stunned silence, they unsaddled their horses and then took their leave of each other, for both were in need of some time alone.

Will retreated to his bunk bed above the stable. He'd never shot a man before — still couldn't believe what he'd done. Though he knew he'd done the only thing he could do in the circumstances, he couldn't stop wondering what would have happened if his aim hadn't been sure. What if he'd killed O'Hara? Would he be up on a charge of murder? He tossed and turned, replaying the scene in his head, worrying about what would happen when the police came, until finally sleep overtook him. The next thing he knew, it was night. He got out of bed, shivering from the cold, and looked out of the window. The lamps were lit at the manor, so he made his way to the kitchen door, hoping that Mrs Dowbiggin might be persuaded to give him something to eat — it had been a long time since breakfast.

When she opened the door, her face told him what he must look like.

'Come in, lad, come in! Master told me what you've done for him today. Get yourself over there and sit down — I've saved you some cold mutton, and there's pickle and fresh bread to go with it.' Hilda Dowbiggin scurried around, fetching things from the larder and fussing over him. 'And when you've eaten, let's get you out of those clothes — they reek of smoke. I'm sure Master won't mind if I run you a bath upstairs and find you some of his old clothes. I'm sure we can find something that'll fit you and he said I was to get you anything you needed.'

Will sat at the end of the table chewing the mutton, enjoying the warmth of the kitchen. He felt much better with a full stomach. What he didn't feel comfortable with was having a bath upstairs in the manor's new bathroom. He was used to having a wash in the tin bath once every six months — if that. Apart from the folk at the manor, he didn't know anyone who had a room just for taking baths in. The only reason he knew there were such things was because of Alice; she'd explained all about it and told him that she expected she'd have one in her house one day. That girl was forever going on about her wants and needs. Why couldn't she be content with her lot? With a rueful shake of his head, Will leaned back into the chair and was just stretching his legs and making himself comfortable when Mrs Dowbiggin came bustling in.

'Come on, then, stir your shanks — the bath's

run. I've put some of Master's old clothes out ready for you, and there's some soap in the dish that'll sweeten you up.'

She ushered him through the hallway and upstairs. Never had Will been in such a room. Through the steam he could see gleaming tiles on the walls and floor, a big bath with gold taps, and all the amenities that went with a modern bathroom. He ran his hand in the foaming water of the bath and sniffed the newly laundered towels.

'Well, get your clothes off and then I can wash them.' Mrs Dowbiggin stood at the doorway, waiting for him to strip. 'You haven't got anything I haven't seen before, young man, so there's nothing there that'll surprise me.'

Will stood there blushing. He had no intention of undressing in front of the housekeeper. For one thing, she'd a reputation for gossip and he didn't want the entire dale to know about his privates.

'Shy, are we? All right, I'll wait outside and you can pass them to me.' Sniggering to herself, she stepped out of the room leaving the door ajar. Will stripped off quickly, wrinkling his nose at the stink of smoke that clung to his garments, then bundled everything up and stuck his hand through the gap in the door. As soon as he felt her take the bundle from him, he quickly closed the door and listened until he heard her depart, chuckling to herself as she went.

Gingerly, Will dipped his toes into the foaming bath, followed by the rest of his body. It was bliss; the warm waters floated around his body, making all his aches and pains disappear. This was a far cry from the old tin bath in front of the fire. For once, he could understand Alice's longing for the life of a toff.

What a day! If someone had told him as he sat on the kitchen-garden wall that morning that by the day's end he'd have shot a man, soaked his weary bones in the manor's bathroom and would shortly be wearing his lordship's clothes, he'd have laughed in their face. His mind lulled into relaxation by the warm and fragrant waters, he was just beginning to lose himself in dreams when he heard the bathroom doorknob turn. He quickly grabbed one of the white Christy towels from the edge of the bath.

'Oh, I beg your pardon. I didn't realize my brother had guests and that someone was using the bathroom. It is customary to lock the door.' Averting her eyes, the intruder quickly withdrew.

So that was Nancy. Though he'd heard a few of her tantrums, Will had never actually seen her. From the fleeting glimpse he'd caught of her, she was beautiful, nothing like the witch he'd imagined. And she didn't sound mad either. Perhaps Alice was right for once and Nancy was just lonely and grieving. It had certainly been a day full of surprises.

Feeling naked and vulnerable, he hastily climbed out of the bath and arranged the towel around him while he put on his lordship's cast-offs. They were in better condition than the clothes Will had given Mrs Dowbiggin to wash, and not a bad fit either. He admired himself in the mirror: in this get-up, he could pass for

102

gentry. Wait until he saw Jack in the morning!

Hoping not to encounter anyone else in the meantime, Will quietly opened the bathroom door and crept downstairs to the safe haven of the kitchen.

'Well, you scrub up decent, young Will Bentham.' Mrs Dowbiggin put her hands on her hips and looked him up and down. 'If I was twenty-one again, I'd be trying to catch your eye! Now go on out of my kitchen, 'cos this old bird's off to bed. It's been a long day and unlike you young 'uns, I know when I'm tired.'

As he stepped out of the kitchen door into the night air, his hair still damp from the bath with the sweet smell of the soap clinging to his skin, Will was wondering whether his new appearance would result in girls trying to catch his eye. With Jack intending to start courting Alice, perhaps it was time he found a nice young lady for himself.

In the stable yard, bats were emerging from their hiding places, screeching as they caught insects on the wing. Will paused to watch them. Tomorrow he knew he'd have to answer to the police, and no doubt Gerald Frankland would want to talk to him again. Yet the prospect of these encounters no longer troubled him. For tonight, he was going to bed clean, well fed and thinking of that fleeting glance of Nancy.

7

Alice sat on the rough granite trough at the base of the drinking fountain, her hand idly playing with the water as it trickled cold and clear into the sparkling pool. The church clock was striking one o'clock, its huge bell announcing the hour to the people of Dent as it had done for centuries. Where was he? There she was, all dressed up in her Sunday best, and he was keeping her waiting. Jack always had been one for doing things in his own time. She kicked her heels against the fountain and adjusted her hat for the fifth or sixth time, fidgeting with her cotton gloves as she sighed and gazed up the road in the direction of Jack's home.

'Have you been forgotten, Alice, or has he thought better of it?' Uriah Woodhead shouted across at his young employee as he stood on the Moon's step, wiping his hands on his apron.

'Looks that way, Mr Woodhead.' Alice sighed and crossed her arms on her lap. 'It's typical of Jack. Him and my brother would forget their heads if they weren't screwed on.'

'He'll turn up soon, lass. He'll have forgotten the time, if I have to bet on it.' Uriah smiled and disappeared into the dark interior of the pub where there were customers waiting to be served.

Alice still wasn't sure why she was spending her precious afternoon off sitting on the fountain's edge waiting for her brother's best friend. She cast her mind back to the previous Friday when Jack had come into the Moon with her brother. The pair of them often came in for a pint or two on a Friday night, so it hadn't struck her as anything out of the ordinary. But on this occasion Jack had downed several pints, and then — in front of her jeering brother and all the Moon's regulars — he had turned to her, stuttering and blushing, and asked her to join him for a stroll the following Sunday. There was no way she could have said no, not in front of all those people. How could he have put her in such an embarrassing position? Why couldn't he have asked discreetly? As for Will, she could have hit him for six when he offered to be chaperone — the whole pub had laughed at that. She tugged her hat down around her head, brushing her burning red cheeks in an effort to get rid of her blushing. And after all that, here she was, sitting outside the church like a stood-up wallflower. Knowing Jack Alderson, the whole thing was probably a joke at her expense. More than likely Will had put him up to it. She wished she hadn't kept asking after Jack every Sunday, but since the fire up at Stone House she'd been worried about them both.

Having decided she'd waited long enough and might as well go on a walk by herself, Alice was about to set off along the churchyard path when Jack came racing up in his horse and trap, the wheels nearly sparking on the cobbles in his haste not to be too late.

'Whoa there, whoa, Patsy.' Jack jumped out of the trap and ran towards her, his jacket flapping and his cap falling to the ground. Pausing to scoop up his cap, he rushed to where Alice stood.

'I'm sorry, Alice. I'm sorry I'm late. I was grooming Patsy, and before I knew it, it was one o'clock already.' Walking back to the horse, he patted it lovingly on its withers, then smiled apologetically at a glowering Alice.

'That's just typical, Jack Alderson — a horse taking the place of me. I've a good mind not to bother walking out with you.' She stuck her chin out and turned to pretend to show interest in the red roses that were growing on the churchyard wall.

'By 'eck, you are bonny when you're in a mood.' Jack couldn't stop himself, though he immediately regretted even thinking it let alone saying it out loud.

Alice turned sharply. 'Jack Alderson, you stand me up and then you accuse me of being in a mood. What sort of a date is this?' She started walking over the cobbles pretending to be heading back into the Moon. 'You can think again if you think I'm walking with you.'

'But, Alice, I've made us a picnic. I thought we could go in the trap up along the high road and picnic by Nellie's Bridge, and then perhaps call off at the manor to see Will.' Jack held tight to the reins of the impatient horse while beckoning Alice to join him.

Alice stopped in her tracks; she loved going along the high road. It was the old drover road where two dales met, and the views up there were magnificent: on a good clear day you could even see the Irish Sea. She turned round and looked at the fretting face of Jack.

'Well, if you've gone to all that trouble, I suppose it wouldn't hurt to come with you. It's only this once, mind.' She pulled up her skirts, giving Jack a glimpse of her ankle while he held her hand as she mounted the trap. She could see him hide his blushes as he got Patsy underway with a quick swish of the whip in the air. Alice held on tight to the wooden seat as it rattled out of the cobbled streets of Dent and joined the narrow track that led up to the fellside. They were silent on the way up the winding track, the horse taking its time and Jack watching Alice's face as she took in the spectacular views unfolding with every turn of the trap's wheel.

'I thought you'd like it up here,' said Jack. 'You can see for miles and it's so quiet apart from sheep and skylarks.'

Alice sat gazing around her, holding on to her hat as the mountain breezes played with it, until finally she gave up and untied it, placing it on her lap, letting her blonde hair blow free across her face.

'I love it up here, Jack — it's so wild and free, and look, you can see the sea.' She pointed at a distant glitter of shining blue between the rolling dales. 'How I wish I could go to the sea. I've never been. My father always promised to take me, but we never got to go.' Her voice trailed off, remembering happier times.

'I love the smell of the peat,' said Jack. 'And the way when you breathe in the fresh air, it makes you feel good. I often come up here if I've something on my mind. It helps me to settle.'

He stopped the horse and trap and the young couple sat for a while, the warmth of the summer's sun on their faces, gazing out at the beautiful sprawling countryside that was their home. Above them the skylarks hovered and sang as they rode the moorland breezes. Below them in the valley, fields of mown grass lay drying in the sunshine, making hay for the winter months ahead. The tranquillity and the warm, pleasant breeze made them feel at ease, content in their own company. The horse chomped on its bit, impatient and wondering why its journey had been interrupted for no apparent reason.

'Do you know, Jack, it's my birthday. I'm seventeen today, but you're the only one who knows, 'cos our Will has forgotten and I've not told anybody else. Last year's birthday seems a million years ago. So much has changed. I miss my mum and dad, and sometimes I feel so alone.' Alice sniffed into her handkerchief and stifled the tears that she could feel welling up. 'There now, I'm even spoiling this beautiful day out with you because I'm feeling sorry for myself.' She sniffed again and swallowed hard, regaining her dignity and pretending not to care.

'Now, Alice, you know we are all fond of you. You've been through the worst twelve months that anyone could have gone through. And as for your birthday, Will hasn't forgotten that it's today. That's why I've picked you up in the horse and trap — we have a surprise waiting for you. Nay, now I've said too much. I promised Will I wouldn't let the cat out of the bag, so stop snivelling and let's be off. Besides, Patsy's had enough of this standing around. She's a bit like thee: no patience. Why I want to spend my time with the pair of you, I don't know!'

'Jack Alderson, are you likening me to a horse? And what's this surprise? Oh, go on, Jack, tell me, please tell me. I thought you had all forgotten!' Alice was bouncing in her seat with excitement. She had thought that it was going to be just another day. Lately they had all seemed to run into one another, and even she had been taken by surprise when she realized that it was Midsummer Day and her birthday.

'I'm not saying another word; you'll just have to wait. But I can say it's something I've never seen either, so we're both in for a surprise today.' Jack flicked the reins and the horse began making its way along the fellside and down the green pathway to the local beauty spot of Nellie's Bridge. In the face of Alice's constant quizzing, he urged the horse to make speed, worried that he might not be able to hold on to the secret until they reached their destination.

Soon they came to the green leafy glades of the riverside, the smell of drying hay drifting in the breeze and the drone of summer bumblebees filling the air as they went about their business of collecting pollen for honey. The meadowsweet, red campion and other hedgerow flowers swayed in the gentle valley breeze and Alice sat back and enjoyed the steady pace of the faithful horse and its driver. She felt content for a change, and she'd made up her mind not to let anything spoil her perfect day. The anger she'd felt towards Jack for being late had given way to anticipation and excitement about what lay in store.

She held on tight as the trap swayed over the rough cobbles of the path that led to the old wooden bridge and the picturesque waterfall that cascaded above it. She could make out the shape of her brother, waving frantically at them as they approached the bridge, but who was the person that stood behind him? Could it be . . . ? Surely not? There was no way that it could be Nancy! How could she be there? She never left the house.

'Well, what do you think of that, then? What's your brother like — he's kept that quiet, hasn't he, the old dog?' Jack blushed and smiled at Alice. 'I've never seen her, but seemingly he met her when he was in the bath with nothing on.'

Alice gasped. 'What was he doing? She's met hardly anyone, let alone our Will in the nude. By, the poor lass — it's not a pleasant sight. I should know, I've filled his tin bath at home often enough.' She covered her mouth, realizing how familiar she had been with Jack.

'Yes, well, it was in a bath he met her . . . But shush now, they'll hear us.' Jack felt awkward. He was the only one who didn't know Nancy and yet he had heard so much about her. He made a conscious effort not to stare at her when he stopped the trap and helped Alice alight to the daisy-covered field.

'I bet this takes you by surprise, eh, Sis?' Will bounded over and hugged his astonished sister.

'Oh, never mind about you giving me a hug,' said Alice, breaking free so she could run to

Nancy, who was standing half hidden under a parasol at the edge of the bridge. 'I can't believe you are here!' Forgetting that the Frankland family were her employers, she reached for Nancy's free hand as she would an old friend.

'I took a lot of persuading, Alice. I'm still very nervous — this is my first time outside in company for years. I had forgotten how wonderful fresh air smells, and how much I enjoy good company like your brother's.' Nancy twirled her parasol coyly and lowered her face so as not to look at the smiling Will.

'Our Will — good company? It must be the sunshine gone to your head. He's a big galoot! But still, it's good to see you outside and enjoying the sun. What I want to know is, how did he manage it? I've been trying to tempt you out for weeks and then he flutters his baby-blue eyes and here you are.' Alice smiled, putting one hand on her hip and hitting her brother's shoulder playfully with the other. 'And look at him, all dressed up like a dog's dinner! Where did he buy that suit? I think it's 'cos of him being around the manor so much; he has ideas above his station!'

'Never you mind, our lass. What you don't know won't hurt you.' Will smiled and called over to Jack. 'Well, lad, did you manage to keep it to yourself, or did my devious little sister wheedle the secret out of you? And what are you doing back there, hanging about like a bad smell? Come and meet Nancy — you know you want to!'

Will was deliberately playing on his friend's

shyness in order to escape telling his sister that he had been keeping Nancy company since the day he had seen her fleetingly in the bathroom. Much to the disgust of the manor's servants — but he really didn't care what they thought or said.

'Pleasure to meet you, Miss Frankland.' Jack reached out his hand in greeting, moving slowly, trying not to look directly at the face of Nancy.

'Please, Jack, call me Nancy. 'Miss Frankland' sounds so stuffy, and as we are to picnic together I don't want you to feel on edge with me.' She smiled and shook Jack's hand, looking him straight in the eye, not hiding the fact that her face was scarred.

Alice could not help noticing the change in Nancy. Today she seemed much less embarrassed by her scars; perhaps it was Will's doing. Having him there seemed to be boosting her confidence and making her life a little more worthwhile. She smiled quietly to herself as Will took Nancy's arm and led her to the tablecloth that had been spread out on the meadow floor with a delicious picnic upon it.

'May I, Miss Bentham?' Jack held out his arm for Alice and grinned, pretending that he, too, was the perfect gentleman.

'I don't mind if I do, Mr Alderson.' Alice took his arm and sat next to Nancy, who was still holding the parasol, both for shade and to shield her scars from prying eyes.

'Isn't it a beautiful day.' Alice leaned back after eating her way through the manor's best pork pie and salmon sandwiches, washed down with home-made lemonade from Jack's mother. 'I wish every day could be like this.'

'Oh, before I forget, I've got a little something for you.' Nancy untied her beautifully embroidered Dorothy bag and took out a small package. 'You admired this so much on the first day we met, the day when I was such a beast . . . ' She handed it carefully to Alice. 'It's just a thank you on your birthday for helping me get my life back. Without you I'd still have been dwelling in the past instead of rediscovering the good things in life.'

Alice looked at the gift that Nancy offered her, so delicately wrapped in purple tissue paper, the perfumed smell of sweet violets rising from the wrapping. 'Oh, no, I couldn't, I really couldn't accept this.' Her eyes filled with tears as she unwrapped the gift, the sun shining on the beautiful glittering jewelled wings of the dragonfly comb that she had so admired on her first meeting with Nancy. 'It's too precious, and it's from your Russian past.'

'Exactly, Alice. Time to put the past and Russia behind me. Besides, it will look so beautiful in that long blonde hair of yours. Won't it, Jack?' Nancy turned and smiled at Jack, turning the scarred side of her face for him to see.

'Yes, yes, it would, it would look good in your hair, Ali.' Jack faltered over his words having finally realizing how badly scarred Nancy was. 'It will suit you down to the ground.'

'Well, if you insist. But really, I shouldn't. It's too fine for a farm girl like me.'

113

'Nonsense! If you were nothing more than a simple farm girl, my brother would not have asked you to be my companion — believe me, he knows quality when he sees it. Especially now that your brother has asked for me to walk out with him. Gerald is thinking about giving him more responsibility at Stone House marble works — he needs a new foreman and is going to give Will a trial run. Your Will has been an inspiration these last few weeks and I'm sorry I've not mentioned him visiting me on the days I have been with you, but we wanted to keep it a secret.' Nancy patted Alice's hand in apology, but Alice withdrew it sharply.

'You're what, our Will? Going to be foreman at Stone House? When were you going to tell me? I'm stuck working my fingers to the bone at the Moon, and you're planning a life without me. I thought we were going to stick together. And you walking out with Nancy — when were you going to tell me that?' Alice tried to keep calm but she was angry with her brother: he should have been the one to tell her, not Nancy.

'Quiet, our lass. If you've anything to say, tell me tonight when I pop into the Moon after seeing Nancy home. I'll tell you all then, not now in front of Jack and Nancy — you're embarrassing them both.' Will stood up, shook the crumbs from his lap and brushed the grass from the back of his breeches. 'Nancy, would you care for a stroll along the riverbank?' He offered her his arm and Nancy quickly accepted, wanting to be free of the situation she had caused.

Jack and Alice watched the couple walking by the side of the river. Nancy's long white dress seemed to have a mellow haze around it, the buttercups giving it a golden sheen. Dressed in his best bib and tucker, Will was the epitome of the aspiring young gent. They made a perfect couple. You would never guess, just by looking at Will, that he was from working-class stock.

'I can't believe it! What's he playing at, going out with Lord Frankland's sister? Has he lost his senses? My father will be turning in his grave!' Alice removed one of her shoes and started banging the heel on the ground in an effort to let out her pent-up aggression.

'If you're not careful, you'll break that heel, and then you will be in a bad mood.' Jack put his hand on hers to spare the shoe from getting any more anger taken out on it. 'Wait and see what he has to say to you tonight. I'm sure he will tell you all.'

'But he's spoilt the day.' Alice pouted and pushed her foot into the abused shoe.

'No, he hasn't. You should be glad for the pair of them. Come on, sulky — I'll beat you to the waterfall.' Jack offered Alice his hand and smiled at her surly face as she stood up. He gave her a little shove. 'Race you, sulky.' And then he took off, running to the waterfall.

'Just you wait, Jack Alderson! I'll catch you — that was cheating.'

'I know, but it's stopped you sulking,' he shouted.

Alice caught up with him, panting, her cheeks flushed. Jack took hold of her hand and they both walked onto the ancient wooden bridge. As they leaned over the railings, looking at the sparkling waterfall and dark frothy waters below, their heads were inches apart. They turned to each other and laughed. Suddenly Jack plucked up courage and gently kissed Alice on her lips, whispering, 'Happy birthday, Alice.'

'Jack Alderson, you can just stop that!' Alice cried. 'What do you take me for? This is our first date!' Then she blushed and turned away, but she was blushing with pride and happiness.

Jack grinned at her. He wouldn't have had her say anything else, but he hadn't noticed her struggling when he'd kissed her. By, she was a grand lass.

* * *

'Look here, our Ali, I'm doing it for both of us. Would you have turned down the chance to potentially become foreman if you'd been offered it?' Will was finding it hard to persuade Alice that the job at Stone House was going to be good for them both. 'There'll be a house, once it's been repaired, and I'll get decent brass if I'm officially put in charge. I've even got my own horse. I've decided I want to make something of myself. It's like you've always said: put your mind to it and you can do better.' He strutted back and forth underneath the little attic window of Alice's bedroom. 'I thought you'd be pleased that Nancy and me are walking out together. What's wrong with that?'

'What's wrong with that? We're farmers, Will

— she's gentry, she has different ways to us, and you'll be the talk of the dale. It was you who kept me away from the manor when I wanted to work there. Now you're going out with Lord Frankland's sister and being bought by him. Wasn't it you who told me he wasn't to be trusted? I thought I knew you better, Will. You've changed this last week or two.'

'You're only jealous. You always wanted money and posh things. Well, I've found out so do I. From the moment I soaked in that bath and put on clean clothes I realized what we had been missing. And by God, even if I have to marry a scarred banshee, I'm going to get it.' Will's temper was getting the better of him.

'You mean you've no feelings for her at all? You're just after her money?' Alice gasped. 'But she's been hurt enough — don't you go hurting her more. If Gerald Frankland finds out, he'll kill you.'

'You bloody little hypocrite! Do you think I've not been hearing about you? The men up at Stone House don't have the manners of us locals; when I heard them talking of the young lass doing favours for Old Todd, I soon put two and two together.' Will's face was thunderous. 'There, I've bloody well said it! I vowed I wouldn't even think it, let alone tell you I knew, but I won't have you lecturing me, our Ali. Not when you carry on like that. Just be thankful that Jack doesn't mix with anybody but farm lads and me, else he'd have heard about it too. Then you would be in bother.'

Alice started to cry. She lowered her head,

unable to look her furious brother in the eye. 'Do you think I'm proud of what I've done? Well, I can tell you I'm not. I didn't do it for the money; I did it because he made me. Can you remember that bacon I gave you, right after I first started at the Moon? He saw me putting it in my pocket. He threatened to tell the Woodheads and said I'd lose my job when they found out. You think I wanted that filthy old man letting his hands wander over me? It's true the old lech gave me money afterwards, and I wish I'd flung it back at him, but I thought I might as well get something out of it. I dread him showing up at the Moon. I was going to tell Annie about the bacon myself — even if she threw me out it'd be better than putting up with that old lech. Please don't tell Jack. How could he love me if he found out what I'm like?'

'Oh, Ali, you stupid girl, what have you done? Now stop crying. With me going up in society, things are bound to get better. Just keep your legs together in future and ignore the randy old bugger. If he tells Annie about the bacon, she'll only laugh. She knows you're no thief.' His anger subsided as he put his arm around Ali's shoulders. 'What I'm doing, I'm doing for us both. Let me get that cottage up at Stone House and make sure that my job as foreman is secure, and then I'll let down Nancy gently. I must admit, it doesn't sit easy with me, using someone like that, but I've found out you've got to look after yourself in this world.'

'That's all I was trying to do, Will. But I couldn't have gone on being Old Todd's floozy.

118

I'd got to the point where I wanted to hit him where it hurts, never mind anything else.' Alice wiped her nose on her sleeve end and grinned at Will in between the sobs.

'What are we like, me and you! Two orphans out in the world and taking it head-on. You stick with Jack and your jobs, and I'll try to make the money and home for us, all right, our Ali?'

Alice nodded, relieved that Will had learned her secret, shocking though it was. She felt as though a burden had been lifted now it was out in the open.

8

It had been a busy morning in the Moon. The drovers who'd taken lodgings for the night wanted an early breakfast before herding their cows and sheep to Hawes for the weekly cattle market. With bacon in high demand, Uriah was kept busy cutting thin strips from the newly cured flitch. It was a job he insisted on doing himself because he reckoned Annie and Alice cut it too thick. When Annie told him to hurry up, he swore under his breath and muttered that he had to make a profit and that meant cutting it wafer-thin. You should be able to feed at least six on half a pound of bacon — and damn them all for rushing him.

'Uriah Woodhead!' Annie yelled at her husband across the kitchen floor. 'If I hear you swear once more, I'll send Alice over with carbolic soap and a scrubbing brush to clean your mouth out. Good decent folk don't want to hear language like that first thing of a morning.' Wiping the sweat from her brow with a tea towel, she went back to frying the bacon over the Yorkshire range that she was so proud of.

'It's enough to make any good man swear — I'm rushed off my feet. Tuesday mornings in this place it's like feeding the four thousand. I've done a full day's job by the time the rest of Dent start to think about getting up.'

'And what do you think us two get up to every

120

day of the week, eh, mister? Don't you think I'd like an hour longer in bed sometimes? Fires always lit and doors open for business before you've even put a toe out of your side of the bed. So just you watch what you're saying. Bugger it!' Annie swore as the bacon sizzling in the pan spat at her, the fat leaving a scald mark on one of her ample arms. 'Now look what you've made me do!'

'Language, dear, language! Else I'll have to send Alice across with the carbolic.'

Alice, catching Uriah's wink out of the side of her eye, gave no acknowledgement beyond a smile as she got on with scrubbing the huge pine table of the Moon's kitchen. She'd found that when her employers fell out, it was best to keep her head down and get on with her work.

'I tell you what's odd this morning: we haven't got Old Todd stopping with us. It's not like him to miss market day at Hawes.' Uriah stopped carving for a moment to think about his absent guest.

'He'll turn up, like a bad penny.' Annie plated up the fried bacon. 'The creeping old devil wouldn't miss going to Hawes on a Tuesday if it were the last thing he did — more's the pity. I can't stand his grubby ways, myself. Have you seen the way he drools when Alice here serves him?' She handed Alice the plates so she could take them to the customers. 'You'll not miss him this morning, will you, Alice? Dirty old man.'

Once again, Alice's only reply was a smile as she lifted the plates loaded with greasy bacon, fried bread and eggs, and hurried into the bar with them. Too true she wouldn't miss Old Todd. After her conversation with Will, she'd made up her mind there'd be no more 'little understandings'. The thought of what the old lech would do when he found out filled her with dread.

The Moon was packed with drovers and farmers who believed in starting the day off with a full stomach and a pint. Many didn't even wait to get to market, preferring to come to agreement over breakfast. Two weathered-faced farmers sitting in the corner concluded their business as Alice arrived with the plates; she saw one of them spit into his palm, then reach out to shake the other farmer's hand, signalling that it was a done deal and that his word was good. He sent Alice to fetch them drinks to seal the deal. She quickly poured two pints of bitter and hurried back to their table. As she bent down to place the two pints in front of them, she caught a snatch of their conversation.

' . . . I knew he was a bugger for the lasses, but this 'un was seventeen! You'd think the old sod would know better.' Oblivious to Alice's presence, the old farmer rubbed his head and took his first sup of the pint.

Alice, eager to hear more, began slowly clearing plates from the recently vacated table next to them so that she could listen in to the conversation.

'It's his wife and family I feel sorry for,' said the younger of the two farmers. 'Fancy being told that your husband's dropped dead in a young lass's bed — on the job, as it were!'

'It's a right rum do, all right. But who can

blame him for going with a young 'un, as long as he could stand the pace?'

'Aye, but it looks as though Old Todd couldn't stand the pace, and look where it got 'im!'

The older farmer spluttered into his beer at this, and then both men burst out laughing.

Alice felt a shiver run down her spine. So that was why Old Todd wasn't here: he'd died bedding a seventeen-year-old girl. How many young girls had he been getting serviced by? Alice felt dirty and sick at the thought of him dribbling and licking his lips as she served him, leering at her cleavage . . .

Suddenly realizing that it could have been her at the centre of the gossip, for ever more the subject of pointing fingers and known throughout the Dales as the seventeen-year-old floozy who finished off Old Todd with her wanton ways, Alice weaved her way through the crowded bar and out into the open air. Faint and flushed, she hurried to the fountain and splashed some of the clear, cold water on her face. Then she sat on the edge of the trough, trying to compose herself.

A blackbird came creeping along the street, head bobbing up and down when it heard a noise. So intent was her gaze that anyone seeing Alice would have assumed she was fascinated by the bird, with its sharp beady eyes and the orange bill that stood out in stark contrast to its glossy black plumage. In reality, she wasn't even aware of the creature; her mind was completely focused on the news she'd just heard.

'Alice, Alice! Where the hell are you, girl!' She

heard Uriah shouting her name. 'Bloody hell, lass, I'm run off me feet.'

'Coming, Mr Woodhead, I'm coming.' She clutched her apron and leapt to her feet, running across the cobbles in the rush to slip unnoticed into the pub. As she entered the bar, she gave a sigh of relief: Old Todd wouldn't be staying in the Moon any more; her worries were over. Her terrible secret would be buried with him.

'There you are!' Uriah glared at Alice. 'What you been up to? I've been shouting my head off.'

'I felt a bit faint and needed some fresh air, Mr Woodhead.'

'Well, you looks all right now. Get them tables cleared. I'm run off my bloody feet in here.' Wiping his forehead, he turned to head back to the kitchen, pausing on the way to thank a departing farmer for his custom.

By eight o'clock the bar was empty. There was still washing-up to be done and floors to be swept ahead of the midday rush, but first they were all in need of a break.

'Time for us to grab something to eat.' Annie placed three plates of breakfast on the table. 'It's been a morning and a half. I'm fair jiggered.' She heaved a sigh and peered at the plate of bacon and egg in front of her. 'I don't know if I can eat this after cooking the stuff all morning. Besides, I heard something earlier that made me feel sick.' She leaned back in her chair and folded her hands on her lap.

'Oh? What was that?' Uriah looked at his wife, curious.

'You mean you haven't heard about Old Todd

124

being found dead in bed with the young barmaid at the Crown? I always knew he was a dirty old devil. Alice, cover your ears — someone your age shouldn't listen to this.'

'Never!' exclaimed Uriah. 'Why, the old devil. Who'd've thought it? Daft old sod, and him with a respectable wife and family. Good job he didn't take a fancy to our Alice here.' He winked at Alice as he tucked into his bacon and egg.

'Uriah Woodhead, how could you even think that? Our Alice is a respectable young lady. Besides, she's walking out with Jack Alderson. She wouldn't be the least bit interested in that old pervert, would you, Alice?'

Alice blushed crimson, wishing the conversation would change. 'No, Mrs Woodhead. He was a nasty old man.'

Uriah quickly caught the escaping mouthful of fried egg. ' 'Course, Mother. How could I think otherwise?' Smirking, he wiped his mouth with the back of his sleeve and gave Alice a long, knowing gaze.

It was the smirk that told Alice: he knew. Uriah had known all along about the 'little understanding'. Her head began to spin and she felt sick deep down in the pit of her stomach. Just when she thought that her secret was safe . . .

★ ★ ★

'Don't forget, the bread's to be in the oven and the steps scrubbed by six thirty. Uriah, don't go to bed till you've made sure there's coal in and

125

that fire's been banked up for the morning.' Annie Woodhead was giving Uriah and Alice their orders before setting off to see her ailing mother in Kendal.

She lifted her skirts and heaved herself up into the trap next to the small body of the driver, still checking and checking again that she had left everything in place for the smooth running of the Moon.

'We've all in hand, Mother. You're back in two days — what can go wrong in that time? Now, bugger off and make sure that the old lass is all right.' Uriah stretched up to kiss her goodbye, then gave the horse a smack on its withers to stir it into action.

'And don't forget to feed the cat,' Annie shouted as the trap set off on its journey.

Uriah turned and went into the Moon. 'Good God, I thought she'd never go. You wouldn't think that I'd run this place on my own, would you? Now, Alice, how about a cup of tea before the lunchtime rush? I could do with a look at today's paper, and then I'll have forty winks.' Picking up his paper from the bar, he went and sat in his favourite seat by the fire while Alice went to make him his tea.

When she returned, the paper was lying scattered on the floor and Uriah was snoring his head off, arms lolling by his side. So this was how it was going to be. She remembered that expression he was so fond of: 'While the cat's away, the mice will play.' Alice had a feeling that this little mouse would not have time for anything — she'd be too busy doing three people's work.

By the end of the day, Alice was shattered. She sat on the edge of the bed in front of the mirror brushing her hair, her cami straps hanging loose from her shoulders. Wearily she poured cold water into the basin, pinned her hair out of the way and stripped down to her bloomers. The cool water felt refreshing as she washed her face and then her body. It was a warm September's night, so instead of scrambling into her nightdress she paused to study herself in the mirror, turning sideways and caressing her firm breasts, wondering at the young woman she had become. As the moonlight from the attic window highlighted the blonde in her hair, she couldn't help but smile at the reflection that she saw in the mirror. What had happened to the ugly duckling? Even if she said so herself, she wasn't too bad to look at.

Hearing a creak of floorboards, which she swore came from outside her bedroom door, she turned sharply. 'Who's there?' she shouted, grabbing her nightdress to cover her nude body. 'Is anyone there?'

There was no reply, just a flutter of bat wings from way up in the eaves of the Moon. Perhaps she had been dreaming. She was that exhausted, it was hardly any surprise she was hearing things. As she pulled the bed sheets back, she glanced at the carriage clock that had once been her mother's ticking methodically on the bedside table. One o'clock: another four hours and she'd have to be up and about, ready for the next day.

She rubbed her eyes, blew the candle out and slid into bed. Sleep came quickly, giving her peace for a few hours.

The following day was wet. Rain battered at the Moon's thick glass windows, making the whole place feel damp and cold. Not many customers came in for breakfast or lunch, which was just as well because Uriah had not banked the fire up the night before and Alice had to light it from scratch. He'd spent the morning walking around the pub like a groaning spectre, suffering the effects of a hangover after one too many 'nightcaps' from the whisky bottle at bedtime. It wasn't hard to see who was really in charge of the Moon when Annie was away.

'You can get yourself to bed early tonight, if you want.' Uriah peered at Alice over the top of his glasses. 'Either that or find yourself something to do. I've a few friends coming round tonight for a card game and they'll not want a young lass hanging about, distracting them from their betting, so you'd better make yourself scarce. Think on you don't say anything to the missus when she comes home — she doesn't like some of my mates.' Uriah fixed his gaze on Alice, seeking assurance that she wouldn't tell of his exploits.

Alice gave Uriah a nod. She'd had enough of being on her own with him, so was thankful for the break. 'I'll be off now, then. All's done for the morning. You know where I am if you want anything.'

Sighing a weary sigh, she climbed the stairs, untying her apron as she approached her

128

bedroom door. Too exhausted for anything else, she lay on her bed watching the raindrops race one another on the skylight. The roof was taking a pounding in the storm and a small trickle of water was gradually forming a pool in the corner of her bedroom. She was not looking forward to spending winter in this cold and lonely little bedroom.

The next thing she knew it was dark and she could hear voices. She must have fallen asleep and been woken by Uriah's friends as they left the Moon by the back door, laughing and calling their goodbyes. She reached out to light her bedside lamp, the golden glow allowing her to read the time on the clock as she sat gathering her senses on the edge of the bed. It was then she heard the creaking of floorboards outside her bedroom door.

'Hello, who's there?' She stood up, half asleep but determined to find out who was out there. Clutching the lamp in one hand, she opened the door quickly. In the lamp's glow she saw Uriah, his cheeks flushed, swaying unsteadily.

'Mr Woodhead, what are you doing here? Do you want some help?'

'Aye, you can help me.' His jovial expression turned into an ugly leer. 'I want a bit of what you gave Old Todd!'

Alice struggled to close her bedroom door on him, but he forced his way in, almost knocking the oil lamp out of her hand as he pinned her against the wall. 'You think nobody knows what went on in that churchyard, you slut? Once Old Todd had a drop or two of the golden stuff, he'd not stop talking about little Alice and how she can't get enough of it. That's why you go to the manor once a week, isn't it? To look after his lordship's needs.' His whisky breath was inches from Alice's face as he held her captive while fumbling to undo his belt buckle.

'It isn't like that! Let me go!' Alice desperately tried to break free of his grip on her.

'Aye, he told us you were a feisty one.' His face broke into a lascivious grin. 'Makes the sport even better.'

Tightening his hold on her wrist, he removed the lamp from her hand and set it down on the table. Then he threw her face down on the bed. With his ample body pinning her down, she was powerless to stop him as he pulled her skirts up and ripped off her bloomers. Alice tried to scream, but he buried her head in the mattress so that it was all she could do to breathe. The iron bedstead dug into her legs as the drunken landlord took his pleasure, grinding the bed into the wall with every thrust. And all the while he was hurling foul-mouthed insults at her, gaining as much pleasure from that as the sexual act itself.

Then suddenly it was over. She felt him withdraw from between her aching, sore legs and he lunged to his feet, releasing her. Kicking his trousers from around his ankles, he stepped out of them and staggered out of the room without a word. She heard him breathing heavily as he descended the stairs.

Alice lay retching and sobbing on the bed, her body aching from the injuries he'd inflicted on her. Pulling her clothing down to cover herself, she curled into a ball, trying to make herself small. How could he? How could he? She felt dirty, worthless and so lonely. What was she to do now? Tears streamed from her eyes as she eased her body off the bed.

Terrified that he might return for more, she wedged a chair beneath the door handle so that it could not be opened. Then she took off her clothes and poured clean water into her washbasin. Desperate to get his filth off her, she scrubbed herself raw, tearing at the bruised intimate parts of her body.

It was some time before she gave up and finally laid her aching body on the bed. Tomorrow, as soon as daylight dawned, she would leave. She didn't know where she would go, but there was no way she would stay another night under the same roof as Uriah Woodhead.

★ ★ ★

'So where's Alice? And why have you not opened up, you big useless lump?' Annie Woodhead had returned from her mother's earlier than expected to find the doors closed at the Moon, even though it was past midday. She clicked her tongue, looking around at the state of the place.

'You'll never believe it, Mother: I found her in bed with Jack Alderson, the little tart. As soon as your back was turned, she had a man in her room! What do you think of that? And I heard she'd been seeing Old Todd and charging for favours. Well, you can see the predicament I was in, on my own with a loose woman. So I threw her out. I couldn't do no other now, could I? And I couldn't run the pub on my own, so that's why we are in the state we are.' Uriah offered his wife a chair to sit in while he hurriedly made excuses for the disappearance of Alice.

Annie looked at her husband, weighing up his explanation. Alice had seemed such a grand lass and Jack was a nice quiet lad . . . On the other hand, she had watched her around Old Todd, making eyes at him, and she'd been forever nipping out of the inn for a few minutes when he was staying with them — the brazen hussy!

'Oh my God, Uriah! And I left her with you. I should have known! She was always a bit too forward for my liking, even though she acted like butter wouldn't melt in her mouth. After we've been so good to her, taking her in and letting her live under our roof! Mind you, look at her father — it had to come out somewhere! We're better off without her. She'd have given this place a terrible reputation, and we don't want people tarring us with the same brush. After all, we have high morals and high standards. No, you did right to throw her out, Uriah. I hope I never see her again.' Annie's teacup rattled with indignation as she lifted it to take a sip of her lovingly prepared tea.

Uriah, meanwhile, was also offering up a prayer that he would never see Alice again. He knew it was more than his life was worth.

9

The grass was long and wet, stinging and sticking to Alice's legs as she made her way along the riverbank, stumbling over tree roots and turning her ankles on boulders in her haste. She was short of breath and the hurts she'd suffered the previous night made her want to cry, but she gritted her teeth and kept moving, desperate to get clear of the village without anyone noticing her slip away.

Unable to sleep, she'd stared up at the skylight window above her bed, waiting for the first glimpse of dawn. Then she had made her escape, gathering up her few possessions and creeping out of the back door of the Moon before the villagers began to stir. Avoiding the cobbled street and the drovers' road, she took to the overgrown path that followed the river to the top of the dale and the marble works, where she hoped to seek refuge with her brother. Will had mentioned that the foreman's cottage renovations were coming along well and it now had a new roof; she was hoping to lie low there for a day or two while she tried to think what to do next.

Pausing to catch her breath, she looked back the way she'd come. The village showed signs of coming to life: she could make out the faint glimmer of candles in windows, and smoke was rising from the bakery in a grey plume that blended with the sullen clouds hanging over the fells. A horse-drawn wagon rolled noisily over the cobbles; soon the road would be full of farmers and tradesmen coming and going.

A spasm of pain made Alice bend over, clutching her stomach. Beads of sweat broke out on her forehead as she sank to her knees, waiting for the nausea to subside. As bad as the pain were the feelings of guilt and anxiety. What was she going to tell her brother? He was bound to ask what she was doing, showing up at Stone House on a work day, but she daren't tell him the truth. If he found out what had taken place, he'd kill Uriah. No, best tell him something else — anything to keep her shame quiet.

She picked herself up and got moving again. After a while, she reached the point where the path passed by the drive to Whernside Manor. Keeping low so that no one would see her, she peeked through the undergrowth and saw Jack leading his beloved horse across the yard. Dear, sweet Jack, he would never hurt anyone. But for all that he was a good and loyal friend to her brother, Alice doubted he would want anything to do with her if he found out what had happened. She wiped her nose and swept the tears away. It was no good feeling sorry for herself; what was done was done. Nothing she could do to change it.

She took a deep breath, pushed her chin out and set off again. As she walked, she began to rehearse the story she would tell Will and Jack. She'd never liked working at the Moon — both the lads knew that — so the best thing would be to tell them that she'd fallen out with Annie. The only person who'd know what had really happened was Uriah, and he wouldn't say, not if he'd any sense. Will had been promising her that if he secured the cottage, she could move in with him. And if Lord Frankland would let her do more than one day a week at the manor, she'd bring in a bit of money. Besides, the manor was more the kind of place where she belonged. She should never have taken the job in the pub. Perhaps there had been a reason for the horrible events of last night, showing her what Uriah Woodhead was really like. Come what may, there was no way she would ever cross the threshold of that godforsaken place again.

★　★　★

It was nearly noon when Alice heard the ring of hammers on stone and the chug of the waterwheel. Then she turned the last bend of the river path at the head of the dale and there in front of her was the marble works. She could see the cottage with its smoke-damaged front; there was obviously lots of work still to be done on it, but thanks to the new slate roof it was looking more like the pleasant home it had once been.

Though she'd been walking since dawn and was exhausted from lack of sleep, Alice's spirits rallied at the thought she would soon see her brother. There was no one in the main yard, so she made a beeline for the cottage, hoping to find Will there. A handful of hens were scratching about by the back door, a sure sign that he was making this his home. There was a strong smell of smoke even now; it probably came from the pile of burned timbers stacked against the cottage wall. Alice shuddered, reminded of the terrible day when Mrs O'Hara died.

'Will, Will, are you there?' she called softly, opening the cottage door and peering into the room. The smell of smoke was even stronger in here. The walls were only half plastered; there was no furniture and no curtains at the windows. With a sigh, Alice crept in and set her bundle of possessions on the floor. She was disappointed that her brother was not at home. The last thing she wanted was to walk up to the works in search of him. She dreaded the thought of the men looking at her; most of them were ex-navvies with no wives and no commitments, and Will had said what a rough lot they were. Feeling sick to her stomach, Alice remembered how Will had gone on to say that they were the ones who'd told him about her doing favours for Old Todd. No, even if it meant waiting all day, she would just have to remain here until Will came.

The stairs had yet to be repaired, so there was no way of getting to the bedrooms. She went through a doorway into the adjoining room. This was obviously where Will was sleeping: in the corner was an iron bedstead, and on it was her mother's patchwork quilt. Alice sat on the edge of the bed. It seemed a lifetime ago since she had said goodbye to her mother; she had been lying in her bed at Dale End Farm, covered with this very quilt.

She picked up a corner of the quilt and hugged it to her chest, tears in her eyes, gently rocking her body. 'Oh, Mum, if you only knew what I'd been through,' she whispered under her breath. 'I miss you so much.' Overcome with grief for all that she'd lost, she collapsed on the bed, her body shaking with violent sobs.

★ ★ ★

'No, no, get away, stop it, stop it!' Alice screamed at her aggressor, flailing at the hands that were trying to grab her.

'Ali, Ali, it's me. Shh, it's me, Will. What's all this about? Why the screaming?' Putting his arms around his drowsy sister, Will hugged her to him, stroking her hair and speaking softly in an effort to calm her down. 'That must have been some nightmare, our Ali — I thought you were going to knock me out!' Will smiled at his young sister, but his eyes were full of concern. He could see she was troubled about something, and he wondered what she was doing at Stone House.

'I'm sorry, I'm really sorry. Did I hit you?' Alice sat upright and rubbed her eyes. She must have been asleep for hours. It was dark outside, and the only light in the cottage came from a couple of flickering candles.

'No, you didn't hit me. But I wouldn't want to be the fellow you were taking on in your dream — he'd have no chance.' Will grinned, released his hold on Alice and sat at the side of the bed.

'Who said it was a man? Has someone been talking? I was only dreaming.'

137

'I was only joking, Ali. Don't get upset. Anyway, what you doing here?' Will got up off the bed and picked up an oil lamp. 'Have you fallen out with Uriah? No, that can't be it; from the way he talks, I get the impression he thinks the world of you.' Will was busy examining the lamp, which had run out of oil, so he didn't see the tears welling up in Alice's eyes.

She gulped hard, fighting back the tears and wiping away all traces with the sleeve of her blouse. 'Yeah, well, impressions can be deceiving. Sorry, Will, I'm still half asleep. I've had words with Annie and she's sacked me. She says I'm lazy and that I haven't been doing my job properly.' Alice sat at the edge of the bed, unable to look her brother in the eye. She hated lying to him. 'I'm not going back. You should have heard her, Will. She accused me of all sorts — and you know how hard I work.' She let the tears out, hoping he'd assume she was upset at the unjust accusations, when really it was sadness and despair at what she'd been through.

'Now then, our lass, don't take on so. It's only a job. That Annie does have a tongue on her. She can make grown men cry when she's a mind to. She'll soon be begging you to come back, once she's had a few days with twice the work to do.' Will came and sat by her side, bemused to see his feisty little sister inconsolable after a telling-off from Annie Woodhead.

'I'm not going back, and you can't make me . . . I'd rather starve than work there.' Alice pulled on Will's jacket, frantically pleading with her brother.

138

'All right, all right, don't fret. I'm not going to make you do anything. I know you never wanted to work there in the first place, and you've no need now, anyway. Matter of fact, I was going to come and tell you my news this Sunday, but I can tell you now instead.' Will got to his feet, looking proud and full of importance. 'Who do you think is the new boss at Stone House? Who's gone and talked Lord Frankland into putting him in charge?'

'Will, you're not! He can't have! You don't know the first thing about cutting marble — we're farmers.' Alice looked up at her brother's beaming face while she dried her eyes with his slightly dirty hanky.

'That I am, pet. The bugger's confirmed it, official like. I've even got this bloody cottage. And look at this . . . ' He walked over to a lamp hanging on the wall and pointed at the gas wick under the glass mantel. 'He's even putting me in them fancy gas lamps like they have at the manor. How about that, our Ali — us with newfangled lights! And upstairs there's going to be a toilet and bath. Now then, how's that for posh, our lass? No more sitting on a cold outside lav for us on a frosty morning. What did I tell you? I've made it, our lass. Now all I've got to do is keep in with his sister and I'll soon own this spot and the works.' He sat on the edge of the bed and slapped his leg in anticipation of the good life he could see ahead.

'And where do I enter into your scheme of things, our Will?' Alice scrubbed the last tear off her face and tossed her hair away from her eyes.

'Am I to skivvy for you and stand by while my true friend is taken for every penny?' Shoving the grubby handkerchief into his hand, she stared at him long and hard. She didn't like what Will was beginning to turn into.

'She's not your friend; she's your employer. Nancy's a toff and she's using you, just as her brother's using me — or so he thinks. But I'm going to turn it round and play him at his own game. She fancies a bit of rough on account of she can't get anyone else, what with that face and her being so moody, nice as pie one minute and screaming like a banshee the next. So I fit the bill — and I intend to take what I can get out of it. And why shouldn't I? It's not like Frankland showed much sympathy for us when Father died, did he? And I've seen the way he looks at you, too. You want to take care, our Ali: I'm sure he'd like you to do more for him than keep Nancy company. I've watched him with them friends of his — right shady bunch of characters. All foreigners, so you can't understand a damn word they say, but it's obvious they're up to no good. 'Business associates', he calls 'em, from Russia. It wouldn't surprise me if the business turned out to be a brothel, judging by the way they carry on.'

'Give over! He's been nothing but a gentleman. And Nancy is a true friend and always will be, so you'd better not hurt her, Will Bentham, else you'll have me to answer to!'

'Well, you'll know all about gentlemen, won't you? After all, you've had dealings with them — take Old Todd, he was a real gentleman!' Will

140

regretted the words as soon as he uttered them. Regretted them even more when Alice once again burst into tears. 'I'm sorry, Ali, I shouldn't have said that. I'd no right. We're both as bad as one another, both of us just trying to make a living by fair means or foul. What a bloody pair! What would our mum and dad think of us?'

'Not a lot, I don't think. At least, not of me. You're doing well for yourself, but I keep going from bad to worse. And now look at me: I'm worth nothing; I'd be better off dead. Father always thought I was a selfish one, and he was right.' Alice went and stood by the window. Turning her face away from her brother, she stared out into the dark night.

Seeing that she was shivering, Will picked up her shawl and placed it on her shoulders. 'Sorry, Ali — I'm a hot-headed idiot. We've both said things we shouldn't. It's that bloody Bentham temper. Let's not fight, eh? We only have one another.' He smiled and kissed her on her brow. 'Things will look different when you've had a good night's sleep. You put your head down in my bed and I'll make something up for myself in the other room. In the morning, we'll sort something out for you. I could do with someone to look after me. Can't you tell from the state of this house? It needs a woman's touch. Come on, our lass, I've said I'm sorry.'

'I forgive you, Will. Who am I to preach? And thanks for putting me up tonight; I'm grateful. I'll get myself sorted tomorrow, I promise.' Alice steadied her breathing and gave Will a kiss on his cheek before removing her shoes and crawling under the bedcovers. Tomorrow would be another day. Any decisions could wait till the morning, when she wasn't so tired and when the world made more sense.

★ ★ ★

Leaves twirled and twisted in the autumn wind, torn from trees that had been battered by the northern gales sweeping over the dale. There had been beautiful hues of orange, russet, yellow and brown as the first frosts nipped, but now the leaves were a nuisance, filling up the gutters and turning to mulch underfoot. It was that time of year when people felt depressed at the onset of winter, the thought of Christmas being the one bright spark, the time to be with loved ones and family.

It was almost two months since Alice's unexpected arrival at the cottage and for weeks there had been no let-up in the wind and rain. The cold, wet conditions were making life difficult at the marble works, with the men growing fractious and unsettled. O'Hara might have been a crook, but at least they could take it easy while he was sleeping off the previous night's hangover. The new boss made sure they kept on working even in the pouring rain. And what was he doing in charge of them in the first place? Barely old enough to grow whiskers and knowing nothing about marble and quarrying. There was only one thing him and his floozy of a sister were good at, and that was hobnobbing with the gentry.

To start with, they waited until Will's back was turned before giving vent to their resentment. But all that changed one particularly foul morning, with the rain lashing down so hard they could barely see the rock face and their tools slipping from their hands with the wet, and Will standing there yelling at them all the while, telling them to put their backs into it and earn their keep. They'd all been muttering under their breath, cursing him, but then one of them spoke loud enough so Will could hear it.

'What did you say?' snapped Will, glaring at the dark, thickset form. 'I'm talking to you, Middleton! Answer me!' The man was one of his best workers, but he was also a ringleader, and if Will let a remark like that go unchallenged, the others might follow suit.

'I said, it's a pity we can't all make our living by shagging the boss's sister.' Middleton rose to his full height. He was a big, burly man who would have no problem holding his own if it came to a fight. 'And I think I can speak for all of us when I say it's not fit weather to make a dog work, let alone us men.' With that, he spat in his hands and bent to pick up his spade.

'How dare you talk to me like that!' Will stepped up and grabbed at the bending man's lapel, hauling on it to bring them face to face.

'Nay, I've said enough — I mean to keep my job. But if the cap fits . . . Think what you will, but I'm right about the bloody weather. We can do nothing on a day like this — and there'll be a lot of days like this 'un in winter.'

Shrugging off Will's hand on his lapel,

Middleton made to carry on shovelling. Two of his fellow workers moved in, crowding Will and making him feel vulnerable and alone on the fellside.

'All right, men, finish for today — but I'm only paying you half a day's wages. And it'll be the same for every day wasted: no work, no pay.'

With that, Will turned and set off walking along the stony track that led to the cottage. He heard mutinous voices behind him muttering curses, and Middleton calling him a 'fucking bastard', but he kept on walking. These were not his sort of men. Most were decent enough, but there were a few who were still loyal to O'Hara. If he was to make a success of himself, he would need to win them over, and the best way to do that would be to prove he'd been given the job because he was worthy of it, not just because of his acquaintance with the boss's sister.

By the time he got home, he was drenched to the skin. Middleton was right: this weather wasn't fit for working in, but he was desperate to get the works running at a profit again. Only then would his position be secure, regardless of his relationship with Nancy.

'By the gods, its bloody wet out there, our lass!' He stopped just inside the back door and threw off his cap and overcoat, leaving them in a wet heap on the floor. 'Fetch me a towel, wherever you are. I swear I'm going to lamp that Middleton one of these days. He's a right bloody troublemaker. I'm going to have to secure a few good orders to win him over. Alice, where the hell are you, woman? I'm drowning in here.'

Alice came rushing into the kitchen. 'Be quiet, our Will — we've company.' She handed him a warm towel from the airing rack above the fire. 'Miss Nancy and Jack are in the front room. Nancy got him to bring her up because she says she's missing you.'

Will towelled his dark hair dry, then ran his fingers through it to flatten and layer it thin to his skull, exaggerating his high cheekbones and sharp features.

'That's what I like to hear, lass,' he whispered conspiratorially. 'Treat 'em mean and keep 'em keen.' Taking the damp towel and aiming a swipe at Alice's bottom, he set off for the front room with a jaunty swagger.

'Nancy, my dear, what brings you here on this terrible wet day? It's a wonder you weren't washed away.' He leaned down and planted a gentle kiss on her cheek, then stood and turned to his friend. 'Jack, what were you thinking, bringing Miss Nancy out in this weather?'

'Don't blame Jack, my love. I needed to see you — it's been a whole week since you've been to the manor. Besides, I was sure that Alice would like to see Jack, now that she is hidden away up here at this terrible place. Did I hear right, my love? Are you looking for more orders? I'll ask Gerald to have a word with his contacts for you. I'm sure he can help.'

'Nay, I can manage. I've got to earn my own points with them men up there, else they'll never respect me.' Will turned to Jack, giving him a playful punch on the shoulder. 'I suppose it's my sister you've come to see, not me. That'll be why she's still lurking out there!' Raising his eyebrows and tilting his head in the direction of the kitchen, Will hoped his friend would take the hint and let him have some time alone with Nancy.

'Well, as it happens, there is something I want to ask her.' For a moment, Jack stood there looking sheepish and twisting his cap in his hands, awkward at being in the way of his friend's courtship. 'If it's all right with you, Miss Nancy, I'll go and see her. Let me know when you want to return to the manor.'

Alice was standing by the kitchen fire, hanging Will's wet clothes in front of the range to dry. She smiled at Jack when he entered. 'So you've had enough of playing gooseberry with the loving couple? Come and sit next to the fire and keep me company. It's not only Nancy who gets lonely, you know.' She plumped up the newly made cushions and offered Jack the chair nearest the fire.

'Aye, well, there's something I want to ask you, and it's a bit awkward, but I've got to know because I'm not being tret right at the Moon. Uriah and his missus have all on to talk to me, let alone serve me. I've a feeling it's something to do with thee, but I can't weigh up what.'

'Don't be silly, Jack, you've done nothing wrong and I've never said anything about you to them. Besides, what is there to say? It's nothing but sour grapes over me leaving. They're taking it out on you because they know we're friends. That'll be all it is.' She reached across and took his hand and held it gently. 'You know I'd never do anything to hurt you. I think dearly of you.'

'Aye, and I think a lot of you, but they are acting strange and folk are talking. Everyone goes quiet when I walk into the pub for the odd pint that I can barely afford nowadays.'

'You're imagining it, Jack. Anyway, what's to do with you not affording to go for a pint? Things can't be that bad.' Alice tried to change the subject from the Woodheads.

'I'm not for saying, but you'll find out soon enough.' Jack's mood lightened and there was a definite twinkle in his eye as he added, 'Let's just say I'm counting the pennies at the moment.'

'Go on, Jack, tell me — what are you up to?' Alice's thoughts were racing. She'd come to realize that there was more to Jack than she'd given him credit for. He might be quiet, and his job at the manor didn't have the same prospects as Will's, but she'd found him to be a caring, sensible lad. What's more, he was good with money — something not to be overlooked.

'Nay, you'll have to wait; I'm not saying anything. But I've got to look after my money, so there will be no more fancy tea and scones in Mrs Handley's tea rooms on a Sunday. Sorry, Alice, but this is more important.' He gave Alice a stern look, frowning slightly as he calculated the saving that he would make by not giving her a Sunday treat.

'Oh, Jack, you mean thing! All you think about is money. You don't care about me one bit. I bet you're only saving up for a bloody horse or a new saddle — anything but looking after me.' Sunday was the only day of the week Alice got treated like a lady and she spent the rest of the week looking forward to it. 'I can't be bothered to talk to you, Jack Alderson. I'm off to join my brother in the other room — at least him and Nancy can think of better things to talk about.'

'Alice, it's only until spring and then you can have scones and tea every Sunday,' Jack pleaded, grabbing her by the arm. 'You'll soon see that it's worth going without for.'

Alice shook her arm free. 'Spring! That's nearly five months off. Things can all have changed by then. I'm not always going to be here — I aim to do something with my life, not spend it waiting for a servant lad.'

Her sharp words stung at Jack's heart and her blazing eyes burned his soul. So that was what she thought of him, a servant lad, nothing more, nothing less. Well, he was going to show her, and by God, she'd want him then, because he loved the fiery Miss Bentham and he was going to get her, no matter what it took.

'Suit yourself, Alice,' he said to her retreating back. 'But you'll still be here. I know you will.' Then he turned and sat by the kitchen fire, hoping that Nancy would not stay long. He wanted to get home and nurse his wounded pride.

* * *

The shadows had lengthened by the time Nancy came through into the kitchen. Jack, who'd been dozing in the comfortable padded chair, quickly roused himself after hearing the farewells exchanged.

'So that's sorted, then, Alice: you'll come to the manor three days a week. You can sleep in the maid's quarters. I'm sure my brother won't complain as the room's not being used. You'll be a great help for Mrs Dowbiggin: she's not getting any younger — but don't tell her I said so! And of course it means that Jack will get to see more of you.' Nancy turned and smiled at him. 'So, it works out well for all. Come, Jack, take me home — it will be night-time before we get there.'

There was an uncomfortable silence from Jack as he put his coat on and opened the kitchen door for Nancy. He remained silent throughout the journey home, and Nancy said nothing, leaving him to his thoughts until they were back at the manor.

'Jack, are you all right?' she asked as he reached up to help her alight from the carriage. 'You seem a little upset.'

'I'm fine, Miss Nancy, thank you. Just in love with the wrong woman — and there's nothing I can do about it.'

10

It was a year since Bess Bentham died and the November day was not dissimilar to the one on which she passed away. A sharp wind blew from the north, whipping around the huge pillars of the Stone House viaduct, nearly blowing the railway workers who were busy repairing the track off the top of it. Alice watched them as she sat sheltered behind one of the limestone walls, alone with her thoughts, apart from the song of a solitary late skylark. She had walked along the rutted track, past the marble works and underneath the railway's towering arches to a secluded spot that had become her thinking place. Where she could sit surrounded by tufts of moorland grass and ling heather, the smell of which she was sure would make a fortune in the fine shops of London if you could only capture it in a bottle.

With a sigh, she gazed out at the view. In the distance she could see Combe Scar, tipped with snow, behind the little village of Dent and the vast slopes of Whernside rising up from the valley. She closed her eyes and covered them with her hands, quietly despairing at the situation she was in. Things had gone from bad to worse since her mother died, and now, to top it all, she had fallen out with Jack, all for the sake of a stupid cup of tea. Her and her sharp temper!

Still, maybe she could make it up with him

once she started working more hours at the manor. Her mood lightened at the thought. She was looking forward to living in her own room at the manor two nights a week, knowing that she'd be warm and well fed if Mrs Dowbiggin had anything to do with it. Besides, she couldn't really call it work. Helping Nancy dress, keeping her company and lending a hand in the kitchen — that wasn't work, especially not compared to the Moon. She shuddered at the very thought of the place and horrid memories came flooding back to her. Alice hadn't dared show her face in the village since she left and hoped she wouldn't have to for a while longer yet.

The cold, biting wind finally got too much for her and, wrapping her shawl tightly around her, she set off down the track to the cottage that she had started to call home. To think that just over a year ago both her parents had been alive and she had been an innocent teenager. Life had certainly forced her to grow up since then, and she'd learned her lessons the hard way. But she hadn't let it beat her. Despite everything, she was still aiming her sights high: today the cottage, tomorrow the manor — and who knew where that would lead? She only hoped Mr Right would come along soon.

She stopped by the water trough at the back door of the cottage to take a sip of the icy-cold water. As she leaned over the pump, she was suddenly overcome by a wave of nausea. Her head felt so light and giddy that she had to support herself by hanging on to the pump until the feeling passed and she felt well enough to continue into the cottage.

'You're white as a sheet, our lass. Are you all right?' said Will, looking up from his seat at the kitchen table. 'I bet you've been up in your new hiding place on the fellside, haven't you? I've never understood why you have to go out in all weathers just to have a think. You must be frozen, you silly devil.'

With shaking hands, Alice took her shawl off and hung it behind the kitchen door. Beads of sweat formed on her brow. 'I feel sick, if you must know. Probably those duck eggs I had for breakfast this morning. I didn't know how old they were when I got them out of the pantry.'

'They weren't old — I only had them given to me the other day. Happen you're sickening for something. You'd better have a lie-down for an hour or two, because whatever you've got, I don't want it.' Will put his coat on and made for the door. 'I'm off out. Will you be all right?'

'I'll be fine. I told you, it's just something I've eaten.' Alice managed a wan smile for her brother, but as soon as he was gone she collapsed next to the fire and burst into tears. She knew all too well what was wrong with her, and it had nothing to do with anything she'd eaten. She'd begun to suspect when she missed two 'monthlies'. Now she knew she was pregnant; the nausea confirmed it. Why did she have to end up pregnant? Uriah and his wife had no children. How was it that he had managed with her something he'd been trying for years with his wife? The last thing she wanted was Uriah's bastard baby. What to do, though? She

152

thumped her stomach hard, making her retch even more, trying to kill the unformed baby. If only she had someone to turn to, someone who would know what to do.

★ ★ ★

'Are you all right, dear?' Mrs Dowbiggin peered at her new help across the kitchen table of the manor. The last couple of mornings she'd come down from her room looking pale and had not even touched her breakfast.

'I'm fine, Mrs Dowbiggin. Thank you for asking.' Alice smiled, trying not to show how she felt. Since moving into her room at the manor, she had enjoyed being part of the little community and the last thing she wanted was to lose her new position. She especially liked the way Gerald Frankland bade her good morning personally every morning as she served him and Nancy breakfast. His dark eyes smiling and watching her as she waited on his every word and instructions for the day.

'Now, dear, I hope that you don't think me presumptuous, but I don't believe you. I've been around long enough to recognize a girl in trouble. You're being sick every morning, my girl — I've heard you. So what are we going to do about this little secret?'

'I don't know what you mean. There's nothing wrong with me.' Alice put on her haughty look; there was no way she was going to tell Mrs Dowbiggin her troubles. She would be the gossip of the dale.

153

'Don't be stupid, girl — you're pregnant. Another few weeks and you'll not be able to hide it on that skinny frame of yours. And then what are you going to do?' Hilda Dowbiggin took a long sip from her teacup and studied the blushing Alice as she did so. She placed her teacup and saucer firmly down on the white linen tablecloth. 'If you don't want it, you need to get on and do something about it. How long gone are you? And who's the father?' Seeing Alice's reaction, she followed this with 'Will he stand by you?'

Alice hung her head and fiddled with her handkerchief, not wanting to look into Mrs Dowbiggin's prying eyes. 'I'm three months, but I don't want anyone to know. It's my secret and I'm not telling you who the father is.'

'Well, it's hardly going to stay a secret, now is it? If it's that Jack Alderson's, I'll give him a piece of my mind. He should have kept it in his pocket!' Hilda Dowbiggin stared long and hard at her. Then she smacked her lips and shook her head. 'You're not the first and you won't be the last, but I thought better of you, Alice. I thought you had more about you than some. There was me, trying to warn you about men, and all along you probably knew more than me.'

'It wasn't like that, Mrs Dowbiggin. I couldn't help it, and it's not Jack's, so please don't say anything to him, please, I beg of you. He would only be hurt.'

'Oh, hold your tears. It's no good crying over spilt milk. What are we going to do now? That's the question. I take it I'm the only one who knows? Else Miss Nancy wouldn't have got you working here three days a week. Let's hope his lordship doesn't find out, or we will be in for bother. Now, do you want to keep it?'

Alice sniffed and looked at Mrs Dowbiggin, bemused. 'What do you mean? I've no option but to keep it, have I?' A glimmer of hope was beginning to shine. Perhaps Hilda Dowbiggin was more worldly than Alice had thought, and perhaps she was going to be her saviour. Even if she didn't have a solution, it still felt better now that someone else was in on the secret and she could talk about her situation with another woman.

'There is a way out, if you want to get rid, but what I'm about to tell you, you keep to yourself, do you hear? And you don't mention me if anything goes wrong. I need my job and, besides, I've my reputation to think of. First, we'll try gin and a hot bath. And if that doesn't work, I'll have a word with Mrs Batty; she's good at her trade and discreet.'

Alice looked at Mrs Dowbiggin in astonishment. She was beginning to see this sweet, dumpy elderly woman in a different light. How did she know about such things? The thought of Mrs Batty performing an abortion on her — those hands of death working on her unborn baby — made her retch. Could she go through with it? She had to; there was no other way. If she wanted to make something of her life, she couldn't afford any bastard children clinging to her skirts. She cleared her throat and tried to draw on her inner strength. 'Does she charge for her services?'

'What do you think, lass? Freedom comes at a price, but I'm sure you'll find the brass if you are determined. Do you want me to have a word with her, then, just in case we can't get rid of it ourselves?'

Alice shook her head and bent it in sadness and horror at what she was about to do to herself. Mrs Batty, the horrible woman who had buried her mother, might soon be killing her baby.

'OK, my love, I'll make it right with her, but we'll try a bath first. Better that way than getting rid with Mrs Batty. You'll be all right, though; it won't be the first baby she's got rid of, I can tell you that.' Hilda Dowbiggin laid her hand on the trembling form of Alice and gently patted her. 'Discreet, she is. There's been one or two young ladies visited her from here — friends of the master, needing to get out of a fix. She does a good service, very professional.'

Alice's jaw dropped at the housekeeper's words. So her brother had been right in warning her against Lord Frankland; he *was* one for the ladies. From here on, she would keep him at a distance. All she wanted to do right now was get on with her life.

★ ★ ★

It was a dark winter's night with only a week to go till Christmas. A few snowflakes fluttered down as Alice stood shivering at the back door of

156

the funeral parlour. Her stomach was churning in trepidation at what Mrs Batty was about to do. After all, it was nothing less than murder of her unborn baby. A baby that was not wanted, born out of rape, and would never be loved — or so Alice had convinced herself. A single quick action and it would be no more; that's what Mrs Dowbiggin had told her.

Losing her nerve, she felt like running, but it was too late. The door opened and, raising her finger to her mouth, Mrs Batty led her into the makeshift surgery she had set up in the mortuary. Alice needed no urging to keep silent; she was too numb to speak. Once inside Mrs Batty helped her out of her coat and then held out her hand for the blood money. Alice dropped the florins into her palm, remembering how she had come by them and the indignities of Old Todd's advances. She waved her to the mortuary table and gestured for her to lie upon it. Still not a word was uttered. Alice wondered whether the woman was frightened that her husband might hear her going about the deadly task. She gave Alice a stick to bite on to combat the pain. And then she finally spoke, whispering, 'You've had your pleasure, now you must pay for it.' And then she set about her cruel practice.

The pain was excruciating. Alice felt dizzy and wanted to yell out for the old crone to stop digging and scraping and to leave her be and for the baby to live. Sweat poured off her and her head pounded with pain; then a deep, dark blackness stole over her as her body tried to block out the agony by numbing her senses. With the deadly deed done, she passed out.

★ ★ ★

The wooden cart rattled up the dale, the wheels and the trotting of the horses drowning out Alice's groans.

'Be quiet, will you — I don't want to end up with a noose round my neck.'

Mrs Batty was panicking. She'd had to load Alice into the funeral cart all by herself, and now she was taking her home: if she was going to die, it was better that she did it on her own doorstep.

Leaving the cart at the bottom of the lane, she pulled Alice's arm over her shoulder and began dragging her towards Stone House marble works. 'For a little frame, you weigh a lot,' she complained. To her relief, the girl was still breathing when they got to the cottage. She gently knocked on the door, fleeing into the darkness as soon as she heard movement from within.

'Alice? Alice, what the hell have you done!' Was that the voice of her brother? Her head was spinning. Her body ached and her clothes felt damp and she could feel snow falling on her face. 'Who's left you in this state? Who knocked on my door and left you like this? If this is anything to do with Gerald Frankland, I'll kill him. I'll bloody well kill him.' She felt Will's tears falling on her face as he gently carried her inside, swearing when he got her into the light and saw her blood-soaked clothes. 'Who's done this to you, our lass? What have you been up to? For God's sake talk to me, I don't want to lose you as well!' he cried, panicking at the sight of his young sister in such a state.

Alice muttered feebly, 'Sorry, Will, I had to do it. I'd no option. I can't be weighed down by a baby. I had to get rid of it.'

'You stubborn, selfish woman! Will you never learn, you bloody headstrong article? Why can't you be content with your lot for once instead of looking for trouble?'

But Will's words were wasted on Alice. Once again a cloak of darkness descended, easing her pain and torment. Tomorrow would be another day and, with the grace of God, she would make it through the night to continue with her search for a perfect life.

11

The snow had been relentless, with biting northern winds clawing at people's faces, making them red and weather-beaten. Snowdrifts were whipped into peaks along the wall tops, and sheep huddled underneath the walls in the belief that they would be safe from the weather, only to find themselves imprisoned in an icy snow grave, trapped until farmers came to free them, alerted by the frantic digging of their sheepdogs. The dale's human inhabitants huddled round their fireplaces, setting aside all thoughts of travel until such time as the blizzards should cease. The workers at Stone House sat in their quarters playing cards and dominoes, venturing out only to collect a few sprigs of holly for Christmas decorations and to curse the weather for stopping their work.

In the foreman's cottage, Will nursed his feverish sister, glad of the weather that covered her sin. Glad that no one suspected the terrible thing that his young sister had undergone, and that the weather would explain her absence from the manor. For four days she had drifted in and out of consciousness, mumbling incoherent phrases; the makeshift abortion had almost cost her her life. The morning of Christmas Eve found her coming out of her fever, able to sip some beef broth that Will gently fed her. After he'd finished spooning the salty, nourishing liquid into her, she laid her head down and dozed off again. Will sat by the bedroom fire, exhausted from worry and lack of sleep. For the first time since he was a small boy, he'd prayed. He prayed that his sister would be spared, that she wouldn't go to join the rest of the family and leave him all alone in the world. He prayed, too, for the soul of the baby whose life had been torn away before it had even begun. Then he sat watching the early grey glow of dawn filter slowly over the great hill of Whernside, and he wondered who the bairn's father was. Anger tearing at his insides, he swore that he would kill the bastard who'd got her in the family way and then paid her to get rid of it.

Alice stirred, gently calling his name: 'Will? Where are you? What day is it?' With her wet, matted hair and dark-rimmed eyes, she looked more dead than alive.

'Quiet now, our lass. You're all right. Mind, I thought I'd lost you for a while there.' He hugged her tight in his arms as she struggled to raise herself from the bed, face cringing with pain as she tried to prop herself up.

'I'm sorry, Will, I'm so sorry. I didn't want you to know. I'm so cold . . . I've been to a dark place in my dreams. I saw Mum and she told me to go back, that it was not my time yet. Will, I'm frightened. Did I die? If I did, I should be in the fires of hell for what I've done.' Alice grabbed her tearful brother's arm, pleading with him for answers. He stroked her damp hair and held her tight, helping her lie down again.

'Never you mind, Ali. What's done is done.

Let's get you better, eh? Go to sleep now. Tomorrow's Christmas Day and we're together; that's all that matters.'

He pulled the covers over her and waited until she had dozed off before getting up to add another log to the fire. Then he crept downstairs to prepare the chicken he had killed for Christmas Day. He had hoped that he would be celebrating Christmas in style this year, his first in his new home. But that would have to wait. Family mattered more, and Alice needed him; there would always be other Christmases.

* * *

'I could have done with that Alice. Trust it to snow and block her off from her work.' It was lunchtime at the manor, there were sauces and stuffings to be prepared, not to mention the huge goose to cook, and Mrs Dowbiggin was on her own. 'Stop standing like a useless lummock and help me set the table.' She was getting in a flap and poor Faulks was catching it. Though she couldn't speak of it to anyone, she was also worrying whether Alice was alive. Mrs Batty had told her the operation had been hard on the girl. 'Oh! Get out of the way. I can do better myself. Men — absolutely useless, no good for anything.'

Pushing the butler out of the way, she polished the cutlery on her apron, then arranged it to her satisfaction on the table. 'See, that's how you do it. There's no secret to it, is there?'

Faulks bit his tongue. It was no secret that Mrs Dowbiggin's husband had run off with a neighbour, but Faulks thought better of telling her he could understand why the man had done it. After all, it was Christmas.

The job done, Mrs Dowbiggin stepped back to admire her handiwork. 'I do love a well-set table.' She was never one to miss an opportunity to sing her own praises. 'Oh my Lord! Is that my soup?' She rushed out of the dining room as the smell of something burning assaulted her nose.

'Nice job, Faulks, very impressive.' Gerald Frankland strolled into the dining room and admired the Christmas table.

'Thank you, sir. It was nothing.' The butler smiled inwardly to himself at getting the praise that should have been Mrs Dowbiggin's. 'Would sir like an aperitif? And will Miss Nancy be joining you?'

'Damn, I think I will — just a small brandy. After all, it is Christmas. Nancy will be along shortly. Smells like Mrs Dowbiggin is going to surprise us with something exotic for lunch. Is Alice helping her today?'

'I believe not, sir. The snow has prevented her getting to work.' Faulks poured a brandy from the sparkling cut-glass decanter and passed it to his master.

'Pretty girl, don't you think, Faulks? I believe Jack has his eye on her. I'd say she was a bit too spirited for him. What do you think, Faulks?'

'I'm sorry, sir, I don't think it's my place to say.' Faulks bowed, then asked, 'Will that be all, sir?' Gerald Frankland's remarks made him uncomfortable and he wanted to escape, even if it meant returning to the hostile kitchen.

'Tell Mrs Dowbiggin that we will be eating at one. And this evening I may have some friends joining us, weather permitting. I'm sure she will conjure something up to delight my guests, even though there is no Alice to help her.' Frankland smiled. Leaning against the huge fireplace, glass in hand, he watched as the mealy-mouthed butler departed for the kitchen.

'Have you been tormenting our butler? I couldn't help but overhear your conversation. You are wicked, Gerald. No wonder you have such a terrible reputation!' Nancy entered the room and beckoned for her brother to pour her wine. Her maroon satin dress rustled as she sat in a chair in the window alcove overlooking the garden. 'You do realize the locals think this is a brothel? Alice told me so; she was quite embarrassed when I asked her what the locals thought of us.' She stared at her brother, smiling at his surprised expression.

'Me? I'm nothing but a gentleman! Can I be blamed if Faulks and Mrs Dowbiggin believe every word I say? I swear I laughed myself sick when Mrs Dowbiggin fell for my story about Mrs Batty — that old woman is the nearest thing to a witch that I've come across. I wouldn't take my dog to her, never mind a young woman in trouble. If they believe that, they'll believe anything.' He tilted his glass, savouring the last drop of brandy.

'One day, Gerald Frankland, you will get yourself in trouble with that sense of humour. You know all too well they believe every word you say and still you tell them tales.'

'My dear, let them believe what they will. No good comes to those who listen behind doors. Besides, they should know better.' He helped himself to another brandy and sat down next to his sister. Outside, a blanket of snow covered the grounds and turned the trees to sparkling white sculptures. 'A white wonderland on Christmas Day. Mind you, it's a bit of a hindrance. I don't think our friends will be joining us, so it will probably just be me and you tonight. There was some doubt as to whether they could make it even without the snow. The situation in Russia is taking a turn for the worse; Tatiana wrote to me the other day to say that the Tsar is not in touch with his people. Many are dying of hunger and there have been protests on the streets of Moscow.'

Gerald gazed out at the falling snow, remembering Moscow and his beautiful Tatiana. In his mind's eye he pictured the way she'd looked the first time he set eyes on her, when she was helping out in the hospital where Nancy had been treated. It was then he had fallen madly in love with his dark-eyed Russian, not knowing that she was a best friend to the daughters of the Tsar. Why couldn't he have loved a normal girl instead of one linked to the royal family of Russia?

'Gerald, you've given me an idea.' Nancy grabbed her brother's hand. 'You've got good contacts in Russia; Will's struggling up at Stone House. How about you sell one of your fireplaces to the Tsar? Now that would be something to talk about and it would get us noticed in this

165

godforsaken place. Imagine the respect those loutish workers would give Will then!'

'Have you listened to a word I've said, Nancy, my dear? Your head is so full of Will Bentham, you've no thought for my worries. And may I point out his absence this Christmas Day? Snow or no snow, I'd have thought that he'd at least have made the effort to see his employer and his beloved sister today.' He finished his second glass of brandy, swilling the last few dregs round the bowl of the glass before pouring himself another.

'Look at the weather — would you go out in this? Let him have one day away from work, Gerald. Will's tried really hard this last six months. He is turning things around for you at Stone House, you know he is.' Nancy offered her glass for a refill and smiled at her brother.

'You are sweet on him, aren't you, my dear. He's only a country bumpkin, you know. Can you imagine what Mama and Papa would have said if they'd caught their special girl going with a farmer's son? Easy with the wine, old girl. We don't want you tiddly before lunch — what would Mrs Dowbiggin say?' He gave her a wink then half filled her glass and handed it back to her.

'No wonder women are demanding the vote, Gerald Frankland. Any more comments like that and I've a good mind to join the suffragette movement. I'll drink as much as I like. Getting back to Will, I am sweet on him, it's true. He's good company, he treats me kindly, and he's not bothered by these terrible scars on my face. We are close.' Nancy blushed and took a deep drink.

Gerald shot her a dark look. 'Oh, don't be so stupid! He's not in our class. A common labourer is not fit for the likes of you. Besides, he's the first man you have really known. However, I will see what I can do regarding the Tsar. That's a good idea of yours — it would be quite something to have the Romanov seal of approval on our marble. I'll suggest it to Tatiana. You never know, it might get us both what we want.' He raised his glass. 'Cheers, old girl. Here's to love and prosperity: long may we have both. But keep away from common menfolk, eh?'

★ ★ ★

Alice tenderly propped herself up on the edge of the bed. Her legs felt like jelly and she couldn't stop shivering as if someone had just walked over her grave.

'There, our lass, slip your arm in here.' Gently Will helped dress his sister and then gave her his arm to lean on, helping her to the warm fireside. 'Not so fast. You're not ready to run the Derby yet,' he cautioned, putting his arm around her thin waist to steady her. 'We're going to have to fatten you up, our lass. There's nothing on you!'

Having gently seated her in the fireside chair, he threw another log on the fire and wrapped their mother's quilt around her to make sure that she was warm enough, before putting the kettle on to boil.

'Well, this is a queer Christmas Day compared to the ones we used to have. With last year's and this one, I'm beginning to doubt it will ever be the same. Remember how Father used to get merry on Mother's sloe gin? By this time, she'd have been playing pop with him for hindering dinner and then, nine times out of ten, he'd hug her and give her a kiss and she'd pretend to be mad with him, but really she was loving every minute. Can you remember, our Alice?'

Alice nodded wearily, feeling sad about times past. 'I'm sorry, Will, you'd probably have been at the manor now, or up at Jack's having dinner with them. And instead you're stuck with me. If I was you, I'd disown me — I've been nothing more than a prostitute, and now I've killed an innocent baby.'

'Quiet, our lass. No doubt you had your reasons. I'm not going to ask who the father is, because I'd only want to go and bloody shoot him, so it's best I don't know. Just promise me it isn't Jack's — although I know he's too much the gentleman for that. He'd have married you if he'd have known you were in the family way. Anyways, as long as you recover and we still have one another, that's all that matters. Because, by God, we've been through enough this year.' He picked up the singing kettle and filled the teapot, stirring it thoughtfully.

Alice wrapped the quilt tightly around her. 'It wasn't Jack's. And you're right: it's best you don't know whose it was, because it would only cause trouble. Don't worry, Will, I feel weak, but I've learned my lesson. Next year I intend to start fending for myself — 1914 is going to be our year, the year when we both prove to each other that we are strong.'

'That's right, Ali — come back fighting! Here, have a sup of your tea and I'll see to dinner. Mother must be laughing her head off up in heaven at my attempt to cook, but I'm determined to have a Christmas dinner of some kind. I've peeled the sprouts and tatties, and the chicken's in the side oven — it may be a bit late, but we'll eat sometime today.'

'You're doing grand. Thanks for taking care of me, Will; I'm so grateful. There's many would have turned their backs on me.' Alice hung her head, gripped by self-loathing.

'Give over, Sis. Now, get your tea drunk and stop feeling sorry for yourself. Listen, I think I can hear the men up at the quarry huts singing — it must be bloody Christmas after all!'

The faint sound of carols filtered into the little cottage, bringing hope and Christmas spirit to the exhausted pair. The roasting chicken and the warmth of the fire set Alice dozing while Will listened to the melodies of his workforce. He didn't know what the next year would bring, but surely it couldn't be as bad as the last one. He prayed for it not to be.

12

'So, Alice, you've made it back to us.' Gerald Frankland contemplated the gaunt, ashen young girl. 'You look ill, Alice. Are you feeling all right? Mrs Dowbiggin informs me that you have had the flu. I hope that you have recovered sufficiently?' He turned and gazed out of the library window.

'I'm recovering slowly, sir, but I'm fit for work. Besides, I wouldn't want to let Miss Nancy down, especially for tonight's New Year Ball.' Alice quickly finished tidying the hearth and turned to make her escape from his questioning eyes.

'Surely you are joining us tonight, Alice? Nancy has been insisting that you must. She would really enjoy your company and I'm sure she has a spare dress you could wear. God knows I've bought her enough dresses, so there's bound to be something suitable, not that I know much about these frivolous things. What do you say, eh? A few dance steps might put a bit of colour in those pale cheeks.'

'I don't think so, sir. I'd feel out of place.' Alice's heart fluttered. She had long dreamed of the moment when she would be asked to the manor's New Year Ball, but she still felt a little unsteady and faint.

'Nonsense! Your Will's invited, so you can keep him company. I'll speak to my sister, see if she

170

can find you something to fit. I'm sure you will enjoy yourself. It'll be nice to see some sparkle in those blue eyes again.'

Gerald Frankland turned from the window to watch as Alice left the room, her cheeks flushed from his last comment. She didn't seem at all well and he wanted to show his concern. Moreover he knew his sister would feel more relaxed with her protégé by her side.

Alice closed the door behind her and leaned against it, brush and pan full of swept embers in her hands. Could she really summon the strength to attend the ball? The mind was willing, but her body felt so weak . . . Yes, she resolved. No matter how poorly she felt, it had to be done.

* * *

'Oh! Alice, you look absolutely beautiful! That shade of blue really suits you; it brings out the colour of your eyes. Here, let me tie the bow tighter to show your waist off.' Nancy studied her companion. 'A bit of rouge on those pale cheeks and then you'll be perfect.'

Alice peered at her reflection, gasping at the sight of herself. The long sky-blue satin dress made her appear tall and slender, while her blonde hair — pinned up with the dragonfly comb that had been her birthday gift — gave her extra height. She almost didn't recognize the woman in the mirror. A fortnight ago, she had been near death and now here she was, attending the dale's largest social event. She smoothed the dress over her thighs and turned sideways to admire the perfectly formed figure. Secretly she couldn't help but be astounded: what had happened to the ugly duckling that she had once been?

'Doesn't Alice look beautiful?' Nancy sighed as her brother entered the room. Alice turned to see Gerald Frankland admiring her, as Nancy clapped her hands in glee at the transformation she'd brought about.

'Now I've two beautiful ladies to accompany me tonight. Alice, you're simply stunning. Heads will certainly turn when you take to the dance floor. As they will when you do, Nancy, my dear.' Gerald kissed his sister tenderly on the cheek. 'Will certainly does not deserve two such lovely ladies. I hope you tell him so, Nancy.'

He smiled and made his way to the door. He'd known Alice was pretty, but this was a revelation. Never had he seen such a perfect creature. The blue dress reflected her eyes, and her hair shone with the Fabergé comb, delicately placed at an angle. If only she was better bred! He didn't mind his sister showing an interest in Will, provided that was all it was; the thought of the relationship getting any deeper was beyond belief. A working-class man and a lady, it didn't bear thinking about! However, with it being common knowledge among their tight circle that Nancy had inherited their mother's weaknesses, it was unlikely that anybody of their own class would take an interest in his younger sister. And at least Will was making her happy. Gerald, on the other hand, could not form an attachment with someone just because she made him happy; it would have to be someone with class, someone to carry on the family name, not a common working-class girl.

'Ladies, I'll see you downstairs. Nancy, don't forget to circulate — we are the hosts, after all, and don't you spend all night with Will!'

'I won't. But some of the guests are so stuffy, Gerald. Do I really have to talk to everyone?'

'Everyone, Nancy. It's expected of us.' Gerald wagged his finger at his complaining sister as he left the room.

'Boring fuddy-duddy,' Nancy complained as she sat heavily on the edge of her bed.

Alice gave herself another glance in the mirror, still amazed at her reflection, then went to close the heavy curtains. When she got to the window, she stopped and urged Nancy to join her. The moon was rising, clear and glimmering white, its smiling face beaming down upon the manor. The sky was purple and pink with hues of the dying day foretelling of the hard frost that was going to cover the dale through the night. The snow twinkled in the moonlight, like scatterings of millions of diamonds, making the view magical.

'Isn't it beautiful? Like something out of a fairy tale. Let's hope that tonight we meet our princes; then it would truly be a wonderful night.' Nancy squeezed Alice's hand.

The two young women made their way down the stairs and into the hallway, their dresses rustling with the weight of material. Nancy's jewellery sparkled in the light as they reached the doorway. The strains of the Beresford Band could be heard throughout the manor, and holly, mistletoe and ivy adorned the hall and adjoining rooms, while log fires burned brightly in the hearths.

'Alice, go warm yourself by the fire and listen to the band while I welcome our guests.' Nancy patted Alice's hand and ushered her into the large ballroom, which had chairs all around the sides for guests who wanted a rest from dancing. The band was in the far corner of the hall, playing the latest refrains.

Leaning against the fireplace in his best suit and with his hair smoothed back was Jack. As Alice entered he looked up from warming his hands and for a moment or two stood gaping at her, lost for words, as she crossed the dance floor, smiling gently at him.

'By God, you scrub up real well, Alice Bentham.' Taken aback by her beauty, Jack had momentarily forgotten where he was.

'Thank you. You're not so bad yourself. No one told me you'd be here; it's a surprise to see you.' Alice bowed her head sheepishly: she hadn't forgotten that last time she had spoken to him, she had been sharp with her words, something that she'd been regretting ever since she said them.

'Aye, well, I came in my father's place. He's not so good — the rheumatics are playing up in this cold weather. By heck, I'm glad I did come, just to see you all dressed up like you are.' Jack grinned and then blushed.

'Jack, I'm really sorry. I was being selfish and self-centred when I lost my temper. I acted like a

174

spoilt school girl. Can you ever forgive me?' She gazed bashfully at Jack. For once she was willing to admit that she'd been in the wrong; if Jack was saving up for something, it was none of her business.

'It's forgotten. Come on, let's help ourselves to a glass of the punch. I've had my eye on it ever since I came in, but didn't want to help myself.'

He held his arm out for Alice to take, which she did, smiling at easy-going Jack. How she'd missed him, if only as a friend. He was very special to her.

* * *

The room was full of Dales people enjoying celebrating New Year's Eve, wishing better fortunes to everyone for the coming year. The band played while everyone danced, drank or chatted, the ballroom alive with noise and laughter. At the stroke of midnight, everyone joined in a large circle, standing next to the one they loved, and sang 'Auld Lang Syne', their cheerful faces welcoming the new year in. Alice held Jack's hand as she rushed backwards and forwards with the crowds to the chorus, Jack admiring every move she made. Then, when the song ended, Jack held her tight around the waist and kissed her passionately, whispering, 'Happy New Year,' and telling her how much he loved her.

Burying her face in his shoulder, Alice tried to hide the tears that were running down her cheeks, as she murmured her best wishes for the

175

new year. But, try as she might, she could not bring herself to tell Jack that she loved him. She wasn't sure: her heart told her one thing and her head another. Jack was many a girl's dream, but he wasn't enough for her. She needed something more than to be a farmer's wife, she needed to see the world and have fun.

Jack lifted her chin and gave her a tender kiss, trying to get the response he needed to hear. She smiled fondly at him, trying not to hurt his feelings, knowing what he was expecting, but unable to say the words. Relief swept over her as Gerald Frankland saved her from the awkward situation by tapping Jack on the shoulder and requesting the next dance with Alice. Jack hesitantly released Alice into the hands of her employer, who immediately took command of the dance floor, sweeping her off her feet as they waltzed round the ballroom.

'Sorry, I thought you needed saving from Jack.' Gerald Frankland spoke quietly as they danced. 'He looked a bit intense and you appeared to be uncomfortable.' He smiled at Alice, who was feeling safe and secure in his arms, unaware of the interest people were showing in the couple as they glided round the room.

'I think he got carried away with the night, that's all.' Alice smiled, spotting Jack in the crowd watching the woman he loved dancing with the lord of the manor. He was taking a long sip from a glass of punch. Next time Alice turned to see him, he'd gone, making her anxious to know where he was but at the same time less nervous of dancing with her new partner.

The night flew by as the couple danced on, making all the locals gossip at the unlikely alliance of commoner and lord. By the time the clock struck two, the ballroom was beginning to empty and Alice was exhausted, nearly collapsing in his arms at the end of their last dance together.

'My poor girl, I've worn you out. You dance so perfectly and I've enjoyed your company so much, I forgot that you've been ill. Forgive me. Here, let me help you up the stairs.' Gerald Frankland unthinkingly offered to carry his dance partner to her room.

'Please, I think we have caused enough scandal tonight, without the lord of the manor carrying me to my room in front of his guests. I'll make my own way, thank you.'

Alice's cheeks were flushed with embarrassment and the excitement of the evening. She had loved every minute, but she didn't want to be the cause of further talk. Shakily she made her way up the stairs and into her bedroom. Heart racing, she lay down on the bed, thoughts of Jack and Lord Frankland racing through her mind. She whispered, 'Gerald,' under her breath, and then her conscience kicked in with thoughts of poor Jack and his confession of love for her. No, she must not think or even fantasize about her employer; she should be true to Jack . . . Giggling quietly to herself, she kicked her shoes off and admired herself yet again in the mirror before stepping out of the borrowed dress and into her nightclothes. Best foot forward, she told herself. This was only the start of the year: 1914, a new year brimming with hope and the love of Jack and the longing glances of Gerald Frankland. Now, which one did she want?

★ ★ ★

'He did what? Over my dead body.' Gerald Frankland was fuming, raising his voice at the breakfast table.

'But, Gerald, I've said yes. I love him, truly I do, and he loves me.' Nancy Frankland pleaded with her brother.

'Will Bentham had no right to ask you to marry him, not without my permission. For God's sake, has the man no manners? You must tell him no, say that I have forbidden it. On second thoughts, never mind — I'll tell him myself. I'll go up to Stone House later this morning. He needs to know he can't simply propose like that — and to do it in our stable after trying to take advantage of my little sister!' Gerald Frankland sliced into his ham and eggs with the fervour of an outraged man.

'So it's all right for you to show yourself up, dancing all night with Alice, but it's not all right for me to accept a proposal from the man I love. No matter how lowly his roots, Gerald, I do love him.' Nancy stood her ground.

'Damn it, woman, it was a bit of fun with a servant, nothing more. I'm not like you, about to lose all status for a bit of rough.' Gerald spat out the words. His head was throbbing from hitting

178

the wine after his guests had departed.

All night his mind had been on the young woman who was sleeping under his roof, and he'd had to fight the impulse to go and knock on her bedroom door in the hope that she'd let him in. Then to top it all, Nancy had come to the breakfast table with news of her engagement to Will. He slammed his knife and fork down.

'Bloody hell, old girl, he's as common as muck. Still, if you love him, we'll have to do something about it. But believe me, Alice was just a bit of fun, someone to dance with in place of darling Tatiana — you know how much I miss her.'

Nancy rose from her seat, put her arm around Gerald and gently kissed his cheek. 'He makes me happy. Please accept that. I don't care if he's no money. And, Gerald, don't shout: Alice is only in the kitchen. You wouldn't want to upset your new sister-in-law now, would you? Love you, sweetie. You'll see, he will make me so happy.'

'Yes, we'll see. This last twelve-month does seem to have revolved round one or other of the Benthams. If you love him, we'll have to do something about it, I suppose. I can't go on ignoring this stupid fancy, but even though he did save my life, I don't agree with the match and never will. At least I know he's honourable, though. So I'll go and see him. And yes, to help him win respect, I'll conjure up an important order for him and that dratted marble works. Anything to make you happy. Now, leave me in peace with my breakfast. I've a thumping headache and I can't do with you sounding so happy around me.'

Gerald grunted and stirred his coffee as he watched his sister gaily running from the room. He wasn't happy, but he'd have to live with it.

* * *

'Well, I don't know what the world's coming to! A farm labourer marrying our Miss Nancy, it's just not right. He might be in charge of the marble works now, but that means nothing. Mr Gerald was only being right with him after that incident with the fire — and he even caused that.' Mrs Dowbiggin stirred the pan of soup, her back to Faulks, complaining about the proposal.

'Too true, Mrs Dowbiggin. I agree with your every word. Things are definitely not like what they used to be. And I'll tell you something else: his lordship is sweet on Alice. You know there was a time you expected your employer to take advantage of a good-looking servant discreetly, on the quiet. Not to dance with her in front of all and sundry. That's not on!' Faulks spat on the shoes he was polishing and brushed with vigour until he saw them shine.

'Quite so, Mr Faulks. Standards are slipping. I blame it on these suffragettes. A woman should know her place: in the kitchen, in the bedroom and married to someone of her own class. There's too much rubbish about equal rights. It hurts me to say this, but men will always be superior. Still, never mind. As long as Miss Nancy's happy, there's nothing we can do but

180

plan for a wedding. I heard Master Gerald saying he was going up to Stone House today, so he might be talking Will Bentham out of it.' She stirred the soup and added salt before trying it.

'What's Master Gerald talking our Will out of?' Alice entered the kitchen. 'What's my brother been up to now?'

'Oh, my dear — I didn't realize you were there. I don't think it's my place to say. You should hear it from your brother first,' Mrs Dowbiggin spluttered as the hot soup burned her lip.

Faulks quickly excused himself, pretending that the shoes he had been polishing were urgently needed. He wanted no part of the cross-examination Mrs Dowbiggin was about to be subjected to.

'What do you mean? You obviously know something I don't, so go on, tell me: what's he been up to?' Alice stood her ground, holding the back of the chair and rising to her full height to slightly intimidate the gossiping housekeeper.

'Well, my dear, I overheard Miss Nancy talking to Master Gerald this morning. It seems your brother proposed to her last night and they're getting married. Miss Nancy is to be your sister-in-law! Now, isn't that grand?' Mrs Dowbiggin watched Alice's face as she absorbed the news. 'I thought that would take the wind out of your sails. I'd have thought one of them would have told you first, but then you were a little busy yourself last night . . . '

'The stupid bloody idiot! What does he think he's doing?' Alice pulled out the chair and sat down, running her fingers through her long hair.

'We'll have none of that language in my kitchen, my girl. But yes, that's what I thought about Miss Nancy. No disrespect, but she is marrying well below her station. Anyway, I've said enough; it's not for me to comment. You know me, I mind my own business, keep myself to myself.' And with that she scurried off to the pantry.

Alice sat at the table, trying to get to grips with the news. Will getting married to Nancy . . . Where would they live? What would become of her? And most of all, how could he afford the wedding that Nancy dreamed of? Oh, why hadn't he talked to her first? She felt hurt and left out. She'd thought she was best friend to both of them, yet they'd not let her into their secret. Even the housekeeper knew before her! How could they? Just how could they!

★ ★ ★

'Alice! I'm so glad that you are here. I wanted to tell you the news, but by the time I came in from talking to Will, you had gone to bed. Alice, I'm going to get married to your brother. Isn't that fantastic news! Can you believe it? He proposed to me last night. My heart's all aflutter. Tell me that you are happy for us — do say you are happy. To think that you are to be my sister-in-law! I still can't believe it — pinch me, I think I'm dreaming.'

'Congratulations, Miss Nancy.' Alice's voice was cold, without sentiment.

182

'Oh, Alice, we are going to be so happy. To think that only last year I was convinced that life held nothing for me, and now I'm about to be married. And to make things even better, Gerald is setting up an order for the marble works from the Tsar of Russia! I suspect he will be the next to announce his engagement. You know he's in love with Tatiana, who's in the Tsar's circle of close friends? He's been waiting for her to come of age, and then I'm sure they will be married. I'm so happy.' Nancy smiled and composed herself on the edge of her bed.

'Master Gerald's to be engaged! I didn't know.' Alice could hear herself nearly scream the words.

'Well, not quite yet, but it wouldn't surprise me. They have been close for a while now. Isn't it exciting, all this romance? We will have to get you and Jack together, and then that would make us all happy.'

Nancy carried on prattling happily, but Alice didn't hear a word. She was thinking that, considering it was still only the first day of January, the new year was not treating her kindly. First she'd discovered that her brother had kept her in the dark, and now it turned out that the man she was beginning to admire and have feelings for was virtually betrothed — to a Russian royal, of all people. Why had she even thought she was in his league? He'd been toying with her. She should have realized that behind those smouldering eyes was a menacing, brothel-keeping ogre. A man who was playing games with her. Yet when she looked into his eyes, her legs turned to jelly. Why couldn't life go smoothly? How was it that Will had it all on a plate: never worked hard, gave enough blarney to get by on and everything fell at his feet?

'Of course, Alice, you will still be my companion, won't you? This should make us closer. Alice, Alice, are you listening to me?' The voice was like a distant echo as Alice automatically tidied and put away Nancy's clothes while her mind was racing with all the news.

'Sorry, Nancy, yes, of course I will. I just don't think you will need my services for much longer.' Alice thought that it was best if she tackled her position first.

'Nonsense. I'll need you even more, especially when Will and I have children . . . although the doctors have warned me it could be dangerous for me to bear children. But what do they know? I want to be a mother like my dear mama, perhaps having three or four darling babies. I'm sure Will is going to make a most perfect father; he has so much patience.' Nancy sat in her morning chair, face rosy and happy, wishing nothing more than to be married as soon as possible to the man of her dreams.

'I'm sorry, Nancy, please excuse me — I'm feeling a little faint. I must have tired myself out last night with dancing. Your brother is very light on his feet and I got carried away with the grandeur of the occasion.' Alice had heard all she could take of Nancy's plans, and in truth she was slightly jealous.

She went downstairs and out of the grand

front door — the same door that only a few months ago she had been brazen enough to knock on, having no idea then of her place in life. Lifting her skirts, she carefully made her way through the snow, shivering in the cold and wishing that she had picked up a shawl before hurrying out in need of some breathing space. The air was curiously still and not a noise could be heard all down the dale. It was as if there were no other souls on the planet, only Alice, alone in her grief.

Once in the stables, she called for Jack. She didn't think he'd be there; if what Mrs Dowbiggin said was correct, he'd probably have taken Lord Frankland to Stone House. Not a sound: good, she was on her own, exactly what she wanted. She needed time to think things out. She walked past the stalls with the horses munching content on their hay bags or oats, the smell of the animals comforting, reminding her of home. She stopped and stroked the nose of her favourite horse; blowing up its nose to make friends with the creature was a trick her father had taught her. The horse snorted, enjoying the attention as she gave it a handful of oats.

'I don't know, lad, what am I going to do? Nothing seems to be going right for me.' She hugged the horse's neck, expecting no response but feeling better for something to talk to that wouldn't answer back. 'Why does everything go wrong, lad? I've no parents, no real home, and I've just got rid of my baby — poor mite, it had not hurt anyone — and now my brother's lost his senses and is getting married to someone he doesn't really love. And then there's Jack. I know he loves me, but he could do a lot better than me because he's a good man. I don't really love him. I know who I do love, but I can't have him and never will.' The horse munched and gazed at her with its big doe eyes, shaking its head as if in agreement. 'I know, lad, you can't answer me, but I needed to talk to someone.' She patted its neck. Shivering, she folded her arms tight around her, then set off back to the manor.

Up in the hayloft Jack stared at the oak beams, lying on the makeshift bed he used when keeping vigil over a foaling mare. He'd heard every word Alice had said and now he realized it was no good. Whose baby had she been carrying? Whoever the baby belonged to, it was no longer . . . How could she? He would have looked after her, cared for her and the baby, if only she'd said . . . She had broken his heart, if she only knew it. Still, he was going to show her. In another month or two he'd be a man of property. The Alderson family owning two farms in the dale — perhaps that would turn her head.

★ ★ ★

'Now, Will, I understand you proposed to my sister last night. Did you not realize there is such a thing as protocol? I should have been informed of your decision before you asked for Nancy's hand. Do you really think that she is the right woman for you? And how are you going to keep her in the manner she is accustomed to?'

As he waited for an answer, Gerald studied his

soon-to-be brother-in-law. He quite admired the fellow, but Nancy could have done so much better if her reputation and appearance had been up to standard.

'We'll manage, Master Gerald. I do truly love and care for her, and I'm sorry I didn't realize that I had to ask for your blessing first.'

Will had expected this visit all morning and had dreaded it. Of course he had realized he should have asked Gerald Frankland's permission first, but he wasn't about to tell him that. He had known that once Nancy said yes, her brother wouldn't dare say no. He'd been counting on the fact that Gerald would do anything to make her happy.

'Well, I don't know, Will Bentham. I always wanted her to marry someone titled, but true to form, my sister has to go and fall in love with a hired man. No house, not a great deal of money and no title does not place you very high in my society. However, if you truly love her, I can't stand in the way. She deserves some happiness in her life. There's not been a great deal of that since our parents died.' He sat, crossing his long legs, and studied the perplexed face of his employee. 'Now, financial matters, of which my sister knows nothing: she receives a yearly allowance of five thousand pounds from our parents' estate. This is paid into my bank account at the moment; of course, it will be transferred to yours once you have become man and wife. I'm also prepared to transfer the deeds to the marble works to you as my wedding present, which would give you this cottage to live in as your secure home. What's more, I'm in the process of finalizing an order that will give you a great deal of prestige in society — I'll tell you more of that shortly. Now, how does that sound? In return, I want you to promise to look after her. My sister's needs must come first.' Gerald Frankland searched Will's face, trying to read his reaction.

'I don't know what to say, Lord Frankland,' said Will, dumbstruck. 'I didn't expect all that. I just wanted the hand of Nancy. Truly, there is no need for your generosity. And, yes, I will put her before my own life always.'

'In that case, Will, welcome to the family. You must call me Gerald from now on. The one proviso I have is that you must make it a discreet wedding. St John's, I think, not Dent parish church; she wouldn't want everyone gawping at her. She still thinks people look at her as if she were a monster. And then a small reception back at the manor. What do you say. That all right?'

'I don't know what to say, except thank you. I hadn't even planned that far ahead. It's all happening so fast.'

Inside, Will was ecstatic. All that money! He couldn't believe it. And the marble works! He wanted to yell for joy, but knew he had to keep it reined in, at least until Gerald Frankland had gone.

'Well, get on with it, man. One more thing. You might need these — they were Nancy's mother's.' Gerald Frankland reached into his inside pocket and pulled out a ring box containing a diamond-encrusted engagement ring and a wedding ring. 'They will mean a great deal to her.' Shaking Will's hand, he passed the box to him. 'Good luck, old man. Make her happy.' He patted Will on the back and then left him in a state of shock and ecstasy.

All that money! Not in a million years had he dreamed of owning all this and having money as well. Small price to pay for marrying a scarred, spoilt bitch. Hopefully their night of passion in the stable would have sealed the deal. He hoped that she was pregnant; then there would be no way of getting out of the forthcoming wedding. Yes, things were definitely on the turn for Will Bentham. Why, he was almost related to nobility now.

* * *

'Master Gerald needs to see you in the study, Alice. He's back from Stone House — don't know if it's good news or bad news, but he's going through his papers. His desk is in a right mess.' Mrs Dowbiggin placed the tea tray on the table and sighed.

'He wants to see me? Did he say what for, and do you think it's urgent?' Alice quickly checked her hair in the small kitchen mirror.

'How would I know? I'm more bothered about my lumbago — it is giving me jip. Besides, I'm not told anything any more. I've worked for this family more than twenty-five years and I'm not told nothing.' She rattled the dirty teapots in the sink and turned away from Alice, muttering to herself.

Alice smiled. In the study on her own with Gerald . . . perhaps there was hope. She pinched her cheeks and checked her dress; she wanted to look her best.

'Ah! Alice, do come in.' Gerald Frankland fixed Alice with a penetrating gaze, gently rocking in his office chair. 'So, what are we to do? My sister is to marry your brother. Neither can be talked out of it . . . Which leaves me with a predicament: what am I to do with you?'

Alice's face dropped a mile. Was she going to be told to go, to make her own way in the world? She couldn't bear that her life was so hard.

'If we are soon to be related through marriage, we can't have you working for us any more. That would not be correct; family and servants should remain separate. However, it's obvious that my sister adores you, so provided you are in agreement I propose that you leave your brother's cottage and move into the manor. You will occupy one of the good spare bedrooms and eat your meals with us — after all, we can't have you telling Mrs Dowbiggin all our news around that kitchen table, can we? In return, you must offer Nancy your devoted friendship, help her plan her wedding, go shopping with her, do whatever it is that you women get up to in your spare time. I've told your brother this morning that Stone House is to be his marital home and I am now in the process of signing the whole works and cottage over to him. Your brother will be a rich man, if he plays his cards right. I'm also willing to give you a small allowance, just to help while you are living with us. I want to make everything above board; you know how people talk. So, what do you think, Alice? Does that sound agreeable to you?'

Speechless, Alice could only nod.

He reached across the desk to shake her hand. 'In that case, welcome to the family. I promise that as long as Nancy is happy we will see that you are looked after.'

Tears of happiness in her eyes, Alice shook his hand. Being part of the Frankland family was something she had dreamed about since those early days when she had toyed with the idea of marrying sultry Lord Frankland and becoming mistress of Whernside Manor.

'What are you waiting for? Go and choose which bedroom you want. I'd choose the blue room myself: it catches all the sunlight in the morning. Faulks will help you move your possessions. And, Alice, I enjoyed our few dances last night. Perhaps we can dance together more often, now we are to be related.'

Gerald smiled as he saw the tears again welling up in Alice's eyes before she turned and hurried from the room. He'd always had her down as a fighter; something must have laid her spirits low. Perhaps it was the Christmas period. Everyone missed departed loved ones at Christmas and New Year; it had been years since his own parents died, but he still felt their absence. She would soon cheer up now that she had been relieved of worries about money and work and where to live.

Nancy had made it clear that she wanted Alice to be part of the wedding package. Who'd hav thought it, after their first encounter? He smiled to himself at the memory of Alice holding her own against the sneering staff and his raging sister. She'd spoken her mind, too full of pride to be cowed by them. Funny old world: he'd travelled the globe, yet he never felt more relaxed than when he gazed into the cornflower-blue eyes of his soon-to-be sister-in-law.

★ ★ ★

Alice leaned against the closed study door. Had she heard right? Was she now part of the family? Was Gerald really signing the cottage and marble works over to Will? If so, all their worries were over. In the space of an hour, she had gone from abject despair to elation. A proper home, with money and good food. And she'd be looking across the dining table every day at the man of her dreams. This really was going to be the year all her wishes came true.

When she got to the kitchen, however, she was soon brought down to earth by the sight of Mrs Dowbiggin and Faulks in secretive discussion.

'I don't think you should be with us. Faulks has told me the scenario. You'll be thinking yourself better than us now. Never in all my days have I heard anything so scandalous! Take heed, my girl: no good will come of this. If I were you, I'd lock my door on a night and warn that brother of yours what he's really taken on. He'll earn every penny he's got out of Master Gerald; you can tell him that from me.'

192

'I don't believe it's any of your business, Mrs Dowbiggin. It's between my brother and Lord Frankland — or Gerald, as I'm to call him from now on.' Alice smiled. Now that it had finally sunk in that she had no more worries, she couldn't resist a bit of mischief while at the same time putting the stuffy housekeeper in her place.

'Well, you've changed your colours! The pair of you have worked your way into this family and now you're going to drag it into the gutter. Well, it'll be over my dead body that you harm this family. Nancy was best off left alone in her bedroom with her memories and us to take care of her — no harm would have come to her then.' Mrs Dowbiggin took the copper pan that she'd been waving at Alice as if she wanted to clout her with it and put it on the pan rack.

'Mrs Dowbiggin, please. I've always confided in you, and the only thing my brother has done wrong is fall in love with someone out of his class. Is that such a sin? Please, we all have to live and work together, and I don't want any bad feeling between us. I'm truly grateful for everything that everyone's done for me these last few months. I'll never forget your help, especially.' Alice squeezed the chubby red arm of her accuser with affection. 'I'm lucky, Mrs Dowbiggin, but I'll never forget where I came from and who helped me get this far. All I ask is that you wish Will and Nancy luck. Because, as you say, they are going to need it. Moreover, I'm going to need your help. I've so much to learn — I don't want to let the family down.' Alice smiled at the blustering housekeeper and hoped that she'd smoothed her ruffled feathers.

'Aye, well, we'll see. But it's still a rum carry-on.' Mrs Dowbiggin threw her tea towel roughly over her shoulder. 'And I don't know what this useless lump's gawping at — he's supposed to be moving you into your new room.' She deftly flicked the end of the tea towel at Faulks, who up till then had stood on the sidelines, saying nothing.

'Don't bring me into your petty argument. Unlike some, I know my place and keep my thoughts to myself. And kindly refrain from using that tea towel upon my personage.' Faulks rose from his chair. 'Which room is to be yours, Miss Alice? Are we to move your belongings now or later?'

' 'Miss Alice' — listen to you! She's Alice, you big galoot,' Mrs Dowbiggin mumbled to herself.

'She is now Miss Alice to me, as I will have to remember when we are in public. Now, which room did Master Gerald want you to have, Miss Alice?' Faulks's face was sombre. Mrs Dowbiggin may not have realized it yet, but changes were afoot at the manor and he had every intention of keeping abreast of the times.

'The blue room, Faulks. And thank you for helping me move my few possessions.' Alice smiled at the poker-faced butler; perhaps he was not so bad. Mrs Dowbiggin bullied him something terrible, and yet he never so much as batted an eyelid.

'Good choice by Master Gerald — it gets all the morning sun. Follow me and we will see to it

194

straight away, Miss Alice.'

'Stuffy old cock,' Mrs Dowbiggin muttered as the pair moved out of the kitchen. 'No good will come of this day, you mark my words.'

13

'You've certainly come off well with my forthcoming marriage, Sis. I'm still in shock myself. I can't believe how much comes with our dear Nancy. Hard to believe no one else has picked her up with her being worth all that money.' Will Bentham sat in his usual fireside seat, his shoes practically smoking from the warmth of the fire as he rested them on the trivet. 'She's worth a mint! We'll never want for a penny.'

'Everything comes at a price, our Will. Do you really know what you've taken on? I can't help but think there's something wrong. A woman of her standing should not be marrying one of us. I don't want to see any one of us hurt — I've had enough hurt lately to last me a lifetime.' Alice took her cloak off and sat in the chair next to her brother.

'Give over — we're made! You're always looking at the downside, you are. Here you are living in the fancy house you've always dreamed of, and here's me with my own business, a wife that'll adore me and a nice income — what more can we wish for? All we need to do now is find you a fellow from the snooty circles you'll be moving in and then we've cracked it.' Will grinned at his sister as she played with her fur-trimmed gloves. 'I see you've been spending their money already: new gloves, dress and cloak.

That lot must have cost a pretty penny.'

'Nancy said I'd to have them when we went to Kendal the other week. She had a fitting for her wedding dress and while we were there she insisted I should have a new dress and cloak. I don't know how much they cost: it was all billed to the manor.' Alice fumbled with the gloves, embarrassed. She had thought that she would enjoy having clothes bought for her and being treated like a lady, but in all honesty, she wasn't comfortable in her new position. She was neither one thing nor the other, with no purpose in life other than being companion to Nancy. She had also felt extremely uncomfortable when the dressmaker measured her, eyeing her up and down, making her feel like something on the bottom of her shoe. Nancy had assured her that the woman was only doing her job and not to be so silly. But still she felt unworthy of the quality material that was being draped on her.

'Well, we'll have to find you somebody, 'cos I see you and Jack have fallen out, else he wouldn't have had Amy Lawson on his arm in the Moon the other night. Can't say I blame him, like. She is a bonny bit of a thing.' He smiled, remembering Jack giving Amy a kiss outside the pub's entrance.

'I . . . I didn't know Jack had found someone else. Is she all right, this Amy? I don't think I know her.' Alice was taken aback. She knew Jack had been avoiding her, but she thought that he would have had the decency to tell her that they'd finished and that he had moved on. She missed Jack's company; he was a best friend who always made everything all right, no matter how bad things were. How she wished that he were still friends with her, just for company and for someone to talk to and share her concerns with.

''Course you know her; she's from Bridge End. Her father once sold us a bull — queer old bloke, said he'd come and do the job himself if his bull didn't perform. She's probably like her father. Knowing Jack, he'll be going at it like a rabbit up in that bed over the stables!' Will grinned, oblivious to the hurt he was causing his sister.

'Don't be so vulgar, our Will! Besides, there is no bedroom at the stables, so he won't be doing any such thing.'

'There bloody well is! He uses it when he's got a broody mare or when he wants a bit of peace and quiet, so that nobody knows he's there. Funny bugger, I've often shouted for him at the stable door with no reply, only to find him laying low up in that hayloft, not wanting to talk to anyone. Come to think of it, you two are a lot alike. He goes up in his loft, and you go up the fell. Funny buggers, the pair of you.'

'I didn't know he had a room up there.' Alice now knew why Jack had been avoiding her. He'd been there in his hidey-hole the day when she was upset and talked to his horse. No wonder he was avoiding her like the plague. She had thought it was because of her new position at the manor; she should have known better. Jack wasn't like that. One day she'd tell him the truth, but not yet. 'I hope he'll be happy with Amy. Me and him just weren't meant to be.'

'Come on, our lass, cheer up. Bloody hell, you're hard work today! Another few months and it's my wedding. What do you think our folks would say? I'll never forget that evening when Gerald Frankland brought Father home. God, the old man was drunk. That's when all this started, if you think about it.'

Alice tried to rally her spirits with thoughts of the wedding. For all her faults, Nancy was a good woman who was in love with Will. 'So have you got a new suit? And who's to be your best man? You know I'm your matron of honour, don't you?' Alice grinned at her brother. 'Don't tell me, let me guess: it's Jack, isn't it? I can't understand why none of their family is coming, not even any of Gerald's friends. It's going to be a quiet affair, because there's not many of our side still standing.'

'Never mind, Sis, we'll all be there that counts. As long as I get a ring on her finger, that's all that matters. Don't worry, I'll tell Jack not to rub your nose in it with his latest conquest. I know you think a lot of him really.' He winked. He'd noticed how upset she'd been when he joked about Jack and Amy, but it would never have worked between Alice and Jack. Too much to handle, was his sister. She'd soon have got bored with his steady best friend.

'Don't care if he does. I've got other fish to fry.' Alice wasn't going to let her brother's words hurt her. Besides, when it came to Jack, she was the one who had done all the hurt; she deserved everything she got. But she was damned if she was going to let her brother know that.

199

'That's it, lass — don't let the buggers grind you down. No matter how bad it gets, keep on fighting, else they've won and that's not what life's about. What's made you come up here today to visit, then? No lords or ladies to entertain or take high tea with?'

'Gerald's going through his tenancies for the year. There'll be tenants going in and out of his office all day today. I thought it would be better if I made myself scarce. We're the talk of the dale as it is, without me being there to add to the gossip. Imagine the embarrassment if Father's friends saw me strutting about, dressed to the nines, when they'd come cap in hand to keep their homes for another year.'

'But we've done nothing wrong, Alice. We've only taken what was on offer to us and made the best of a bad situation. Come on, lass, it's what you've always wanted: big house, good clothes, full belly — a lot more than we've had in the past.'

'You don't understand. We have all the material things that we ever needed, but I realize now it's not them that's important. It's knowing who you are, being your own person and having your freedom. I love being part of the family, but I need that little bit more security, same as you have.' Alice reached for her cloak and put it around her shoulders. 'I've got to go. I'm meeting Mrs Dowbiggin at St John's. We've got to decide how to decorate the church. Thank God you both chose April — at least there will be spring flowers to decorate it with!' She opened the cottage door and smiled at Will.

'Ali, if you don't like it, change it. Set your head and go for it — bring me back my stubborn, headstrong little sister, the one with the attitude, please.' He got up and kissed her tenderly on her cheek. 'Stick me some dandelions in a jam jar — that'll do for their wedding. Let's bring 'em down to our level.'

'Nay, we can't have that, our Will. They'd be wetting the bed all night — isn't that what Mum used to say when we picked dandelions?' Alice grinned and closed the door.

Will was right: she needed a kick up the bum. After all, she was now Miss Alice, not plain Alice Bentham; she had an allowance and was about to help arrange her brother's wedding to Lord Frankland's sister. Enough moaning — time to get on with things.

* * *

The walk to the church was exactly what Alice needed. Although it was only the end of January, the weather was quite mild and she enjoyed the two-mile stroll from Stone House to St John's, breathing in the sharp, clear air and seeing early signs of spring all around her. Lichen covered the tops of the walls and the bark of the bare trees, making everything greener than the grey day should have permitted. In another week or two, the grassy banks would be full of celandines, primroses and wood sorrel and the pungent aroma of wild garlic would fill the air along the riverside. The trees would be filled with nesting birds and the dark nights would

201

soon be gone. It was a time to look forward, to get on with life and stop dwelling on the past.

'Where have you been? I thought me and Faulks were going to freeze to death in this little church. It isn't like the one at Dent; there's nothing grand about this one. There was me getting in a tizz, worrying about all the preparations that needed doing, and Faulks has just told me that there's only going to be ten at the wedding. Lord Frankland doesn't want a big do, doesn't think Miss Nancy could handle it.' Mrs Dowbiggin shook her head. 'It gets stranger by the minute. I always dreamed that a Frankland wedding would be a splendid affair. I was really looking forward to decorating the church and manor, cooking for a huge wedding party and making the finest wedding cake, and now Master Gerald's saying immediate family only. It's a rum do, is this wedding.'

'I like St John's. It's a lovely little church, nestled here among the yew trees and with the river running by. I don't think Nancy and Will would have felt comfortable in anything bigger. This is charming.' Alice surveyed the wooden pews and glittering altarpieces and felt a peace she hadn't known in a long time. 'It's not all about status, Mrs Dowbiggin; it's about being right for the moment.' She watched the old housekeeper wrinkle her nose and run a finger along the altar. 'I hope that they will be very happy together and that their union will be blessed with children.'

'Hold your tongue! That's the last thing we want to hear at the manor — you couldn't have cursed this union more if you tried!' Mrs Dowbiggin's eyes flashed as if Alice had sworn in the house of the Lord.

'Mrs Dowbiggin, enough! Miss Alice only meant well, didn't you, dear?' Faulks intervened.

The two servants exchanged looks. Though no words were spoken, they were remembering Nancy's mother teetering on the brink of insanity after child-birth. It was a curse that had plagued generation after generation of Frankland women.

Observing them, Alice curbed the impulse to snap at the old housekeeper and instead took her by the hand and said softly, 'Of course I meant well. Everyone wants to see children from a marriage. Why do you call it a curse, Mrs Dowbiggin? You seem certain that this marriage is doomed and I don't understand why, especially when Nancy is so happy.'

Mrs Dowbiggin took her handkerchief out of her coat pocket and began patting her eyes. Putting an arm around her, Alice led her to one of the oak pews and they sat down. Faulks, sensing that women's talk was imminent, made himself scarce. He only hoped that he had been sharp enough to stop Mrs Dowbiggin from saying anything out of turn.

'I'm being overprotective, Alice, that's all. The worst pain that any woman can have is childbirth. I'm almost like a mother to that girl and I don't want her to go through that. You know how it is.' Mrs Dowbiggin, obviously flustered, stuffed her handkerchief into her coat pocket.

'But you can't protect her for ever. She's of an age to make her own life, and she loves our Will so much; I hope he returns that love and looks after her. Now come on. With some daffodils and narcissi we'll make this church the bonniest in the dale on their wedding day. And I'll bet you've a cake already made in the kitchen, soaking up alcohol as we speak.' Alice took her hand and patted it and they both quietly walked out of the church and along the pathway to where Faulks stood waiting.

'What do you say, Faulks? Time to celebrate and look forward, eh? How can they not be happy? They have everything and more besides.'

'Indeed so, Miss Alice.'

Alice turned to close the church's black cast-iron gate, just missing Faulks putting his finger to his lips, urging Mrs Dowbiggin not to continue with the conversation.

'Right, I'll not be heading back to the manor with you on the main road. I realized as I came through the dale to meet you that I need some time to myself, so I'm going up there.' Alice pointed to the top of the fell.

'But your clothes, Miss Alice — that beautiful cloak!'

'My sanity is more important. I need my thinking time. I'll see you at suppertime — do lay me a place.'

As she watched the two servants set off along the road, she could imagine Mrs Dowbiggin commenting, 'You can't make a silk purse out of a sow's ear,' as soon as she was out of earshot. Frankly, Alice didn't care. Let them think what they would; she knew what mattered to her and she had just begun to realize that it wasn't money.

* * *

Alice hurried up the drive to the manor, her dress hem plastered with mud from taking shortcuts across the fells and a tear in her cloak where she had snagged it on a hawthorn tree in her hurry to climb a stile on the way home. She realized with a jolt of alarm that she'd lost one of her gloves. She resolved to hunt for it later. The light was fading and she could see the candles and gas lamps had been lit in the manor. She decided to chance the front door rather than the back, not wanting to have to explain the state of her clothes to Mrs Dowbiggin. First she stopped to wipe the mud off her beautiful tight-buttoned boots. The leather had been spotless and shiny when she had set out, but now looked in need of at least an hour's polishing if not repair. She wiped them roughly on the grass verge, then brushed herself down. Seeing the state of herself, she felt a little frisson of alarm, but told herself what the hell, she'd only been for a walk. It wasn't as if she'd stolen the Crown jewels. She walked up the steps and quietly opened the front door, wiping her feet on the doormat and hurrying through the hall without anyone seeing her.

'Evening, Alice.' Gerald Frankland was just closing Nancy's bedroom door as Alice, head down, came running up the stairs. 'Nancy's been enquiring as to your whereabouts. I told her that you had gone for a walk after your meeting with Mrs Dowbiggin at the church.'

'Sorry, Gerald, I lost track of time. I'll get changed and go in to Nancy straight away.' Trying to hide her distressed attire, Alice brushed past him to get to her own bedroom.

'I trust, by the state of your dress, you enjoyed your walk. It's certainly brought colour to your cheeks. Perhaps you can entertain us at the dinner table by telling us where your walk took you.'

Uncertain whether he was being serious, Alice simply nodded and darted into her room, closing the door behind her. Of all the people to run into! She was mortified that he'd seen her in such an unkempt state, and conscious how ungrateful he must think her, getting her expensive new clothes in such a mess. Anxious not to keep Nancy waiting, she changed clothes, placed her boots outside her door to be cleaned by Faulks, and hurried along to Nancy's room.

'Where do you think you've been? I've been on my own all afternoon, without any company, no explanation, nothing, cast to one side like a disused doll!' Nancy yelled, her hair unbrushed, her scarred face even more distorted with rage. 'I will not be on my own! You are getting paid to be my companion twenty-four hours a day, not just when you feel like it.' She thumped the mattress that she was sitting on with her clenched fists and glared at Alice.

It had been a while since Alice had seen

Nancy in one of her tempers. She'd forgotten just how frightening and domineering she could be.

'I was never told I was to be a twenty-four-hour companion. I thought I was to be tret more like family, now you are to marry my brother.' Alice spoke softly but firmly; she wasn't going to kowtow. The few hours that she had enjoyed walking had made her realize that, since New Year's Day, she had not had a single hour to herself. 'I'm sorry, Nancy, I should have asked you first, but I thought you and your brother were busy with the tenants today.'

'Tenants? What do I know about tenants? They are my brother's business. I can't be bothered to sort out rents and finances. I needed you here. I haven't felt well all day and now my bloody brother is threatening me with the doctor.' She pounded the mattress again, then fixed Alice with her blazing dark eyes. 'Whatever gave you the idea you were going to be family? You are Alice, the poor girl we took pity on — nothing more! Now get out of my room. I'm not dining with you tonight. I've told Gerald I need dinner in my room — and you can just go down to the kitchen and see to it. Go on, get out!' Nancy threw her hands up in the air.

Alice said nothing but walked to the door with as much dignity as she could. It was a replay of her first encounter with Nancy, that day when she'd told her she was a spoilt, rich brat and she never wanted to see her again. As she closed the door behind her, she heard the crash of something being thrown against a wall.

So that was how it lay, she thought to herself as she went downstairs: Alice, the girl everyone took pity on, never to be treated like real family. Well, she wouldn't put up with it. Wedding or no wedding, there was no way she would be staying where she wasn't wanted. If she hadn't spent the day getting her thoughts together up on her beloved fells, she would probably have been crying. But no, she was a Bentham, her roots were in the Dales, and she was better than any off-comed family, with or without money.

★　★　★

'You're very quiet tonight, Alice. Is something the matter? I know Nancy is in one of her moods — is that it?'

Alice looked at Gerald. A few weeks ago, she'd have thought it a dream come true to find herself alone in the manor's dining room with the man she was beginning to have feelings for. Now she gave a wan smile and replied, 'I think it'd be best if I left the manor tomorrow. I know you've only taken me in out of pity — Miss Nancy made that clear tonight — and I have my pride.' She carried on eating her dinner, waiting for Gerald to comment.

'Damn that woman! She comes out with such rubbish when she's in one of her moods. I don't know what has come over her — today's episode was one of the worst I've seen.' He cast aside his knife and fork and held his head in his hands. 'We did not take pity on you, Alice. You are her only friend and she is to marry your brother. Sometimes her mouth runs away with her. Forgive her, Alice. She truly does not mean it.'

'I know,' Alice said sadly. 'I went for a walk, but I needed time to think — so much has happened this last week or two. I was only gone a few hours. I'd never hurt Nancy.'

'You are entitled to as much time as you wish to yourself if Nancy is otherwise occupied. She was supposed to be with me at my tenants' meeting today, but she came downstairs barely dressed and started dancing in the hallway in front of my stockman. The embarrassment of it! I had to escort her to her room. We must be the talk of the dale. It's no wonder we have such a bad name.'

Hearing the catch in his voice and seeing the tears welling in his eyes, Alice got up from her seat and rushed to his side. 'Don't worry, Gerald. I'll look after her twenty-four hours a day until the wedding, and even afterwards if Will wants me to.' She squeezed his hand. 'She'll be all right, I promise. I'll stay and keep her mind occupied. It's probably the pressure of the wedding that's getting to her.'

Suddenly remembering whose hand she was holding, Alice hurriedly released it. Blushing violently, she returned to her seat.

'I'd be grateful if you could, Alice. I have a feeling that this may be the beginning of a very rocky month or two. I hope that your brother knows what he's taking on and that he has a great deal of patience. But let us talk of cheerier things, shall we? Where did your walk take you? You look as if you have benefited from the fresh air. It does one good to have some time to oneself. I sometimes head up to the Occupation Road and sit gazing upon our lovely valley. Makes you forget your worries, those fells rolling gently, dale after dale, until they reach the sea. Have you ever been to the sea?'

'No, I haven't. My father always said he would take me, but we never got to go. The nearest I've been is to the top of Leek Fell, where you can see it in the distance.' Alice cast her mind back, remembering the sight.

'Then we shall go! We'll all go. In the summer, once the wedding is over, we'll have an outing.' Gerald smiled, his mood lightening as he picked up his knife and fork and continued with his meal. 'By the way, Alice, I almost forgot to tell you: Jack is to be the new owner of your old home, Dale End. He made me an offer, and I agreed. It couldn't be in safer hands. Eventually he will be leaving his work here and I'll be sorry to lose him when that time comes. I do believe he must be thinking of settling down. He'll be a good catch for someone.' Gerald smiled and winked, not knowing that Alice and Jack were no longer courting.

Alice's heart pounded. She felt as if she was going to be sick. Jack in her old home — how could he? She had always hoped for Dale End to be hers one day. Only this afternoon she had passed it on her walk and noticed it was still empty. Peering in through the kitchen window had rekindled old memories; she couldn't bear to think of anyone else living there. And now Jack was considering settling down ... She didn't know what to think. Was it jealousy she was feeling or anguish? If she wasn't careful, she was going to be left on the shelf, and that would never do!

14

'February fill-dyke, that's what it is. Have you ever seen rain like it? How am I supposed to get these sheets dry?' Mrs Dowbiggin moaned to Faulks as she lifted the damp sheets onto the clothes drier above the fire. Pulling at the rope, she wound it tight round the hook before the pulleys let it slip again. 'It's rained all blinking February. What with the weather, my lumbago and her upstairs carrying on, it's a wonder I'm not mad.' She stretched and peered out of the window. 'Anyway, the doctor's coming to see her this morning. Master Gerald says she needs something to calm her nerves. He still thinks it's the wedding that's getting her worked up.'

Faulks grunted while he read his newspaper.

'Morning, another beautiful day.' Alice entered the kitchen carrying Nancy's breakfast tray. 'I thought I'd bring you this, Mrs D — save you entering the ogre's den. I'm afraid Nancy's moods are not improving. If this keeps up, I'm going to lose my temper. I have come so close to telling her what I think of her this last day or two. My mother would have put her over her knee and walloped her, no matter how old she is.' Alice helped herself to a cup of tea from the teapot.

'Get him to serve you — he's doing nothing.' Mrs Dowbiggin kicked Faulks's foot and glared t him. 'Doctor's coming today; she'll calm down once he's been. I must admit we haven't had a session like this for a while.'

'What makes her like this, Mrs Dowbiggin? I used to think it was her scars hurting her, or not having anything to do, but she says she's not in pain, and with the wedding she has plenty to occupy her at the moment.'

Mrs Dowbiggin mouthed some words and pointed downwards.

'What?' Alice was lost.

'Cover your ears, you.' She swiped poor Faulks round his head with a damp pillowcase, then leaned conspiratorially towards Alice. 'Women's problems. Nerves, you know.'

Alice blushed. 'I see.'

'Her mother was the same. Nearly insane with it, she was. Too highly bred, if you ask me,' Mrs Dowbiggin whispered, half covering her mouth. 'Dr Bailey will give her something and then she'll be right again.'

'I'd better go up to her. I said I'd play whist with her until lunch — not that I dare win a game: it'd probably be more than my life's worth!' Alice gave a mirthless laugh and went back upstairs, thinking that if her brother only knew what he was taking on, he'd surely think twice.

She knocked gently on the half-closed bedroom door and then entered. Nancy was sitting in front of the mirror, examining her face.

'Look at me! How could anyone want to marry me? Your brother's only marrying me out of pity; he doesn't love me. I'd be better off dead!' she wailed. Then, wrapping her arms

213

around herself and rocking back and forth, she repeated over and over, 'I'm nothing to no one. I'm nothing to no one . . . '

'For God's sake, Nancy, I've had enough of this self-pity! You're getting married in another month. You should be looking forward to having a new home and a man to love you. I've no man and no real home. Do you hear me complain? Stop this relentless moaning. I can't take it any more. I'm going to my room until your mood's improved!' Then Alice marched out, slamming the door behind her.

Back in her own room, she agonized over whether she should tell her brother how much worse Nancy's moods were becoming, and how she'd inherited them. How near to the edge of insanity had her mother been? Alice wondered. Even though Will said he was marrying Nancy for her wealth and her tantrums were a small price to pay for what he would get in return, would he feel differently once they started married life and he had to live with her? The Stone House works were now safely in his hands, the deeds having been signed over last week, so it was probably already too late for him to back out.

Her thoughts were interrupted by the sound of the doorbell: Dr Bailey had arrived. A few minutes later she listened as Gerald talked to him on the landing before opening Nancy's bedroom door. Then she heard Gerald's tread on the stairs as he left the doctor to examine Nancy. Quietly Alice closed her bedroom door and crept downstairs. Knowing that Dr Bailey would stop

214

by Gerald's study on his way out, she slipped into the adjoining room, hoping to eavesdrop on the doctor's prognosis in case there was anything that her brother should know. Sure enough, she heard him knock on the study door and go in, but when she tried to listen through the wall, it was too thick. She couldn't hear a word.

After a while, the two men left the study together. Gerald was escorting the doctor to the front door. Alice opened the morning-room door a crack and peeked out.

'I'm sorry you have had to come out in such bad weather,' said Gerald, passing the doctor his hat and cloak.

'Not at all, Gerald. Let me know when you come to a decision. As I said, we can do something about it, but it might be as dangerous as seeing things through to their natural term. And you never know, she might calm down in another month or two. I've given her a draught to calm her, so she will probably sleep the rest of the day. You know where I am if you need me. Good luck, old man.' Dr Bailey patted Gerald on the back before dashing out to his carriage in the pouring rain.

'Damn, damn, damn the man. I'll bloody kill him!' Gerald Frankland picked up his riding whip from the hall stand and thrashed the side of his leg with it. 'I'll bloody kill him. Alice, Alice, where the hell are you?' He shouted loud enough for all the manor to hear him.

Alice came out of the morning room and stood in front of him, defiant but frightened by his show of temper.

215

'Get your cloak on. You're coming with me, else I won't be responsible for my actions when I catch up with your brother.' He thrashed the whip against his side again. 'I'll wait for you outside — and no gossiping with them downstairs.' Then he was gone, pulling the huge door behind him with a bang.

Alice ran and grabbed her cloak, putting her hood up to stop her hair from getting wet. Following the sound of Gerald's raised voice, she caught up with him at the stable.

'Damn it, man, are you going to take all day doing this?' Gerald Frankland was bellowing at Jack, who was harnessing the team to the carriage as fast as he could, his fingers fumbling with the buckles.

At last everything was ready. Elbowing Jack aside, Gerald ordered Alice to get into the carriage, while he sat on the board. He lashed the team with the whip and they set off. The rain was torrential and the horses slipped on the treacherous surface, but Gerald, drenched to the skin and looking like a mad man, drove them faster and faster until they reached Stone House. Pulling the carriage up abruptly at the cottage door, he shouted for Alice to get out. Then he stormed up to the cottage door and swung it open, whip in hand, his cloak dripping with rainwater and his eyes flashing with rage. Will was sitting at his kitchen table with his back to them. He turned round in shock at the intrusion into his home.

'Get up! Get up and fight me!' Gerald swung his cloak off and grabbed Will by the neck. 'I'm

216

going to bloody well kill you, you stupid fucking man! The doctor reckons she's pregnant — my bloody sister, pregnant! — and it can only be yours, you bastard.' He held Will by the neck, pinning him against the kitchen wall. 'Couldn't you keep it to yourself till you got married? I'd have told you then that she can't have children. It'll drive her mad; her mind can't take it. Already she's had to be sedated. Now we'll probably lose her, you fool!'

Alice stood watching her brother gasp for breath as Gerald Frankland squeezed tighter.

'You marry her in April, by God. You stand by her and your bastard child, no matter what state she gets into, else I'll kill you.' Gerald's hand shook while he kept his hold tight upon Will's neck. 'And another thing — you can keep the works and the cottage, but you're not going to get a penny of her allowance, nor any more orders through me. Thought me a fool, did you? Thought you'd make sure I couldn't renege on my promise by getting her pregnant? Well, your little plan's backfired. Now you can watch her getting worse and worse with her rages, just like my mother did. You will earn every penny that this place is worth. Not that it's worth a lot — I've been propping it up for years. Italian marble is all the markets want now, not this common black limestone marble.' He sneered at Will, gasping for breath. 'You'll find you're not much better off than you were when you started, but now you'll have a wife and child — and you'd better treat them right.' He released Will, then punched him hard in the stomach.

Will knelt, bent double and gasping for breath, on the flagstone floor. Alice rushed to his side. Even though he had confessed to her that it was only the money he was after, she had hoped that secretly he did think something of Nancy. Now there was a child to consider as well. If only she had known of Nancy's problem, she could have told Will not to bed her and not to use her to get his own back on his employer. He should have been more respectful. He'd seen the agony and torment his sister had gone through at Christmas, after she had destroyed her baby. Will had only to spend an hour with Nancy to realize that her mind was on the brink of a dark precipice. And he was the cause of it.

Gerald kicked Will's crumpled body. 'Get up, you bloody coward! Get up and talk to me. I've done what I wanted to do, without actually breaking your neck. Now we sort it out. Alice, get him a drink of water. I won't give him the satisfaction of choking to death, because I need him alive so he can stand by my sister.'

Alice passed Will a cup of water. He drank it down and spluttered, thanking her with a hoarse voice. Both men then sat down at the table while Alice stared out of the kitchen window at the incessant rain on the mountainside. She wished herself far away, away from this rain-sodden dale with all its problems, away from Nancy and away from the two men arguing at the table, their voices bitter with the fine line of love and hate running through them, both fighting for what they needed and what they thought was best for them.

'The first Saturday in April, one o'clock — you'd better be there, else I'll come and shoot you myself.' Gerald Frankland rose from his chair, picked up his whip and smashed it down on the table. 'If you lay a hand on her or deny her the attention she deserves, so help me God, I'll break you.' He turned to Alice. 'Are you coming, or is blood thicker than water? You do know Nancy will need you?'

Alice looked to Will. Hands clutching his sore neck, he nodded for her to go. She didn't want to leave her brother; she'd have liked to stay with him — as much to give him a piece of her mind as to make sure he wasn't badly hurt — but she knew her own security depended on the Franklands. Besides, Nancy needed her, and she was carrying Will's baby. That little nephew or niece would be a Bentham, part of her family. Though she didn't know what would happen to her after the wedding, for now Alice would stay by Nancy's side.

She pulled her cloak around her and climbed into the carriage. The horses, drenched and sweating from their chase up the dale, were eager to make the return journey so that they could be unharnessed and get back to their stables. Gerald and Alice rode in silence, their mood matching the weather. Rain pounded the roof of the carriage, competing with the deafening roar of the river as the waters surged, frothing and swirling round the smooth grey limestone formations.

When they finally arrived, Gerald handed the reins to Jack and stormed off across the yard without a backward glance. Alice climbed down from the carriage and followed as Jack led the team into the shelter of the stables. She was in no hurry to return to the manor.

Jack lifted the tack off both animals and began to brush the withers of the first horse. He kept his eyes on the horse, not even glancing in Alice's direction as he spoke. 'He's pushed these horses hard. They've a fair sweat on them, even in this weather. Must have been something urgent that you were both about.'

Alice leaned against the stable door, not knowing what to say. Gerald had warned her against gossip, but Jack could be trusted. 'He'd every right. I don't think I've ever seen him in such a mood.'

'Oh, aye, he's got a temper, has our master. Only once in a blue moon, but when he blows, he blows and there's no holding him back. He once whipped a dog that bit him to within an inch of its life. He'd every right then; according to him it needed to learn a lesson. What's he in a temper for today, then?' Jack carried on grooming, chewing on a straw as he spoke, still averting his eyes from Alice.

'Our Will. I suppose everyone will find out soon enough,' Alice sighed. 'Nancy's having Will's baby and she's going to be real ill while having it — her state of mind can't handle it.'

'Same old story for his lordship then: a dog's bit him again. And you don't bite the hand that feeds you.' Jack led the first horse into its stall and combed out his curry brush. 'Your Will's been a fool. Miss Nancy loved him without him getting her pregnant. He should have taken more care.' Finally he looked at Alice. 'It must be something in the water up at Stone House.'

'What do you mean by that, Jack Alderson?' Alice glared at him in defiance, now certain that he must have heard her talking to the horse.

'Nay, nothing. I'm not saying anything. Next time I see him, I'll tell your brother to keep it in his pocket. Happen he's not the only one who should. By the way, I found this outside Dale End's kitchen window.' He fished out the fur-trimmed glove that Alice had lost the day she went walking up the fell. 'I take it that's yours? I saw you wearing a pair like it on the day you came back with Miss Nancy from Kendal.'

'Thanks. I've been searching for that everywhere. I hear you're buying Dale End — are you going to be living there? It seemed so deserted.'

'Well, you can't live at home for ever and I thought it was time to be settling down and making my own home.' Jack started grooming the second horse. He still couldn't look at Alice; he loved her so much, but when he'd found out the things she'd kept from him — that she'd been untrue and slept with another man, then got rid of a baby — it had caused a hurt in him that was going to take a long time to heal.

'I see. I'm sure it will make you very happy.' Alice could feel a lump forming in her throat. 'Thanks for the glove.' She waved it at him as she turned to cross the yard towards the manor.

If she didn't love him, then why did her heart feel so heavy? And then she thought of the dark and brooding Gerald. Why worry about Jack? He was nothing but a boy she had grown up with, more like a brother than the lover Gerald could be. She swallowed hard, raised her head high and walked into the manor without giving him a backward glance.

★ ★ ★

Low clouds hung around the small church, wrapping it up in grey cotton wool and making it feel oppressive and dark. It may as well have been the middle of the night, not one o'clock on a Saturday in early April. The church bell, muffled by the low cloud, rang out across the top of the dale. Outside the main door, daffodils nodded in the light breeze as if in conversation with one another about the coming wedding, anticipating the arrival of the bride.

Will, dressed in his new suit, fumbled in his pocket, playing with the family wedding ring. He felt sick with apprehension. If he'd been able to run away, he would have done. But he knew that Gerald Frankland would hunt him down no matter where he went. Jack stood beside him talking to the vicar, who was expressing concern at the size of the congregation. Obviously no one had told him that this was to be a shotgun wedding.

Suddenly the organ sounded the opening bars of Handel's 'Wedding March' and Will, heart heavy with the knowledge that this was his last minute of freedom, turned to see his bride walking down the aisle with her brother at her side. Alice walked behind them with a delicate bunch of primroses in her hand, flashing a reassuring smile at her big brother. Jack nudged Will out into the aisle and encouraged him to take Nancy's hand, while Gerald Frankland stepped to the side of the couple, giving Will a threatening glance as he placed her hand in the hand of her soon-to-be husband. Nancy gave her bouquet to Alice and smiled at Will, her nerves held at bay by the medication the doctor had given her that morning.

With her face covered by a veil and her dark hair standing out in stark contrast against the cream of her wedding dress and flowers, Nancy looked beautiful. If it hadn't been for her scars, she would have been many a man's fantasy: rich, young and with child by her husband-to-be. To Will, she was a millstone. For the rest of his days he would be in service to her, her brother and his unborn child. He'd thought everything he'd ever wanted was being handed to him on a plate, only to discover he was taking a lunatic for a wife, and thanks to her brother he didn't have a penny in the bank to support them. He went through the vows as if in a trance, wanting to run but at the same time rooted to the spot. Never had a wedding service taken so long.

Then finally it was over, and they were walking out of the church, watched by a few curious locals who had gathered on the bridge, wondering who the happy couple might be and wishing them well as they drove off in their wedding coach.

* * *

223

'They're here! They're here! Get a move on — open the doors.' Mrs Dowbiggin was in full cry. Even though it was only a small wedding breakfast, she was determined that it should go exactly the way she'd planned.

Faulks opened the front door and welcomed the new couple in while Mrs Dowbiggin stood clapping in the hall, along with a young servant girl who had been hired for the day. Nancy smiled, happy that everyone was making her day special. There had been a tense atmosphere between her and her brother these last few weeks, but now she had the man she loved and a baby on the way, everything would be all right. She didn't know what everyone was making such a fuss about.

'Congratulations, Miss Nancy. Congratulations, Master Will.' Faulks smiled and led them to their seats, laying napkins out on their laps and pouring a liberal glass of wine for the newly-weds.

'Thank you, Faulks. What a very strange day. I always thought the sun would be shining on my wedding day. Don't you think the sun should be shining? Instead it's dull and dreary, and I feel quite lightheaded.'

'It's spring, miss. Sometimes the sun shines; sometimes it rains. As long as you are happy, miss, you'll radiate sunshine.' Faulks smiled, trying to offer encouragement, but at the same time he cast a worried glance at Gerald.

'That's me, Faulks — a ray of sunshine, shining out over everyone, apart from my sulky brother, who looks like the rain clouds outside.

Make him smile, Faulks: he's spoiling my day.'

'He's just concerned for you, miss, as we all are. He knows you are unwell and is worried about your new life.' Faulks moved on to Gerald, his eyes never straying from the wine pouring into the glass — anything rather than meet his employer's gaze.

'My Will is going to take care of me ever so well. Besides, Alice is coming to Stone House with me too. I wouldn't have it any other way.' Nancy beamed at Will and Alice, reaching out for their hands and squeezing them tight.

'Now, Nancy, we haven't decided on Alice yet.' Gerald stirred his soup, which the young serving maid had placed in front of him. 'I'm sorry to embarrass you, Alice, but I'm at a loss as to what to do with you under the circumstances.' He took a long slurp of his soup and gazed across the table at a subdued Alice. 'I'd have thought that you would prefer to stay here at the manor, but my sister seems to think you will be moving into Stone House with your brother and her. I think we had better discuss this after the newly-weds have departed for their home. You can always follow them to Stone House in the morning — that is, if you wish to do so, and if Will is happy with that arrangement.'

Will gave a nod. He'd few words to spare for his new brother-in-law and he was counting the minutes until he could escape the stuffiness of the manor and return to his home.

Alice watched Gerald sitting back in his chair and staring across at the newly-weds, knowing full well he was making Will uncomfortable. 'I'll stay here tonight,' she said. 'It's their first night together — a sister in the next bedroom is the last thing you want.' And then she blushed, realizing she had been forthright. But there was no other way of saying it, as far as she could tell.

'I'm afraid that moment has well and truly passed, Alice, my dear. As we all know, your brother put the cart before the horse, as they say — hence the atmosphere around this table on what should have been a day of celebration.' Throwing down his napkin, Gerald got to his feet and made his apologies, then stormed out of the room.

'I'm sorry, Will, it came out wrong. I shouldn't have said that.' Alice could have kicked herself.

'It doesn't matter, Sis. I've had enough anyway; this food was sticking in my throat. I'm off up the dale and taking Nancy with me. Can you get her things?'

'They're already packed and waiting in the front hallway. Let Nancy say goodbye to Gerald before you go, though — it'll only make him worse if you don't.'

They both turned to Nancy. She seemed confused and sad. She was angry with her brother, and couldn't understand what she had done so wrong to upset everybody. All she wanted was to have a lovely wedding day and to marry the man she loved. She knew they were going to be so happy; if only she could rid herself of this feeling of not being in control and stop these anxiety attacks, things would be all right.

'Come on, old girl, go and say goodbye to your brother. I'll wait outside in the horse and trap.' Will helped Nancy up from her chair.

'But the dinner — we've only had the first course.' Nancy was even more confused.

'I'll make you something when we get home, Mrs Bentham.' Will put his arm around her, smiling as he led her out of the dining room.

Alice tugged at his elbow. 'Look after her: she needs your support. And mind you stand by her — she's having your baby, remember.'

'What do you take me for? We'll be all right. Make sure you look after yourself tonight — remember what I've said in the past.' Will winked at her.

'That's the pot calling the kettle black, Will Bentham.' Alice kissed her brother on the cheek.

When Nancy came out of Gerald's study sniffling into her handkerchief, Alice was on hand to give her a hug. 'You'll be fine, Nancy. I'll come and be with you tomorrow, but for now go and be happy with my big brother. And if he doesn't take care of you, he'll have me to answer to.' She walked with her to the manor's steps and waved at the couple as Will whipped the horses into motion.

Behind the study curtains, Gerald watched them set off down the drive. He had lost his little sister to a man he suspected didn't love her. He prayed that she'd survive childbirth. At least once the baby was born, there would be hope.

★   ★   ★

'Oh my Lord! All this food and nobody to eat it! I've never known a do like this in my life. What's folk going to think of us? Think on, young Betsy, you say nothing to anyone in Dent about this wedding day, 'cos if I find out you've been gossiping, there will be hell to pay.' Mrs Dowbiggin wagged her finger at the poor serving girl as she set off home, her services no longer required now the wedding party had broken up. 'I feel all faint. I could do with some smelling salts, Mr Faulks. What a to-do!' She planted herself in the Windsor chair and fanned her cherry-red face with the tea towel. 'You shouldn't be helping clear away. You're not one of us any more,' she chastised Alice for carrying in the wasted food from the wedding breakfast.

'And who do you think I am? I can't sit about here and do nothing. Besides, it hasn't exactly been the day I wanted either.' Alice was as annoyed as Mrs Dowbiggin. She no longer knew where she stood in life; her brother wouldn't really want her at Stone House, yet there was no reason for her to stay at the manor. It was all very well Nancy saying she needed her, but she didn't realize that Will was going to struggle to feed them all.

Having cleared the kitchen table of food, Alice set about placing it in the pantry and cellar in the hope that it would keep fresh enough for everyone to eat it over the coming week. 'You're all going to eat well, if nothing else,' she said, washing her hands.

'That ham will last longer than a week if there's only us and Master Gerald. What a waste! And all my fancy sweets — nobody even got to see them.' Mrs Dowbiggin held her apron to her eyes, almost in tears.

'Never mind, at least there was a wedding. At one point, I did wonder if my brother would turn up; I was afraid he'd get cold feet. He went through with it, though. Now he'll have to get on with his lot and take care of Nancy and the baby. It'll hit home now he's got responsibilities. There'll be no more spending his spare time having a pint or going shooting with Jack.' Alice shook her head and walked past Mrs Dowbiggin as she headed back upstairs.

Mrs Dowbiggin caught her hand as she passed, gripping it tight. 'Your Will, he will take care of our Miss Nancy, won't he? She may be a handful, but we all think a great deal of her. And you'll be there for her, won't you?' There were tears in the old housekeeper's eyes as she pleaded with Alice.

'I'll be there for her. I'm going to talk to Gerald now, find out where we go from here. I'm neither one thing nor the other, and someone is going to have to make him see sense over Nancy and her baby — they still need his support even though she is pregnant by my brother. He didn't know of her medical problems when he got her pregnant, else he'd not have even touched her.' Alice patted the faithful Mrs Dowbiggin's hand, more resolved than ever to try and salvage something of the day.

Alice knocked gently on the study door. Through the narrow gap underneath the door she could see the flickering light from the open fire, but nobody answered. She knocked harder, knowing that Gerald was in there and not wanting to retreat from the mission she had set herself, even though her stomach was churning. She was about to knock again when the door opened ever so slightly, showing the dark figure of Gerald Frankland. He left the door ajar and Alice went in, following as he returned to his chair by the fire.

'Well, Miss Bentham, have you come to chastise me, to give me the benefit of your considerable knowledge? Because that's what I'm expecting, you and your quick tongue.' Gerald Frankland poured himself another glass of port from the decanter and gazed into the fire.

Alice sat down in the chair opposite, her hands in her lap, trying to remain calm. She could see that Gerald had been drowning his sorrows. 'I'm only making sure you're all right. I know it's been a bit of a day for you, for all of us.'

'A bit of a day? A bit of a day — ha! That's a bloody understatement.' He swigged his drink. 'It's been a bloody fiasco, that's what it's been. It was like the Mad Hatter's tea party, sitting around that wedding table. My mad bloody sister, not knowing what the hell was going on, and your brother desperate to run away . . . I just want to wipe the whole damn day out. So, yes, it was a bit of a day.' He poured himself another drink and indicated for Alice to get a glass and join him. 'Cheers! Here's to the happy couple.'

'But Nancy *is* happy. Perhaps she doesn't always know what's going on, but she's happy with Will and with the baby coming.' Alice took a quick drink and coughed as the warm port went down her throat. She'd never drunk port before.

'How can she be happy, married to your brother? He hasn't got a penny to his name. She's left here for that hovel at the top of the dale. She's not in her right mind, what with having that bastard baby.' Gerald glared at Alice with his wounded eyes.

'Money isn't everything. Nancy loves my brother. Now, I don't know if he deserves her love, but if she's happy, does it matter? She'll have the baby; things will be all right. Perhaps living up the dale with my brother will do her good.' Alice took another sip of the port; it made her feel warm and relaxed. 'You're going to be an uncle — that's something to be proud of. You haven't lost a sister; you've gained a nephew or niece.'

'She's so ill, I might yet lose her! If she dies, it will be all your brother's fault. I could kill him for what he's done.' Gerald spat the words out.

Alice leaned towards him, trying to hold his gaze. 'He didn't know about the danger. The only thing he's done is to love your sister — what's wrong with that? We've all loved someone we shouldn't have.' Words were flowing freely out of Alice as she allowed Gerald to pour her another drink. 'They're going to struggle, though, with no money. But my brother will provide for them. Rabbit stew never hurt nobody.'

She hoped that the mention of rabbit stew would make Gerald realize how tough life was for his workers. Surely he wouldn't want his sister to endure such hardship, regardless of what he thought of Will.

231

'Don't try and make me feel guilty, Alice; it won't work. I might have had a bit to drink, but I'm still compos mentis. I'll reassess the situation in the morning, when I take you up to Stone House. I might have been a bit hard, especially on Nancy. But can you blame me? My whole family is going to the dogs — even I'm sitting here talking to my sister's maid as if she was my closest friend.' He placed his glass on the table and looked at Alice.

Alice blushed, the warmth of the port making her complexion glow. 'I'm sorry I've overstepped my place. I only wanted to make a case for them both because my brother is hopeless at standing his ground. The port must have given me added courage.'

'Too bloody right! But you never have been one to know your place. To tell you the truth, you amuse me with your forthright ways, but now is not the time. Leave me to my thoughts and this bottle; I'm best sorting my own head out, without a blue-eyed temptress sitting across from me.' He raised his glass and grinned at her. He could see that she knew all too well what she was doing. Alice was not as innocent as she would have him believe. Trouble was, one day he might not be able to resist those cornflower-blue eyes.

'I'll see you in the morning.' Alice smiled and walked past him. Another drink and she would probably have been putty in his hands. There was something about Gerald Frankland that made her lose all control of her feelings. Perhaps he'd come to her later . . . How she wished he would — to hell with reputations!

15

Alice lay back in her bed watching the sun's rays stream through the half-drawn curtains. Specks of dust floated like dancing fairies in the early morning light. She snuggled down under the covers, content with the warmth of the bed and her thoughts of Gerald Frankland. She'd half hoped that she would wake up with him next to her, but common sense told her that it was a good thing she hadn't. Better to hang on to her dignity. Besides, she didn't want him to think she was easy.

She listened to a family of sparrows cheerfully chattering in the wisteria outside the window. They were busy nesting, preparing for their young and enjoying the spring sunshine. It made her think of her brother and Nancy preparing for the new arrival. Would Gerald have changed his mind and decided to give Nancy her dowry? Alice hoped so; there was not going to be enough business at the marble works to keep the labourers and the foreman's new family fed.

Throwing off the covers, she got up and pulled the curtains fully open. It was a beautiful day. The sun was shining, the sky was blue, and the surrounding fells were turning green again after the long, hard winter. They beckoned Alice. She longed to go walking from dale to dale until her legs ached and her stomach needed food. But there was no time for that today; she was off to

Stone House, to join her brother. Conscious that she might never again wake to the luxury of her bedroom at the manor, she lingered by the window, making the most of the view.

Downstairs, the clock in the hall chimed six o'clock. Not a soul was stirring; it would be another hour before Mrs Dowbiggin started making breakfast. That left Alice with time enough for a quick walk. She washed and dressed, tiptoed downstairs and out through the front door, then across the stable yard to the path that led to the fellside. The hedgerow along the bottom of the fell was filled with the new buds of spring, with violets, wood sorrel and primroses in bloom along the grassy banks. The fresh morning air was clear and sharp and Alice breathed it in as if it was the elixir of life as she made her way to the stone wall that separated the meadowland from the rough grassland of the fell. It was the perfect vantage point from which to gaze down on the valley below while she pondered what life was going to throw at her. She sat on a stone next to the gateway to the fell, watching the hazy mist that lay along the river evaporate in the heat of the sun, leaving the river glittering like a silver ribbon as it meandered down the dale. She was sitting there, basking in the sun and daydreaming, when she heard the chain on the gate being opened. It was Jack, leading one of the horses that had been grazing on the fell.

'You're an early bird. I never usually see a soul up here at this time.' Closing the gate behind him, he tied the horse to one of the crossbars.

He pulled a packet of cigarettes out of his pocket and lit one, then leaned on the wall next to Alice.

'I couldn't resist. It was as if the sun was calling me. Besides, I needed to think things through before I go up to Stone House this morning.'

'Aye, I reckon your lad's taken on more than he can chew. He'll not be happy with that one. She's used to getting her own way, whereas he's like me and you — bit of a free spirit. Wild birds die if you cage 'em; he should know that.' Jack took a long drag on his cigarette.

'I'll remind him, but it's too late now. He should have thought about that when he was busy plotting how to get his hands on Nancy's money.' Alice couldn't help but confide in Jack that she knew Will had only married and got Nancy pregnant for her money.

'I thought this baby was an accident. Has he got her in the family way on purpose? By 'eck, my father would kick my arse if I'd have done that.'

'Now you know why there was such an unwelcoming feel about the wedding. He'll be right with Nancy, but it's her brass that he's after. I don't know what's got into our Will. He's changed since Mother and Father died.' Alice picked up a pebble and threw it hard, watching it bounce and settle on the stony path.

'Aye, well, I haven't seen him much this last month or two — haven't had much time for owt lately.' He untied the horse and stamped out his cigarette with his boot.

Alice stood up, brushed her skirt and linked

her arm with Jack's. 'I'll walk with you. They'll be waking up at the manor now. How's that girlfriend of yours — Amy, is it? Must be serious if you're thinking of settling down.'

'Nay, I've given over taking her out. She was costing me a fortune and she couldn't bake. What I need is a lass that's good with money and can make something out of nowt. Amy was no good for me.'

Alice smiled. She'd had a narrow escape from thrifty Jack; she wanted a bit more from life than working and she'd had her fill of having to make something out of nowt.

* * *

Mrs Dowbiggin was busy lighting fires and getting the kitchen going for breakfast when Alice walked in.

'What on earth are you doing up and about this hour of the day? I've only just got dressed myself!' She pulled a new tablecloth out of the large oak drawer and shoved it into Faulks's hands so that he could set the breakfast table in the dining room.

'It's such a beautiful morning, Mrs D, I couldn't waste it lying in bed. I needed to get out while I have the chance. Once I'm up the dale, I'll not have much time to myself.' Alice helped herself to a glass of water, sipping it while she watched Mrs Dowbiggin stir the porridge.

'Must be something in the water, because his lordship is up and about too. He's just demanded a cup of tea in his study. I told him he'd have to wait until the kettle's boiled and I've only one pair of hands.' Wiping her fingers on her apron, she began getting the breakfast crockery out.

'Leave that to me. I'll take it through to him. I need a word with him anyway.'

Alice put a cup and saucer and teapot on a tray; then, while she waited for the kettle to boil, she ran outside and picked a small bunch of violets. Mrs Dowbiggin tutted as Alice arranged the violets in a small vase and put it on the tea tray before carrying it off to Gerald's study.

As soon as Alice was out of earshot, the housekeeper shook her head and said, 'I don't know what's going on in this family any more, Mr Faulks, I really don't. Perhaps it's best that we are where we are in life, 'cos I wouldn't want to be young again.'

★ ★ ★

'Morning. Isn't it a beautiful day? It'll be a nice ride up the dale this morning.' Alice breezed into Gerald's study, placing the tray of tea in front of him.

'I suppose it is, but my head doesn't think so.' Gerald squinted at Alice. 'I'm afraid I drank too much last night and now I'm suffering, hence the tea.' He took a deep slurp of tea and eased into his chair. 'Having drunk myself stupid and considered the matter from every angle, I've come to a decision. I will give them Nancy's allowance — they'll need it to bring the baby up. But I want your assurance

237

that you will be there for her, no matter what. She trusts you and I know that she's going to need all the help she can get in the next few months. No taking sides, Alice; you do right by me and mine, because you know your brother's plotted his way into this family and I'll not fall for any more schemes.' He looked intently into Alice's eyes, as if questioning her motives.

'I'll be right with her, Gerald. I'll be there when she needs me, and I promise neither Nancy nor the baby will come to any harm if I have a say in it.'

'Right then, let's wish them all the best this morning when we go to Stone House. I'll drop you off at the cottage and then I'll look around the works with Will. I've been going through the books and, to be honest, I don't know what we are going to do. We can't compete with these foreign imports. Bloody Italians — thanks to them, our marble's worthless. For a month or two I thought we were doing well, but orders have dropped off. I need to discuss it with Will.' He flicked through the accounts book and sighed.

'Thank you, Gerald.' Alice smiled at her new brother-in-law, glad that she'd secured her brother a decent living. 'Don't worry, things will come right in the end.'

'Go on, go on, get your breakfast.' He waved his hand at her. 'And, Alice, I like the violets.' He smiled, leaning back into his chair as he watched her leave his study, inspired by her determination. She wasn't one for giving

238

in; that he was sure of. His sister would be in good hands as long as Alice was with her.

* * *

The ride up to Stone House was pleasant, the team of horses trotting steadily while the early spring sun shone down on Alice and Gerald. There was little conversation between them; both were lost in their own thoughts. Alice had packed a small bag with a few possessions to take with her and then closed her bedroom door with a long backward glance, not wanting to leave the comfort of the manor for the spare room at Stone House. She had to go; that she knew. She owed it to Nancy and her baby; and her brother, who until now had had no idea how much his new wife was suffering from her nerves, was going to need her support.

She looked at Gerald, his eyes on the road ahead as he sat next to her at the reins. This was the man that she had been warned about, the man who ruled her life, and now he was her brother-in-law and she felt at ease with his charms. In fact, she could honestly say that there was not a minute in the day when she did not think about him. His dark hair, his dry smile and his smooth voice . . . Yet below the gentle side to him Alice could see there was a man of passion, the side that one day perhaps she would see more of. She gathered her thoughts as the trap went over the small arched stone bridge that had crossed the River Dee for centuries and up the short path to her new home. Gerald held her hand as he helped her to alight; then she hurried to the open kitchen door, where Nancy was standing with arms outstretched.

'Will said you were coming, but I thought he was teasing. He's even put some of Mrs Dowbiggin's cakes out on a plate for us. I don't know how to make cakes. Do you, Alice? I fear I'm not going to be a good wife and mother; I've so much to learn.' Nancy sat down and fidgeted with her fingers, a look of hopelessness on her face.

Alice removed her hat and shawl and took Nancy's hands in hers. 'That's why I'm here: to take care of you and the baby, to make sure you eat and get enough rest. All you have to do is take care of yourself and Will and be happy.' She smiled reassuringly at her sister-in-law, who looked as if she had finally realized what she had let herself in for.

'Aye, our Alice will look after you, lass. She can cook, so tha needn't bother your head over that.' Will put his hand on Nancy's shoulder just as Gerald came into the room.

'Will, you and I need to make a fresh start. You're married to my sister now; I might not agree with it, but as long as you promise to stand by her and care for her, then you'll have my backing, along with the allowance that we originally talked about. You can thank your Alice for that.' Gerald looked at Alice as she knelt on the floor next to Nancy. 'She made me see sense last night. We've got to take care of this baby now it's on its way.'

'Well, that takes a weight off my mind.' Will's

face lightened. 'I can't thank you enough for helping us out. I didn't know how we were going to manage; the stone works is not doing much at the moment and the men are all grumbling. We need to find a better seam of marble soon if we are to keep working.'

Will had been dreading seeing Gerald Frankland all morning. One night of being with Nancy had made him realize just how bad she was, but at least the money gave him some hope.

'Right, let's go and take a stroll up to the works so I can take a look around. How many men have we working for us at the moment? If you haven't the work for them, perhaps you could get rid of one or two — that's what I advise, anyway.' Gerald danced around his words, remembering that he no longer actually owned the marble works.

'Aye, well, any advice you can give, I'd be grateful. You'll have seen by my accounts that we aren't breaking even at the moment. The market's just died.' Will was clearly uncomfortable.

'Nancy prompted me a while ago to secure you an order from the Tsar of Russia — I have contacts over there, as you know. However, there is turmoil in the country at the moment and I'm sure that ordering a fireplace from Dent would be the last thing on their minds. For the time being we will have to come up with another way of boosting profits.'

Alice was struck by the words 'turmoil in Russia'. So things were not going well over there. Come to think of it, she hadn't seen any letters

241

arriving with the delicate feminine handwriting on the envelope; perhaps that was one of the reasons Gerald had been so moody lately. She felt herself looking at him and blushing at the thoughts that were going through her head. Perhaps he was fair game after all. With his beloved Tatiana off the scene, she could woo him and keep his attention. How she hated the sound of that Russian woman's name. If as a result of this turmoil she were to vanish from Gerald's life, Alice would be a happy woman.

'Do excuse us, ladies. We are going to take a stroll to the stone works so we can draw upon one another's knowledge and see what can be done. Nancy, dear, I'll have a talk with you later, but I'm sure you and Alice have plenty to catch up on in the meantime.' Gerald put on his hat and stepped out, followed by Will, who turned to wink at them as he closed the door. There was a broad smile on his face; he felt much more comfortable not being at loggerheads with his brother-in-law.

Alice bustled around the kitchen, tidying up and sweeping the hearth, then filling the kettle before placing it over the fire to boil.

'I'm so useless. I'm Will's wife — I'm supposed to be doing this, but I don't know what to do,' Nancy wailed as she watched Alice scurrying around.

'And as I said that's precisely why I'm here: you and your baby will be wanting for nothing. Talking of babies, you need to stop wearing those corsets. The poor mite will be getting squashed in there.' Alice nodded to Nancy's cinched-in waistline. 'You need some loose-fitting clothes. Tell our Will to put his hand in his pocket and take you to Kendal. You need to be comfortable, not make a fashion statement.'

Nancy's face immediately clouded over. 'I don't want to lose my waist. It'll have to be squashed — I'm not spoiling my figure for a baby.' She pouted and launched into a tantrum that a ten-year-old would have been proud of, screaming, 'I wish it was dead. It has spoilt everything!'

Alice did her best to calm her down. 'You don't mean that, Nancy. Why, only the other week you were saying how much you were looking forward to being a mother. In five months you'll be wearing the tightest corsets you can find. Don't wish the baby ill; it'll bring a lot of joy to you both — a new baby always does.' She could see that Nancy was struggling to come to terms with the course her life had taken and that she didn't really wish any harm to the baby.

Nancy sobbed, 'I've made a mess of my life. What am I doing here instead of at the manor? Look at it — a worker's cottage — and me four months pregnant the day after a shotgun wedding. My life's a mess, a horrible mess.'

Alice put a comforting arm around her. 'We all make mistakes. I should know — I've done things that I'm really ashamed of. But you have so much to look forward to. You've got money, a good cottage, a man who loves you and a baby on the way — and when he or she is born, I'm sure you'll love that baby with all your heart.

Things will get better. You've just to get on with it. I'm here to do all the work and take care of you both and I'll not let you down.' She rocked Nancy's trembling body, gazing over her shoulder at the beautiful spring day outside the kitchen window. It was going to be a long five months, and even then she didn't know how things would be. She only hoped and prayed things would improve.

16

It was payday and the burly marble workers formed a line at the doorway of Stone House Cottage, collars turned up and caps pulled down to protect them from the fine drizzle. The grey skies matched their mood.

'I've not had to carve anything for over a month now,' said the oldest man in the group. 'I can't see us carrying on. There's no work, and we can't go on like this for ever.'

Josiah Middleton nodded in agreement and carried on trying to wind the men up. 'If O'Hara had still been here, we'd have had full bellies and full pockets, but this arse-licker only looks after himself. I tell you, O'Hara might have been turning Frankland over, but he took care of his own. With this 'un we'll get bloody nothing, 'cos he's neither one thing nor t'other. The man's a traitor to his own kind!' Middleton shoved his hands in his pockets and spat on the clean step of the cottage. 'Come on, you bugger, open up — we want our brass,' he brayed at the kitchen door.

The green-painted door opened and Alice stepped out, wiping her hands on her pinny. She glared at the great hulk towering over her in the doorway. 'Will you be quiet! Miss Nancy is resting and my brother's trying to count out your wages. You'll not get them any sooner by bellowing.' There was no trace of fear in her voice, but inside she was quaking. The huge man could easily have picked her up off her feet, and well he knew it.

'Oooh, lads, did you hear that? Miss Nancy's resting. From what I hear, both these so-called ladies are at their best on their backs,' Middleton roared at his workmates, who rewarded his wit with rumbling laughter.

'Don't you make fun of me, Mr Middleton, or you'll live to regret it.' Alice could feel her temper rising. Her face was flushing not with embarrassment but with fury. How dare he, the crude, vulgar man. 'I'm warning you, mind who you are talking to.'

'And who's that, then? A lady's maid — if you can call that wild thing a lady. As for the 'maid', why she's no better than a prostitute, or so I've heard.' Middleton continued playing to his admiring crowd, unaware of Will coming to the door.

'Middleton, you've insulted my family enough — get yourself in here now, and close the door.'

Will was sharp and hard with his words; this troublemaker had riled him once too often. He went and sat behind the kitchen table, where the allocated wages and his accounts were all laid out, and began counting out a few extra shillings alongside Middleton's wages. The man had taken his cap off and relaxed his stance in anticipation of receiving his week's pay. Alice looked on, her eyes burning into Middleton's back. Her hands were clenched into fists by her side; she was so angry she wanted to lash out at him for calling her those things.

Will counted the money out as he placed it in the big man's outstretched palm, and carried on counting until the man was holding two weeks' wages. Then he rose to his full height and looked the grinning man straight in the eye. 'Middleton, you're fired. I've had enough of you and your troublemaking. I don't need your sort round here. There's an extra week's wage in your hand. Now, I want you off my property by the end of the day.'

'You dirty rotten bastard — you can't run that works without me. You're nothing, you jumped-up piece of shit.' Middleton grabbed Will by the collar, pulling him halfway across the table and sending the rest of the wages scattering across the floor.

'Oh, but I can,' said Will, breaking free from his aggressor's grasp. 'There isn't going to be a marble works any more — I've just closed the place down and now you're all out of a job. So you can threaten me all you like but there's nothing you can do about it.'

'You bastard! You've sold us all out! Taken care of yourself, haven't you? Made sure you're all right, but you don't give a damn about the rest of us — we're nothing to you.' He made a fist and was about to throw a punch at Will when he felt something poke him in the middle of his back.

'I wouldn't do that if I was you. Now you'd better calm down, walk out that door and keep on walking else I'll pull this trigger — and believe me, my brother taught me how to handle a gun real well. I don't just lie on my back, as you so quaintly put it.' If Alice could have pulled the trigger without fear of being prosecuted for murder, she would have done it. She hated the ugly brute of a man.

Middleton went quiet, bent down to pick his cap up and slowly made his way to the door. The whole time Alice held Will's shotgun to his spine. He opened the door, spat once again, put his cap on at an angle and walked out of the yard without so much as a glance at his fellow workers. Alice and Will stood on the doorstep watching him, his coat flapping and arms swinging as he turned the corner and disappeared from sight.

Having heard every word of what had gone on inside the cottage, the rest of the men stood silent, their faces sombre as they awaited their final paypacket. They were regretting the times that they had moaned about their work; it might not have been up to much, but at least it put food on the table and a roof over their heads. Now things looked bleak. As each man emerged from the cottage clutching his money, he paused to solemnly shake hands and mutter promises to stay in touch. In reality they didn't know what the future held for them.

Once the last worker had left the kitchen, Will breathed a sigh of relief. It had been the worst day's work he had ever had to do and he felt sorry for his ex-workers. Work was hard to come by and he didn't know where they would end up.

'Thank God that's over,' said Alice. 'If that Middleton had said another word, I swear I'd have shot him. Ignorant brute.' She was sweeping the kitchen floor, pushing the broom with a vengeance as she cleaned up all traces of the muddy boot prints that had been left on the stone slabs. 'I'm glad Nancy didn't wake up when he started losing his temper and shouting: it would have made her nervous and upset her.'

'Aye, he's one that I'll not be sorry to see the back of. I'll miss some of the others, though. Still, if all goes well, I might be able to rehire them.' Will took his accounts book and the few pounds he had left over and locked them in his sturdy sideboard.

'That was a good idea the pair of you came up with. Shows what you can do when you put your heads together. Once the conversion's done, the marble works will make two good houses. And as soon as they're sold, you can build them two new houses. All in all, it should make a good investment for the both of you.' Alice set aside the broom and busied herself washing dishes.

'Aye, I can't wait. Starting next week, I'm going to have a hell of a tidy-up. I need to get hold of the scrap man first — might as well get what money we can from the old machinery. But that's all I can do for the time being. I wish that architect friend of Gerald's would get a move on with the plans. Last thing I want is to be sitting around here with nothing to do.'

Alice turned from the sink to look at her brother. 'Nancy will enjoy having you around. She needs your support.'

'Aye, but do I want to be around her? She's near driven me mad of late. I tell you, lass, if she hadn't any brass, I'd be thinking about doing a runner. I didn't know what I was taking on — why didn't you tell me how bad she was?' Will was standing in the kitchen doorway, staring out at the drizzle and the mist that was starting to form around the fell.

'She'll get better once the baby's born. Not long to go now, so be patient; you'll soon be a dad and that will change everything.' Alice went to her brother and put an arm around him. 'With all this money you and Gerald will be making from your new project, you'll be lord of your own manor before you know it.'

'Aye, well, we'll see. It'll take a while to get everything in place. In the meantime, we'll have to live on Nancy's allowance and be content with that.'

'Is someone talking about me?' Nancy, fresh from her afternoon nap, entered the kitchen.

'No, Nancy. It's been a bit of an afternoon, that's all. Will's just laid off the workers — I'm surprised the shouting didn't wake you up.' Alice beckoned for her to sit down. 'Will was only saying it's a good job we have your allowance to live on, until the houses get built.'

'What houses? What are you talking about? Nobody ever tells me anything!' Nancy demanded in an aggravated tone.

'You were there when Gerald and Will talked about closing the marble works and changing it into houses. That way they can keep Stone House turning a profit for them.' Alice squeezed her hand.

'I can't remember. I can't remember anything. My head feels all fuzzy. I can't think straight any more.' Nancy turned to Alice, her eyes pleading for an explanation.

'Don't worry, love. You let us worry about that. We'll take care of things, won't we, Will?'

'Aye, nothing to fret about, all's in hand.' Will grabbed his coat and cap from the hook by the door. 'Right, I'm off up to the works to make sure all's straight. It'll be funny to walk up there and not have any workers around.'

In truth, it was just an excuse to get out of the cottage. Will was fed up with humouring his new wife and listening to baby talk, and having to endlessly repeat things because Nancy couldn't remember having been told. Already he was sick and tired of this being-married lark. Given the chance, he'd welcome being free and single again.

17

'Are you ready, you two? The horse and me are waiting. I don't know why you women take so long. God only knows what you get up to.' Will waited in the bright sunshine, impatient to set off. He was meeting Gerald at the manor to go over the plans that had been drawn up for the new houses.

'We're coming. You should know better than to rush a pregnant woman — we had to make sure we looked our best, didn't we, Nancy?' Alice helped her sister-in-law into the trap, Nancy's swollen belly showing that the unborn baby was growing. 'You're going to have to be more patient when you're a father, what with all the sleepless nights and nappies. But I'm sure you'll cope.'

She climbed in and sat opposite Nancy in the back. Behind her she could hear Will grunting and mumbling under his breath in response to her dig at him.

'We do need to get there for dinner time, not supper — get a move on,' Alice prompted.

Will finished lighting the cigarette that hung from the corner of his mouth and whipped the horse into motion.

With the trap finally moving, Alice and Nancy sat watching the countryside go by and listening to the steady pace of the horse's hooves. In the dale, farmers were cutting the grass to make into hay and the warm air was filled with the smell of sweet grass drying. It was a beautiful day and even Will began to relax a little, breaking into a merry out-of-tune whistle.

'It's nice to see home.' Nancy gazed at the manor with tear-filled eyes as the trap slowed to a halt by the front steps. 'I forget how much I love this place. Not that I don't want to be with Will, but it would be nice if the cottage was a little larger.'

'It won't be long now. Gerald and Will have agreed that the first house to be built will be for the two of you and the new baby to live in. Then you can rent your cottage out.' Alice knew Nancy had been missing the luxuries of the manor and she could understand how she felt. She had forsaken so much for the love of Will and he did not appreciate it.

'Nancy, my love, you're blooming!' Gerald took hold of his sister's hand to support her as she alighted the trap.

'Thank you, Gerald. I feel fine sometimes, but how I miss this place.' A tear rolled down her cheek.

'Now, don't get upset. You know we are always here and that you are always welcome.' He escorted her into the manor, then turned to help Alice alight. 'Alice, how are you keeping? I see you've brought the sunshine with you.' His eyes twinkled with mischief, but he lowered them when he noticed Will watching him.

Alice couldn't take her gaze off Gerald as he escorted her up the steps. It had been a few weeks since she had seen him and every day she had fantasized about his dark features. Crossly she reminded herself that she had no business thinking about him in that way. So far as he was concerned, she was just a servant girl. She chattered brightly in an effort to cover her inner turmoil.

'Thank you. It's such a beautiful day, we had a lovely journey, and Nancy's been coping ever so well. She just got a little tearful when she saw the manor. You must admit, there is quite a difference between this and where we live.'

'Ah, but that will soon change. You should see the plans I've had drawn up; the new family will not want for anything with the house we are to build. Come on, Will, leave that animal to Jack and come and join us in the study.'

Once the men were engrossed in their discussion of the plans, Mrs Dowbiggin came in with a tea tray and began serving the two women. 'Miss Nancy, it's lovely to see you.' She gave Nancy a hug and fussed over her as she poured tea and passed out the cups. 'How's things with the baby?' she whispered, not wanting the men to overhear 'women's business'.

'Mrs Dowbiggin, I miss you. Are you taking good care of my brother? And where's Faulks? Is he well?' Nancy, shaking with emotion, clutched Mrs Dowbiggin's hand.

'We are fine, Miss Nancy, so stop bothering about us and just look after yourself and that baby. That's all that matters now.'

Mrs Dowbiggin blew her nose on a lace-trimmed handkerchief, disguising the fact that her eyes, too, were brimming with tears. Having looked after Miss Nancy since she was a girl, she had missed her terribly. At times she'd even found herself missing the tantrums, wishing she could hear her screaming upstairs and smashing ornaments. Life had been so quiet without her.

Putting on her cheeriest voice, the housekeeper brushed Nancy's arm and said, 'Not long now — another three months and we'll be hearing the patter of tiny feet. Your mother would have been so proud. I'm knitting, you know — it gives me something to do of a night.' And then she began sniffing into her handkerchief again, upset but trying not to show it, as she shuffled out of the room.

Alice sipped her tea and watched the two men reading the plans in the bright light that was streaming through the open study windows. She liked the study, with its green walls lined with bookcases; it gave her a secure feeling. Seeing Gerald seated at his desk like a proud statesman, she couldn't help but think how things had changed since her first meeting with the Frankland family. Then her mind returned to the present as she observed Nancy, her features drawn and tired. Thankfully, this was one of her better days. There were times when it was all she could do to remember her own name, let alone anything else. The sooner the baby was born, the better for all concerned.

'Beg your pardon, sir, but I thought you might want to see this.' Faulks entered the study waving a crisply ironed newspaper. 'The paper boy sends his apologies at the lateness of his delivery, but as you can see by the headlines it could be grave news, especially for your Russian colleagues.' Flustered, he set the paper on the desk in front of his employer.

'What's all this fuss, Faulks? What on earth are you talking about?' Disgruntled, Gerald picked up the paper and scanned the front page. The colour drained from his face as he read.

'What is it? What's wrong?' said Will, seeing his reaction.

'Archduke Franz Ferdinand, heir to the Austro-Hungarian throne, has been assassinated in Sarajevo by a Serbian nationalist. This could have terrible consequences if the Austrians retaliate by attacking Serbia. Russia is sworn to defend the Serbs, while Austria will turn to their German allies for support.' Gerald placed the paper on his knee, his face grim as he contemplated what would happen if, as he feared, the great powers of Europe went to war.

'Oh, so it's nowt for us to worry about, then, just a load of foreigners fighting among themselves. From the way you were looking, I thought good old King George had died! Come on, let's get back to these plans; never mind the paper.' Will leaned over the architect's drawings, trying to make sense of them all.

'For God's sake, man, there are people I love in Russia! If war breaks out, their lives may be in danger. And you expect me to put all thought of that aside for the sake of building a few houses? There are more important things in this world than making money.' Thrusting the plans away, Gerald sprang to his feet and went to the window, the newspaper still clutched in his hand.

'A beautiful day like today, sun shining, family all around me, but I feel a dark cloud blotting the horizon.'

Nancy went to her brother's side and laid her hand on his shoulder. 'You've always got us, dear. It's better we forget our ties to Russia. The time has come for us both to move on and find happiness here.' Smiling, she kissed him lightly on his cheek before returning to her seat next to Alice.

'Aye, come on, man, nothing's happened yet. Don't go looking at the black side. These bloody foreigners always kiss and make up; the whole thing'll have blown over by next week.' Will patted him on the back.

'I hope you're right, old man. I pray that you're right and I'm wrong, because otherwise we'll be building these houses for nothing.' Gerald came away from the window and poured two whiskies from the decanter on his desk. He handed one glass to Will and downed the contents of the other in a single gulp.

Will looked at the crystal whisky tumbler filled with golden liquid. Never having drunk the stuff before, he followed Gerald's example and threw it back in one gulp. Coughing and spluttering, eyes watering and cheeks turning red as the spirit warmed his insides, he wheezed, 'Now I know why they call it firewater! Give me a pint of best bitter, any day.'

Gerald patted him on the back and laughed. 'It's a taste that grows on you after a while. Same thing's true of bloody foreigners.'

'Aye, you can keep them and all. Nearest thing

to foreign I've ever seen is Lancashire, and that was enough for me.' Will laughed and coughed again as he leaned over the desk.

'Let's hope, for all our sakes, that you never go any further,' said Gerald, pouring another drink. This time he sipped it slowly and thoughtfully.

★ ★ ★

'Gerald seemed to be very worried by the news. I think he might know more about it than he let on.' Alice was sitting with Will on the wooden bench outside the cottage watching the sun set over Combe Scar. For fear of upsetting Nancy, they had not spoken of the incident in the study while in her presence; the journey home had been spent chatting about the new houses and their visit to the manor instead. Only now that she had retired to her bed, leaving brother and sister to sit outside until it was time for them to sleep, were they able to discuss it.

'It'll be nothing. I've never even heard of this fellow that got killed, so how could it make any difference to us that he's dead? We'll get them houses built and we'll make as much brass as Gerald. Then we'll give everyone a run for their money.' Will finished cleaning his shotgun and blew down the barrel. 'It's a grand night. I'm just going to have a wander up the fell and pot a rabbit or two. Are you coming with me?' He jangled some cartridges in his pocket and put his cap on.

'No, I don't think I will. I want to sit here a while longer and mull things over. Nancy's been good today, but who's to say what she'll be like tomorrow? She wears me out some days.'

'Aye, that's why I'm going up the fell — need a bit of time to myself. I tell you, Sis, it's a high price I'm paying for a bit of extra brass.' He put his shotgun over his shoulder and walked away.

'You've only yourself to blame,' she retorted, but he didn't hear her. Alice shook her head. Will had everything to look forward to — new big house, doting wife, a baby on the way — and he still wasn't satisfied. He'd only been married a couple of months and already his patience with Nancy was wearing thin. Hopefully, when the baby came along, things would be different.

Her thoughts returned to Gerald and the expression on his face as he studied the newspaper. Something had disturbed him a great deal, and that worried Alice. Unlike her brother, Gerald knew all about politics and world affairs. Not only had he travelled the globe and lived in Russia for a while, he'd attended Sedbergh School and been a cadet. He wouldn't have been alarmed without cause.

The glorious sunset soon made her forget her anxieties, bathing the countryside in shimmering hues of gold and orange. The screeching of diving swallows made way for the high-pitched squeak of bats as they clambered out of their daytime hiding places to glide through the dusky skies on dark, leathery wings. Alice shivered as the temperature fell with the disappearance of the sun. It was time to go in and wait for Will's return, although, knowing him, it could be early morning before he ventured home.

She lit the oil lamp and placed it in the window, catching sight of her reflection in the glass. What a state she was in! Alice took a loose strand of hair and twisted it behind her ear. She'd gone to the dogs since moving out of the manor. Maybe now that plans for the houses were coming along, she could convince Will to buy her a new dress and perhaps a hat to go with it. Tomorrow she would suggest that they take a ride into Kendal for some baby clothes and then she would try and steer Nancy past that shop she liked, the one on Stramongate. They always had such beautiful materials in the window. Yes, that would be the best way to go about it: once Nancy came around to the idea, Will wouldn't be able to say no. She hummed to herself as she sat at the table darning Will's socks. When they visited the manor to show off the new baby, she'd be all dressed up in her new dress, new hat, maybe even new shoes. She wanted to look pretty next time she saw Gerald, because it would be her he'd be looking at, not the baby.

18

'Gerald, good to see you.' Colonel Fredericks stood up from behind his desk and shook Gerald's hand firmly. 'I wondered if you would be showing interest. I take it you've heard that Germany declared war on Russia yesterday? It's only a matter of time till good old Blighty gets pulled into it. Damned shame, but we'll soon show them.' He indicated for Gerald to take a seat. 'So, what can we do for you, old man? D'you fancy a posting?'

'That's what I was hoping for, sir. I reckon I'd be more use with a gun in my hand fighting for my country than potting the occasional pheasant or rabbit.' Gerald had thought long and hard before catching the train to Carlisle and requesting an interview with his father's old friend, the colonel of the Border Regiment. The news that Germany and Russia were now officially at war had made up his mind.

'Seriously, lad, do you really want to risk everything to go and fight in some foreign field?' The colonel's usual bluff manner was replaced by a much more serious tone. In the days when Gerald's parents were alive he had attended many dinner parties at Whernside Manor; fascinated by his dress uniform, the young Gerald would follow him around, begging to be allowed to play with the sword that hung by his side. 'I owe it to your father and mother to warn you, Gerald, that this could turn out to be the war of all wars if England does get involved. You've a lot to lose. And then there's that sister of yours . . . '

'What's the point of wasting my training sitting in the Dales, pretending to be lord of the manor, when everything I know is changing?' Gerald looked the colonel in the eye. 'As for Nancy, she's now married and is expecting her first baby.'

'Is she, by God! Then congratulations are in order. Who's the lucky fellow? Anyone I know?'

'No, Colonel, he's no one you would know.' Gerald wasn't about to tell him that his sister's new husband was just some local and that it had been a shotgun wedding. Impatient to return to the matter at hand, he declined the colonel's offer of a celebratory cigar and pressed on: 'Do you think you can find me a commission?'

'If that's what you want, I will write a letter of recommendation to the War Office informing them that one of the finest cadets Sedbergh ever produced is applying for a commission. They'll want to see your birth certificate and a medical certif — ' He broke off as Gerald produced the documents from his pocket and handed them over. 'Well, my boy, you really are determined, aren't you? With these I can get you gazetted more quickly. But, Gerald, you take care. I wouldn't want the son of my dearest friends to end up dead because of me.' He smiled at the serious-faced young man sitting across from him.

'Thank you for your concern, Colonel, but I

am determined to volunteer. When this country does get drawn in, I want to be one of the first to take up arms. There's far too much at stake for me to ignore my obligations.'

The two men got to their feet and shook hands. The colonel looked tired and too old to take on a new war. But Gerald couldn't wait for his papers to come through so that he could do the job he'd trained for as a cadet at Sedbergh and fight for King and Country.

★ ★ ★

'Read all about it, read all about it! Britain declares war on Germany.' The newsvendor on the corner of Stramongate was doing a roaring trade, barely managing to give out the papers and take the money fast enough. People were clamouring to get their hands on the latest edition with its shocking news of Britain's entry into the war against Germany and its allies. Will, Nancy and Alice dodged the throng and crossed the road to the haberdasher's, the bell above the door chiming loudly as Will ushered his womenfolk into the shop.

'I've never known a morning like it,' said the shopkeeper, turning from the window where she'd been watching the commotion. 'That's the second printing of papers that young lad has sold today. Folk are carrying on like they've been given a pot of gold 'stead of getting into a war. I can't see any sense in it, myself. Why should we go and rescue those Frenchies? The world's gone mad.' Observing Nancy's bulge as the three drew closer, she added: 'Just be glad that you're married. At least you won't be going to war. And you won't be letting him go, will you, love, not in your condition?'

Already unnerved by the hubbub in the street, Nancy became even more confused and scared at the mention of war. Alice hurried to reassure her as Will stared through the glass door at the crowds still gathering.

'Here now, take the weight off your feet.' The stout middle-aged shopkeeper came out from behind the counter with a chair and set it down beside Nancy. 'I remember when I was having our Alf — by 'eck, I was tired and my feet ached. I used to say to the old man he had no idea what I went through to give him a son. They've no idea, haven't these fellows, no idea whatsoever what we women go through.' Catching sight of Alice casting an admiring glance at a ream of delicate pink calico, the astute saleswoman swiftly changed topic: 'Now that is a lovely bit of calico, just come in from Liverpool docks last week. I can give you a good deal on it if you buy two dress lengths, and it'll last well.'

'Thank you, but we've come for some of your baby clothes. We noticed them in the window last time we were in Kendal.' Alice spoke on Nancy's behalf.

'Aye, I've a good stock in: wool vests, liberty bodices, nappies . . . and I've some lovely flannelette nighties — any baby's right in them until they start crawling. Is this your first?' She turned to Nancy, studying her with enquiring eyes.

'Yes, it's my first.' Nancy looked down at the floor, not wanting to engage the old woman's stare.

'Well, I hope it's a lad, for your sake. Then you mightn't have to go through it again. The pain when I had our Alf was unbearable. I vowed I'd never have another after that. I tell you, these fellas take their pleasure but don't know the other half of it.'

'Can we have a look at the vests, please?' Alice cut in, hoping to get the shopkeeper off the subject. She didn't want Nancy subjected to a long drawn-out description of the agonies of childbirth. From the look of the woman, the son whose birth had proved so much of an ordeal must be a grown man by now.

'I'll just get my steps — the vests are up there on the top shelf. Do you want a fairly big size? You can make them do for six months if you get them big enough. Same with the liberty bodices. Little mites are better warm than cold; they need at least three layers on, even in this grand weather.' She pulled out some rickety wooden steps and climbed slowly up. Balancing three flat cardboard boxes under her chin, she made a wobbly descent with one hand on the steps. 'These are our finest wool vests. Now, I'm only advising, but if I were you, I'd take three of them.'

Alice took one out of the box and passed it to Nancy, who held it up and then squeezed it tight to her face, feeling the softness of the wool and playing with the tiny drawstring ribbon round the neck. 'Will, darling, come and look at these

— aren't they adorable?' Nancy's eyes filled with tears as it suddenly dawned on her that she was about to be a mother.

'I'm just watching these crowds, Nance. I've never seen anything like it in my life.' Will walked reluctantly from the shop doorway, glancing over his shoulder, unable to take his eyes off the crowds gathering around the newsvendor.

'What do you think? Aren't they sweet?' Nancy held a baby vest up for Will to inspect.

'Aye, aye, you get whatever you want, lass, and I'll settle the bill when you're done. While we're here, might as well treat yourself an' all. And knowing our lass, I'm sure she'll have her eye on something too. Just pick out whatever you want and give me a shout when you're done — I'm going to nip outside, see what's going on. It's like Christmas out there.'

Alice winked at Nancy as Will walked out of the shop. Time for them both to get what they wanted.

'We'll have half a dozen of the vests and the same of the liberty bodices . . . ' Alice took charge of the orders as Nancy admired the ribbons and small buttons that fastened the tiny garments. 'Two dozen nappies ought to do it, and can we see those nighties that you were suggesting? After that, we'd both like to look at some material. Do you do dressmaking as well?' The woman nodded. 'Oh, good, that makes it easier all round. Can you take our measurements before my brother comes back — it's a case of what the eye doesn't see, the heart doesn't grieve, if you know what I mean.'

'Anything you want, we can do it,' said the starry-eyed shopkeeper, overjoyed that she'd had second thoughts about opening up that morning. Because the way these two were spending, there would be no need to open for the next month. 'Would you like your order parcelled and sent to you? It'd save you both any awkward questions. Now, what about a pair of these pink gloves? They would go lovely with that calico you had your eye on . . .'

Soon the shop counter was covered with goods as Nancy and Alice took Will at his word and picked out whatever they wanted. It was like turning two children loose in a sweetshop.

'By 'eck, I didn't realize a baby could cost so much! Does it really need all that? We'll be living on bread and dripping with the money I've spent today.' Will shook his head as he put the receipt into his pocket.

'You want your son to be dressed right, don't you?' Alice replied, giggling at her sister-in-law. Nancy was smiling, enjoying a good day out shopping.

'And how do you know that it's going to be a lad? Mind, I hope it is a lad, 'cos God help us if it turns out to be a lass that takes after her aunty Alice.' Will grinned at Alice as they walked through the crowds. 'I bought a paper off that lad. I thought we could drop it off at the manor, show it to Gerald. Looks as though he was right — all hell's going to break loose. But the folk I were talking to say it'll be over by Christmas. Won't take us long to teach Kaiser Bill a lesson and send him running home with his tail between his legs. Nancy, are you up to calling off at your brother's? You're not too tired, are you?'

'No, it'll be good to see him. Then I can tell him about the sweet little baby clothes.' Nancy glowed as if it would make her day complete to see her darling brother.

'Right, let's get out of this madhouse and go see what Gerald makes of the news.' Will untied the horses and, realizing that they'd been spooked by the hullabaloo, led them away from the bustle of central Kendal. As his womenfolk chattered happily in the back of the trap, he posed a question, keeping his voice low so only the horses could hear: 'War declared — what the hell is that going to mean to all of us?' Then he mounted the trap and drove them slowly home.

* * *

'I tell you, Gerald, all hell's broken out in Kendal. The papers are stirring everybody up — the place was full of crowds cheering and young lads lining up for a chance to take on the Hun, and their mothers were crying, not wanting them to go. I've never seen anything like it.' Will was pacing up and down the sitting room of the manor, trying to describe the atmosphere in Kendal.

'I read it this morning.' Gerald sat stony-faced until his brother-in-law had finished, then he knelt beside his sister and took her hand in his. 'Nancy, love, forgive me, I should have told you earlier: I've signed up and am about to join our gallant lads. I'm so sorry, but I have to go — not

268

only am I fighting for England but also for our friends in Russia. I join my regiment next week. They've appointed me second lieutenant — I'll be shipped out to France straight away.' His eyes pleaded with Nancy as she started to tremble and sob. 'Try to understand, Nancy, I must go. You've got Will and Alice to look after you, and if, God forbid, anything happens to me, the manor and everything that's mine will be yours.'

'Don't leave me. Please don't leave me. You are all I've got in this world.'

'Nonsense, you've got Will, who loves you dearly, and faithful Alice, who is always by your side. And soon there'll be the little one as well. I'll come home to find you with a bouncing baby on your knee and probably another one on the way. And I will come home, you know me — just like a bad penny.' Gerald smiled at his sister, fighting back the tears that were beginning to well up in his eyes.

Nancy cried inconsolably as he rose from his knees and walked over to Will. 'I'm afraid the build will have to go on hold until I return, old man. You understand, don't you?'

'Aye, I understand. If you feel it's your duty, you must go. No doubt you'll be the first of many. To be honest, I wish I were coming with you — see a bit of other lands, shoot a Hun or two. It'd only be like potting rabbits.' Will slapped him on the back. 'She'll be all right, don't worry.' He nodded in the direction of Nancy. 'Me and our lass will take care of her.'

'Alice, will you wish me luck and look after my little sister and her new baby?' Gerald turned to

Alice, who had remained silent when he made his announcement.

'I'll wish you luck and I'll look after Nancy, but I think you are wrong to go and leave us all. We need you here. Let someone else fight this war; it's nothing to do with us here in Dent.' Alice's blue eyes blazed with fear and hatred of the war that was going to take Gerald away from her.

'My dear Alice, the world is a much smaller place than you think. I'm going to fight for all of us, to make our lives safer and to let people like you say what they think. I know you're angry with me — those blue eyes give you away — but I have to go.'

As Alice looked up at him, silhouetted against the evening sun shining through the sitting-room window, it seemed to her as if a cloud of darkness enveloped the room. The war had come to Dent and nothing was going to be the same.

19

Alice sat on top of the limestone wall, resting from hoeing the small piece of earth she called her garden. She'd claimed it from a strip of land between the stream that ran by the side of the cottage and the lane down to the main road. All spring she'd dug and weeded the long strip of rough land, and now with summer drawing to an end her labours had been rewarded with a display of vibrant dahlias and chrysanthemums flowering in one part of the garden while a thriving vegetable plot occupied the remainder.

The weeds didn't stand a chance with Alice venting her anger on them in the early morning sunshine. The lettuce, beetroot and cabbage patches had never been weeded so fast; while her brain had been doing overtime, her body had mechanically gone on with its chores until there were no more weeds left. Still gripping the hoe, Alice stamped it on the ground, shaking her head in disgust at herself for not saying goodbye the way she'd wanted to. She'd stood there on the platform, waving as Gerald boarded the train in his smart army uniform, when what she should have done was taken him to one side and told him how she felt. But that class thing had got in the way as usual: she was a maid and he was her master, and no matter how much she wanted to show her feelings, she was afraid of showing herself up if he refused her advances.

Alice stamped the hoe down once again, this time slicing an earwig in two. Alice watched its death throes, the life ebbing from its body. Normally she'd have been satisfied with flicking it off the dahlia it was making a meal of, but today she needed to vent her wrath on something.

The previous morning they'd taken the winding hill road to the station. The fell was shrouded in fog that clung to the landscape like a damp cobweb, obscuring the view. Nancy had sobbed inconsolably as she clung to Gerald in his khaki uniform, his cap and stick making him look every inch the officer and a force to be reckoned with. The steam train had come shunting out of Rise Hill tunnel, puffing grey smoke as it made its way on the upward line to Settle and then on to Leeds. The claret-coloured carriages were packed with khaki-clad troops from the barracks at Carlisle and with enthusiastic volunteers eager to go and teach the Hun a lesson.

As the train had drawn in, Will had shaken Gerald's hand, promising to take care of Nancy and her newborn. Then he'd prised Nancy's fingers from her brother's uniform and dragged her away, still frantically pleading with him not to go. It was then that Alice had stepped forward, wanting to put her arms around him and tell him of her feelings, but unable to say the words. Even when his dark brown eyes had looked into hers and his soft voice had murmured, 'Alice, take care,' as he kissed her on the cheek, she'd remained silent. Not so much as a 'Take care.

272

Keep your head down' — not a word, let alone 'I love you'. She had stood on the platform as he boarded the train, cheered on by the occupants, and slammed the carriage door. She'd gone on standing there as the train pulled out with him waving from the window. Then she had turned to Will and told him that she would walk home rather than ride with them in the trap. The fog had lifted by this time, and from the first bend of the road on the hill she could just make out the last carriage going over the top viaduct at Dent Head before disappearing into Blea Moor tunnel. There she had stood, tears in her eyes, whispering, 'Take care, my love.' Then she had picked a bunch of heather from the roadside in remembrance of the day.

A cry of 'Delivery for Will Bentham!' brought Alice back to the present with a jolt. The post lad was coming up the road with a huge parcel balanced on the front of his bike. 'Can you sign for it, miss?' Alice looked at him with her blue eyes but said nothing. 'Miss, can you sign for it?' He puffed and caught his breath as she took his board and pencil from his hand and signed, then returned it without saying a word. He untied the string that held it secure on his bike and passed it to her, hesitating for a minute or two, expecting a tip, for it was a long, hard pedal up the dale from Dent to Stone House and he'd hoped to be given something for his trouble. But seeing that nothing was forthcoming, he mounted his bike and carefully picked his way past the larger stones on the path to the main road, then freewheeled most of the way back to

Dent. Some folk just did not appreciate his deliveries, and it was usually the same lot, the snobs.

Alice wiped her hands on her pinny and carried the parcel into the kitchen, placing it on the table and cutting the string tie with a carving knife. It was the baby clothes and the dresses that they had ordered on their visit to Kendal. She examined the tiny baby clothes, smiling at the smallness of the garments and feeling a twinge of guilt at having ended her own baby's life so cruelly. Surely the delicate, beautiful clothes would make her smile. She then unfolded the floral-patterned dress that Nancy had ordered; it was pleated and loose-fitting, which should make her more comfortable in the last months of pregnancy. At the bottom of the pile were the pink dress and gloves. The dress was beautiful; the seamstress had done an excellent job. Alice held it to her waist, twirling round the kitchen table with it held close to her. What a pity there wasn't going to be a single man left in the dale, let alone Gerald, who would surely have admired her in this. Bloody war, spoiling everything. The sooner it was over the better!

★ ★ ★

Will leaned on the oak table in the Moon and took a sip of his pint, the frothy white head giving him a creamy moustache, which he wiped off with his jacket sleeve. 'So, what do you reckon, Jack? Are you going to join up and see a bit of action?'

274

'I'm not off anywhere. I'm farming with my father and that's where I'm stopping. I'm not going to be cannon fodder for the toffs, bugger 'em. I'm best off at home, same as you are.'

'Aye, but haven't you ever wondered what it'd feel like to shoot a fellow dead? I nearly did — remember t'other spring when I shot O'Hara? It was such a feeling, I could hear my heart beating. Nothing like shooting rabbits: they just sit there and let you pull the trigger.' Will downed his pint and got to his feet. 'Another, Jack?'

'OK, one more, then I'm off home.' He set his pint glass down on the table and watched Will head over to the bar. He remembered all too well the day that Will shot Sean O'Hara. The man had been an evil bastard, and after the way he treated that horse he deserved everything he got, but Jack wouldn't have wanted to be the one to pull the trigger.

Will returned with two frothing pints. 'Here you go, lad. What's all this talk of 'One more, then I'm off home'? It's not that late — sun's not even set yet.'

'I've a cow that's about to calve, so I'll need to be up early in the morning. I'm not like you, a man of leisure.'

'Nay, be fair — I've been busy tidying up at the mill the last few weeks. I'd be helping dig the foundations out for the new buildings, but everything's on hold now until Gerald gets home from playing soldiers. To be honest, the last thing I want is to be a man of leisure — bloody Nancy is starting to turn me mad, never mind herself.'

'Well, you've only yourself to blame. Back when we were both working at the manor, how many times did we hear her screaming and carrying on? You knew what you were taking on. We always used to joke that she was mad — well, now you know she is.' Jack took a mouthful of his fresh pint and looked at his friend. He had that faraway expression on his face that he always got when he was plotting something.

'Did you know Gerald got fifty quid to fit himself up for his new uniform? All the officers get that. He went to Moss Bros in Leeds with his allowance. Fifty quid — that'd last me a lifetime in clothes.'

'Aye, they might last his lordship a lifetime — the way he shoots, he'll be lucky to last a week. You should know what he's like with a gun: can't hit a pheasant, let alone a Jerry.'

'Jerry who?' Will frowned, his pint stopping midway to his mouth.

'That's what the papers are calling the Germans on account of their helmets are like Jerry pots that you put under the bed.'

Will spluttered into his pint. 'Fancy having helmets like pisspots! We're bound to kick their arses. I tell you, Jack, it'll all be over by Christmas and life will get back to normal. Still, I wouldn't mind having a pop at one or two of them. I'd soon get their numbers down.' Will mimed shooting Jack with his fingers.

'Don't even bloody well think about it — you've a baby on the way and your Alice will need you,' Jack growled.

'Our Alice, need me? She doesn't need

anybody, that one. She's as hard as nails and feisty with it. You should know — you've had plenty of do's with her!' Will grinned cheekily.

'She'll more than get feisty with you if she hears you talking about going off to fight. Just behave yourself and keep out of trouble for once in your life.' Jack drained his pint and stood up. 'Right, I'm off. Knowing my luck, I'll get home to find this cow will have started to calve.' He pulled his cap low over his eyes and walked out of the Moon.

Will watched him go. There had been a time when the two of them had dreamed of going off to see the world. No way Jack would be doing that now — he was too content with his lot. Still, it might not be too late for him. And perhaps now was the time to do something about it.

★ ★ ★

Will wrote his note quickly and left it on the kitchen table in clear view for Alice to find it. He cut himself a slice of bread, spread it with butter and ate it while he gazed around the kitchen. God, Alice would go mad when she found out he'd left, but he couldn't take living with Nancy any more. Besides, she'd be all right: she had money, and Alice would take care of her and the baby. He swigged a pint of milk to wash down the bread. Then quietly closing the kitchen door behind him, he led his saddled horse down the lane.

An early morning mist hung over the river and the smell of autumn was in the air, with a hint of

277

frosty days to come. He turned to look back at the huge pillars of Stone House viaduct and the cottage that had been his marital home. A wave of guilt washed over him: was he being selfish? It couldn't be helped. He had to get away. As he'd crept out of bed, tucking his shirt in and pulling on his braces, he'd watched Nancy sleeping peacefully. Another month and the baby would be here, and then it would be too late to leave. He didn't love her, he never had. How could anyone really love someone whose moods changed like the weather? She had worn him out. No, it was definitely time to go. He mounted his horse and kicked its sides. He had an urgent appointment with a recruitment officer and after that . . . who could say?

★ ★ ★

Alice sat at the kitchen table, her hands shaking, tears dripping from her cheeks onto the brief note until the ink ran down the page. How could he? The stupid bloody idiot, how could he walk out on his wife and soon-to-be-born child? And how could he leave her with all the worry of looking after them both? She screwed the note up tight in her hand. Selfish bastard! He wasn't going to join up because he was patriotic; he was running away from his responsibilities. Her heart ached, with sorrow at not having a chance to say goodbye to her brother, but also with worry at the thought of how strong she was going to have to be. Would she ever see him again? She prayed to God that for once he would do the sensible thing and keep his head down instead of trying to prove himself.

Her first problem was how to break the news to Nancy. How do you tell an eight-month-pregnant woman that her husband has gone to war rather than standing by his family? This poor baby was already facing the prospect of being born to a mad mother; now it looked as though it might never know its father. And with the war raging in Europe, who knew what the future might hold for the poor little mite? Alice vowed that, no matter what anyone else did, she would stand by the baby. This little niece or nephew would need her, and she needed him or her; by caring for this child she would make up for what she had done to her own baby.

The sound of Nancy moving about upstairs brought Alice to her senses. She sniffed and wiped her eyes on a tea towel, putting the kettle on to boil before trying to deal with the mess Will had left her. Best she told Nancy of Will's absence straight away: it would have to be done sometime. She'd make a pot of tea for them both and then show her the letter. Alice felt so sad for her; it was bad enough that Gerald had gone to war, but for her husband to abandon her when she was eight months pregnant . . . that would no doubt tip the poor girl over the edge.

Hearing footsteps on the stairs, Alice took a deep breath, stuck her chin out and dried her tears, and then turned to face Nancy. The weight of the baby slowing her down, she entered the kitchen and smiled at Alice as she pulled out a chair and sat down. She took a long sip of her tea before speaking.

'That's good — just what you need to start the morning off. Do you know where Will is? I woke up this morning and his side of the bed was empty.' She peered at Alice over the edge of her teacup. 'I expect he's gone out with that terrible gun of his. I do wish he'd realize that he no longer has to kill things to keep us fed.' She took another sip of tea, and only when there was no answer from Alice did she look at her face and see the tears welling up in her eyes. 'What's wrong, Alice? Why the long face?'

Alice didn't say a word. She couldn't — the words wouldn't come out; instead there was this huge lump in her throat that she kept forcing down, along with the tears. Silently she passed Nancy the letter with a trembling hand and then wiped the escaping tears from her cheeks.

Nancy read the letter. She read it once and then she read it again, trying to take the news in. Not believing that her husband would rather go to war than be with her, would rather be killed on some foreign battlefield than hold his newborn baby.

'No, no! I don't believe it. He wouldn't leave me, he wouldn't walk out on me in this condition, he wouldn't, he just wouldn't. Help me, Alice, help me! I don't want to be left on my own. I've nobody, nobody, and I hate this baby and what it's doing to me.' She rocked her body, screaming and yelling with the grief of Will leaving her.

Alice hugged her sister-in-law, tears running down her face as she comforted her. What had he been thinking? How were they going to cope without a man about the house? Desperate to calm her down, she offered her an arm to lean on and suggested that she return to bed, murmuring words of encouragement as they climbed the stairs to the empty bedroom. The last thing they wanted was for the upset to result in the baby being born early. As she mixed her a tonic to help her sleep, Alice caught sight of yesterday's newspaper by the side of the bed, its front page full of news of the war and of patriotic propaganda, with Lord Kitchener pointing his finger and declaring, 'Your country needs you.' Alice pulled the covers over a sobbing Nancy and grabbed the paper. Well, that can go on the fire, she thought; it's done its job! And now because of it there were two heartbroken women and a baby about to be born without its father present. She pulled the bedroom's curtains and stroked Nancy's hair as she sobbed into her pillow.

'Hush now, we'll be all right. You know Will — he had to go. Where there's trouble, that's where he's got to be. I know he loves you — he's always telling me that he does and he'll always be there for you and the baby.'

She kissed Nancy's forehead, then left the room and went downstairs. She was fed up with lying, especially for her brother. He didn't love Nancy, he never had done, and he would never be satisfied with life. Well, there was only one thing to do and that was to get along without him. Somehow they'd get by — who needed a man anyway?

20

Gerald lit a cigarette and leaned back on a wooden crate, exhausted. Since the moment he had disembarked from the troop ship at Le Havre, he'd been on his feet virtually twenty-two hours a day. What little time he did get for sleeping was interrupted with the constant sound of shellfire and gunshots. He remembered the Channel crossing: the waters had been so rough that everybody had been sick and what had started off as smart uniforms were mostly covered with vomit by the time they reached the shores of France. Then there was the marching: a fifty-pound backpack plus weapons and ammunition to be carried all the way to the Belgian border. And on their arrival they'd taken a pounding from a gun that the soldiers had nicknamed Little Willie. Gerald remembered throwing himself on the ground as he heard a shell whistle overhead. All the soldiers who'd been stationed there carried on as if nothing had happened and didn't give the new officer a second glance. Since then he'd got used to gunfire, exploding shells and the never-ending casualties and deaths. Some of the young comrades he lost were as young as eighteen. These young officers, fresh out of Eton and Uxbridge, had arrived at the front line full of patriotic fervour and eager to fight for their country. Now, those that survived looked like him: gaunt and weary. Any illusions that dying for their country would be a glorious thing had vanished like the smoke that hung over the mud-laden fields of war.

Gerald drew on his cigarette and decided it was time to write home. He wondered whether Nancy was a mother by now and hoped that things were going well for her; she'd been so upset when they had parted that early morning at Dent station. He remembered kissing Alice on the cheek, and her standing watching the train pulling out of the station. What a fool he had been! He should have taken her in his arms and kissed her properly to say his goodbyes. Life was too short to abide by formalities. There were boys dying around him who had never kissed a girl, lads so young that they had only known their mother's love. And there he'd been with a beautiful young woman under his roof, ignoring her because of her class! Life was stupid. Death was stupid.

He cast aside his cigarette butt and dragged his boots through the mud-filled trench to the officers' dugout. There he found a pen and some paper and sat down to write home. How he missed home! What he wouldn't give right now for the comforts of the manor and his evening meal with a good glass of port . . . He must not think about it; Blighty needed him to fight and he was here to do his bit. Picking up his pen, he wrote:

My dear loved ones,

It has been some weeks since we said our goodbyes and I think of that moment with great tenderness. You really have to be here to understand what it's like, and I don't want to be too graphic about what goes on out on these flat French fields. However, I will tell you about my billet. I am sitting in a hole dug in the trench, five feet by three feet, with a board stuck up in the middle to support the roof. At present there are two of us in here. Later on, I will try to get my other officer in. It is raining and the mud at the bottom of the trench is a foot deep — in some places it's so deep it goes over your knee. Across the entrance of the hole is waterproof sheeting, now daubed with mud like everything else around here, but it provides some shelter. We are continually under bombardment and the earth vibrates with the big shells the Boche keep chucking at us. Despite this, morale is good. We are supplied with cigarettes, port and brandy, and reasonable food. The one thing that is not so good is the water. It is transported in petrol cans from our stores and they sometimes forget to clean the cans out before filling them with water. Tea flavoured with petrol is not to be recommended.

I'm sitting here wondering if I'm an uncle yet. Promise you will write and tell me — some good news would be cheery. Give my best to Mrs Dowbiggin and Faulks. I know the manor is in good hands while they stay there. I

miss you all greatly, but it won't be long before I'm home.
   Your loving brother,
   Gerald

He sealed the letter and put it in the pile of documents to be posted. Hopefully it didn't sound too downbeat. He didn't want Nancy to worry about him: she would have enough on with the baby. A shell exploded directly overhead and a whistle sounded; time to organize his troops and go over the top. How many would die this morning?

*   *   *

A fortnight of hard training had taught Will that, wherever he was going, it would be no picnic. He'd excelled in gunnery, but he was finding it hard to follow orders. If he could have rammed a grenade down the sergeant major's throat, he would have done. He was sick of training with full kit on, saluting and being shouted at. Now the order had finally come through: they were being shipped across to help hold the line at Ypres. Instead of bayoneting straw men and yelling at the pretend Hun, they'd be let loose on the real thing. At last they could do their bit for King and Country.

'Give us a light, mate.' The young lad next to him was trembling as they neared the shores of Calais. He seemed so young, Will wondered if he'd given the recruitment officer his true age. They'd heard the guns as they stood on the docks at Dover and now, as they were nearing French soil, they sounded even louder. The young lad's hand shook as he held the match to Will's cigarette. He flinched as an extra-loud shell exploded somewhere on the Belgian border.

'You're going to have to get used to that, mate. We'll be right under them in twenty-four hours.' Will winked at the young lad.

'I know. I just can't do with the noise. I've never heard anything so loud. I didn't think it'd be like this.' His face was strained and frightened.

'What's your name, and where you from? I'm Will, come from a little town called Dent in Yorkshire, which seems a million miles away now.' Will held his hand out.

'I'm Billy, from Buxton in Derbyshire. Me mam and dad farm, but I'd had enough, wanted to see the world.' He smiled and shook Will's hand.

'Well, Billy, you stick next to me and we'll get through it together. We'll show these bastards not to take us farm lads on. We'll make your mum and dad proud of you.'

Will looked at young Billy, still wet behind the ears, yet desperate to prove himself. How could he have envisaged what he was going to be up against? The way the lad was quivering every time a shell went off, he'd be a sitting duck on the front line. Will decided he'd make it his business to keep an eye on the young lad, keep him alive as long as possible. For the sake of Billy's mam and dad, who must be going out of their minds with worry, he'd be the lad's guardian angel without letting him know it.

His thoughts returned to his own life and the way he'd walked away from his responsibilities. By now things should have calmed down. Alice would have cursed him, and Nancy would be doing her usual wailing, but she'd soon have a baby to keep her busy. His thoughts were interrupted as the sergeant major gave orders to get ready to disembark. The clank of rifles, ammunition and backpacks being gathered up by hundreds of intrepid soldiers echoed around the ship. The atmosphere was so laden with fear, you could almost taste it and smell it as the aged troop ship docked.

'Stick with me, lad — I'll look after you. Keep your head down and your mouth shut and we'll make it.' Will pushed his protégé down the gangplank in front of him.

Orders were being yelled out left, right and centre as they marched out of the docks and down the road that led to the Belgian border at Ypres.

Ten miles from the Allied trenches, the troops rested for the night in a holding camp; even that far back from the front line, they could smell gunpowder and hear the pounding shells and gunfire. Will could hear Billy in the bunk above him sniffling and crying.

'Quiet, lad, you can't go home to your mother now — it's too late. You'll have to grow up and be a man. Get some sleep, 'cos this will be the last good night's kip you'll have for a long time.' Will looked up at the wooden boards of the bed

287

above his head and heard the young lad turn over. Not another word was spoken as Will gazed into the night. In truth, he too was frightened. He longed to be back at the little cottage in Dent, even if it meant putting up with Nancy's screams and his sister's caustic tongue. He knew now what a fool he'd been.

★ ★ ★

'For fuck's sake, Billy, keep your bloody head down — a good sniper could pot you off as easy as shaking hands.' The two men lay with their backs against the trench wall, both caked with mud, breathing heavily after making a dash from one trench to another. Will watched a rat run along the trench wall, squeaking as it went. It had no fear of the two men watching it; there were rich pickings among the dead and dying and it knew how to survive. 'Bloody flea-infested things! I woke with one of 'em running across my face t'other night.' Will lit a cigarette and offered it to Billy before he lit one for himself.

Billy inhaled the smoke and then exhaled slowly, watching the smoke rise above the edge of the trench. 'I hate 'em an' all. We used to have them on the farm, around the pigpens mainly, but never as big as this. These French rats are nearly as big as dogs.' Billy turned on his side and examined his canteen. It had taken a battering as he flung himself into the trench.

'Well, that looks knackered to me. We'll pick one up somewhere en route, or Sarge will issue you with one.' Will threw his cigarette stub into the filthy mud. 'Give us ten minutes and then we'll make our way over the top, back to our own trench. I'm a bit like your canteen — knackered. It's hard keeping alive with them bastards always taking a pop at you.' Will shut his eyes and pulled his cap down.

As he catnapped in the wet and filthy trench, Billy sat watching him. Will had found out everything there was to find out about him, even down to the name of his pet dog. But Billy knew nothing about Will, apart from the fact that if he hadn't had him as a guardian angel, he'd have been killed fifty times over. The rough Yorkshireman was a crack shot and a good comrade, but he kept himself to himself, never talked about his family or home. Billy closed his eyes; he couldn't sleep, but he might as well rest while he could. The non-stop pounding of the big guns and the cracking of rifle fire meant someone else was probably meeting their death right this minute. How he wished he'd not joined up. He'd seen things this last fortnight that a man his age should never see. His mind raced with faces that he'd never see again and the cries of dying men. Then a hand grabbed his shoulder.

'Some guard you are!' Will was shaking him awake. 'Come on, get ready — we'll make a run for it. All's a bit quieter at the moment.' He adjusted his tin helmet and stood ready with his rifle. 'You make the run first and then I'll follow. I'll cover you, but be bloody quick — no dawdling like an old fellow.' Will raised his head over the trench. 'Go on, then — there's nothing about. It must be Jerry's tea time.'

Billy's heart was pounding; he hated these desperate scrambles between trenches where you felt like one of those ducks in the shooting gallery at the fair. He climbed the wooden ladder up the side of the trench, his boots slipping on the mud-covered rungs and his hands shaking as he hauled himself to the top.

'Go on, fuck off then, else Jerry's going to blow you to bits,' Will urged.

He gave Will a quick glance and then scrambled the few yards to his battalion's trench, heart pounding, running half bent to dodge any bullets aimed for him. Overcome with relief, he threw himself into the relative safety of his unit. He'd just picked himself up and was about to peer over the trench wall when a shot rang out. So distinct and clear, it was a shot that would be with Billy for the rest of his life. As he stuck his head above the wall, Billy saw Will sink to the ground, a bullet hole straight through his head, blood streaming down his face. His eyes were wide open, staring at Billy as he fell with arms outstretched, trying to reach for the safety of the trench. He was dead; Billy's guardian was dead. The young man slid down the side of the trench, curled up in a ball and sobbed, every bone in his body aching and shaking. Why couldn't it have been him? Why Will? He'd always been able to hold his own, he didn't fear anything, and now he'd left him on his own.

Will's body lay on the sodden, mud-covered ground of no-man's-land until nightfall; then he was retrieved along with the other fallen, his details noted and his corpse buried in a mass grave. No ceremony, just another statistic, another life claimed by the endless pounding of the guns of war.

21

Alice sat at the kitchen table, Gerald's letter in her hands. She'd just finished reading it aloud to Nancy and was trying to head off the inevitable flood of tears by playing up the few positive points: 'At least he's well, Nancy, and he sends us all his love. It doesn't sound too bad: he's got food and drink and — '

'He's going to die! They are all going to die! He'll never come back. I'll never see him again. He'll be buried out there in one of those filthy trenches stabbed by a Hun carrying a bayonet just like Will will be and all because of me.' Hair uncombed and still in her nightgown even though it was mid-morning, she began rocking herself backwards and forwards in her chair. 'Everyone who loves me dies! I'm cursed!' she wailed, tugging at her hair.

'Nonsense! Lots of people have bad times in their lives, and right now there are thousands of young men out on the front lines. The one I can't forgive is my brother — trust him to take care of himself, leaving us like this with his baby due any minute.' Alice put another log on the fire. It was a cold, frosty day and the autumn leaves were falling from the trees. 'Go and get some clothes on — you can't sit around like that all day. We can't have the local gossips thinking that you are going around half dressed.'

Alice was at her wits' end. Ever since Will had

absconded to join the army, Nancy had been impossible. If it hadn't been for Jack occasionally popping in on his way up the dale to see his dad, she was sure she would have gone mad. It was Jack who'd brought the mare back after a traveller who'd been staying at the Royal Shepherd in Kendal delivered Will's message saying that he'd stabled the horse at the inn and asking Jack to come and collect it. He was the one who listened as she poured out her worries and cursed her brother for leaving them and going to fight in a war that had nothing to do with them. The rest of the time she kept her worries to herself, knowing there was nothing she could do and that sitting around moping would get them nowhere.

'Come on, let's get you up those stairs so I can brush your hair and make you look respectable.' She pulled at Nancy's arm to ease her up out of the chair.

'Alice, I don't feel well today. I keep getting a pain in my stomach. I've been feeling it for a while. I didn't want to say anything when you were reading the letter, but now I think I better had . . . ' She looked down at her wet nightdress and the puddle of fluid that had appeared on the floor underneath her chair. Then she screamed, not knowing where it had come from.

'Shh, shh, keep calm, your baby's on its way. Now, let's get you up those stairs and in bed while we can.' Though her voice remained calm, Alice was filled with panic as she ushered her screaming sister-in-law up the stairs. She needed the doctor, or at least old Mrs Batty, but the thought of her entering the house made her skin crawl. 'We'll get you into bed and then I'll have to run and ask someone to go and get the doctor.'

'Don't leave me, Alice, please don't leave me — the baby's coming,' she cried, grabbing Alice by the neck.

'Stop it, Nancy — it takes hours for babies to be born. My mother was on three days when she had Will, I remember her telling me. It'll not come yet, don't worry. Now that I've got you settled, I'll go and put some hot water on — we'll need it to wash the baby.' She paused until Nancy, gripped by another spasm of pain, had finished screaming. 'I'll not be long. Stop in the bed until I come back up and you'll be all right.'

She rushed downstairs, grabbing her shawl from behind the kitchen door, and ran as if the devil himself was after her across the fields to the neighbouring farm of Cow Dubb. Banging on the door and fighting for breath, she pleaded with young Ben Harper to go get the doctor from Dent and to be quick about it. As she raced back across the fields to Stone House, Alice looked over her shoulder and saw Ben galloping round the first bend in the road, his jacket flapping around him. By the time she reached the lane end she could hear Nancy's screams. It was all she could do to keep going. The muscles in her legs were burning as if they were on fire, her heart was pounding, and her lungs were struggling to take in air.

Somehow she found the breath to yell up the

stairs between pants: 'I'm coming, I'm coming, Nancy. I'm just putting some water on.' Hurriedly filling the kettle and putting it on to boil, she hauled herself upstairs to Nancy, who was screaming so loud Alice thought her eardrums would burst.

'The baby's coming, the baby's coming,' Nancy panted, perspiration running off her brow.

There was nothing else for it: Alice was going to have to deliver it as best she could.

She grabbed some towels from the bathroom and arranged them under Nancy. 'Breathe, Nancy, breathe. Try not to scream . . . I think I can see it coming . . . That's right. I think I can see the head . . . Push, Nancy, push . . . One more big one . . . Go on, you can do it.'

With an almighty scream from Nancy, the baby was born, its red face all screwed up and angry-looking. Alice wrapped the little mite in one of the towels, hoping that her attempt at cutting the umbilical cord would be acceptable to Dr Bailey, who was hopefully on his way. Exhausted and soaked with perspiration, Nancy lay back, grateful that the ordeal was over. Alice wiped the newborn's face and handed the swaddled bundle to its mother.

'You have a little girl, Nancy, and she's beautiful — just look at her!'

The new arrival's eyes were closed tight, as if she had no desire to see the world she'd been thrust into.

'She's beautiful, and she's all mine.' Nancy gazed down at her daughter with tears in her eyes. 'I wish her father was here to see her. Will he ever be able to see her, Alice?' A tear dropped onto the new baby's head, christening her with love.

'I don't know, Nancy. I really don't know. But she will always have us two, and we are all she needs.'

'I'll call her Alice — after all, you've brought her into the world. Alice Rose. Rose was my mother's name.' Nancy bent and kissed Baby Alice on the head. 'Hello, Alice Rose. I'm your mother and this is Aunty Alice.' She smiled at Alice and yawned.

'I'll go and get the cot; then we can wrap Baby Alice up and put her in it. The doctor's on his way — no doubt he'll want to check you over on his arrival.' Alice dragged the heavily draped cot next to the bed and gently placed the sleeping baby inside. 'Now then, let's tidy you up a bit, and then you can have a little sleep. You'll need all your strength with a new baby to feed.'

She helped Nancy into a clean nightdress and changed the bloodstained sheets, then lit the oil lamp in the window before leaving the new mother and baby. As soon as she got to the kitchen she threw the soiled sheets on the floor while she poured boiling water into the dolly tub, adding a good handful of soda crystals. Then she put the sheets in to soak. Once that was done, she sank into the kitchen chair. What a day! Screams, tantrums and now a new baby. Wherever Will was, she hoped he was paying for the sin of walking out on them.

The knock on the door gave her a start. She must have dozed off in the warmth of the kitchen. Alice stirred herself, checking in the mirror to make sure that she looked presentable before opening the door to Dr Bailey. The colour drained from her face when she saw it was not the doctor but the delivery boy from Dent post office. In his hand was a black-edged envelope.

'Beg your pardon, missus. Message for Miss Bentham.' The boy looked down at his shoes, his face red. Then he turned and mounted his bike in a bid to get away as fast as possible. This one wasn't the first he'd delivered and he didn't want to be around when the contents were read.

Alice was shaking as she opened it. She read the message once and then she read the message again.

It is my painful duty to inform you that Private William James Bentham, No. 289645 of the Northumberland Fusiliers, was killed in action on 4 October 1914.

By His Majesty's command I am to forward the enclosed message of sympathy from Their Gracious Majesties the King and Queen . . .

Not Will. It couldn't be Will. He'd have kept his head down. He thought too much of life to get killed! Then Alice thought of the new life asleep in the cot upstairs, oblivious to the cruel world she had just been born into. Poor little thing, she'd never know her father.

Alice sank into the chair, trembling as she read the lines over and over again. There'd been a mistake. Surely there had been a mistake? Will had not long gone. Surely they meant Gerald? Why had it been addressed to her? Nancy was his wife and next of kin. Alice lay her head on her folded arms, the message crumpled in her hand, tears rolling down her face and her small frame heaving with sobs, oblivious to the fact that she'd left the kitchen door open. She felt a hand on her shoulder and lifted her tear-stained face up to see the doctor standing by her side.

'Alice, are you all right? I met the telegram boy on the road up here.' Dr Bailey spoke kindly to her in a soft voice. 'Is it Gerald . . . ?'

Alice rubbed her red eyes and blew her nose. 'It's Will, Dr Bailey. He's been killed in action.'

'My dear, I didn't even know he'd gone to war! My condolences. I always seem to be bringing bad news to your door. Now, I must see Nancy, but I will talk to you once the baby's been delivered.' Dr Bailey was already on his way to the stairs, upset to think one of the local lads had become a war casualty.

'The baby was born about half an hour ago. Both mother and baby are doing fine. Nancy's exhausted — you'll need to take a look at her — and the baby's tiny, but she's all in one piece. I delivered her.'

'Does Nancy know about Will?'

Alice shook her head. How could she tell her on the day their baby had been born?

'It would seem you have had your fair share of

worry today, my dear.' He patted Alice on the shoulder. 'Put the kettle on and we will have a talk once I've examined mother and baby. I'm a good listener!' He smiled and picked his black bag up, taking his time as he climbed the stairs. He was beginning to feel his age and the cold northern climate was not kind to his rheumatics.

By the time he came down, Alice had stoked the fire and made a fresh pot of tea.

'Mother and baby are fine, Alice. You did a good job. Now, what are we to do with you? Are you all right, my dear? Life does seem to be throwing everything at you.' He pulled a chair up to the table and stirred a spoonful of sugar and a dash of milk into his tea while studying Alice's face. 'Will you be able to manage tonight with all this responsibility? The death of your brother is bound to take its toll, and on top of that there's the baby — I doubt Nancy will be able to cope with her. I'd keep the death of your brother to yourself as long as you possibly can. It's liable to send Nancy over the edge, and we want the baby to have the best start in life now, don't we? After all, she may well be the next heir to all the Frankland estates. God willing, Gerald will come back in one piece, but if he doesn't, that little girl will be worth a fortune. Of course, I shouldn't be commenting on this, but it would be in your interest to look after the baby, keep her safe, and one day you'll get your reward.'

Alice was taken aback. She'd known Dr Bailey was the Franklands' family doctor, but she didn't realize he knew so much about the family's affairs.

'I'll take care of her as if she was my own. And I'll break the news to Nancy when I think she can handle it.' Alice offered him another cup of tea.

'Good girl, I knew I could count on you. Now, I've given Nancy a sleeping draught for tonight. Have you everything you need to feed the baby by bottle? Ben Harper's cows give good creamy milk; it'll not hurt her to be on that for a day or so. It'll take a bit of pressure off Nancy — that is, if you think you can cope with giving the baby her night-time feeds? You don't want Nancy up and about, wandering on her own in the early hours.'

Alice nodded. She'd rather be in charge of the baby; at least that way she'd know that it was getting fed.

The doctor rose and put his hat on. 'Take care, Alice. I'm so sorry for your loss. I have a feeling there will be many more to follow, leaving behind a lot of broken hearts. I'm getting too old — I know what this world is capable of.'

Alice watched the aged doctor mount his horse with some difficulty. As he trotted off down the lane, her eyes filled with tears. She needed peace to mourn her brother. She longed to go up and talk to her Maker on the wild fell, but instead of the balm of fresh mountain winds on her tear-stained cheeks she would have to make do with the snug warmth of the kitchen.

22

Alice held the letter from the solicitors in Kendal in her hand, shaking her head in disbelief. What a state of affairs! She couldn't believe how men ruled the world when it came to money. She'd had a much better business brain than her late brother, yet here she was, left with nothing. Worse still, Nancy was penniless too. On Will's death, Nancy's inheritance had reverted to Gerald, leaving them with nothing to live on except the vegetables in the garden. What were they going to do now?

She stared out of the kitchen window, trying to organize her thoughts and come up with a plan as to what to do next, but it was impossible to think with Baby Alice screaming the house down. It seemed to Alice that her namesake had started crying the moment she was born and hadn't stopped since. Perhaps the baby could pick up on the tension that was building in the cottage. Alice clenched her hand in anger, screwing the letter into a tight ball. Shut up, just shut up for one hour, just sleep!

It looked as though she was going to have to pacify the screaming baby, because as usual Nancy was oblivious to the child's needs. She seemed to be oblivious to everything since the baby's birth. All she did was sit in front of the dressing-table mirror, staring at her reflection as she combed her hair. When she could be bothered to come downstairs, she'd sit gazing out of the living-room window. Although a month had passed since Alice had learned of Will's death, she still hadn't got round to telling Nancy. Given her current state of mind, it was too risky. For the time being, she was better off living in her own world and not knowing the truth. Oh, that dashed baby and her screams! There was nothing else for it — she'd have to go and get her.

'Now then, you awkward little devil, what're you screeching for?' She lifted the angry, red-faced bundle of noise from her cot. 'You've come to test us all round, haven't you, Baby Alice? I see — or should I say, I smell? — that we need our nappy changing. Where's your mother at? I'm sure she could do this — let's find her.'

The baby continued to scream as Alice carried her downstairs. A cold blast of air greeted them as they entered the living room. Nancy was sitting in her usual place, with the top sash window wide open and the wind blowing the curtains wildly about as she stared unseeing at the outside world.

'What are you up to? Shut that window. It's the end of November, not the middle of the summer! Here, take the baby while I close it.' Alice passed the baby to Nancy, making sure she was wrapped up warm in the cold of the living room. She slammed and fastened the window. 'What's the point of wasting money on coal for the fire if you're going to have all the windows open? Anybody would think we'd money to burn. I had to go scavenge the bit of coal we have off the railway batters as it is. Give me Alice back — she needs her nappy changing. Do you want to watch again? Then perhaps you can do it next time.'

Alice looked at Nancy as she took the baby from her, the little mite still screaming and yelling for attention. There was no response; Nancy acted as if she hadn't heard.

'Go and put some more clothes on, Nancy. You must be freezing, sitting in that draught with that thin dress on.' Alice lifted the baby over her shoulder and patted the screaming child on her back, hoping that she would stop screaming just long enough for her to get Nancy to put more clothes on.

'Did you not hear him?' said Nancy, as if in a trance. 'Did you not hear him shouting my name? I heard it on the wind. I've seen him walking up the path on a moonlit night as clear as day.'

'Who? What are you talking about? It's just the wind. It's blowing a gale.' Alice rocked the baby and patted her as she watched Nancy with her wild eyes.

'I'm not telling you! I'm not sharing with you. He's always been closer to you than me! Well, not this time; this time he's mine.' Nancy laughed a strange laugh and rose from the chair. She seemed to float past Alice, her silk dress swishing softly as she left the room.

'Since she had you, little woman, your mother's been getting worse, not better. I swear some days she acts as if she doesn't know you exist.'

Alice took the baby into the warm kitchen and removed her full nappy, replacing it with a clean one from off the airing rack. While the baby lay on the table kicking her legs, she filled a bottle with warm, creamy Jersey milk. Sitting on Alice's knee in front of the kitchen fire, the angry little body relaxed and suckled contentedly. 'You don't like being ignored by your mother, do you? That's why we have these tantrums. I'd be the same if I was in your shoes. I was lucky: I had a perfect mother. She was my best friend, my guardian and a wonderful mother, and I didn't even have the manners to say goodbye to her as she lay dying. How I regret that. No matter what your mother's like, she's still your mother.'

She stroked the little girl's rosy cheeks until she fell asleep. Alice gazed at her, thinking of the baby she'd lost, her mother and father dying, and what her brother must have gone through on the battlefield. Now he lay buried in a foreign land. Life had dealt her some hard blows in the last two years, but each time she had managed to bounce back. And she'd go on bouncing back. Somehow she would sort out the money problem. Gerald would surely have made some provision for the baby his sister was carrying before he went to war. She would book an appointment with the solicitor in Kendal, see what he had to say. Once she told him what had happened, Jack would probably offer to take her. She'd mention it to him when he next called by.

★   ★   ★

'Don't you worry about a thing, Miss Alice. They'll both be all right with us. I'm fair looking forward to having this little mite for a day.' Hilda Dowbiggin was cuddling the baby so tight it was a wonder she could breathe. 'And Miss Nancy will enjoy the change, so don't you worry, we'll be just fine.'

Alice looked over her shoulder at the plump housekeeper waving them off from the steps of the manor.

'I hope they know what they're in for with Nancy. Instead of getting better she's been getting worse since the birth of the baby.' Alice shuffled her clothes and made herself more comfortable next to Jack.

'Aye, she's in a bit of a state. I can see why you've not told her about Will yet. That would push her right over the edge. It's taken me a week or two to realize that I'll never see him again. I keep going over and over our last night in the Moon. If I'd known the silly bugger was serious about wanting to shoot the Huns, I'd have played hell with him. I thought it was all talk.' Jack flicked the reins and the horses broke into a canter along the flat road under Helmside and on towards Kendal.

'I miss him so much, Jack. He was the only one I had left. If it hadn't have been for Baby Alice being born on the day the news came, I think I would have probably fallen to pieces myself.' Alice smiled at Jack. She'd come to appreciate his company more and more, regarding him as her closest friend.

'I know, lass. I miss him too. I've no one to

have a pint with or go shooting with now. He may have been an awkward bugger, but he isn't half missed.' He squeezed Alice's hand with his free hand and gazed longingly at her. 'Do you mind if we pull in for a minute or two when we get to the Black Horse under Killington Fell? I'd like to give these two a bit of a break before climbing the fell road.' He nodded at his team of horses.

'No, that'll be fine. I haven't set a time with the solicitor. I only hope he can see me today, else it'll be a waste of our time.'

'No, Alice, I don't call it a waste of my time. We're back talking. Just like I miss Will, I've missed you all this time. You don't know how much I've missed you. I've never let on until now, but I heard you that day talking to the old horse in the stable.' Jack couldn't bring himself to look Alice in the eye while he confessed. 'I wish to God that I hadn't overheard — it broke my heart to think what you'd done with that baby.'

'But . . . but what you heard wasn't anything to do with you. I'm so sorry I hurt you, but believe me, the baby couldn't be born. Every time I saw it I'd have been reminded of the shame of that night . . . ' Alice's eyes filled up with tears. Had he really thought she was capable of destroying a baby she could have loved? As it was, the father would never have loved it, and she doubted that she could bring herself to love a baby if she couldn't even look at it without being reminded of the humiliation and hurt of being raped.

Jack reined in the horses. 'What do you mean, 'the shame of that night'? What happened, Alice? I thought you'd just been carrying on behind my back, like a bloody floozy. What happened? Tell me!' His face was red with anger as he looked at her tearful face.

'You don't understand,' Alice sobbed.

'Too right I don't bloody understand. I don't understand how a grand farm lass can turn into a common hussy!' Jack glared at her.

'I was raped, Jack! I was raped by Uriah Woodhead while his wife went to see her mother. Now do you understand?' Burying her head in her hands, Alice sobbed uncontrollably. She had been carrying her secret for so long, it was a relief to get it off her chest.

Jack jumped down from the trap, steadied the horses and went to help her alight. 'Oh, lass, I didn't know. I'll kill that bloody Uriah! He's always had a wandering eye, the dirty old bastard. It's the last bloody time he'll get my trade. I'll swing for him, so help me God. Why didn't you tell me earlier?'

Alice stammered: 'Because I didn't want anyone to know. I felt so dirty, so vulnerable — and who'd take my word against his?' She sobbed into Jack's jacket.

'Everybody would have listened to you! He'd done it before, with a lass from Gawthrope. He's a mucky old bugger when he's had a drink or two, and Annie does nothing about it except cover for him. She daren't do anything else.' Jack held her tight and gave a mirthless laugh. 'Like, I knew it wasn't mine, seeing you wouldn't let me get that far, but raped — I never dreamed that. The bastard!' He hugged Alice tighter still. He still loved her; if anything, he loved her more than ever now he knew she'd been faithful to him.

Alice held him close, loving the feel of the tweed material of his jacket on her skin and the security of his arms around her. She had even missed the smell of the carbolic soap that his mother washed his shirts in. He was all she had left of her old world and she was so glad that he was there. She held him tight while the cold November winds blew around them, glad to have him back as a friend.

23

'Now, Miss Bentham, how can I help you? Does this have something to do with your late brother?'

The solicitor's offices were dark, the green velvet curtains blocking most of the faint November light, and the air was filled with the smell of musty papers and books. Alice was nervous; she had never dealt with someone in authority before.

'Yes, that's right, sir — my brother, Will Bentham, and his brother-in-law, Lord Gerald Frankland.'

'I see. Well, carry on, Miss Bentham.' He looked at her over the top of his spectacles, eyes burning through to the bone, judging her character.

'My brother, as you know, was the beneficiary of his wife's allowance, set up by her brother, Lord Frankland. Since my brother's death we have not been receiving any payment because it has been withdrawn, yet I'm sure that Lord Frankland would want it to continue, especially as he is now uncle to a baby girl.'

'I see . . . Please give my congratulations to, er . . . Nancy? Is that correct? I see your brother was put in charge of the allowance because Nancy is not able at the moment to look after her own affairs. Is that still the case?' He flicked over page after page of documentation with his bony fingers.

'Yes, that's correct.' Alice felt as though she was being cross-examined in court.

'And am I also correct in thinking at this moment in time you are looking after her and the infant's welfare?' Once again he peered at Alice over the top of his spectacles.

'Yes, I am.'

'Would you give me a moment to read these notes? There may be something in here that will help with your request. I see that Lord Frankland does mention you in his instructions, so please bear with me for a moment, Miss Bentham. Unfortunately this war is making extra work and I've had no time to acquaint myself with these documents.'

He studied the folder while Alice surveyed the dreary office with its stacks of files and documents.

Eventually the solicitor looked up from the papers in front of him. 'Well, Miss Bentham, you are indeed mentioned — I have here a note in Lord Frankland's own hand assuring me of your good character and your dedication to his sister's interests. He has made provision that, in the event of his or your brother's death, Miss Nancy's monthly allowance should be issued to your good self. Thankfully, we have had no notice of Lord Frankland's death. Rather than wait for communication from his lordship, I think we can act on his behalf — after all, he has quite enough to be getting on with, fighting for dear old England.'

He signed a note to that effect and passed it to Alice, who took it gladly with shaking hands.

'Give this to my secretary downstairs and she will see to it that the allowance is paid to you. You may also be interested to learn that Lord Frankland states that, in the event of your brother's death, Miss Nancy, her baby and your good self are welcome to live in Whernside Manor. He must value your services highly, Miss Bentham.'

Conscious once more of coming under scrutiny from those penetrating eyes, Alice got to her feet. 'Thank you, sir. Thank you for your help. You don't know what a relief this is.' She couldn't believe it — they could live at the manor! She could have her old room back, and Mrs Dowbiggin and Faulks would be able to help with Nancy and the baby.

'Thank you, Miss Bentham. Regards to your sister-in-law and her child.' The solicitor busied himself with his paperwork, not even opening the door to show her out. After she had left his office, he sat back in his captain's chair and stared at the door. A young slip of a thing — working class, too, from the sound of her — and he'd just handed her the keys to the best house in Dent, and a good monthly allowance to boot. Some people had all the luck.

* * *

'Well, how did you get on?' Jack was waiting outside the solicitor's when Alice emerged.

Alice grinned. 'Let's just say I can afford to buy you a cup of tea and a cream cake at Simpson's café, if you wish, kind sir?' She gave a

311

playful curtsy, happy with her good fortune.

'Too right, lass — I'm blinking frozen. I'll not say no to a warm-up, and then we'd best get back. Looks like rain's going to set in and it's nothing of a job sitting sodden on this buckboard for twelve miles.'

'Right, take my arm if you wish, kind gentleman.' Alice linked arms with Jack and they walked across the road to the tea shop, giggling all the way.

'I have missed you, you know that, Alice, and I do still love you.' Jack leaned across the table where they were now seated and took her hand.

Alice blushed. 'Jack, we are in company — don't be silly.'

'I don't care if the whole world knows it. You've always been the one for me, ever since we were little. I'm sorry I weren't there when you needed me most. You promise me you'll come to me if there's anything you want.' He squeezed her hand tightly.

'I promise.' Alice smiled. It was good to have him back in her life. 'Come on, let's go — it'll be dark before we know it.' She linked her arm through his again as they left the shop, making their way to the horse and trap.

* * *

'Who's put that there? Who's dared to put that there?' Jack was visibly upset as he pulled a white feather from the tied-up reins. 'I'm no coward! I'd fight for my country if I really had to.' He squashed the feather in his hand, disgusted at

312

being branded a coward. He was doing his bit for the country by farming and making sure local shops were supplied. He glanced around the marketplace but no one met his eyes.

'Hush now, Jack, they don't know what you do. Whoever left it obviously watched us go into the café and assumed the worst. Forget it.' Alice pulled on his arm as the crumpled feather was thrown down in the road. 'Come on, it's been a long day and I want to get home. Things were going so well; let's not let a stupid feather spoil it.'

Jack spat in the street, then climbed onto the trap, pulling Alice up next to him. 'Isn't it enough I've lost my best friend, my boss is on the front fighting, and my father has made me go back farming? Mind, I'm not about to be made into cannon fodder, so perhaps a white feather is right.'

He whipped the team into action and drove them hard out of Kendal and across the wild moorland up to the Dent road. He was silent all the way, never looking at Alice, who felt that a good day had been ruined by a stupid, unthinking gesture by a total stranger. By the time they arrived at the manor it was pouring with rain and the grey clouds had come down the fellside, turning late afternoon as dark as night.

'You'd be best stopping the night here, if you can. You don't want to take the baby out in this weather — it'll catch its death. I'll come and take you all back up to Stone House in the morning.' Jack barely glanced at Alice as she alighted from the trap.

Her clothes sodden, hair dripping down her face, Alice looked up at him. 'Jack, please stop worrying about that blasted feather — it means nothing. You're doing enough for the country without having your brains blown out.' She shook her wet hair out of her eyes and gave him a smile. 'I'll see you in the morning, and thanks again for taking me — it's been a good day.'

Alice watched Jack ride off, his hand waving to her as he turned the bend of the path and went out of sight. She stood leaning against one of the pillars of the grand porch for a while, just watching the rain pelting down. So Jack still loved her! It was a good feeling to have. Trouble was, it didn't feel good enough. There wasn't that flutter that she got when she talked to Gerald, but since he would never be hers, perhaps she had better set her cap at Jack. At least he was a safe option. Was he the right one? Oh, she just didn't know! Her heart said one thing and her head another. With a sigh she turned and went into the manor.

'Aye, lass, you're soaking! Let's have them wet clothes off and get you into fresh ones. There's one of your old dresses still upstairs in the blue bedroom.' Mrs Dowbiggin passed her a warm towel from out of the airing cupboard and escorted her upstairs.

Having tousled her hair dry and got out of her wet things, Alice felt much better. She put on the dress and pulled a woolly cardigan over it. 'Where are Nancy and Baby Alice?'

'Miss Nancy's in her old room and the baby is

314

asleep. Pretty as a picture, she is, the image of her mother.'

'Thank you, Mrs Dowbiggin. Have they both been all right for you? Baby Alice can be a bit demanding and, well, you know how to cope with Nancy.'

'Aye, well, I thought I knew how to cope with Nancy, but she's terribly confused at the moment, doesn't seem to want to settle to anything. I even read her a letter that we got from Gerald, but she wouldn't sit and listen.' Mrs Dowbiggin picked up Alice's discarded clothes. 'I'll put these on the airing rack. They'll be dry by the morning.'

'You've got a letter from Gerald? We haven't heard from him in weeks. Is he all right? Is he injured?' Alice couldn't ask the questions fast enough.

'He's fine — or rather, he's tired, fed up of fighting and complaining of the food, but he sounds cheery enough. I'll give you it to read later. I thought you'd have received one from him. Although, I have to say I'm glad that you haven't, just in case he mentioned Will dying and Nancy read it.'

'It's so difficult trying to keep it from her. I've been waiting and waiting for the right moment, but she's so fragile. I dread to think what it will do to her.' Alice sat down on the edge of the bed and sighed.

'Aye, I'm sorry, pet. For someone so young, you haven't half been through the mill. Come on, come down into the kitchen while all's quiet and read Gerald's letter. I'll make you a nice cup

315

of tea before we serve dinner. It'll be a novelty for me and Faulks looking after folk again. Since his lordship went to war, we haven't been standing on ceremony round here. The old devil and me have lived in the kitchen. I doubt things will ever be the same after this blasted war.'

Alice settled in a chair by the kitchen fire and began to read the letter. Before long her face was glowing red with the heat of the blazing fire and the passion that she felt as she hung on every sentence of the precious letter. When she came to the line *Remember me to Alice and thank her for looking after Nancy — I really do appreciate her,* she stared at the letters on the page so hard it seemed they would be engraved on her memory for ever. She prayed that he would stay, keep his head down and come home soon. If only he would return to her, she might pluck up the courage to tell him how she felt. To hell with the consequences.

24

'Marry me, Alice, please marry me. I've loved you since we were little. There will never be anyone else but you for me; I know that now,' Jack pleaded with a dumbfounded Alice over the kitchen table as she nursed the baby. Baby Alice gurgled contentedly, granting her permission.

'Oh, Jack, how can you ask me to do that when you know what I've done? You know I'll always love you, but as a friend. You deserve better than me.' Alice blushed and played with the baby's rattle as if trying to draw attention away from her embarrassment.

'You know I'm a man of few words. I wouldn't be asking you if I wasn't true with my feelings. I can provide for us well. You know I've bought your old home and, after my father's and mother's day, I'll have my home and all. I'm worth a bob or two, lass, if it's brass you're worrying about.' Jack leaned over the table and then sat back, rubbing his head with his cap in frustration.

'It isn't that.'

'Then marry me. We are made for one another.' Jack was not for giving in.

Alice didn't know what to say. She didn't want to hurt his feelings by saying no, and she knew Jack was a good safe catch. But in her heart of hearts, she wasn't truly in love with him. He was too much like part of the family. She had grown up with him and he was beginning to be like a replacement brother to her.

'Give me till Christmas to think about it — it's only a month away, not long to wait for an answer.' Alice smiled at crestfallen Jack. 'I just want to be sure. Everything is happening so fast and I'm not over losing Will yet.'

'Sorry, Alice, I wasn't thinking. 'Course you're still in mourning. Still, I've got to say, Christmas can't come quick enough. Aye, lass, make it a yes and I'll be the proudest man up the dale.' A huge smile lit up Jack's face. 'I'd always be right with you, you know that.'

'I know, Jack. I just need time. I don't know what I want myself — all's wrong in the world. All of them young men fighting and dying for our country and here am I looking after Nancy and this baby here. I can't leave them — what would become of them? Mrs Dowbiggin and Faulks couldn't manage; neither of them is getting any younger. Give me until Christmas; by then we'll have moved back into the manor. And who knows, Gerald might be home by then and the war might be coming to an end.' Alice felt quietly ashamed of herself, making up any excuse rather than saying no.

'Right, Christmas it is. And if you say yes, we'll get married on New Year's Day, 'cos I'm not going to give you time to change your mind. Until then, I'll leave you in peace.'

Jack opened the door and Alice could hear him whistling as he walked down the lane. She didn't want to break his heart again, but while Gerald remained alive, there was still hope of her winning his affections, she just knew it — how could he resist? The thought of marrying Jack when she knew it was Gerald she had feelings for filled her with dread. Come Christmas, she was going to have to tell Jack the truth and hurt him. She'd written to Gerald, giving him the good news that he was now an uncle, and then informing him of Will's death. She'd cried as she'd written the letter, thinking of her father's saying 'One going out of the world and a new one in, always happens like that.' How true it had been that day.

She'd come to a decision about Nancy, too. By the end of the week, she'd break the news about Will's death. How she'd take it, Alice didn't know, but it had to be done. Alice could not carry the burden any more; she was worn out with their endless conversations about what a dead man might be doing in far-flung fields.

* * *

Nancy sat motionless. Not a tear, not a whimper, just a constant to and fro of her body, swaying in her chair as Alice told her of Will's death. She twisted her handkerchief tighter and tighter in a knot and gazed out at the rain trickling down the glass panes of the window.

'Do you understand, Nancy? You do know that Will's not going to be coming home to us, that we are on our own now?' Alice put her arm around Nancy as she stared out of the window.

Nancy lifted her hand and traced the downward path of a raindrop on the glass with her finger. She didn't say a word, but a trail of tears ran down her cheeks, mimicking the raindrops on the windowpane.

In the end, Alice left her there, not knowing what to say. It had been bad enough when she was heartbroken over Will choosing to go to war. Now she had to mourn his death and face the fact that she would never see him again.

★ ★ ★

The shells had pounded all morning, the constant barrage of guns and noise sending men almost to the edge of insanity as they wallowed in the thigh-high mud amid the dreaded lines of barbed wire strung out between the trenches.

Gerald Frankland was leading an attack on a patch of land just the other side of the Belgian border. It was only a few yards, but if they could gain it, the morale of his men would be lifted. A few yards meant a lot in this war.

'Right, men, listen for my whistle. On my signal, we go over the top.' Gerald lined up his exhausted and battered men. Their eyes betrayed the fear they were feeling; while some prayed to their Maker, others took deep drags on their cigarettes in an effort to combat nerves.

Gerald blew loud and clear on his whistle and the assault began, men scrambling over the trench, bayonets fixed, voices screaming and guns firing, both sides refusing to give an inch. Shells exploded, sending limbs and bodies flying. Smoke hung all around, and the smell of sulphur and the blood of dying men mingled in the air.

Gerald charged forward, yelling at the top of his lungs, bayonet drawn, leading his men into battle. He stumbled, only to get up again, yelling all the while. Then the ground gave way beneath him as a shell exploded inches away. Bleeding, injured and half buried, he lay fighting for his life in no-man's-land, while all around him his men were falling one by one. Consciousness came and went, and Gerald found himself crying out in pain with no one there to hear him apart from his dying comrades. The last thing he saw was the grey gun-smoke skies clearing and the blue of a frosty December morning shining through. The clear, sweet voice of a skylark trilled its song over the devastated battlefield. For a moment he smiled, remembering the clear blue skies of the Yorkshire Dales, and then darkness fell, his pain winning the day.

25

The rain had fallen every day since the trip to Kendal, never giving anyone the benefit of seeing a clear winter's sky for more than a few hours. The streams down the fellsides were in full flood with waterfalls splashing into deep pools and entering into the River Dee with force. The river had risen well above its banks, surging through the dale, uprooting small trees and dislodging boulders in its urge to get to the sea.

Alice stared out at the rain, unwittingly rocking the baby to and fro in her arms. She was turning out to be more of a mother than Nancy. Since learning of Will's death, Nancy had barely left her bed.

'I don't know, little one, this weather's getting worse. It's the first time I can remember hearing the river from here — it must be terribly high. It'll do some damage if it's not careful.' She folded the blanket around the baby's head and gently placed her in her cot. Baby Alice chortled happily, gazing at the woman she thought was her mother.

'That wind's getting up — just listen to it blowing down the chimney. We'd better get some coal in from outside before it gets dark. We're going to have to keep that fire going tonight, aren't we, my darling?' She tickled the smiling baby girl under her chin, then picked up the coal scuttle and went outside.

Leaving the door ajar behind her, Alice ran through the driving rain to the shed where the coal was stored. Behind her, the wind caught the back door and slammed it with an almighty bang. Moving as fast as she could with the full scuttle, Alice returned to the house and closed the door behind her.

'There, my love, we can close the door on the world now.' Grabbing a towel, she went to stand by the baby's cot so she could carry on talking to her while she dried her hair. When she lifted her head, Nancy was standing in the doorway, looking at the pair of them.

'Nancy, love, come and sit by the fire — you must be cold in that nightdress. I'm sorry, did I wake you up with the door banging? I've been out for some coal. It's such a wild night out there. Just listen to the wind blowing down the chimney! I wouldn't want to stop out in this.' Taking Nancy gently by the arm, she guided her towards the warmth of the fire. 'Why don't I make us something to eat? Would you like Baby Alice to hold?'

Nancy shook her head as she sat next to the fire.

'Here, let me put a blanket around you. There's a real draught blowing through them windows, even though I've closed the curtains.' Alice pulled a blanket from the old oak bedding box that had belonged to her parents and wrapped it around Nancy's shoulders.

'Have you heard the voice? I heard it as plain as day when I was lying in bed. It called to me from outside. Did you not hear it? It called my name.' Nancy gripped Alice's hand hard.

'Don't be silly, Nancy, there's nobody out in this. It's the wind you're hearing, that's all. There, do you hear it whistling down the chimney?'

Both women jumped as a loud knocking was heard on the door. Nancy shrank back in terror as if it was the devil himself knocking.

Alice hesitantly went to answer, nerves on edge after listening to Nancy and her story of voices calling for her.

There in the pouring rain was the telegraph boy. 'Sorry, missus, but I've got a telegram for Mrs Bentham. I had to deliver it even in this weather.'

The wind howled around him and the battered winter leaves blew into the house as the drenched telegram boy stepped over the threshold, his dripping waterproofs leaving puddles on the floor as he fished inside his leather bag for the all-important telegram.

'We don't want it! Whatever you've got for us, we don't want it — you must have the wrong house!' Alice didn't want to take the envelope from the boy: she knew what it would contain.

'Give it to me. It's addressed to me — I'll read it.' Nancy snatched the telegram from the boy's hand and went into the front room, clutching the rain-soaked telegram in her hand.

Alice looked at the shivering young boy standing on the flagstone floor of the kitchen. She knew what he'd brought and she didn't want him in the house a moment longer, but at the same time she couldn't send him back to Dent in this weather.

'Do you want to stay? It's not fit to return to Dent tonight — that river sounds really swollen.' She looked at the shivering, white-faced boy. He could only be twelve or thirteen at most; his mother must be worrying where he was.

'No, me mam said I'd to get home and not go near the madwoman. I'm more frightened of her than the weather.' He reached for the door handle, job done and his instructions from his mother calling him home, no matter how bad the weather was.

'Just a minute, I'll give you something for coming out.' Alice went to the kitchen drawer to get her purse. As she did so, a blood-curdling scream came from the front room. She turned to the ashen-faced boy.

'Thanks, missus, but I'm off. Me mam said the madwoman'll have me if I don't get home straight away.' Banging the door behind him, he disappeared into the wild night before Alice could give him anything for his bother.

Replacing her purse in the drawer, her heart heavy, she went to join Nancy in the living room. The baby had joined in with the cries of her mother, but Alice was more concerned with the contents of the telegram.

'What does it say, Nancy? Give it to me.' She snatched the paper from her.

'I told you I could hear him crying out my name! He's on the wind. I can hear him calling me.' Wild-eyed, Nancy got up, pulled the curtains back and looked out of the window, the palms of her hands flat against the windowpane.

Her hands shaking so much it was all she could do to focus, Alice read the telegram:

It is my painful duty to inform you that Second Lieutenant Gerald William Frankland No. 598624 of the Border Regiment is missing in action and presumed dead.

Please accept our sincere sympathies in your loss.

How many of these letters did the armed forces send out? Alice looked at the telegram, thinking about the wording and how the people who sent them must be almost immune to the constant stream of grief that they wrote every day.

'Nancy, he's missing in action; they are only presuming he's dead. It's not the same as the one I received about Will — Gerald might still be alive.'

'He's dead. I know he's dead. Can't you feel it? Something's wrong. I keep hearing his name.' Nancy made no effort to soothe poor Baby Alice, so Alice picked her up and rocked her in her arms as tears rolled down her own cheeks.

'He can't be! Both our brothers can't be dead; he's just missing.' Alice hugged the baby tight, needing a cuddle in her grief and the baby giving her some reassurance. 'Nancy, come and sit down. We don't know that he's dead. They will surely write again and confirm his death or tell us that he's been found safe and alive.'

She put the baby back in her cot and guided

Nancy to the fireside, settling her in a chair and stroking her long black hair. All the time she was trying to comfort her sister-in-law, she wept silent tears. Two deaths in two months; this was the second time in Alice's short life that two deaths had come close together. What had she done to deserve all this sadness?

That night she lay in her bed exhausted by grief yet unable to cry herself to sleep with the wind gusting around the chimney and the rain pelting down on the tin roof of the stables. It was the wildest night she could remember. Seeking the comfort of Baby Alice's presence, she crept to the cot, smiling at the sight of the perfect little girl with her arms stretched above her head, content even though a force-ten gale was blowing outside. Suddenly she heard the familiar creak of the top stair: Nancy must be awake. Alice opened her bedroom door and got to the stairs just in time to see her sister-in-law going into the kitchen. Perhaps she, too, was unable to sleep for thinking of her loss.

By the time Alice got to the kitchen, Nancy was unbolting the back door. 'What are you doing? You can't go outside in your nightdress in this weather!'

'Can't you hear him? He's up at the old marble works and he's calling for me to come. Will's there too — can't you hear them?' Nancy turned wide-eyed, then carried on pulling the bolt and lifting the latch.

'Nancy, come back. Don't be so daft — it's the wind! It's only the wind you can hear.' She snatched at Nancy's nightdress, trying to pull

327

her away as she opened the door, the wind and rain gusting into the cottage, snatching at the curtains and the clothes on the airer.

'Don't stop me, Alice. I must go — he needs me; he needs my help.' She pushed Alice aside with all the force of a madwoman, but Alice stood firm.

'Nancy, come, my love, come to bed. There's no one there; it's only the wind. Let me close the door and we'll go to bed.' Holding Nancy tight, she leaned against the back door, closing it on the wild night outside. 'Here, carry a drink of milk upstairs and let me tuck you into bed. There's no one there, believe me.'

'But I heard him! I heard him, Alice — he's out there in the wind and rain.' Nancy stared at Alice, eyes wild and tearful as she climbed the stairs to her bedroom.

'Shh now . . . ' Alice stroked Nancy's long black hair and pulled the sheets up to her chin. 'See? Nobody's there.'

Nancy lay in the bed and closed her eyes. Alice could hear the baby moving and the familiar muffles that usually turned into tears. She prayed that Baby Alice would hold on another minute or two before she started crying; she daren't leave Nancy till she was certain that she had settled. Thankfully the little one obliged.

By the time she crept out of the room a few minutes later, the first splutters of a cry were erupting.

'Now then, young lady, I've had quite enough of your mother tonight, without you starting as well.' She hugged the baby to her, the warmth of her body and the security of being held quietening the little mite. It wasn't long before Baby Alice was fast asleep, and Alice herself began to drift in and out of sleep, trying hard to stay awake but finally succumbing to exhaustion.

She didn't know how long she'd slept when she was jolted awake by a loud bang. Was that the back door slamming? She quietly withdrew her arm from around the baby and went to the top of the stairs. The kitchen appeared to be empty and everything was quiet. Then she crept along the landing and peered into Nancy's bedroom only to find the bed empty and Nancy gone.

* * *

Out into the wild, dark night Nancy ran, her sodden nightdress clinging to her skin, the voices urging her on. Through howling wind and driving rain she ran and ran . . .

Alice tore down the stairs, stumbling and banging her head hard against the banister in her haste. Lightheaded and with blood trickling down her face, she pulled herself upright and continued to the door. Supporting herself against the doorframe, she stood yelling into the night: 'Nancy, Nancy, Nancy . . . ' She kept on yelling until her voice was too hoarse to continue. Blood from her head wound was dripping down the back of her neck, and her body and face were drenched from the rain and battered by the wind. Upstairs she could hear Baby Alice crying. Reluctantly she closed the door, giving up on Nancy returning. Hopefully she'd have taken sanctuary in one of the old workmen's huts, but only daylight would reveal that. The baby was yelling loudly now, demanding attention. Alice hauled herself up the stairs and looked at the little one's angry face. As she leaned over the cot, she realized that she was dripping water on the baby. She pulled off her soaking nightdress and put a clean one on before picking the screaming bundle up.

'Hush, little one. Quiet now. Your mam's gone to look for your pa, but you've still got me. You'll always have me.'

26

When morning came, the skies had cleared and the wind had dropped. Her head aching, her eyes red and sore from the tears she had wept over all she had lost, Alice went to the kitchen window and looked out. Storm debris lay scattered on the ground, and the sound of the river in full flood filled the air. The sun was rising over Whernside, its weak rays caressing the reddish-brown tops of the fells.

After feeding the baby, Alice had spent the rest of the night in the kitchen, sitting by the dying embers of the fire and anxiously watching the back door, hoping that Nancy would return. She thought of Gerald and Will, both lost to the war, and the promise she had made Gerald: that no matter what happened, she would look after Nancy. She cursed herself for not looking after her, and not stopping her from going out into the night.

Wearily she climbed the stairs and tiptoed to the cot. Baby Alice was breathing heavily, fast asleep. Alice got dressed and put her boots on, then set off in the direction of the viaduct. From up there she would have a view over the marble works, maybe see where Nancy was. Leaving the back door open so she would be able to hear if Baby Alice awoke, she ventured up the hillside. The cobbled path was awash with small tributaries flowing downhill into the swollen

River Dee, and the stream that powered the polishing machine for the marble works had turned into a full-blown river. As she climbed, Alice called Nancy's name over and over, and when she came to the remains of the marble works, she searched the remaining workmen's shed, in the hope of finding her there. Not a sign.

She carried on up the slope until she reached the arch of the viaduct. From there she could see right to the far end of the dale. Somewhere out there was her sister-in-law; she only hoped she was safe and not, as she had feared in the middle of the night, lying dead and alone. The chill December air was crisp and pure, and the smell of fresh water cleared her heavy head. Alice gazed around her: even the sheep had gone, deserting the fell for lower ground where they might find shelter from the pounding rain that had fallen for the last few days. It was time to head home; Baby Alice would be waking soon, and her needs must come first. She picked her way down the rough cobbled road, her skirts getting wet and dirty. As she reached the final few yards, she saw a figure emerging from the kitchen doorway.

'Jack! I'm here, Jack, I'm here!' Alice yelled to him, desperate to stop him before he disappeared.

'By God, I thought you'd done a runner on me, but then I heard the baby making a noise upstairs.' He began to walk up the slope towards her. 'I was just checking the sides of the river — I've lost some sheep; silly bloody things crept down here to get away from the storm and ended up drowning — and since I was almost at your bridge, I thought I'd pop my head in to see that you're all OK after last night's storm.'

Hearing Jack rambling on about lost sheep, Alice covered her head in her hands and began sobbing uncontrollably.

'What's up, lass? Whatever's wrong?' Jack ran to her and put his arm around her. Only then did he see the cut on her forehead. 'Are you all right? Did you bang your head? What happened?'

Alice buried her head in the familiar smell of his tweed jacket, sobbing and pouring her heart out, telling him of the past night's events, of Gerald going missing and of Nancy running out into the night.

'Are you sure you feel all right after that bump on the head? In that case, go put the kettle on and make a brew. Get that young 'un upstairs fed and this house warmed up. I'll organize a search party — she can't have gone far. And stop fretting. You couldn't have stopped her: she's been off her head for months now. The news of Gerald must have been the last straw.' Jack gave Alice one last comforting hug as she sniffed and filled the kettle with brown floodwater from the tap, ready to boil for tea. 'As soon as I've got any news, I'll come back and tell you.'

Though he managed a smile for Alice, in his heart he feared the worst. Nobody could survive out in the open on a night like this. He only hoped that Nancy had found shelter.

★ ★ ★

It was nearly dusk by the time a weary and down-hearted Jack entered the kitchen at Stone House. He didn't want to break the news; he felt sick with the day's findings.

'Well, did you find her? Has anyone seen her? Please, Jack, tell me. I've been going out of my head with worry all day. I've felt so helpless, stuck in the cottage with the baby, not able to do anything.' Alice tugged at his jacket as he steered her to the chair next to the fire and sat her down.

'Aye, we found her. I'm sorry, Alice, I don't know how to tell you . . . ' He bent over and gazed into the fire, rubbing his head with his hand. 'There's no easy way to say this: we found her drowned, in the river at Cow Dubb. She was washed up, tangled in some tree roots. She must have fallen in last night. She wouldn't have stood a chance: the river's still in flood today and it was a torrent last night.'

'No, she can't be! She just can't be! That's everyone gone. There's nobody left.' Alice crumpled in a heap on the pegged rug in front of the fire and wept. 'I'm so fed up of fighting, of being strong. Now I've no one.'

'You've still got me, lass. I'll always be yours, you know I will. I'm not sure what to do for you, but I promise you I'll always be there.' Jack sighed, looking at her distraught face. 'To make matters worse, they've found young Tommy Goad, the telegram boy, just below Bath Bridge. He must have tried to take a shortcut home down the back lane and been swept off his bike. His mother will be heartbroken too. It's a right do. I've never known anything like it.' Jack put his arm around Alice as she rested her head on his knee, sobbing and wishing that she had persuaded the young lad to stay, regardless of what his mother thought of Nancy.

'Where have you taken Nancy's body?' Alice wiped her eyes and raised her head. 'Did you not think to bring her back here?'

'Nay, lass, you wouldn't want to see her, the state she was in. We took her to old Mr Batty's. He'll see to her. No doubt he'll be coming to see you once the river subsides a bit. Old devil will be rubbing his hands, thinking of the money he can make with this funeral. I shouldn't say it, but you know what he's like.'

'Well, he needn't bother. Nobody bothered with her when she was alive, so they'd only be hypocrites if they turned up for her funeral.' Alice was angry that she would once again have to do business with the Battys. She hated them, and even in her grief she was determined that they were not going to get the better of her.

'Now, what are you going to do, lass? You're in a funny position. I suppose if Gerald is missing, presumed dead, Baby Alice is the rightful heir to all his estates. Poor little mite, good thing she's too young to know of all these carryings-on.'

'I don't know . . . Gerald's solicitor will have to be informed of Nancy's death and Gerald being declared missing. We were going to move into the manor before Christmas, and I think I will still take Baby Alice there. It's where she belongs and, besides, I don't want to stay here. There's too many bad memories here for me.' Alice rose up from her knees. 'We'll manage

335

— you have to; no matter what life throws at you, you've got to get on with it.'

★ ★ ★

Alice looked at the concentration on Ernie Batty's face as he bent over his notepad writing down her wishes for Nancy's funeral.

'Satin inlay, did you say, Miss Bentham?' He had his professional slimy voice on and he smiled at Alice, showing his black stumps of teeth to her.

'Yes, we agreed on that — bright red, if we could, Mr Batty.'

'Oh! But, Miss Bentham, I don't know if that's proper in a coffin. I've a lovely shade of oyster silk that would be more fitting.' He rubbed his hands, thinking of the price he could charge.

'Red was her favourite colour and it showed her hair off so nicely. I want red, Mr Batty.' Alice returned his sickly smile, gazing innocently at him, while what she really wanted was to scream.

'Right, red it is. Horses, Miss Bentham — do you need a horse-drawn hearse? Nothing looks finer than horses with plumes . . . ' His hand made waves in the air, conjuring the forms of fine horses.

'Mr Batty, she's lying in your mortuary not twenty yards from the church. Do you honestly think I need horses and a hearse? Four bearers will be sufficient, thank you.'

'And finally, how many are you expecting for the funeral tea, and where would you like it arranging? Should we say tea for a hundred to a hundred and fifty?'

'Mr Batty, I don't know where you are getting those numbers from, but there will be four of us there. And what tea we will be needing will be ready and waiting for us at the manor.'

'I thought that you'd wish for her to have a funeral that befits her brother's title; that's why I came up the dale to sort it.' His smarmy act was starting to fail as he realized that there was not going to be a lot of profit to be had.

'Aside from her brother and husband — one of whom lies dead in France, the other missing and presumed dead — Nancy Frankland was loved by two good friends and two faithful servants. Those four were the only ones who really knew her, so those are the ones whom she would want at her funeral, no one else. We wouldn't want to be seen as hypocrites now, would we?'

'Certainly not, Miss Bentham. I'll see to it — her funeral will be small but professional.' He rose from his seat and put his tall black hat on. 'Thank you for your time. Your wishes will be carried out.' He grimaced a smile as he reached for the door.

'Just one more thing, Mr Batty — please send your bill to Bramble & Partners Solicitors. Their office is on Stramongate in Kendal. They will settle with you once they have dealt with Miss Frankland's estate. I'm afraid you might have a wait, as they are busy with a lot of estates given the times we are living in.' Alice couldn't be certain, but she was sure he swore as he closed the door behind him, mumbling under his breath.

She leaned against the door and surveyed the empty kitchen, remembering how Ernie Batty had asked for money up front from her heartbroken father after the death of her mother. She could still see her father throwing the few pence that they had onto the table for the money-grabbing couple to put into their pockets. Well, at least she had given Nancy the coffin she deserved and not the flimsy board one that her mother had been buried in.

She moved away from the door: time to pack. She was looking forward to moving into the manor with Baby Alice. The prospect was a ray of sunshine in the gloom. If she never saw Stone House again it would be too soon; there had been nothing but heartache since the day she'd moved in.

★　★　★

'Oh, Alice, it's so good to see you and the baby! At last you're back where you both belong. I just wish Miss Nancy was with you. We'll miss her so much.' Mrs Dowbiggin dabbed her tear-filled eyes. 'It's such a terrible, terrible time. Have you any news of Master Gerald? Is he still missing?'

Alice and the baby couldn't get into the manor for the endless questions that were being thrown at her as she climbed the front steps.

She gave Mrs Dowbiggin a kiss on the cheek and then passed the sleeping baby to her before taking off her black hat and hanging it up on the hall stand.

'We've not heard a thing, Mrs Dowbiggin; I only wish we had. It's the not knowing that's the hardest part.'

'Aye, and this little one's left all alone in the big bad world.' Hilda Dowbiggin smiled and tickled the chin of the dark-haired baby. 'It's a good job she's too young to know owt about it all. Now, I've put you in your old room and I've made what used to be the nursery up for this little one.'

'That's lovely, thank you. I'll just say goodbye to Jack and make sure he's all right for Friday and the funeral, and then I'll catch up with you and Faulks over a cup of tea.' Alice left Mrs Dowbiggin holding the baby and went outside to thank Jack for bringing them and their belongings down to the manor.

He was unloading the last case as she caught him.

'I suppose you're glad to be back here. You always wanted to live in a big house; that's what you used to dream of.' Jack looked at her, dressed in her mourning outfit; even in black she was beautiful.

'It's not for ever; it's only till I know what's going to happen to the baby. Are you all right for Friday? Can you still pick us all up and take us into Dent for the funeral?'

'Aye, I said I would. I'll pick you all up about eleven. I hope it's reasonable weather, I've had enough of this wet stuff. It's no good for nothing.'

Alice planted a kiss on his cheek and he returned with a kiss on the lips, holding her close and looking into her blue eyes.

'See you Friday. Behave yourself.' With a smile he climbed into the trap and whipped his horses into action.

Alice watched him go. He would want to know where he stood with her before long. Trouble was, she had no idea what she wanted: her head said marry him, but her heart said no.

★   ★   ★

The cobbled streets of Dent were empty as the small procession walked the few yards to the church, following the beautifully carved coffin along the iron-railed path, passing the ancient tombstones inscribed with the names of people long since gone. Mist gathered around the fells, making the air heavy and dank as the small funeral party entered the church. The vicar, who had never met Nancy in her lifetime, preached a quick sermon on good morals and the way to lead a decent life. The few mourners bowed their heads and listened as his voice echoed from the pulpit.

Alice sat staring out of the window. She'd no time for religion: God had not been kind to her, so why did she need Him? But at the same time there was something inbred in her that made her still respect the church. She bowed her head as the Lord's Prayer was said; she'd been taught the words as a child, but she was too bitter to say them. They meant nothing to her. If God was so good, why had He taken so many people away from her? Jack squeezed her hand and sneaked a quick look at her as the vicar came to the end of his prayers. She smiled bravely and stood up, ready to follow the coffin out into the graveyard. Faulks put his arm around Mrs Dowbiggin, steadying the distraught cook, who had been more mother than housekeeper where Nancy was concerned. They walked, the vicar continuing the prayers, down the grassy bank to where Nancy's final resting place was going to be, and there they gathered around the grave watching the bearers gently lower the coffin into the deep, dark hole.

As the coffin disappeared into the depths, Alice turned her eyes to the surrounding fells. She'd done this too often; she didn't want to be here again. Once the coffin had been lowered, she walked over to her mother and father's grave, knelt down and said a few words to both, tears in her eyes. There would never be a grave for Will; he'd never be with his family, where he belonged, under the home turf of Dent. Instead he was lost on the battlefields of France, buried with hundreds of unknown soldiers. She got to her feet, crying, Jack by her side. Once again she turned and sobbed into the comfort of his jacket, but at the same time she was angry, she was so angry. Why had life dealt her such a bad hand? Perhaps it was time to play it at its own game. She'd had enough unhappiness; that she was sure of.

'Come on, pet, there's nothing you can do about what life throws at you. Time to move on.'

Jack put his arm around her and walked with her out of the churchyard and across to his horse and trap.

Faulks and Mrs Dowbiggin were waiting, both looking sombre as Jack gave Alice a hand up into the trap, making sure that her black skirt was all gathered in and that his two extra passengers were sitting comfortably.

'I never want another day like this one. My nerves couldn't stand it.' Mrs Dowbiggin dabbed her eyes with her violet-scented handkerchief. 'And to think it's Christmas Day in a week! When I think back to last year at this time, everything was so different. This blasted war is to blame for everything. I still can't understand why we are in it!'

'Hush now, Hilda, don't you go having one of your do's. We've tea to serve when we get back to the manor.' Faulks kept his cool as he tried to stop Mrs Dowbiggin from getting in a fluster.

Alice watched the familiar countryside go past as Jack's team of horses made their way quietly home to the manor. She looked around her at the bare brown fields and dark silhouettes of the trees in winter. It'd soon be spring and the vibrant greens of the new season would be showing through. With the new year would come new hope and new aspirations. She just needed to get over the next few weeks and then things would seem better with the spring sun shining. She sighed and folded her gloves, which caught Hilda Dowbiggin's attention.

'Are you all right, my dear? It's been a terrible time for you, more so than for any of us

— you've been in the thick of it.' She reached across and patted Alice's knee.

'Yes, I'm fine, thank you, Mrs Dowbiggin. Just wondering what the next year will bring. Surely it can't be as bad as the last two.'

'Well, let's hope not, my dear. Do you think Baby Alice will have behaved for her new nursemaid? It was good of Mr Bramble to engage one so fast on behalf of Master Gerald. At least it gives you your life back, my dear. What will you do with yourself now?' Hilda Dowbiggin enquired, her curiosity getting the better of her as they pulled up at the steps of the manor. Jack opened the trap door and gave Mrs Dowbiggin his hand.

'I tell you what she's going to do, Mrs Dowbiggin — she's going to wed me, that's what she's going to do.' Jack looked up at Alice as the stout housekeeper sat gaping at him. 'I've waited long enough for an answer, Alice. Now marry me, and come and live back at your old home, back where you belong.' He stood his ground, waiting for Alice's answer, taken aback by his own forthright manner.

Alice looked at him. Should she? He offered stability; he was worth money; she knew all about him . . . There was just one thing wrong: he wasn't the dashing Gerald! She looked at the two elderly servants standing on the steps like a pair of statues, waiting for her answer. She blushed and fiddled with her bag, not knowing what to say.

'Well, what's your answer?' Mrs Dowbiggin prompted her.

Alice looked at the three faces beaming at her. 'Yes! My answer is yes, I'll marry you, Jack Alderson, and we'll make Dale End our home.' She could feel a lump in her throat and wanted to burst into tears. She'd no option but to marry him: it was security and he was a good man.

'You will? You've said yes! I can't believe it! I'll turn the trap round and set a date with the vicar straight away.' Jack was over the moon with delight.

'You will not, Jack Alderson — we've just come away from a funeral; show some respect,' Alice chastised her husband-to-be. 'We'll both go and see him after Christmas when we have finished mourning and have shown respect to the ones we have lost.'

Jack held her tightly around the waist and kissed her on the cheek, nearly making Mrs Dowbiggin faint with the sight of him being so forward. 'We'll be happy, my love. I'm sure we'll be happy.'

'Aye, well, that's enough of that. Remember we've just come back from a funeral and there's a baby in there without a mother. Keep the celebrations quiet for now.' Alice climbed the steps and watched Jack as he led the horses away. She sighed. She'd said it now: she was going to have to marry him. For better or for worse, she was getting married.

27

'Come on, Miss Alice, you're going to have to get a move on — it's ten o'clock already. Another two hours and you'll be walking down the aisle. Just look at the garden; you can tell it's the first day of spring. I've never seen as many daffodils. The lawn is covered with them.'

Mrs Dowbiggin bustled around as Alice gazed out across the grounds of the manor. It would be the last time she looked out of the huge bay windows and admired the well-kept grounds. After today she would be back to low ceilings and the small windows of Dale End, with no beautiful garden or wallpapered walls. Ah, well, she should have known that none of this could ever be hers. She ran her fingers over the back of the leather Chesterfield suite and made her way up to her room to change into her wedding dress. It was all laid out for her on the bed, simple but beautiful, with small satin buttons that fastened the high neckline round her slim neck and circled her dainty wrists, every inch of her body being flattered by the elegant design. The dressmaker had said she was a dream to make a dress for because of her slight figure. She'd stood while pins had been stuck into her and tucks had been made at strategic points until the beautiful dress had been finished and everyone had stepped back and admired the craftsmanship that had gone into it and how

345

beautiful she looked.

To Alice, it felt more like dressing in slave chains. She didn't want to go back to farming, getting up first thing in the morning to milk cows, and having to eke out a meagre existence on a bleak fellside. She'd enjoyed the few months she had lived at the manor. Baby Alice had settled with her nursemaid, leaving Alice with time on her hands — perhaps not a good thing, as her mind had been doing overtime. The devil making work for idle hands, as her father once said when she'd done something wrong instead of helping him.

She pulled her silk stocking up her leg and fastened her suspenders, slipped her silk cami down over her body and studied herself in the mirror of the wardrobe. She looked tired; after all, she hadn't slept for a night or two, wondering if she dared go through with the wedding, wondering whether to pack a bag and walk over to the next dale, where nobody knew her. But that wasn't her style. She'd never walked away from anything, and she couldn't break Jack's heart again. He was a good friend; happen in time she'd grow to love him. She slipped the wedding dress over her head and did up all the buttons, then sat on the edge of the bed to put on her shoes.

There, she was dressed. She just needed the hat from downstairs and the bunch of primroses and violets that Jack had picked for her. She flicked her long hair over her shoulder and walked down the sweeping staircase. She remembered the first time she had walked down those stairs, conscious of the stares of all the Frankland ancestors in their picture frames, watching the young country lass with attitude, saying what she thought, regardless of her class. She'd learned a lot since then.

★ ★ ★

'Miss Alice, you look beautiful, absolutely beautiful! We are so proud of you.' Mrs Dowbiggin brushed tears away as she watched Alice glide across the hallway. 'Say something, you big useless lump.' She dug Faulks in the ribs as he stood next to her.

'You do indeed, my dear. I don't think I've ever seen a more beautiful bride.' He smiled at Alice and then scowled at Mrs Dowbiggin. 'I believe your carriage awaits outside, Miss Alice. There is a stable boy with a decorated trap. I understand your husband-to-be has sent it for you.'

Alice couldn't resist opening the front door for a quick peek at her transport before putting her hat on. Standing in the courtyard was Jack's trap, decorated with white blossom from the hedges, and his team of horses had their manes plaited with blossom threaded between the braids. It must have taken him ages.

'Good morning, Miss Alice. Mr Jack says he hopes that you like the trap and he's waiting for you at the church.' The young stable boy smiled and pulled at the horses' harnesses as they reared their heads.

Alice blushed and closed the door, checking

herself in the hall mirror and arranging her hat so that the white veil from around the large brim fell about her face.

'Here's your flowers, love. I've put a bit of ribbon round them and tried to make them look posh.' Mrs Dowbiggin passed her the posy and squeezed her hand, and then Faulks opened the door for her to mount the trap.

'I'll miss you both, you know that.' Alice hugged the stout figure of Mrs Dowbiggin and kissed Faulks on the cheek. 'You've both been good to me.' Her eyes were filled with tears.

'Get away, go on, be gone with you — your man's waiting. You know where we're at. You know you can always come and see Baby Alice at any time. Now go on, get gone, before I start crying.' Mrs Dowbiggin shooed her out of the hallway and down the steps.

It was too late to turn back. Alice could hear the church bells ringing out in the distance. It was her wedding day and Jack was waiting.

★　★　★

Alice stepped out of the trap onto the cobbled street of Dent. A few locals were gathered around the church gate to wish the new couple well and they watched as she nervously walked up the path. Her stomach was churning and her heart was still asking her head why she was going through with the marriage. She reached the porch entrance and swallowed, keeping her stomach in check, then stepped up to the doors of the church. Jack's father took her arm as soon as she entered. He was a man of few words and just smiled as he offered her his arm. They walked up the aisle to the traditional wedding march until she was at Jack's side. He looked nervous, scrubbed to within an inch of his life, with shiny cheeks and pink blossom in his button-hole that matched them. He smiled and shuffled his feet, looking at his beautiful bride.

The vicar smiled at Alice, his long, thin body towering in front of them in his white surplice.

'Please be seated.' The few people present duly sat, and then he cleared his throat and continued with the service.

Alice glanced nervously at Jack as the congregation rose to sing the first hymn. The notes from the ancient church organ were not quite in tune with the congregation as both organ and vicar sang in a higher key.

It was at the end of the last verse of the hymn that everyone turned their heads when they heard the church door open. Slowly a figure entered, gradually emerging from the shadow of the clock tower and into the spring light that was streaming through the windows. Thin and unsteady on his crutches, Gerald Frankland walked up the aisle, his face scarred and drawn. He stopped three pews away from the couple, just standing in the aisle, before sitting awkwardly down.

Alice couldn't believe what she was seeing. Forgetting where she was, she dropped her wedding posy and rushed to his side, dropping down on her knees, speechless, with tears in her eyes. Jack just looked on, not knowing what to do. The vicar tactfully gave a small cough, urging Alice to rejoin her husband-to-be. She rose to her feet, tears streaming down her face. Gerald was alive! The man she secretly loved and adored was back, and there she was, getting married to a farmer's boy.

'Ladies and gentlemen, I want to remind you that we are gathered here today to join together John Richard Alderson and Alice Bentham in holy matrimony.' The vicar looked down into his prayer book and coughed.

'Just hold on, Vicar.' Jack looked at Alice, her eyes red with tears. Then he lifted her veil and kissed her.

'This is highly unusual! You can do this after the marriage, Jack.' The vicar looked displeased.

Jack blushed, uncomfortable. 'There's not going to be a wedding. I'm not going to be second best and marry a lass that doesn't love me. I don't think she ever has. She's never looked at me the way she looks at Lord Frankland there. And I don't blame you, lass. I'm just an ordinary fellow that does his best, but you will always want more than I can give you and he's got everything I haven't got.'

Alice sank into a heap, still clutching her posy, and wept. He was right: she didn't love him. She was marrying him for security, but now Gerald was back and everything had changed.

Jack reached for his cap and put it on. Placing his hand on Alice's head, he whispered, 'Don't cry, lass, you'll be all right. As for me, I'll just stick to my horses in the future.'

He walked down the church aisle past Gerald

and his family and out into the spring sunshine. The congregation listened to the sound of his horses and trap driving off across the cobbles, whispering and feeling uncomfortable at the unfolding event.

'I'm sorry, ladies and gentlemen, I'm afraid there will be no wedding here today.' The vicar walked down the steps. 'It seems that I nearly undertook a most unwanted service by one of the party.' He ushered the congregation out of his church, leaving Gerald and Alice alone.

Gerald gripped the pew and pushed himself up onto his feet again, making his way towards Alice.

'I'm sorry, Alice, I've ruined your wedding day. I shouldn't have come, but I had to see you. Every day when I was fighting for my life in that awful Red Cross hospital I thought of you — your blonde hair, those blue eyes, that mischievous smile and the way you can make me lose my head, like drinking the most exotic wine. When I went home to the manor and Mrs Dowbiggin told me you were here, getting married, I knew that I had to make speed and stop you from making the biggest mistake of your life.'

Alice sniffed and wiped her eyes, then looked at Gerald's face and smiled.

'That's better! Where's my feisty Dales lass?' Gerald made fun of her Yorkshire roots. 'Don't you know how much I love you? It's taken a bloody war to make me realize it and to know that class is nothing.' He hobbled forward on his crutches, then lifted her chin and kissed her on the lips. 'Come on, Miss Bentham, let's go home. I know at least three bodies who will be pleased to have you back where you belong, and Mrs Dowbiggin is going to be so busy with a proper wedding to plan, she isn't going to have time to gossip with Faulks.'

'Do you really feel the same way as I do, Gerald?' Alice lowered her tear-filled blue eyes, not daring to look him fully in the face. She felt sick with happiness and relief. She had almost settled for second best, until Gerald had rescued her. Poor Jack — she hoped he'd understand.

'If you'd been through what I have been through, you'd know just what you wanted. I know I love you with my every breath. Now, where's that reprobate brother of yours and my sister? I didn't see them as I entered the church.'

'Didn't Mrs Dowbiggin tell you?'

'Tell me what? I didn't stop. I had to get here and see you. What is there to tell? Is there another baby on the way?'

'Oh, Gerald, if only there was, if only it was such good news. I'm afraid both Will and Nancy are dead.'

'Dead? No, they can't be; they were both safe here in Dentdale. It was me who went to war to give them life and hope.'

Alice held his hand while she sat with him on the church pew and told the sorry tale of the two deaths. Then they walked out into the spring sunshine and she showed him Nancy's grave. Gerald bent down, his army cap in hand, and prayed for his lost sister. The newly sprung yellow cowslips nodded on the earthy grave in agreement with his prayers as a low cloud passed over the spring sun in keeping with the mood in the little village churchyard.

28

'Well, I nearly dropped down dead when I saw Master Gerald on the step. I hadn't time to tell him anything — he turned round as fast as he appeared soon as I said everyone was at Miss Alice's wedding. It wasn't half good to see him. Looks frail, mind you, but we'll soon build him up now he's home.' Mrs Dowbiggin kneaded the loaf of bread that was going to be wanted now that Gerald Frankland had returned. 'That poor horse of his got the biggest whip across its backside I've ever seen. I suppose he wanted to see Alice getting married. It'd be a change after dreary army life.'

'I'm just glad he's back — a fellow man in a house full of women. We can stand together against you females.' Faulks folded his newspaper.

'You, classing yourself in the same bracket as Master Gerald? He's twice the man you are, you old goat.' Mrs Dowbiggin patted her hands against her apron, causing a dusting of flour to cover the kitchen floor, before putting the loaf of bread to rise next to the open fire.

'You'd be lost without me, you know you would, you old fool.' Faulks winked at the blushing Mrs Dowbiggin, then buried himself in his newspaper.

'Happen I would. We go together like a pair of well-worn shoes. Life wouldn't be the same without you.' She busied herself and cleaned the pine table, not looking at the smiling Faulks. They'd been in service together for years and she was content in his company.

* * *

'Put the kettle on, Mrs D — we are home,' Gerald Frankland yelled across the hall after slamming the front door. 'We'll be in my study.'

'We? Who's we?' Mrs Dowbiggin looked at Faulks in puzzlement. 'Well, go and see who's with him. You need to welcome him back; that'll give you an excuse to see who's there.'

Faulks folded his paper, rearranged his waistcoat and solemnly made his way to the study. He coughed before knocking on the door and entering.

'Come in, Faulks. How have you been, old man? There was many a day when I could have done with your service, when my boots needed cleaning and my buttons shining.' Gerald Frankland held his hand out to be shaken by his trusted old butler.

'It's good to see you, sir. May I say it's a pleasure to see your smiling face. It seems a lifetime ago that you left us for the front. Was it terrible out there, sir? From what I understand, we've suffered a shocking loss of young life.'

'I prefer not to talk about it, Faulks. I'm trying hard to forget the whole terrible episode.'

'Of course, sir. I understand.' Faulks coughed politely. 'Did sir say he wanted tea? One cup, is it, sir?' Faulks had spotted the delicate white lace of a woman's dress from behind the winged chair that was facing out of the study window.

'No, Faulks — allow me to introduce my wife-to-be. I'll be needing two cups of tea and, I suspect, smelling salts for Mrs Dowbiggin. Alice, take my hand, my darling. Rescued in the nick of time, Faulks: the woman who kept me alive. All those months in those dreaded trenches and hospital, this face of an angel kept smiling at me and I knew I had to survive to marry her.'

Alice stood up, bashfully holding Gerald's hand, not quite knowing what to say to the gobsmacked Faulks.

'But Miss Alice was marrying Jack. I don't understand.'

'She was, Faulks, but I saved her and now we are to marry. Go! Go and tell Mrs Dowbiggin — no doubt she will have something to say. And ask the nursemaid to bring me my niece. I want to see who she takes after. If it's her delightful aunt, then I'm doubly blessed.'

Alice smiled at Faulks as he walked out of the study door. Gerald grabbed her by her waist and held her tightly in his arms. 'I see nothing's changed here: the servants still need to be the first ones to know the news.' He smiled and kissed her hard on the lips. 'That tastes good. You don't know the times I've dreamed of that when I was lying in that dreadful hospital bed.'

'Gerald, behave yourself! What would Faulks think if he walked in? Besides, they have been wonderful to me since Nancy and Will died; they've always been there for me.'

'To hell with them. I'll kiss you when I want.

You're mine now and I want everyone to know it.' Gerald's dark eyes flashed as he held Alice tight and kissed her more firmly. 'Tonight you'll sleep with me. I've needed company for so long.'

'Gerald, I can't, it wouldn't be right. This was supposed to be my wedding night, in case you've forgotten.' Alice was horrified. 'We need to take things slower, do this the right way.'

'Nonsense. Just pretend it is your wedding night, that I'm your husband. I assure you I won't be as disappointing as your farm boy.'

Gerald released Alice when the nursemaid knocked on the door and entered the study carrying Baby Alice in her arms.

'So this is my niece.' Gerald peered over the cream lace blankets at the dark-haired baby.

'Would you like to hold her, sir?' The portly nursemaid offered the gurgling baby for him to hold.

'Oh my God, no. Babies are for women. You won't catch me holding one. Is she perfect? Nothing wrong with her? Is she showing signs of having all her faculties?'

'She's perfect, sir. Aren't you, my little angel?' The nurse tickled under Baby Alice's chin, making her smile and blow bubbles.

'Good, good, I'm glad to hear that. I was worried, you know. You can't be too sure. Er, now I've returned and Miss Alice is to be my bride, I'm afraid I won't have need of your services.' He looked at the distraught nursemaid and then at Alice. 'Of course, I will pay you to the end of the week, and then Miss Alice will take charge of your ward.'

The nursemaid fought back tears. She had been so contented looking after the beautiful little girl and it had given her a purpose in her life, but now she was without a home and pay.

'Thank you, sir. I'll pack my bags and be gone by Friday.' She curtsied with the baby still in her arms and left the room.

'Gerald, that was hard. Of course I'll be glad to look after Alice, but an extra pair of hands would be useful around the place.' Alice frowned, wondering what was going on in Gerald's mind.

'We don't want a nursemaid wandering around the place. Besides, she isn't exactly an oil painting — a bit dour in that black dress.'

'She's just lost her husband: he was killed at the Somme. I thought you'd be more understanding of a war widow who was trying to make a living.' Alice turned and stared at Gerald. Even in the few hours that she had been with him she'd realized that he'd changed since he'd come home from the war.

'She'll make a living somewhere else. Now, where is that blasted Faulks with our tea? I could have made it myself at this rate.' Gerald stormed out of the study in pursuit of his elusive cup of tea, shouting for Faulks as he crossed the hallway.

Alice flopped into her chair. Had she done right? She did love him, but she wanted to take things more slowly, not be bedded on the first night of his return. Perhaps she could talk him out of it. Besides, her mind would only keep wandering to thoughts of Jack; after all, it was his bed she was meant to be in. Poor Jack, he'd been a good friend and always would be. She only hoped that he'd forgive her for the way she felt about Gerald. He had to be the one: he had the looks, the charisma and most of all the money — what else could a girl want?

* * *

Gerald sat in his study before retiring to his bed. Will was dead, likewise Nancy. Leaving just Alice, his flight of fancy, the one he had to have. Just why he had become obsessed with her when he was in the trenches, he could not understand. A waiflike commoner, yet she'd been the fantasy that had kept him alive through the fighting. What a sight she'd looked, marrying that oaf of a farmer. Gerald swilled the last dregs of brandy around his glass and smiled. He'd enjoy bedding her. The ever-willing Alice was waiting and he could resist no longer.

* * *

Alice lay back beneath the crisp sheets of the master bed, the morning's sun shining through the windows and an early visitor of a swallow was tweeting outside. She sighed and ran her fingers through her long blonde hair, feeling the warm imprint of where Gerald had lain. It had been a night of lust and passion, neither of them holding back their hunger for sex. Alice had soon forgotten that she should have been in the arms of Jack as the experienced hands of Gerald held

359

and caressed her most intimate parts, making her feel more pleasure than she ever had in the hands of a man. At first she'd been frightened, remembering the feeble fumblings of Old Todd and the aggression Uriah Woodhead had shown her when she was raped in the bedroom of the Moon, but these memories had all faded into insignificance as Gerald held her close and spoke his words of magic.

He must have woken early and crept out of the bedroom; it was still well before six and the manor was silent. Alice sat on the edge of the bed looking at herself in the full-length mirror for a moment, then pulled her dressing gown around her. On her way to the bathroom she saw Gerald in his nightshirt, leaning over the baby's cot in the adjacent bedroom. Not a sound did either of them make; he was just staring at the sleeping baby. She walked into the room behind him and slipped her arms around his waist.

'Penny for them?' Alice smiled and kissed him behind his ear.

'What's that? What did you say?' Gerald spun round and faced her. 'Don't you ever sneak up on me again.'

'I only meant a penny for your thoughts. You looked so intent as you stared at little Alice. I'm sorry if I disturbed you.' Alice loosened her grip as Gerald turned back to the sleeping baby.

'I thought I heard her screaming, but she's asleep. I must have been dreaming. Do you think she's all right, Alice? She isn't showing signs of being like her mother, is she? I worry for her.'

'Don't be silly — she's perfect in every way.

She's got her mother's good looks with that mop of black hair, but she's as bright as a button.' Alice stroked the sleeping baby's cheek and linked her arm into Gerald's. 'Come on, come back to bed. Mrs Dowbiggin's beginning to stir and here's us in our nightclothes.'

'No, I'm getting up. I need to have a ride around my land before breakfast, see what's been going on while I've been away. So stop tempting me, woman, I've things to do . . . but tonight is another matter.' He slapped Alice firmly on her buttocks and chased her back to his bedroom. Then he quickly got dressed and set off, slamming the front door behind him.

Alice lay in bed listening to the horse's hooves clattering across the gravel and down the rough path. She'd got her man and a family. For the first time in her life she felt content; this was where she belonged, warm and secure in the fine bedlinen of the manor with the sun shining through the windows and breakfast being prepared just for her. Life couldn't get any better.

★   ★   ★

'Well, I don't know what on earth he's thinking about. He must have lost his senses — and she hers: fancy sleeping with another man on what should have been your wedding night! As for him, he's only having his bit of fun.' Mrs Dowbiggin was turning the spitting bacon in the huge frying pan as she shouted to Faulks,

361

without realizing Alice had appeared in the room.

Faulks's muffled cough made her aware of Alice's presence.

'Please don't stop on my account,' said Alice. 'You're entitled to your opinions. But let me make one thing clear: Gerald and I are to be married, so you will soon have to give me some respect as I will be the lady of the house.' Alice turned, her skirts rustling as she marched out of the kitchen, calling over her shoulder, 'I'll have my breakfast in the study, please, Faulks. Master Gerald's gone out on his horse and he may be some time.'

Alice was angry. How dare they gossip about her as if she wasn't there? She'd show them. She'd ask Gerald for an engagement ring and then they'd know he was serious. Maybe that would make them respect her.

* * *

'Mrs Dowbiggin didn't mean any harm, Alice. We both think a great deal of you. She was only trying to protect you. You see, we know Master Gerald, and he has always been hasty in his actions, especially when he sees someone else getting something he wants.' Faulks put the tray down next to Alice as she looked out of the window.

Alice was still angry as Faulks made his apology. 'That's just it, Faulks: he wants me and he is to marry me. Tell Mrs Dowbiggin I need to see her. We'll start talking about wedding plans this afternoon. I'm sure Gerald will agree. I think Midsummer Day will be ideal, don't you, Faulks? That is my birthday, after all.'

'I'm sure it will be ideal, Miss Alice. And once again I'm sorry if we were talking out of turn. I'll tell Mrs Dowbiggin to start thinking of some plans for your wedding day.'

He closed the door firmly behind him, leaving Alice playing with her scrambled egg like a sulking toddler, pushing it around the plate, uninterested in eating it. She would have the perfect wedding. He did love her — it was so obvious to her. Why could no one else see it?

★ ★ ★

It was nearly noon before Gerald arrived back at the manor. Alice had been wearing the carpet thin pacing up and down the study, preparing her instructions for Mrs Dowbiggin and her questions for Gerald.

'Gerald, you've been ages. I've been counting every minute.' Alice rushed to his side as he entered the study.

He poured himself a drink and sat down heavily in his chair. 'Bloody hard morning, Alice. I've called in at my lettings — nearly all of them have a lad missing or still over there fighting. I feel a fraud being discharged and back in my old life. You know half of them could have stopped at home; all they had to do was say they were needed by their fathers to keep the farms going. But instead they've chosen to fight. And for what? A bloody government that's using them for cannon fodder.' He swigged the last of his port and rose to pour himself another.

'I'll ask Mrs Dowbiggin to make us some lunch. You'll feel better once you've eaten.'

'Better? You think a bit of lunch is all it will take to make me feel better? Nothing's going to make me feel better, stop me hearing the screams and the faces of the dead, the rats and the squalor of the trenches. Yet here I am, safe and secure, lying to those poor, blissfully ignorant tenants of mine, telling them their sons and brothers will be fine, that they should be proud that they are fighting for their country.' He swigged his port and idly twisted the glass in his hand.

Frightened, Alice slipped out of the study. Gerald had changed; the war had left its mark on him.

'Are you all right, Miss Alice?' Faulks appeared, on his way to the study.

'Yes, thank you, Faulks. Could you take Master Gerald some lunch, please? And can you tell Mrs Dowbiggin that I won't need to see her this afternoon? I'll make it another day. Master Gerald isn't up to discussing weddings at the moment.'

'Very well, Miss Alice. Will you be partaking of lunch with Master Gerald?'

'I won't, thank you, Faulks. I'm going for a walk.' Alice thought she detected a smirk on the butler's face, but she wasn't going to rise to it. She knew why she'd cancelled and it had nothing to do with servant intervention.

She climbed the stairs and went into the

makeshift nursery. Baby Alice was asleep in her nursemaid's arms.

'I was hoping to take Alice for a walk. Would that be all right?' Alice leaned over and kissed Baby Alice on her brow.

'She's due for her bottle in half an hour, ma'am. I reckon she'll scream all the way without her feed. She likes her food, does our Alice.' The nursemaid smiled at the rosy-cheeked infant as she slept content in her arms.

'I'm sorry that Master Gerald said we could manage without you. Will you be able to find work elsewhere?' Alice looked at the nursemaid; she was good at her job.

'I'll go back to Sedbergh. I'm sure I'll find some job in service, or perhaps at the private school there. I will miss this little one, though. She keeps my mind off things.' She smiled and turned her head to the baby, her eyes filling with tears.

'I'm sorry. I hope life improves for you.' Alice pulled the nursery door closed behind her and left the manor. She wanted to be alone with her thoughts; in the last twenty-four hours her world had been turned upside down, and she didn't quite know what was going to hit her next.

29

Alice looked at the empty space next to her. The sheets and pillow were uncrumpled: Gerald's side of the bed had not been slept in. Hugging her pillow, she gazed at Baby Alice sleeping in her cot, blissfully unaware of her namesake's worries.

Three months had passed since his return from the front; three months of turmoil, getting to know the new Gerald with his moods and temper tantrums. At first, Alice had put it down to the fact he was still recovering from the horrors of war, but now she was worried. He no longer looked at her in the way he had done that day in the church. She felt he was bored with her already, and all talk of an engagement or wedding had long since been forgotten. She was his nursemaid and easy lover, the one who kept his bed warm when he was not out gambling with his so-called friends or drinking and womanizing. Mrs Dowbiggin and Faulks must have seen how things were, but they said nothing, keeping their heads down and getting on with their jobs as if his behaviour was nothing out of the ordinary. How wrong she had been to think that he loved her. He'd wanted her, but that's all it was. There was no love there. She should have known that; after all, she'd been warned by just about everyone.

A tear trickled down her cheek. To think she'd

let Jack walk away from her for this cad. Once again she'd ended up being used, all for the sake of trying to better herself and for trying to keep Baby Alice close to her. Better to have no home at all than be treated like a prostitute. What was it that made men look at her in that way? Did she have 'Tart' written across her forehead, invisible to women but there to be seen by all men? She sniffed and controlled her tears as she heard the front door go and Gerald swearing as he took his riding boots off in the hallway before making his way up the stairs and into bed.

'You still here? God, I thought you'd be long gone.' He slurred his words as he lunged across the bedroom and collapsed on the bed. Mumbling and smelling of drink, still dressed in his clothes, his breeches covered with mud from riding, he pulled the bedcovers over him.

Outside Alice could hear his horse pawing the gravel. The poor creature, he hadn't even unsaddled and stabled it before coming indoors. Jack would have seen to it if he'd still been employed at the manor, but since the onset of war he'd only worked for himself and his father. Alice lay still until she heard him snoring; then she quietly rose and dressed before picking the sleeping baby up in her arms and going downstairs. Placing the still-slumbering baby on the large sofa in the drawing room, she arranged the cushions to stop her from falling on the floor, and then went outside to unsaddle the distressed horse. The sun was shining, but there was a slight hint of autumn frost in the air with the early morning mists clinging to the river in the valley below.

'Shh, now. What a state you're in. He must have ridden you like the devil.' She approached the sweat-flecked horse, whispering softly as she took hold of the harness and stroked it on its neck. Once it was calm, she began leading it in the direction of the stables.

'I'll take that for you, Miss Alice. It isn't a job for a lady.' Faulks appeared out of the kitchen door and came towards them with his hand outstretched. 'I thought I heard the master return. I can't believe he'd leave his horse in this state. He used to be such a proud horseman.' The butler shook his head as he took control of the reins. 'Mrs Dowbiggin's got the kettle on, if you want to join us for an early morning cuppa.'

Alice nodded and, leaving him to take the horse into the stables, headed back to the drawing room to check on Baby Alice before joining the housekeeper in the kitchen.

Mrs Dowbiggin was still in her flannelette nightie and dressing gown, her long grey, thinning hair in cotton rags to give it a bit of curl.

'Oh my Lord — Miss Alice, I didn't expect you in the kitchen at this hour. Look at me, I'm not even dressed. What will you think of me?'

'Don't worry, Mrs Dowbiggin. I'm only glad you're up and that the fire's going. It's cold out there. Faulks says there's tea on the go. Is it all right if I join you?'

'Don't be silly, lass, you don't have to ask. Here, sit yourself down and I'll get you a cup.

It's been a while since you've sat in here with us. I must say, I've missed your company. I don't get much out of old Faulks nowadays.'

Alice sighed and gazed into the fire, silently clasping the cup in her hands as Mrs Dowbiggin busied herself in the kitchen.

'You look troubled, Alice. What's wrong? Do you want to tell me? If not, just say I'm to mind my own business.'

'I can't tell you . . . You all warned me, but I thought he loved me. I thought I was the only one and I was besotted. I've been such a fool!' Alice hid her head in her hands, tears dripping through her closed fingers.

'Now then, pet, you were only trying to better yourself, and I don't blame you for that. But even before Master Gerald went to war, he used to play games with young women. Yours won't be the first heart he's broken.' Mrs Dowbiggin put her arms around her and held her tight. 'Just make the best of it, lass. At least you've got a roof over your head and you're well fed. Baby Alice needs a mother and you are all she's got, because her uncle never looks at her twice. Poor little thing — no mother or father, and an uncle who doesn't have the time of day for her. If I were you, I'd tell him that you are moving into the spare bedroom with her because she's teething. He won't mind — he's coming home drunk most nights anyway. And it'll give you a bit of peace for a night or two.' Mrs Dowbiggin squeezed Alice, hugging her extra tight. 'There, I'd better get dressed before Faulks comes back in. You sit there and have your tea. I'll pop in and

369

see if Alice is still asleep.' The old housekeeper bustled out of the kitchen shaking her head. She'd known it would all end in tears, but there was no telling a lass when she was head over heels in love.

Alice sniffed and wiped the tears away with the back of her hand as Faulks walked in.

'The horse is seen to, Miss Alice. She's stabled and wiped down and fed. I still can't believe that the master would leave his pride and joy like that. I don't know what the world's coming to.'

'Neither do I, Faulks,' Alice sniffed. Conscious that Faulks was uncomfortable at the sight of her crying into her tea, she made an effort to smile.

'May I say, miss, I can't understand the way he's acting. I've known Master Gerald all his life and he's not the gentleman I thought he was, miss.' He coughed apologetically into his hand.

'He's definitely no gentleman — we've both been fooled. But what to do about it, I don't know.' Alice smiled and got up to return to Baby Alice. At least she was welcome in the kitchen once again and had allies in Faulks and Mrs Dowbiggin.

★ ★ ★

It was a true autumn day: the rain hadn't stopped, and the winds howled around the manor. Alice and the baby were cosy and warm in the nursery with the fire blazing in the hearth. As she watched the little one playing with her teddy and ball, Alice felt more content than she had in a while. Gerald had been gone a few days now and she was thankful for a bit of peace. Since she'd moved into the spare bedroom, he'd been less attentive, virtually ignoring her sometimes.

Suddenly she heard the front door slam and the sound of Gerald's voice laughing and booming as he ran up the stairs. But he was not alone; there was an answering peal of high-pitched laughter, and then the sound of a woman talking in a foreign language that Alice couldn't understand. She froze as she listened to them frolicking on the landing, the shrieks and laughter getting louder as they went into Gerald's bedroom and closed the door behind them.

Alice stared out at the pouring rain. How dare he bring one of his whores into the bed he'd shared with her? Her temper started building as she heard the giggles from the adjoining room and imagined Gerald muttering words of love. She looked at the baby playing contentedly and decided to walk in on the loving couple. Gathering her skirts and jutting out her chin, she marched out onto the landing and threw open the bedroom door.

'What the blazes! How dare you enter my bedroom!' Gerald looked out from the bed, eyes blazing with anger. 'Get out! Get out now!'

'Who is this, Gerald?' The dark-haired woman gave Alice a disdainful look.

'She's nothing, Tatiana, just a servant who doesn't know her place.'

'Surely no maid would be so bold as to enter your room when they know you are busy?'

Gerald leapt up from the bed, pulling his braces up and buttoning his flies, as Alice looked at the Russian beauty who had taken her place. Or rather, whose place she had taken, for this was the woman he'd always been in love with, while Alice had never been more than a plaything to him.

'Get rid of her!' commanded Tatiana, her foreign accent making the words sound even more contemptuous. 'I don't want a maid who's so rude to her mistress. She's obviously not been trained well.'

Alice protested, 'Tell her, Gerald — tell her I'm more than a maid, that we were to be married. Tell her.'

His face as black as thunder, Gerald pushed her out of the door, then slapped her hard across the face. Grabbing her arm, he forced her into the nursery and picked up the innocent Baby Alice under his other arm, making her scream in shock and surprise. The cries of Alice and the baby echoed through the manor as he stormed down the stairs dragging them with him. He released Alice's arm just long enough to open the front door, then threw her down the steps and set the baby on the ground. As Alice crawled, sobbing, to shelter the baby from the rain, her blonde hair lank and wet, he stood in the front doorway looking down on them.

'Get away from here. You're nothing but a common whore. And you can take the brat with you. I don't want to see you or it ever again — you are both mistakes.' His white shirt clung to his chest as he bellowed the words that cut through the air and into Alice's heart. 'Go on, get off my property before I set the dogs on you.'

Alice stood in the pouring rain, holding the crying baby. She could see there was no love in his heart for them, not a scrap of affection. He glared at her, as if waiting for her to plead, but she wasn't going to beg; she'd never begged for anything. Her tears mingling with the cold rain, she turned and walked away, Baby Alice screaming in her arms. She had her dignity, if nothing else. As for Gerald — good riddance; he wasn't worth it. If that was a gentleman, then Old Nick himself had better manners.

The rain fell like stair rods, cold and biting, while Alice clung to the shivering baby, trying to shield her from the rain with her body. Her heart felt heavy and tears stung her eyes as she set off down the road, walking without knowing where she was going. With all the strength in her little arms and legs, Baby Alice fought against her guardian, still screaming at the top of her lungs.

On and on Alice walked, into the village of Dent, past the closed doors of the Moon, past the Battys' yard, with the coffins still propped against the walls, and on past the fountain where she'd flirted with Jack. There was no door where she could find sanctuary, no one she could turn to with the little bundle that now lay quiet in her arms, too exhausted to struggle. She was a stranger in her own village. Remembering all the past hurts, a wave of desperation swept over her.

By the time she got to the church bridge that spanned the beer-coloured waters of the River Dee, the baby's body felt cold and limp in her arms. She stood on the parapet, looking down at the white foam swirling round the willow roots and crashing over boulders as the floodwaters swept down the valley to the sea. Her long blonde hair dripped onto the wet, frozen body of Baby Alice as she bent her head over her.

'Forgive me,' she whispered, kissing the baby tenderly on the forehead. Then she clambered to the top of the bridge, clutching Baby Alice to her chest. Tears filled her eyes and she was trembling as she looked down into the gushing waters.

'Oh, no, you don't. I can't let you do that.' A strong voice came from nowhere and an arm clasped her around the waist, preventing her from leaping into the pounding waters. 'I'll not have your death on my conscience.' The strong arm pulled them both back from the edge and deposited them by the roadside.

Jack stood over Alice and the baby as they huddled together, a picture of despair. Tenderly he bent down and picked up both frozen bodies in his strong arms and carried them to his waiting trap.

As he lifted her in, Alice put her arm around him. It was Jack, the one she had hurt so badly, the one who had every right to turn his back on her. She cried into his soaked jacket and looked desperately into his eyes as he laid her underneath a horse blanket, wrapping Baby Alice up next to her.

'Right, you're coming home to Dale End

where you belong, with me.'

For once, Alice did not argue. She wanted so much to belong. Perhaps life was going to be all right, now she finally knew her place.

30

November 1918

The sky was heavy with snow, and the biting wind made Alice's cheeks glow red as she sat behind the fell wall watching the lights go on down the dale. No lights were visible at the manor; it was in darkness, empty and cold like Gerald's heart. He was long gone. Taking Tatiana with him, he'd fled the dale in the middle of the night, bankrupt and in disgrace, with creditors lining up from Dent to Kendal. Rumour had it that he'd left the country.

The two loyal servants he had abandoned to their fate were now doing very nicely for themselves. Mr Faulks had wasted no time in asking Mrs Dowbiggin for her hand in marriage, and the pair of them were now running a successful tea room in Sedbergh. Alice was glad they would have security in their old age. Although they still argued like cat and dog, they couldn't live without one another.

Wrapping her shawl around her against the cold, she smiled as she watched Jack and little Alice in the yard down at Dale End. Jack was feeding the dogs and the little girl was helping collect the eggs from the hen house, holding her skirt up to carry them into the house, just the way Alice herself used to do when she was a child. Daintily carrying the eggs across the yard

376

with the help of her dad. Dad — how easily that rolled off the tongue; but that was what Jack had become and young Alice knew no different. She didn't remember the night that they'd been thrown out of the manor in the pouring rain, and Jack had found them and taken them home with him to Dale End. There they had stayed, loved and content, in the cottage that had been Alice's childhood home.

Alice watched as Jack lit the oil lamp in the window; time to wander down and make the evening meal and sit contented next to the fire. Her finger played with the wedding ring that Jack had so lovingly put on her finger last New Year's Day. How she loved him, and he her. Young love was foolish; she knew that now. All the time she'd been searching, he'd been there, under her nose, with everything she ever wanted. What a fool she had been, her head turned by everything false, when she'd had the love of a good man all along. Her hands rested on the bulge of her unborn baby; soon their family would be complete, a little brother or sister for Alice. A new life to nurture and care for in the family home.

Getting to her feet, Alice carefully picked her way down the path, the first snowflake of winter slowly melting on her face. Perhaps they would build a snowman tomorrow, or perhaps the little family would just keep warm indoors and watch through their window as the dale turned into a winter wonderland. Whatever they did, they would do it with love, the two Alices safe and secure with a good, strong, loving man by their side. A Dales man, one of few words but every one of them true, and with a love so strong that she knew they would take on the world together, for ever.

Author's Note

Dentdale lies in the Yorkshire Dales surrounded by beautiful rolling fells. Until recently, access to this remote area was difficult. It is the place where generations of my family hail from, and the place I call home.

Some of the things mentioned in my story have factual roots, and I thought that you, the reader, would be interested to know them.

Whernside Manor was originally known as West House. It was owned by the Sill family, who made their fortune from West Indian sugar and built the manor with the proceeds. They also brought slaves to Dent, and there are some who say that those slaves built the limestone walls that are a feature of the dale. It is rumoured that Emily Brontë, who along with her sisters went to school with the Sills in nearby Cowan Bridge, based Heathcliff in *Wuthering Heights* on stories she'd been told of life at Whernside Manor.

Dent marble is a black crinoidal limestone, much sought after for its fossil remains. It is mostly deposited around the rocks of Arten Gill, and its presence led to a boom in quarrying and works in the Dentdale area. The main works were located at Stone House, which was famed for its beautifully polished fireplaces. By the mid-nineteenth century, Stone House products were being exported worldwide, including a superb fireplace that was shipped to the Tsar of

Russia in St Petersburg. Later, however, cheaper Italian marble began flooding the market and Stone House was forced to close.

The impressive granite fountain near the entrance to St Andrew's church was built to commemorate Dentdale's most famous resident, vicar's son Adam Sedgwick (1785–1873). Educated at Sedbergh School and Cambridge University, he went on to become Woodwardian Professor of Geology at Cambridge. He was a close friend of Queen Victoria and Prince Albert, and also taught the young Charles Darwin.

Other titles published by
The House of Ulverscroft:

YEW TREE GARDENS

Anna Jacobs

Sisters Mattie, Nell and Renie have escaped from their bullying father. Building new lives for themselves, the youngest sister, Renie, lives with the newly married Nell. Working as a waitress at the King's Head Hotel, she becomes increasingly harassed by the new assistant manager, Mr Judson. So, also eager to escape from Nell's unpleasant husband, Renie is delighted to be offered a new job in London. Making new friends she soon settles, yet worries about how Nell is treated by her husband. When tragedy strikes Nell and her family, Renie feels horrified and helpless; finding her only comfort in her growing friendship with the injured Gil. But can their relationship progress from just friendship? And how will the return of the threatening Judson affect their future?

WHISPERS IN THE TOWN

Pamela Evans

For West London sisters Sal and Ann Storey, 1957 should have been one of the happiest years of their lives, but their world is turned upside down when two family tragedies strike in quick succession. Left to run the family's sweetshop with their grandmother, Sal's new-found flair for business doesn't make up for everything she and Ann have lost. When Sal meets and falls in love with taxi driver Bob Beck, her luck seems to have changed. Bob becomes her one constant, particularly when Ann finally uncovers her long-held guilty secret, which could have explosive consequences for the sisters. The last thing Sal needs is Bob's scheming ex-fiancée Kate's reappearance in his life — especially as Kate is preparing to make a stunning revelation . . .

LIGHTS OUT TILL DAWN

Dee Williams

Before World War II has even been officially declared, ten-year-old Hazel Morgan and her eight-year-old brother, Peter, are evacuated, leaving London for the safety of the Sussex countryside. With her children gone and her husband John in the army, Rene Morgan misses her family terribly. When she learns that John has become a prisoner of war, she has to take on the highly dangerous job of Fire Watcher. Meanwhile Hazel and Peter, desperate to go back home, return to the city, overjoyed to be reunited with their mother and Gran. But their father is still far away and the worst of the war is yet to come. As the air raids increase, the Morgans must face the terror of the Blitz together . . .